HEAT, THERMODYNAMICS, AND STATISTICAL PHYSICS

Heat,
Thermodynamics,
and
Statistical Physics

Franzo H. Crawford

Williams College

HARCOURT, BRACE & WORLD, INC.

NEW YORK · CHICAGO · SAN FRANCISCO · ATLANTA

Preface

This text is intended for junior or senior students interested in physics, chemistry, and engineering. The aim is to provide a background of the experimental as well as the theoretical growth of the study of the thermal properties of matter. During long experience in teaching thermodynamics, the author has become more and more impressed with the desirability of integrating the study of matter in bulk (thermodynamics) with an introduction to the molecular, or statistical, study of matter (statistical physics). The present work has grown out of a senior year's course devoted to such a program. It is, of course, necessary to develop the bulk view first, to the point where the student begins to think in this new (and often rather baffling) way. However, a great deal of the beauty and power of the subject is lost if it is not followed immediately by the molecular approach, with all the insight it gives into the problems discussed.

In general, then, the first fourteen chapters of this book deal with thermodynamics, and the remaining five with statistical physics. The role of entropy, a central one, serves as a major link between the two concepts. Many, for example, will wish to follow Chapter 9 (on entropy) with Chapter 15 (on entropy and probability).

The chapters on thermodynamics pay particular attention to the question of independent variables and their proper selection, introducing and applying extensively a Jacobian scheme for systems of two or more variables, and emphasize thermodynamic methods and the use of curve differentials in the treatment of heat and work. The chapters on statistical physics are concerned with kinetic theory, statistical mechanics, the uses of statistical physics in determining thermodynamic functions, and various applications. Throughout, the author defines both heat *and* work *added* to a system as *positive*. Although thermodynamics arose from the historic interest in engines as sources of external work, the usual convention is almost as confusing and unnecessary as calling paper money positive and coins negative in preparing a bank balance.

The examination of such large topics as thermodynamics and statistical physics puts great strain on any notation. Even with upper-case, lower-case, and script letters, the combined Latin and Greek alphabets are inadequate. It has accordingly been expedient, but without undue violence to long-established conventions in mechanics and atomic and molecular spectroscopy, to present many symbols in multiple contexts. Thus, to mention only one case, the overworked S does duty for entropy, the S state, and the total spin quantum number of the atom. Subscripts and superscripts make many symbols self-explanatory and therefore prevent ambiguity.

Although this book is designed for a year's course, it can readily be adapted to a semester's course by suitable omissions and curtailment. For a one-semester course, the author suggests the following chapters: 1, 2 (Secs. 2.1 to 2.9), 4, 5, 6 (with the omission of Sec. 6.8 through 6.11), 7 (Secs. 7.1 to 7.11), 8, 9, 11, 12, 15, and as much of 16 and 17 as time permits. Conceivably a class might cover 60% of the text in one semester.

The author owes much to the standard works on thermodynamics, especially the books of Epstein, Roberts and Miller, and Zemansky in thermodynamics and of Mayer and Mayer and Fowler and Guggenheim in statistical mechanics. It is a pleasure to express thanks to my wife, who typed the entire manuscript and helped prepare the drawings, and without whose efforts the book might never have been completed. My colleague David Park read several of the later chapters and gave excellent criticism and advice. The staff of the library of Williams College was most helpful in locating hard-to-find journals. Last but not least, the author is grateful to the President and Trustees of Williams College for granting a sabbatical leave that enabled him to finish the manuscript at this date.

FRANZO H. CRAWFORD

Contents

CHAPTER TWO

Temperature

CHAPTER THREE

The Equation of State

CHAPTER FOUR

The First Law of Thermodynamics   *82*

CHAPTER FIVE

Work and Heat in Various Systems   *109*

CHAPTER SIX

Heat Capacities of Gases

CHAPTER SEVEN

Solids, Liquids, and Change of Phase

CHAPTER EIGHT

Heat Engines and the Second Law   *200*

CHAPTER ELEVEN

Thermodynamic Methods

CHAPTER FOURTEEN

The Physics of Low Temperatures   *413*

CHAPTER SEVENTEEN

Advent of the Quantum Theory — *529*

CHAPTER EIGHTEEN

Quantum Statistics — *566*

CHAPTER NINETEEN

Applications to Various Systems   *618*

Appendixes   *669*

CHAPTER ONE

Introduction

1.1 Introduction to Thermodynamics

The subject of thermodynamics arose historically from the study of heat engines and the problems involved in converting heat into mechanical work. It is based on two fundamental laws of great generality. The first of these is due largely to the efforts of Count Rumford (1753–1814) and James Joule (1818–1889). This law rests on the recognition of heat and work as different manifestations of energy. It is essentially a special formulation of the law of the conservation of energy. The second law derives from the work of Sadi Carnot (1796–1832), Rudolph Clausius (1822–1888), and Lord Kelvin (1824–1907). Although it has many formulations, it deals primarily with the natural *limits* on the conversion of heat into work.

Since the middle of the nineteenth century the scope and generality of these two laws have been greatly extended. The ideas and methods peculiar to thermodynamics have in consequence become of value throughout the subjects of physics and chemistry. They find basic application not only in the study of steam engines and turbines but also in the study of jets and rockets. They have laid the basis for refrigeration and the general theory of cooling and have thus led to the whole field of the production and study of very low temperatures. Other applications include the theory of electric cells, thermocouples, piezoelectric crystals, paramagnetic salts, and heat radiation. The understanding of chemical reactions and a good share of chemical engineering likewise depends on the use and interpretation of these two laws.

1.2 Large-Scale or Macroscopic View

The two basic laws of thermodynamics are primarily empirical laws. Their truth depends on direct observation of the way samples of matter behave when subject to various operations and processes. These involve changes in large-scale or *macroscopic* properties such as volume, length, pressure, and temperature. Studies of this sort can be carried out on the greatest diversity of systems without any assumption or knowledge about the structure or constitution of matter. For such purposes temperature is simply a numerical value read off an instrument called a thermometer. We need have no more precise ideas of temperature—other than that it is a measure of relative hotness or coldness. This enables us to detect uniformity of temperature and changes in temperature, whether the scale be a standard or a purely arbitrary one.[1]

Thermodynamics deals with matter in bulk. The systems used contain such vast numbers of atoms that the properties and behavior of individual particles average out. Among the bulk properties of interest are most of the quantities listed in handbooks of physics and chemistry as so-called "constants of matter." These are, of course, constants not in the sense of having invariable numerical values, but rather in the sense of being characteristic of the *substance* in question and independent of the size, shape, etc., of a particular specimen. These bulk properties include such things as specific heats, coefficients of linear and volume expansion, heats of vaporization, heats of chemical reaction, and compressibilities.

Typical thermodynamic results furnish us with *relations* among these bulk properties. No thermodynamic argument purports to give the absolute value of a quantity, but simply to relate it to other properties of the same material. Since no hypotheses about the nature or even the existence of atoms are made, these relations have a dependability limited only by the generality and precision of the empirical laws from which they come. Since the two fundamental laws of thermodynamics are among the most general in the exact sciences, these relations, properly deduced, have a correspondingly wide validity. Once the applicability of the two laws has been established, the results accordingly remain unmodified as atomic theories are revised and atomic "models" altered or discarded altogether. This is simply to say that thermodynamic results are large-scale or *macroscopic* relations whose truth is independent of atomic or *microscopic* details.

1.3   Molecular or Microscopic View

The very generality of the macroscopic treatment of physical systems is the source of a serious disadvantage. It can never be expected to give us any insight into why a given truth should be so or what is taking place on a molecular or microscopic level. The desire to obtain just this latter sort of insight has led to the great development of the kinetic theory of matter. Owing to inherent mathematical and physical difficulties, the greatest quantitative success has been obtained in the simplest case, that of a dilute gas. Here a sample of gas is regarded as an assemblage of mass particles (molecules) subject to the laws of

---

[1] Pressure is given by the reading of a suitable manometer. Although a knowledge of what these quantities mean on an atomic or molecular level gives us an insight into physical happenings, lack of this knowledge does not affect the formulation or application of the two laws.

Newtonian mechanics. Then on the basis of reasonable assumptions about the mutual forces between these particles, an attempt is made to obtain expressions for pressure, total energy, and temperature in terms of particle velocities, configurations, etc. The results obtained by this analysis are specific and clear-cut. They are also very illuminating as to molecular processes and behavior. Their precision is, however, limited by the provisional state of our knowledge of the exact nature, size, and behavior of molecules. It is also usually restricted further by approximations made to overcome inherent mathematical difficulties.

In the broader view the two approaches to the study of matter are, of course, complementary. Thermodynamic relations leave absolute magnitudes to be determined by other means. One of these other means is offered by the kinetic theory. By judicious use of the results of both methods, we can expect to gain the fullest understanding of the natural world. But it is quite essential at all stages to keep the two methods separate and distinct. Otherwise, only confusion can result.

1.4 Systems and Their Surroundings

A system, as used here, is a definite portion of matter thought of as distinct and separate from its immediate environs and the rest of the universe. We imagine a closed surface acting as a *boundary* to this system. Everything without is nonsystem. If we wish to talk of a piece of iron, for example, then the outer surface of the metal itself is the system boundary (Fig. 1.1). Everything outside, including the immediate environs and all the rest, is excluded. In practice only a very modest bit of the excluded part of the universe will ever be affected by our system or react back upon it. For this reason it is convenient to call the immediate environs that have any physical reaction with or on the system the *surroundings*. Then for practical purposes we can ignore the rest of the universe as being independent of local happenings in the system and its neighborhood. The interactions mentioned include all sorts of energy exchanges: heat flows from or to the system; the system performs mechanical work on its surroundings, or they do work on it; electrical energy, in the form of a current, flows into the system and is degraded there into heat; etc.

FIGURE **1.1**

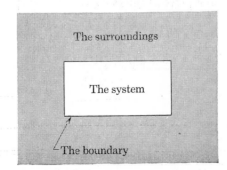

The surroundings

The system

The boundary

1.5 Walls and Boundaries

System boundaries are of all sorts. Sometimes they are real physical surfaces, as in the case of the bar of iron or of a cylinder containing a gas. In other cases the boundary is a purely mental one. In our minds we may draw a "dotted surface" about a certain mass of moving fluid. As the system moves, the boundary may change its size and shape as energy interchange takes place with the surroundings. In several cases of special interest in thermodynamics, the boundaries are formed by physical walls of certain idealized types. Of these the following are of particular importance.

Rigid Walls. Systems contained within rigid walls are effectively protected against changes in volume and thus not subject to having work done on them by hydrostatic or other forces of a mechanical nature.

Cylinder and Piston. In the case of a liquid or gas, it is often convenient to confine the system in a cylinder with a smoothly fitting piston (Fig. 1.2). The volume, V, and pressure, p, can then be controlled at will. The piston is at once idealized as leakproof and frictionless.

Diathermic Walls. These are literally walls "permeable to heat flow." Although metal walls are the best as far as rapidity of flow is concerned, most solids may be considered diathermic if *thin* enough.

Adiabatic Walls. These are walls of such a nature that they permit the transfer of no thermal effects whatever. They prevent all passage of heat, whether by conduction, radiation, or convection. They are approximated by many solid materials, such as wood or asbestos, if *thick* enough, but the nearest approach to the ideal adiabatic wall is provided by a good Dewar flask with silvered walls and a high vacuum between. Adiabatic walls play a very important part in thermodynamic arguments.

Semipermeable Walls. In the case of systems consisting of solutions, such as sugar and water, it is often desirable to have a portion of one wall made up of, say, wet parchment, which retains the sugar but allows the water to pass freely. The parchment then constitutes a semipermeable membrane, a wall whereby the mass and composition of the system become variable at will.

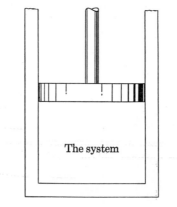

FIGURE **1.2**

The system

Isolating Walls.   These are walls or boundaries that prevent all *inter-action* between the system and its surroundings. Since they must preclude all thermal, electrical, magnetic, and radiational effects, they require careful specification. In the first place, there is no insulator against gravitational fields. Hence we must rule out gravitational effects altogether. This is equivalent to taking our system mentally to a point where no gravitational field exists or to confining the discussion to cases where gravitational effects are so small as to be negligible. We prevent magnetic and electric interference by removing all sources of such disturbance to a remote distance. If then the outer wall is mechanically *rigid, tight,* and *adiabatic,* we have in effect an *isolating* boundary.

It is clear from the description of these various types of walls and boundaries that they are all schemes for giving us *control,* of one limited sort or another, over the system under examination.

1.6   Thermodynamic Equilibrium

It is a matter of common experience that systems, if left to themselves long enough, tend toward a final, steady, persisting state, which we call the *equi-librium* state. The attainment of equilibrium seems to be a universal property of *isolated* systems. Given enough time, temperature differences tend to vanish. Pressure differences cause material flow, reducing the original differences. Diffusion tends to iron out differences of concentration. Mixtures of reacting chemicals come to a static condition where no further observable reaction takes place. Electrical charges migrate over the surface of conductors until a final static distribution results. These are examples of the apparently universal tendency of isolated systems toward a state of complete mechanical, thermal, chemical, and electrical—or, in a single word, *thermodynamic—equilibrium.*

All gradients in the system cause flows, which tend to reduce the very gradients causing the flows in the first place. When the final state of equi-librium has been reached, no further experimentally measurable changes can occur. The system's properties become independent of time. In this sense equilibrium systems are *timeless* systems; there is nothing in such systems to differentiate one instant from any other. Of course, equilibrium systems are timeless only in a macroscopic sense. Molecular activity continues as before but is of such a nature as to cause no large-scale local properties to vary, either with time or with location within the system.

1.7   Thermal Equilibrium and the Zeroth Law

At this point we must examine the concept of *thermal equilibrium* in greater detail. Our intuitive idea of temperature derives from the physiological sensa-tions of hotness and coldness. We can, in fact, arrange a set of bodies (at least roughly) in a series of increasing hotness, so that each is as hot as, or hotter than, its predecessor. We say that they are arranged in order of increasing temperature. This arrangement, of course, does not provide us with a continuous "degree-of-hotness" or *temperature* scale, nor does it attach a numerical measure to the "temperature" of a particular body in the sequence. If two of the bodies with different temperatures are put in physical contact, the hotter body is observed to become cooler, and the colder body to become warmer, until a steady state is reached at which the two bodies have a common intermediate temperature. They are then said to be in *thermal equilibrium*. We then go a step further and define *heat* as the physical entity the passage of which from the hotter body to the colder body brought about the temperature equalization and the attainment of thermal equilibrium. We say that heat is that entity which flows from hotter to colder bodies when they are in contact and tends to cause them to come to the same condition of hotness or coldness.

We must now develop a logical operational approach to the subject, as against the preceding intuitional approach based on qualitative sense perceptions. For this purpose we need two types of walls mentioned in Sec. 1.5, namely, adiabatic and diathermic walls. But now we shall define them entirely by operations involving thermal equilibrium. Let us consider two systems, *A* and *B*, which, for simplicity, we may take to be two gases. Let each be placed in a metal cylinder with a gastight piston (Fig. 1.3), and let the two be isolated from the rest of the universe by a suitable wall and separated from each other by another wall (wall #1). Now allow the values of the pressure, *p*, and the volume, *V*, of gas *A* to be changed in any way. If these changes produce no effect whatever in *p* and *V* of gas *B*, we say that wall #1 is an adiabatic wall. Suppose, on the contrary, that in general when we alter the *p* and *V* values of *A* there is a corresponding *spontaneous* change in the *p* and *V* values of *B*, so that *A* and *B*, regarded as a single system, form a *timeless* or *equilibrium* system. Then the wall is a diathermic wall, and *A* and *B* are in *thermal* equilibrium. Actually, of course, the metal cylinders in which *A* and *B* are contained are diathermic, and placing the two cylinders in physical contact would suffice for the argument. It is merely necessary that, in the absence of magnetic or electrical influences, a diathermic wall be capable of preventing the physical leakage of gas from *A* to *B* or the transmission of physical forces. Thus diathermic walls permit thermal equilibrium, and adiabatic walls prevent it.

FIGURE **1.3**

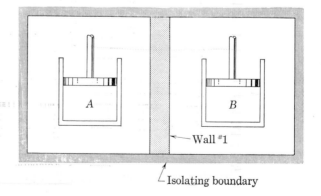

Wall #1

Isolating boundary

Suppose we now have *three* systems: A, B, and C (Fig. 1.4). Let B and C be separated from one another by an adiabatic wall, and let each be separated from A by a diathermic wall. Once thermal equilibrium has been reached, B with A and C with A, we find that the replacement of the adiabatic wall by a diathermic one produces *no further changes* in B and C. Thus B and C are in thermal equilibrium. (Here we speak of bodies as being in thermal equilibrium even when they are not in direct contact through a diathermic wall. It is merely necessary that they *would* be in thermal equilibrium if they *were* so separated.)

We may state this important fact in this general form: *if each of two systems is in thermal equilibrium with a third, they are in thermal equilibrium with each other.* This is such a basic idea in thermodynamics that R. H. Fowler has termed it the *zeroth law* of thermodynamics.

This fact or law we now recognize as the basis of the concept of temperature and of the operation of the thermometer. For with three systems in thermal equilibrium, one, say, C, may consist of a quantity of mercury in a glass bulb attached to a narrow capillary. A change in the volume of the mercury would be indicated by a change in the height of the mercury thread. If this system is in thermal equilibrium with two other systems, A and B, then they are in thermal equilibrium with each other. And the height of the mercury thread may be taken as a measure of that common property of A and B whereby they are capable of existing in thermal equilibrium. This common property is called *temperature*. To obtain a numerical measure for temperature, we need only make a set of arbitrary marks on the stem of the mercury-in-glass system. This system then becomes a thermometer.

In a similar way, once we have defined temperature as the common property of bodies in thermal equilibrium, we may define heat as the agency that brings about thermal equilibrium. For this purpose no hypothesis is made about the nature of heat.

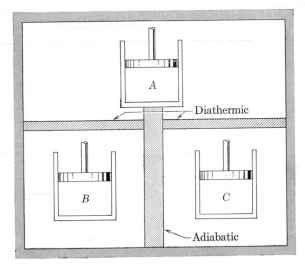

FIGURE 1.4

1.8   Temperature as a Property of a System

At this point it is worthwhile to examine temperature from a somewhat different viewpoint, namely, its existence as a parameter having the same value for all systems in thermal equilibrium.[2] Consider now two bodies. Although these might be any two bodies, let us assume for simplicity that they are the two gaseous systems of Fig. 1.3. Suppose that gas A has a mass m_1 and pressure and volume p_1 and V_1. Likewise, let m_2, p_2, and V_2 represent these properties for gas B. It is assumed throughout that the masses are fixed. We know from experiment that if p_1 is fixed, we may, within limits, choose V_1 at will. Thus p_1 is not fixed by V_1 alone, nor p_2 by V_2 alone. Now place the two gases in thermal contact, and allow equilibrium to ensue. In general, if p_1 and p_2 are fixed, V_1 and V_2 will change, but always in such a way that *one is related to the other*. This means that the four variables (p_1, p_2, V_1, and V_2) cannot be varied *independently*. There must therefore exist a functional relation connecting the equilibrium values of these variables, say,

$$f_{12}(p_1, V_1, p_2, V_2) = 0 \qquad\qquad (1.1)$$

Of course, it is possible that the two gases were in thermal equilibrium in the first place (that is, at the same temperature). In that case no change would occur in any of the variables (whether p_1 and p_2 or V_1 and V_2 were fixed initially makes no difference).

Suppose a third gas, C, is also brought into thermal contact with A and found to be in thermal equilibrium. If p_3 and V_3 refer to this gas, we write the consequences of this fact in terms of the zeroth law of thermodynamics. For now A is in thermal equilibrium with C as well as with B, and therefore B is in thermal equilibrium with C. The functional relation expressing the result of the original equilibrium is given by Eq. 1.1. We may write two other equations expressing the same truth for the other cases; namely,

for A and C $\qquad\qquad f_{13}(p_1, V_1, p_3, V_3) = 0 \qquad\qquad (1.2)$

for B and C $\qquad\qquad f_{23}(p_2, V_2, p_3, V_3) = 0 \qquad\qquad (1.3)$

Two of these three equations contain p_1. Solving for this value gives

$$p_1 = F_{12}(p_2, V_1, V_2)$$

and

$$p_1 = F_{13}(p_3, V_1, V_3) \qquad\qquad (1.4)$$

or

$$F_{12}(p_2, V_1, V_2) = F_{13}(p_3, V_1, V_3) \qquad\qquad (1.5)$$

This last equation essentially implies a relation involving only the variables of gases B and C, since their equilibrium is inferentially true irrespective of gas A (and the value of V_1). Consequently, the functions F_{12} and F_{13} must be of such form as to permit the elimination of the common variable V_1. A little

---

[2] See Born, *Physik. Z.*, **22**, 218, 249 (1921); Balamuth, Wolfe, and Zemansky, *Am. J. Phys.*, **9**, 199 (1941); and particularly R. A. Smith, *The Physical Principles of Thermodynamics*, Chapman and Hall, London, 1932, Chap. 1, to which the present account is largely due.

consideration shows that V_1 must occur either in an *additive* function or a *factor* function or both. Hence we must be able to write

$$F_{12}(p_2, V_1, V_2) = f(V_1)[g(V_1) + G_2(p_2, V_2)]$$

and
$$F_{13}(p_3, V_1, V_3) = f(V_1)[g(V_1) + G_3(p_3, V_3)]$$

Since these terms are equal, the unknown functions $f(V_1)$ and $g(V_1)$ cancel, giving

$$G_2(p_2, V_2) = G_3(p_3, V_3) \qquad (1.6)$$

Of course, the same type of argument can be carried through for another of the pairs, say, A and B.

Finally, then,

$$G_1(p_1, V_1) = G_2(p_2, V_2) = G_3(p_3, V_3) \qquad (1.7)$$

This relationship means that *a function of p and V exists for each of our three gases* (or bodies, since the argument is readily generalized) *and that its value is the same for all three.* Each function therefore must equal some parameter; this parameter we call the temperature, t, and we are able to write

$$t = G_1(p_1, V_1) = G_2(p_2, V_2) = G_3(p_3, V_3) \qquad (1.8)$$

Thus temperature is that parameter which is common to bodies in thermal equilibrium. Of course, we need not regard Eq. 1.8 as defining a unique temperature. Any single-valued function of t would do as well. The important point is that such a common parameter *does exist* for all bodies in thermal equilibrium. The argument can clearly be extended to systems requiring other variables than p and V (see Problem 1.4).

1.9   The Equation of State and the Temperature Scale

The equation

$$t = G(p, V) \qquad (1.9)$$

where p and V refer to any body in thermal contact with the three bodies mentioned in Sec. 1.8, constitutes the so-called *equation of state*. It is a relation involving the three variables p, V, and t so that when any two are fixed the third is determined. It is assumed that the system is subject to no forces of mechanical, electric, or magnetic nature save hydrostatic pressure. Of course, the actual *form* of the function $G(p, V)$ remains undetermined until a numerical scale for t is agreed upon. But we may study the experimental relation of p to V, when t is a constant, without knowing the value of t. The experimental values of p and V plotted at fixed t are quite independent of any special scale. In fact, they are simply a plot of the curve

$$G(p, V) = \text{constant} \qquad (1.10)$$

which we call an *isotherm* for the system or body.

In 1660 Robert Boyle showed that in the case of a gas the isotherms were very nearly of the form

$$pV = \text{constant} \qquad \text{(1.11)}$$

This, of course, is Boyle's law and expresses an empirical truth quite independent of any presumed temperature scale.

To attach a numerical value to t, we proceed as follows: we select one particular body, say, the gas A, as our reference body or *thermometric* material. Since for this substance p_1 and V_1 in $t = G(p_1, V_1)$ are independently variable at constant t, we agree to fix one of them, say, p_1, and set $p_1 = p_0$, a constant. Then

$$t = G(p_0, V_1)$$

which essentially determines t as a function of V_1 alone. This may as well be written simply as

$$t = F(V_1) \qquad p_1 = p_0 \qquad \text{(1.12)}$$

where we are at liberty to make this function $F(V_1)$ *anything we like*. From general considerations it is clear that this functional relation should be single-valued and as simple as possible. The simplest relation that is not trivial is a *linear* one which we write either as

$$
\begin{aligned}
V_1 &= \alpha' + \beta't & p_1 &= p_0 \\
t &= \alpha + \beta V_1 & p_1 &= p_0
\end{aligned}
\qquad \text{(1.13)}
$$

or

The same argument could now be carried through for this gas with $V_1 = V_0$ a constant. The result would be a *new scale* with p_1 and t related by

$$
\begin{aligned}
p_1 &= \delta' + \gamma't & V_1 &= V_0 \\
t &= \delta + \gamma p_1 & V_1 &= V_0
\end{aligned}
\qquad \text{(1.14)}
$$

or

The next chapter will be devoted to the many problems involved in the fixing and comparing of the various possible temperature scales given by relations such as Eqs. 1.13 and 1.14. But the important point for the present discussion is that only after the *arbitrariness of the temperature scale has been settled can we, in principle, determine the form of the equation of state for the body.*

If we accept Boyle's law as true for gas A and agree to measure temperature by Eq. 1.13, we have simply to multiply the first of these equations through by p_0. This gives

$$p_0 V_1 = \alpha' p_0 + \beta' p_0 t$$

But with p_1' and V_1', any two other values of the pressure and volume at the same temperature and with the same gas in the thermometer,

$$
\begin{aligned}
p_0 V_1 &= p_1' V_1' = (p_1' V_1')_t \\
(p_1' V_1')_t &= \alpha'' + \beta'' t
\end{aligned}
\qquad \text{(1.15)}
$$

Thus

where $\alpha'' = \alpha' p_0$ and $\beta'' = \beta' p_0$, becomes the equation of state of the gas A used to define its own temperature scale.

When experimental results for the isotherms of other gases and other materials are available, we may determine empirical equations of state for them also. Equations of state will play an important part in future discussions, and we shall return to the subject many times.

The existence of equations of state is assumed even when the form of the equations is unknown. Frequent use will be made of the functional form of Eq. 1.9, and we shall always assume that it is possible in principle to solve this relation for either of the other two variables at will. Thus the equation of state may appear in the explicit forms

$$t = G(p, V)$$
$$p = H(V, t)$$
$$V = I(p, t)$$

$$(1.16)$$

or even in the implicit form

$$F(p, V, t) = 0$$

One further convention should be mentioned. Since functional relationships occur very frequently, we eventually find ourselves short of symbols. If we see $G(p, V)$ or $I(p, t)$ occurring alone, we must remember that the first is the temperature function and the second the volume function. To avoid confusion, it is customary in thermodynamics to write Eq. 1.16 simply as

$$t = t(p, V)$$
$$p = p(V, t)$$
$$V = V(p, t)$$

$$(1.17)$$

This practice has one disadvantage. If in some case we should change the variables p and V to others (x and y), we should have $t = t(p, V)$ and $t = t(x, y)$, where the *analytic forms* of the two functions are in general quite different. With care this possibility need lead to no ambiguities.

1.10   Intensive and Extensive Properties

When we endeavor to describe the status of a system, we are forced to consider only *equilibrium* systems. In such cases, instead of the pressure, temperature, etc., for every small part of the system, we require merely a single pressure, a single temperature, etc., for the system. Only for equilibrium does the *system* really possess a pressure or a temperature. Of course, in some cases it is difficult to say whether or not true equilibrium has been reached. These cases of *pseudoequilibrium* usually involve more complicated systems in which some chemical process in progress either is very slow or requires a catalyst for its completion. Examples are furnished by a mixture of hydrogen with oxygen or a bar of ordinary steel. The first is in a metastable state, since on exposure to spongy platinum the two gases combine explosively to form water. The mixture may, however, be treated as an ordinary inert mixture. Likewise, the piece of steel may be treated as a homogeneous stable solid, despite the fact that when vibrated protractedly it crystallizes out some of its excess carbon, with a marked change in its properties. Hereafter, then, when thermodynamic systems are mentioned, equilibrium systems will be understood.

In discussing thermodynamic systems, it is convenient to divide their physical properties into two classes or categories. The first class includes all properties that are *local* in character or can be defined at a *point* in the system. Thus pressure can be defined as the ratio of a force to the small local area over which it acts. Density is the ratio of mass to volume and can be defined in as small a volume as we choose. Temperature is a property that can, at least in principle, be measured for a system comparable in size to our smallest thermometer. If we subject a system to an electric or a magnetic field, the intensity of the field is capable of definition at a point. Such local properties are said to be *intensive* properties. Other intensive properties are refractive index, thermal conductivity, dielectric constant, concentration of an ingredient, specific heat, etc.

In general, the definition of intensive properties at a point in a system involves difficulties due to the atomic nature of matter. If we consider the mass density, ρ, we write for any arbitrary element of volume

$$\bar{\rho} = \frac{\Delta m}{\Delta V}$$

where $\bar{\rho}$ is the average density over ΔV. If we now attempt to pass to the limit and set the density at a point to be

$$\rho = \lim_{\Delta V \to 0} \frac{\Delta m}{\Delta V} = \frac{dm}{dV}$$

the value of the result will depend on whether the point around which ΔV shrinks to zero does or does not contain any matter. With mobile particles as in a gas or liquid, ρ may be expected to fluctuate with time, and a usable point density could be defined as the average over a long time interval of the instantaneous densities—an average that we would expect to be independent of the point chosen. This definition, however, would not necessarily be true for a solid. It is customary, therefore, to regard the actual mass in all thermodynamic systems as being spread uniformly over the whole volume of the system, with a consequent continuous (and uniform) density function for the equilibrium system. Thus we write

$$\rho = \bar{\rho} = \lim_{\Delta V \to 0} \frac{\Delta m}{\Delta V} = \frac{dm}{dV}$$

or

$$dm = \rho \, dV$$

and the average value of the density over the whole system, $\bar{\rho} = m/V$, becomes equal to the value at any point.[3] Similar considerations apply to other local properties.

---

[3] By this means we avoid the awkward statement that dV is not a mathematical differential but in fact large enough to contain many particles (a so-called physical differential—whatever that might be!).

The second class of properties can be defined only for the system as a *whole*. It includes mass, volume, length, total energy, and a number of other properties that depend on the scale of the system. Such properties are called *extensive* properties and, in general, other things being equal, they vary directly with the extent or mass of the system. Thus for a gas with all its intensive properties fixed, the volume is proportional to the mass; and for a solution of salt in water, the total amount of salt present (if the concentration is fixed) is proportional to the total volume, which in turn depends on the total mass.

Generally if we take a system and add another just like it to form a larger system, all extensive properties will be exactly doubled, while all intensive properties will remain unchanged.

It is often convenient to use so-called *specific* properties, such as specific volume, the volume per unit mass. In this case the volume of the whole system and the specific volume are designated by upper and lower-case letters, respectively, that is, V and v and

$$V = mv$$

Since v is a volume per unit mass, it can, in principle, be defined for any point in the system and is thus an intensive property. Writing the equation of state for a unit mass system as $v = v(p, t)$, we have either

$$V = mv(p, t) \qquad (1, 17)$$

or

$$V = V(m, p, t) \qquad (1.18)$$

as the equation of state including m. The first equation, showing the explicit effect of mass, is often more convenient than the second.

It appears that equilibrium is closely related to the uniformity of *intensive properties*. In this connection certain intensive properties are more fundamental than others. Differences in pressure actually cause mass flow inside the system that tends to reduce these differences; differences in temperature cause heat flow; differences in concentration cause diffusion; etc. Other intensive properties such as refractive index or specific heat are not themselves directly concerned with the attainment of equilibrium but simply change with pressure, temperature, concentration, etc.

Uniformity of all intensive properties is not always reached at equilibrium, as witness steam and water together or water and melting ice. These are examples of polyphase systems, where phase is a term introduced by Gibbs to designate the individual states of aggregation in which matter may exist—solid, liquid, and gas. In a single-phase system all intensive properties are uniform throughout the system. With more than one phase present, only the temperature and pressure attain uniformity; other properties, such as density, refractive index, and composition, change abruptly at phase boundaries.

1.11 Thermodynamic States of a System: Degrees of Freedom

We are now in a position to ask the general question: how can we best describe the status of a thermodynamic system? For simple systems such as a gas in a

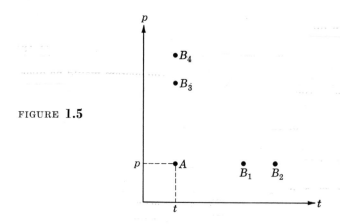

FIGURE **1.5**

cylinder (Fig. 1.2), a complete description is furnished by giving a few quantities only, say, p, V, t, and the mass, m. In other cases many more are required. But in the simple case of the gas we do not need all of the four quantities. If m, p, and t are the same for two samples of gas, then *all the other properties* of the samples are found to be identical. In fact, if the equation of state is taken into account, there are four variables, m, p, V, and t, and a single equation involving all of them. Hence, mathematically speaking, three variables can be varied independently. If it is assumed specifically that *mass* is constant, there are four variables, two restricting equations or *equations of constraint*, and only two independent variables. In this case we may choose at our convenience *any pair* of the three p, V, and t. If we agree to select p and t as the independent pair, the state of the system can be described in the so-called *p-t* plane. For this plane we choose rectangular axes and represent p, say, vertically and t horizontally (Fig. 1.5). Any equilibrium state, that is, any thermodynamic state of the single-phase gas system, is representable by a single geometric point in this plane.

Thus in Fig. 1.5 A, B_1, and B_2 represent states of the system at the same pressure (*isobaric* states), whereas A, B_3, and B_4 represent states at the same temperature (*isothermal* states). We shall often refer to a system as "being" at a point A and "moving" from a point A to a point B, etc. This is simply a locution for saying that the geometric point representing the state of the system, the so-called *image* or *state* point, is at A and moves from A to B, etc.

It is found experimentally that once the state point of the gas is determined in the *p-t* plane, then all other intensive properties of the gas—density, ρ, dielectric constant, K_e, velocity of sound, Υ, etc.—are likewise determined. Thus the name "equation of state" is really very appropriate. When the variables in the equation are fixed, the state of the system is determined.

It is instructive to treat this problem in a somewhat more formal way. In general, if we have a number of independent restraining equations, n_{eq}, and a number of variables, n_{var}, then n, the number of variables that may be varied independently, is given by

$$n = n_{\text{var}} - n_{\text{eq}} \tag{1.19}$$

Of course, we cannot have $n_{\text{eq}} > n_{\text{var}}$, since then the system would be over-defined. When $n_{\text{eq}} = n_{\text{var}}$, the state of the system is uniquely determined, and no properties can be altered.

If we make a formal list of the variables and the independent restraining equations for the gas, we have

Variables	*Equations*

$$p, \ V, \ t, \ m, \ \rho, \ K_e, \ \Upsilon$$

$$n_{\text{var}} = 7$$

(1) $m = \text{constant}$
(2) $\rho = m/V$
(3) $V = V(m, p, t)$
(4) $K_e = K_e(p, t)$
(5) $\Upsilon = \Upsilon(p, t)$

$$n_{\text{eq}} = 5$$

There are five equations, of which the first is a conventional (but arbitrary) restriction, the second is a definition, and the last three are laws of nature. Finally we have

$$n = 7 - 5 = 2$$

the result noted earlier. If we had added more variables to the first list, we should have added more equations to the second list, so that the difference would remain unchanged. It is, of course, necessary to avoid adding equations that say the same thing in a different way. Thus we must not add $\rho = \rho(p, t)$, for although this relationship is true enough, it can be obtained by combining Eqs. 2 and 3. If we write the equation of state in the alternate form $V = mv(p, t)$, then $\rho = 1/v(p, t)$, which is simply another function of p and t.

The preceding arguments can be extended at once to *liquid* systems. In the case of *solid* systems, we have to take precautions to see that the solid is subject to no *stresses* other than pressure and that the pressure is *uniformly* applied to

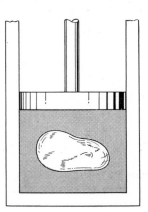

FIGURE **1.6**

all points of the body's surface. Accordingly, the solid may be immersed in a neutral liquid (Fig. 1.6) that will transmit the piston pressure directly to the solid surface. If the body is to be treated this way, it must be homogeneous and noncrystalline, or at least made up of many small crystalline parts arranged in random fashion. (Otherwise, the contraction under pressure will not average the same in all directions and will depend on how the body is cut from the crystalline sample.) Such solids are said to be *homogeneous* and *isotropic*. Like liquids, they have equations of state. The argument for the gas therefore carries through for any single-phase system with these reservations.

Generally it is convenient to call n, the number of independent variables, the number of *degrees of thermodynamic freedom* possessed by the system under the particular restraints imposed. Here degree of freedom is used in the same sense as in mechanics, where we state that a mass point has three degrees of freedom in space, a solid body six, etc.

1.12   The Two-Phase System

Two phases in equilibrium present certain features not possessed by a single pure phase. Consider, for example, water and water vapor (or steam) in equilibrium together (Fig. 1.7). A single value of p and a single value of t exist at every point in the system. But, unlike the single-phase system, this system does not permit p and t to be varied separately. If we push the piston down, instead of increasing the pressure, we merely condense some of the vapor. If the heat released by the condensation is allowed to flow out of the system so that the temperature is held constant, no alteration of pressure occurs. In fact, the only way we can change p is to alter t; that is, p is a function of t, say $p = p(t)$. This functional relation, called the *vapor pressure function*, is quite independent of the relative amounts of liquid and vapor, provided, of course, at least some of each is present.

With this knowledge in mind we may prepare our lists of variables and equations as before. But now the masses, volumes, and densities of the two

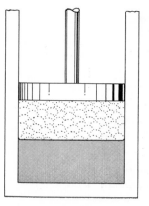

FIGURE **1.7**

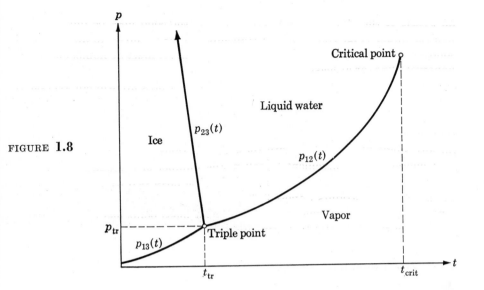

FIGURE **1.8**

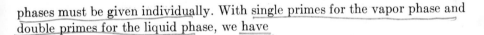

phases must be given individually. With single primes for the vapor phase and double primes for the liquid phase, we have

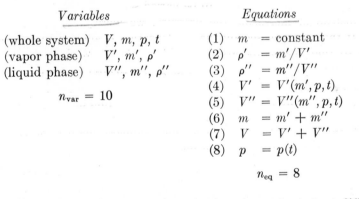

Variables		*Equations*
(whole system) V, m, p, t	(1)	$m = $ constant
(vapor phase) V', m', ρ'	(2)	$\rho' = m'/V'$
(liquid phase) V'', m'', ρ''	(3)	$\rho'' = m''/V''$
	(4)	$V' = V'(m', p, t)$
$n_{var} = 10$	(5)	$V'' = V''(m'', p, t)$
	(6)	$m = m' + m''$
	(7)	$V = V' + V''$
	(8)	$p = p(t)$

$$n_{eq} = 8$$

The result is $n = 10 - 8 = 2$ as before, but there is one important difference. We may choose either p or t but not both for the independent set. With a maximum of one intensive variable permitted, we have what is called a *univariant* system. A great many other choices of variables may be made, including p and V, V and t, and V' and p.

Similar behavior is exhibited by the other two possible phase combinations, the ice-vapor and the ice-water systems. In the first case, the pressure under which the system exists is the vapor pressure of the solid. In the second case, the melting temperature of the ice shifts with pressure, and this dependence fixes the shape of the melting (or freezing) curve. The general relations are shown in Fig. 1.8, where the three pressure functions are designated as $p_{12}(t)$,

$p_{13}(t)$, and $p_{23}(t)$, the subscripts referring to the pairs of phases in equilibrium. These three curves divide the p-t plane into well-defined regions of existence for each pure phase. (The liquid-vapor curve terminates at its upper end at the so-called *critical* point. Above the temperature fixed by this point, no pressure, however large, can liquefy the gas.)

In each domain p and t are independent, so that we have a so-called *bivariant* system (a system with two independent intensive variables). On the boundaries of the single-phase domains, where two phases coexist, the systems are *univariant*. The three curves intersect at the *triple* point, and here the three phases exist stably together. At this point both p and t are clearly fixed, and the system is *zero-variant* (that is, all intensive variables are fixed). Any two-phase system can readily be made zero-variant by simply fixing the pressure. This is the best method of obtaining reproducible fixed temperatures for thermometric purposes, as we shall see in the next chapter.

1.13 Other Systems

There are many other simple mechanical and electrical systems for which the number of independent variables may be determined in much the same way as in the preceding sections.

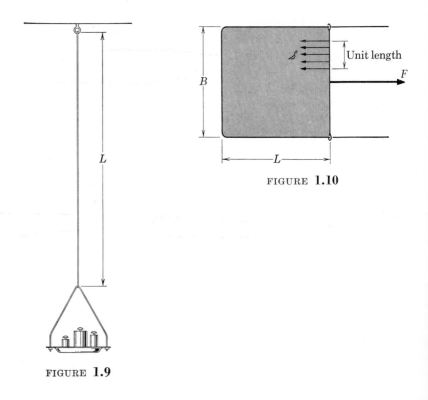

Unit length

F

B

L

L

FIGURE **1.10**

FIGURE **1.9**

Thin Uniform Filament under Tension. Imagine a thin filament with one end attached to a rigid support and the other to a pan containing weights (Fig. 1.9). If the filament is so light that its own weight is negligible compared with that of the pan and weights, the system may be considered under uniform tension, say, T. If the weight of the pan and its contents is W, the cross-sectional area of the filament is A, and the length of the filament is L, we have for the lists of variables and equations

<table>
<tr><td align="center">Variables</td><td align="center">Equations</td></tr>
<tr><td align="center">p, V, t, m, T, W, A, L</td><td>(1) $m = $ constant</td></tr>
<tr><td></td><td>(2) $V = AL$</td></tr>
<tr><td align="center">$n_{\text{var}} = 8$</td><td>(3) $T = W/A$</td></tr>
<tr><td></td><td>(4) $V = V(m, p, t)$</td></tr>
<tr><td></td><td>(5) $L = L(W, p, t)$</td></tr>
<tr><td></td><td align="center">$n_{\text{eq}} = 5$</td></tr>
</table>

Thus $n = 8 - 5 = 3$. A convenient set of independent variables would be W, p, and t, say; or perhaps, since the external atmospheric pressure would in general be fixed, we might reduce n from 3 to 2 and have W and t, T and L, L and t, etc., as possible sets.

Systems with Surface Tension. Consider next a thin film of liquid stretched on a wire frame (Fig. 1.10). When the force, F, is increased, the film may, within limits, be stretched to larger and larger values of the area, A. If $\mathcal{J}$ is the surface tension (the force exerted by the surface film along a line of unit length on whatever is beyond the line), d the thickness, B the breadth, and L the length of the film, we have

<table>
<tr><td align="center">Variables</td><td colspan="2" align="center">Equations</td></tr>
<tr><td>$p_{\text{atm}}, V, t, m, F, A,$</td><td>(1) $p_{\text{atm}} = $ constant</td><td>(5) $B = $ constant</td></tr>
<tr><td align="center">$\mathcal{J}, d, B, L$</td><td>(2) $m \quad = $ constant</td><td>(6) $A = 2BL$</td></tr>
<tr><td></td><td>(3) $V \quad = Ad/2$</td><td>(7) $F = 2B\mathcal{J}$</td></tr>
<tr><td align="center">$n_{\text{var}} = 10$</td><td>(4) $V \quad = V(m, p_{\text{atm}}, t)$</td><td>(8) $\mathcal{J} = \mathcal{J}(t)$</td></tr>
<tr><td></td><td colspan="2" align="center">$n_{\text{eq}} = 8$</td></tr>
</table>

Here Eq. 4 is just the equation of state of the liquid in the film. Eq. 7 states the fact that force F is determined by $\mathcal{J}$ and B, where B is assumed constant. Finally $\mathcal{J}$ is found to be independent of A and hence to be determined by t alone, Eq. 8.

Charged Soap Bubble. Consider now a soap bubble of radius r charged with an electric charge, z, and held in equilibrium by a pressure, p, from an

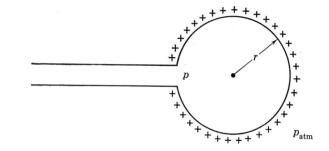

FIGURE **1.11**

external source of gas (not shown) (Fig. 1.11). Making up a set of variables, we have (excluding p_{atm}, which is taken to be fixed)

Variables	*Equations*
$p, V, t, r, A, z, \mathscr{S}$	(1) $V = \frac{4}{3}\pi r^3$
$n_{var} = 7$	(2) $A = 4\pi r^2$
	(3) $r = r(p, \mathscr{S}, z)$
	(4) $\mathscr{S} = \mathscr{S}(t)$
	$n_{eq} = 4$

The third equation expresses the fact that the equilibrium radius must be fixed by the expanding factors, z and p, and the contracting ones, $\mathscr{S}$ and p_{atm}, the latter being constant. Eqs. 3 and 4 are laws of nature, whereas Eqs. 1 and 2 are geometric relations. With $n = 7 - 4 = 3$, useful choices might be p, t, and $z, r, \mathscr{S}$, and z, etc.

It is clear from the foregoing examples that the mere statement that a given system has two or three degrees of freedom is ambiguous unless the definite restrictions involved are stated or implied. Other interesting cases are left for the exercises.

1.14   Quasistatic Processes and Reversibility

Whenever a change is made in the thermodynamic coordinates of a system, we say a thermodynamic *process* has taken place. Thus, if the system undergoes a change in pressure, every part of the system undergoes the same change. If the system originally at A_1 ends at B_1 (Fig. 1.12), we must *not* draw a straight line between these points and say that this line, C_1, represents the "path of the change." For this line represents an infinite succession of states with the same temperature and a gradually rising pressure. In fact, C_1 represents an *infinite succession of equilibrium states*. For a system to change in this way, it is clear that the change must be carried out infinitely slowly, so that at every instant the system is in complete equilibrium and thus actually has thermodynamic coordinates at all times. Such processes are called *quasistatic* processes and can, of course, only be imagined as the ideal limiting cases of real processes carried

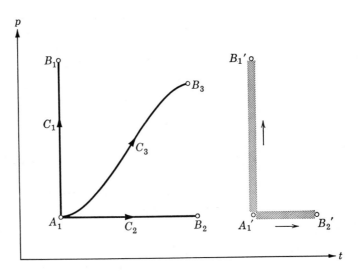

FIGURE **1.12**

out more and more slowly. In the figure, C_1 represents a quasistatic isothermal increase in pressure, C_2 a quasistatic isobaric increase in temperature, and C_3 a general quasistatic change from A_1 to B_3.

In contrast, any process taking place at a *finite* rate is, of necessity, non-quasistatic. Thus a sudden compression, say, from A_1' to B_1', is composed of a rapid succession of nonequilibrium states. The system possesses thermodynamic coordinates only at A_1' and B_1', the beginning and the end of the process. As the piston falls, the pressure and temperature directly beneath the piston are higher than elsewhere. There are mass flow and heat flow, eddy currents arise, shock waves pass through the gas, etc. The state of the system cannot be represented in a simple two-dimensional diagram.[4] For this reason all nonquasistatic processes will be indicated by *hatched* lines ($A_1'B_1'$ and $A_1'B_2'$). This practice will serve as a warning that the system has lost its simple character and may no longer be adequately described by thermodynamic coordinates until equilibrium has been reattained.

In principle, during a quasistatic process the system is always under control. We can stop the process when we desire, have it proceed in the opposite direction, etc. If a gas expands quasistatically (and isothermally) from B_1 to A_1, we can reverse the process in detail and return the system to B_1 by the same path, C_1, by which it originally changed. Under these conditions we say that the quasistatic process is *reversible*. As far as the system is concerned, we have

---

[4] We might imagine the whole system divided into a large number of cells so small that t and p would be essentially uniform in each. Then we could describe the state of the system by giving the values of t and p for each cell. With l cells there would be $2l$ "coordinates" in terms of which to describe the process, and a hyperspace of $2l$ dimensions would be necessary to describe the system at any instant. The image point could be thought of as beginning at A_1 in the plane of Fig. 1.12, moving along some hypercurve in $2l$-dimensional space, and finally ending at B_1' in the plane when the final equilibrium state is reached.

exactly reversed every detail of the original process. This type of reversibility is called *internal reversibility*. The more general sort of reversibility will be taken up in Chap. 5, where we must consider not only reversing the internal effects of a process but also *all external effects*. In general, whenever *frictional effects* of any sort are present (such as friction in the piston-cylinder arrangement used for compressing the gas), there will be definitely irreversible external changes. The gas can be compressed from A_1 to B_1 quasistatically, and we can return the system to A_1 as it was before. If friction produces heat, however, taking the system from B_1 back to A_1 will not convert this heat back to work but will simply produce *more* heat. Thus the external world will not be returned to its original status even though the system itself was!

The sudden compression, A_1' to B_1', in the figure is irreversible also, because we lose control over the details of the process within the system. We are able to control only the piston speed and position. The succession of changes in each minute portion of the gas constitutes the real process, and this succession we cannot control in detail, much less reverse in direction. To be sure, we can expand the gas suddenly from B_1' to A_1', but then another succession of changes will ensue in each minute portion of the gas, and these will definitely not be the ones from the earlier process with simply a change in order. All nonquasistatic processes are in a very literal sense, then, *irreversible processes*.

In summary, processes are irreversible for either or both of the following reasons: (1) they are nonquasistatic; (2) they involve inherently irreversible effects, such as friction.

We must be careful not to confuse irreversibility of a *process* with nonreturnability of a *system* to its original state. It is always possible, in theory, to return a system to its original state after an irreversible process. But in so doing, changes in the outside world take place that can never be undone. In what follows we shall assume that all quasistatic processes are reversible. The simplest way to ensure this is to assume that the mechanism whereby the change is brought about is *frictionless*. More general cases are reserved for later discussion.

Problems

1.1 Make a list of as many properties of physical bodies as you like, and divide them into *intensive* and *extensive* properties.

1.2 Given the equation of state written as

$$V = mv(p, t)$$

how would you write the corresponding forms solved for p and t?

1.3 Make up some complicated systems for yourself, isolate them, and examine the behavior of various intensive variables as equilibrium is reached.

1.4 Carry out the argument of Sec. 1.8 when one of the three bodies has its states fixed not by p and V but by a pair of variables x and y. What are the equations of state for the system? Would complications arise if, say, three variables (x, y, and z) were required for this body?

1.5 Given that the length L of a thin wire under the action of a stretching force F can be expressed as

$$L = a + bF$$

what experiments would be necessary to obtain an equation of state? (Use temperature as defined in Sec. 1.9.)

1.6 In the following cases apply the analysis of Secs. 1.11, 1.12, and 1.13 to obtain a suitable value for n, the number of degrees of freedom. Select a possible set of independent variables in each case.

(a) A gas is confined at constant volume.

(b) A soap bubble is formed at the end of a tube connected to a metal reservoir of gas.

(c) A three-phase system consists of the solid, liquid, and vapor phases of a pure substance.

(d) A three-phase system is made up of solid salt, salt solution, and water vapor.

1.7 Plot the curves that separate the p-t plane for water into the stable domains of ordinary ice, liquid water, and steam.

1.8 Consider a condenser, C (Fig. 1.13), bearing a charge, z. Suppose the charge is supplied by a potentiometer so that the charging potential, E, may be varied by sliding the contact to right or left. Taking the condenser and its dielectric as the system, discuss the problem of independent variables, and choose a possible set.

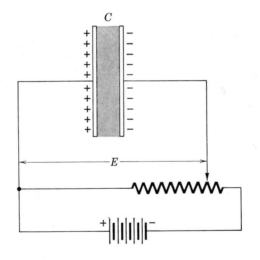

FIGURE **1.13**

CHAPTER TWO

Temperature

2.1 Measurement of Temperature

In the first chapter we examined the idea of temperature as an expression of the physiological sense reactions to hot and cold. The physical concept was then deduced from the zeroth law of thermodynamics as that property which is common to all bodies in thermal equilibrium. This deduction led directly to the existence of an equation of state, which for a body under hydrostatic pressure was written

$$t = G(p, V)$$

To put this equation in a more general form, we now imagine the whole argument of Sec. 1.8 to be carried out for three bodies or systems in thermal equilibrium. Let each of the bodies or systems have two degrees of freedom as before, but suppose that for one of them, say, the third, the variables required are not p and V but some other variables (X and Y). Then the analog of Eq. 1.8 becomes

$$t = G_1(p, V) = G_2(p, V) = G_3(X, Y) \tag{2.1}$$

where, as before, the three functions G_1, G_2, and G_3 are undetermined, since the temperature scale has not been settled upon.

Next choose the third system as the *thermometer*, and, since X and Y by definition can be varied independently, keep one of them constant, say, Y at Y_0. Then

$$t = G_3(X, Y_0) = F(X)$$

where $F(X)$ is now the thermometric function and X is the *thermometric property*. If this function is chosen as before to be a linear one, we have from Eqs. 1.13 and 1.14

$$X_t = \alpha' + \beta't \tag{2.2}$$

and
$$t = \alpha + \beta X_t \tag{2.3}$$

where the two forms are equivalent and X_t is written to emphasize the fact

TABLE **2.1**

Thermometer	Thermometric property
Mercury in glass	Length of liquid column
Constant-volume gas	Pressure of gas
Constant-pressure gas	Volume of gas
Platinum resistance	Electrical resistance
Platinum-rhodium thermocouple	Thermal emf
Nitrogen vapor	Vapor pressure of liquid

that X is the value of this variable corresponding to a value of t. Then Eq. 2.2 provides us with a continuous temperature scale as soon as we settle upon a suitable property of a suitable system.

Naturally the thermometric property should be one readily and precisely measurable, but otherwise a wide choice is available, since most physical properties change with temperature. All materials expand on being heated, and so we could perfectly well choose the length, L, of a metallic rod as X. This would give us a thermometer in which constancy of X indicated constancy of t. In practice, the linear expansion of solids is so small that the property is used only in thermostatic devices, rather than in direct-reading thermometers.

Fortunately the volume expansion of liquids is much greater than the linear expansion of solids. It can also be greatly magnified in effect if the expanding liquid in a confining bulb is allowed to overflow into a capillary tube. The length, L, of the liquid column is then X. In this case the external atmospheric pressure should be held constant, although its effects are small.

So many different thermometers have been devised that a few of the more generally used types are listed in Table 2.1, together with the thermometric property, X.

2.2   General Temperature Scales

To set up a specific temperature scale using either Eq. 2.2 or Eq. 2.3, we must determine the two unknown constants. To be definite, let us choose the second equation. To determine α and β, we need two basic or standard temperatures as fixed points. If these standard temperatures are to be the basis of all other temperature scales, it is essential that they be provided by two systems that really provide accurately reproducible temperatures.[1] Accordingly, as shown in Sec. 1.12, we need zero-variant systems. In a zero-variant system all intensive properties, including the temperature, are automatically fixed by the nature of the system. This condition at once suggests a *three*-phase system of a pure substance such as water. And indeed we might employ the triple point of

---

[1] Reproducibility can, in principle, be determined without having a scale defined. Arbitrary marks on the device will do to detect *changes* of temperature.

TABLE **2.2**

t_i	t_s	Name of scale
32°	212°	Fahrenheit
0°	80°	Reaumur
0°	100°	Celsius

water as one of the fixed points were it not for the inconvenience of having to work at a partial vacuum of 4 .5 mm of mercury.

The practical solution, as was pointed out earlier, is to take a pair of two-phase systems that are *univariant* and make each zero-variant by fixing the pressure. The universal choices have long been ice-water and water-steam systems, at a standard atmospheric pressure of 76 cm of mercury at sea level and 45° latitude. The first gives the *ice point* of temperature t_i, and the second the *steam point* of temperature t_s. To obtain a reproducible ice point, it is essential to keep the water in the ice bath saturated with air at all times.[2] For the steam point, it is necessary that the water be boiling actively and that the thermometer be *in the steam and not in the water*. The reason for this requirement is that the actual temperature of the water is affected by the presence of small amounts of solid impurity, whereas the region above the water is maintained at the fixed temperature of pure steam and freshly condensed pure water.

The property X is now measured at the ice point and at the steam point. If the values are X_i and X_s, we substitute in Eq. 2.1 and have

$$t_i = \alpha + \beta X_i$$
$$t_s = \alpha + \beta X_s$$

which, on solving for α and β, give

$$\alpha = t_i - \frac{(t_s - t_i)}{(X_s - X_i)} X_i \tag{2.4}$$

$$\beta = \frac{(t_s - t_i)}{(X_s - X_i)} \tag{2.5}$$

On substituting Eqs. 2.4 and 2.5 in Eq. 2.3, we obtain the defining equation for a general scale based on the property X. This is

$$t = t_i + (t_s - t_i) \frac{(X_t - X_i)}{(X_s - X_i)} \tag{2.6}$$

Particular scales result when numerical values are assigned to t_i and t_s. The three most common assignments are given in Table 2.2.

---

[2] Here the air is not merely an inactive gaseous medium used to transmit pressure to the water-ice system. We have actually a system of *three* phases and *two* nonreacting chemical substances or components. It is, however, univariant, although the temperature at which equilibrium is reached under 1 atm of pure air is slightly *lower* than if the pressure were transmitted by a neutral piston. This complication does not arise in the steam bath, owing to the active boiling of the water. See Beattie and Blaisdell, *Proc. Am. Acad. Arts Sci.*, **71**, 362 (1936); and Beattie, Huang, and Benedict, *Proc. Am. Acad. Arts Sci.*, **72**, 300 (1938). See also Sec. 11.9.

The Celsius or centigrade[3] scale is used throughout the scientific world, and for it Eq. 2.6 becomes

$$t = 0° + 100° \frac{(X_t - X_0)}{(X_{100} - X_0)} \tag{2.7}$$

2.3   Various Celsius Thermometers

We must not conclude that all arbitrariness of the temperature scale has been taken care of in Eq. 2.6. In this equation we have merely fixed the numbers to be assigned to t_i and t_s. X may now be selected from a large number of *properties* of a large number of bodies or *systems*. Each combination will produce its own unique scale. Thus if X is taken to be the length of a metal rod, Eq. 2.7 gives

$$t = 0° + 100° \frac{(L_t - L_0)}{(L_{100} - L_0)} \tag{2.8}$$

where L_t, L_0, and L_{100} are the respective lengths of the rod at t, 0, and 100°C. If we choose a *copper* rod, one scale results; if we choose a *tungsten* rod, another results. The two thermometers agree at the fixed points 0 and 100°C by definition but nowhere else. (For example, the copper rod thermometer reads 50° when the tungsten one reads 54°.)

When X is taken as the electrical resistance, r, of a coil of wire, then

$$t = 100 \frac{(r_t - r_0)}{(r_{100} - r_0)} \tag{2.9}$$

In this case, the *resistance* scale of copper agrees very closely with the *length* scale of tungsten but not with the *resistance* scale of tungsten.

The quantitative behavior, between 0 and 100°C, of several of the thermometers listed in Table 2.1 is given graphically in Fig. 2.1, where the horizontal scale represents temperature readings on the constant-volume hydrogen thermometer, indicated by t_{H_2}; the vertical scale gives the correction, Δt, that must be added to the reading, $t_{X,Z}$, made on any other thermometer using property X of substance Z. Thus $\Delta t = t_{H_2} - t_{X,Z}$.

It is apparent that the corrections are largest for the electrical thermometers and smallest for the gas thermometers. Among the gas thermometers the deviations are greater for a nonpermanent gas such as carbon dioxide than for air or nitrogen, for which they are too small to show on the scale of Fig. 2.1. None of the scales agree exactly except at 0 and 100°C, where they agree by definition.

These differences naturally raise questions of a fundamental character. Why do the various thermometers differ, and which is correct?

To the *first* question, we can answer only that each thermometer provides its own unique scale. There is no a priori reason why similar properties of

---

[3] The Ninth General (International) Conference on Weights and Measures (1948) decided to drop centigrade and adopt the new name of Celsius for this scale.

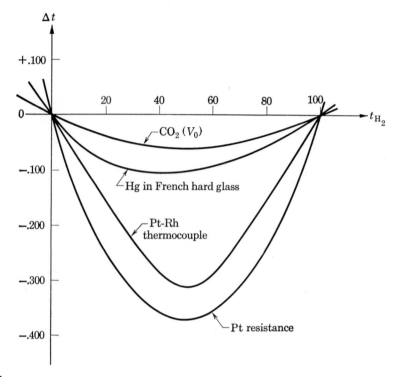

FIGURE **2.1**

different materials should march together with rising temperatures, and, in general, it is pure coincidence if they do. There are as many Celsius scales as there are combinations of property X and substance Z. As to the *second* question, they are of course *all* correct. We must select one arbitrarily to be a *standard* empirical scale. Readings on any other scale must then be corrected to this standard one.

2.4 Criteria for Good Thermometers

A number of criteria govern the choice of a thermometer for a given purpose. For a clinical thermometer, smallness of size, directness of reading, and, to some extent, accuracy may be desirable. For attempts to determine the surface temperature of the sun, however, readability at a distance would be of paramount importance.

In selecting a thermometer for a universal scientific standard, there are similarly well-defined criteria—basically *range, accuracy,* and *reproducibility.* All questions of cost, size, convenience, etc., must be sacrificed to these requirements. Standard thermometers must be capable of giving readings of high precision, and these readings must be reproducible under identical conditions, with the same high precision.

On this basis a number of thermometers fail at once for one reason or another. The ordinary mercury-in-glass thermometer, by using large bulbs and fine capillaries, attains a very open scale. Nevertheless peculiarities in the behavior of the glass prevent such a thermometer from being anything but a convenient secondary instrument. Glass exhibits volume *hysteresis;* that is, its own volume depends not only on its present temperature but also on its *past* thermal history. A glass thermometer heated to a high temperature and then cooled and placed in an ice bath apparently comes quickly to equilibrium. However, the bulb continues to shrink slowly, causing a corresponding secular rise of the ice point, called a *zero-point creep.* This creeping of the ice point evidently presents an asymptotic approach to some limiting bulb volume and may go on for years. Joule kept records for 40 years on the zero point of one of his thermometers; when the thermometer was last examined in 1930, the creep was still in progress and had totaled 0.642°C since 1844.[4] Although modern borax glasses are a great improvement over earlier glasses, they still exhibit this unfortunate property. Zero-point creep renders the fixed points and hence the whole scale of liquid-in-glass thermometers uncertain and so precludes them as standards.

Each of the electrical thermometers has characteristic limitations. The resistance thermometer normally employs chemically inert platinum, but platinum readily absorbs furnace gases and changes its calibration. At very high temperatures the metal also tends to vaporize with a further change. Thermocouples, depending on the thermal emf at the junction of dissimilar metals, are not sensitive to resistance changes but are very sensitive to the purity and method of preparing the metals as well as to subsequent stressing. Convenient as the electrical types are, then, they are not suitable as primary standards.

Their limited range eliminates vapor pressure thermometers and radiation pyrometers as possible primary standards. Only the gas thermometers remain, and, for a number of reasons, they are quite satisfactory. Owing to the large coefficients of expansion of gases, gas thermometers are not only very sensitive but also little affected by vagaries in the relatively much smaller coefficients of expansion of the containers in which the gases are placed.

2.5 Gas Thermometers

There are two important types of gas thermometers, as we have seen: in one the *volume* remains *constant* while $t = t(p)$, say t_p for short; in the other the *pressure* remains *constant* while $t = t(V) = t_V$. Since in actual use as standards these instruments are quite complicated, only a rough indication of their essentials can be given here.[5] The precautions and instrumental corrections are

---

[4] J. H. Poynting and J. J. Thomson, *Heat*, 5th ed., Griffin, London, 1928, p. 8; Ashworth, *Mem. Proc. Manchester Lit. & Phil. Soc.*, **75**, 37 (1930/31).

[5] For details see, for example, Beattie, Jacobs, Gains, Benedict, and Blaisdell, *Proc. Am. Acad. Arts Sci.*, **74**, 327 (1941) (constant-volume type); and Eumorfopoulos, *Proc. Roy. Soc. (London)*, **A81**, 339 (1908) (constant-pressure type).

also numerous and involved and require special treatment for each installation. For this reason gas thermometers are used only for standardization purposes and not for routine measurements; the smaller, cheaper, and more convenient electrical thermometers are always employed routinely.

The Constant-Volume Thermometer.   This instrument consists of a large bulb, B_1, for the thermometric gas, connected by means of a thin capillary with one tube, B_2, of a manometer filled with mercury (Fig. 2.2). The level of the mercury in B_2 is brought to the zero mark, **0**, by raising or lowering B_3, a tube open to the atmosphere and connected to B_2 by a flexible hose. The difference in levels, h, of the mercury in B_2 and that in B_3 can be read on a scale. The total pressure, p, in the gas is then given by $p = p_{\text{atm}} \pm h$, where it is customary to measure all pressures in terms of mercury column heights reduced to their equivalents at 0°C.

To obtain the temperature of a system with this device, we need three pressure readings, p_0, p_{100}, and p_t, made while B_1 is in, respectively, the standard ice bath, the standard steam bath, and the system of which the temperature is desired. Then with $X = p$ in Eq. 2.7 we write

$$t(p) = t_p = 100 \frac{(p_t - p_0)}{(p_{100} - p_0)} \qquad V = \text{constant} \qquad (2.10)$$

The Constant-Pressure Thermometer.   When we attempt to confine a gas at constant pressure, the volume naturally changes with temperature.

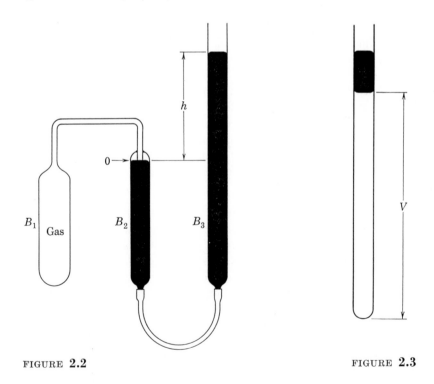

FIGURE **2.2**   FIGURE **2.3**

If we are to make t a simple function of the volume, we must ensure uniform heating of the gas either as a whole or in several parts. Fig. 2.3 illustrates a simple prototype of the constant-pressure gas thermometers in which the gas mass is trapped in a tube of uniform bore by a small drop of mercury. The constant pressure is made up of the atmospheric pressure plus the constant pressure exerted by the small bit of mercury.

Here as before the whole device is placed in the two standard-temperature baths and in the system of which the temperature is desired. If the respective volume readings in these three cases are V_0, V_{100}, and V_t, Eq. 2.7 gives

$$t(V) = t_V = 100\frac{(V_t - V_0)}{(V_{100} - V_0)} \qquad p = \text{constant} \qquad (2.11)$$

In practice such a device as that in Fig. 2.3 must be replaced by a more elaborate one in which the overflow from the main bulb at temperature t is trapped and measured in a second bulb kept at a lower temperature, usually 0°C (see Fig. 2.5). Thus the constant-pressure thermometer is more trouble to construct and use than the constant-volume thermometer. However, the constant-pressure instrument is more satisfactory at high temperatures, since the bulb is not subject to as large a pressure distortion.

2.6   The Thermodynamic Celsius Scale

The tendency of gas thermometer readings to group together more closely than those of other types was mentioned in connection with Fig. 2.1. If we include only the more permanent gases, this tendency is even more striking. Finally, as the density of the gas in the bulb is reduced, the readings draw together even more closely and eventually, in the limit of *zero* gas pressure, converge to a common reading at any particular temperature. This property is illustrated in Fig. 2.4, for two temperatures observed with eight different thermometers. For comparison the temperatures as given on the extrapolated helium scale as a standard are 50 and 150°C, respectively. The two types of thermometers are used for each of the four gases: helium, hydrogen, neon, and nitrogen. In each constant-pressure type the two "unknown" temperatures are measured with the bulb filled to 1 meter of mercury and so on for successively less gas. In each constant-volume type gas is introduced into the bulb to make the ice-point pressure 1 meter, 0.75 meter, etc. The readings vary linearly with p_0 (the *constant* pressure or the *ice*-point pressure, as the case may be), which is plotted horizontally. Actually, at 50°C the constant-pressure helium and the constant-volume neon readings—indicated as He (p_0) and Ne (V_0) in the figure—have already reached the extrapolated value at $p_0 = 1$ meter. The discrepancies are largest for the two constant-pressure nitrogen instruments, but even here are only $+0.056$ and -0.025 at the highest pressure.

It is this remarkable behavior of gases that has led to the universal adoption of the *gas scale extrapolated to zero pressure as the standard temperature scale.* Since it depends on the properties of a gas in the zero-pressure or *ideal* state, it is often called the *ideal gas Celsius scale*. Readings on this scale will be indicated simply by t, or, to emphasize the extrapolation to the limit of zero pressure, t_{lim}. From Eqs. 2.10 and 2.11 this scale is then given by

$$t = t_{lim} = 100 \lim_{p_0 \to 0} \frac{(p_t - p_0)}{(p_{100} - p_0)} \qquad (2.12)$$

where p_0 = filling pressure at the ice point,

or by
$$t = t_{lim} = 100 \lim_{p_0 \to 0} \frac{(V_t - V_0)}{(V_{100} - V_0)} \qquad (2.13)$$

where p_0 = constant pressure of gas. The limits refer to smaller and smaller masses of gas in the bulb as zero pressure is approached.

FIGURE **2.4**

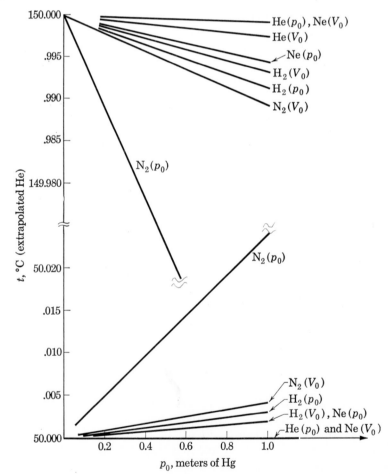

2.7   Boyle's Law and the Ideal Gas Celsius Scale

Since the two limits of Eqs. 2.12 and 2.13 are experimentally identical, we should try to combine the results into a single relation for $t_{\lim}$. Multiplication of Eq. 2.10 top and bottom by V_0 gives

$$t_p = 100 \frac{(p_t V_0 - p_0 V_0)}{(p_{100} V_0 - p_0 V_0)} \tag{2.14}$$

Similar treatment of Eq. 2.11 by p_0 gives

$$t_V = 100 \frac{(p_0 V_t - p_0 V_0)}{(p_0 V_{100} - p_0 V_0)} \tag{2.15}$$

The appearance of the pV product in each equation at once suggests that we examine the bearing of Boyle's law on the problem. This law, although only an approximation to the behavior of real gases, becomes more and more accurate as a gas becomes less dense. It states that the isotherm of a gas for any given temperature may be written

$$pV = \text{constant}$$

Since a rise in temperature will inevitably increase the pV product, this constant must therefore be some increasing (although empirical) function of t. To emphasize this relationship, we write

$$pV = (pV)_t \tag{2.16}$$

where $(pV)_t$ is a constant at fixed t but varies with t.

For a gas at 0°C with pressure p_0 and volume V_0,

$$p_0 V_0 = (pV)_0$$

If the same mass of gas is heated to 100°C and then to any temperature t,

$$p_{100} V_0 = (pV)_{100}$$

and

$$p_t V_0 = (pV)_t$$

These three results in Eq. 2.14 give

$$t_p = 100 \frac{(pV)_t - (pV)_0}{(pV)_{100} - (pV)_0} \tag{2.17}$$

Similarly, if the gas with p_0 and V_0 at 0°C is heated to 100°C and t_0, respectively, with $p = p_0$ throughout,

$$p_0 V_{100} = (pV)_{100}$$

and

$$p_0 V_t = (pV)_t$$

Consequently, Eq. 2.15 becomes

$$t_V = 100 \frac{(pV)_t - (pV)_0}{(pV)_{100} - (pV)_0} \tag{2.18}$$

Thus, for *any gas that obeys Boyle's law*,

$$t_p = t_V$$

and hence the *constant-volume* and the *constant-pressure scales* will be identical.

This conclusion suggests that for any *real* gas we take as the definition of the actual gas Celsius scale simply

$$\left.\begin{matrix} t_p \\ t_V \end{matrix}\right\} = 100\,\frac{(pV)_t - (pV)_0}{(pV)_{100} - (pV)_0} \qquad (2.19)$$

according to whether V or p is constant.

Since, as the pressure is reduced more and more, all gases approximate to Boyle's law behavior, we may *define* the thermodynamic Celsius scale as the common limit of Eq. 2.19 as $p \to 0$. Finally, then,

$$t = t_{\lim} = 100\,\frac{\lim_{p \to 0}(pV)_t - \lim(pV)_0}{\lim(pV)_{100} - \lim(pV)_0} \qquad (2.20)$$

2.8   Empirical Behavior of Gases

Let us now examine the behavior of real gases to see the reason for the behavior of gas thermometers as illustrated in Fig. 2.4. For this purpose we need an exact experimental or empirical equation of state, and the best one[6] represents the pV product as a power series in p; that is,

$$pV = A + Bp + Cp^2 + Dp^3 + Ep^4 + \cdots \qquad (2.21)$$

The coefficients A, B, C, D, etc., are called *virial coefficients*. We refer to A as the first virial coefficient, B as the second, and so on. They are determined to fit the pV data at a given temperature. Eq. 2.21 is thus an empirical *isotherm* for the gas. The virial coefficients should, accordingly, be written A_t, B_t, etc., to indicate their temperature dependence.

Particularly accurate isothermal data of this sort have been obtained at the Reichsanstalt in Berlin by Holborn and Otto.[7] They worked with the most important gases for thermometry, including helium, hydrogen, neon, argon, and nitrogen. The temperatures varied from 400 to $-260°$C (for helium) and involved pressures up to 80 meters of mercury. The temperatures were measured with a platinum resistance thermomometer corrected to the extrapolated helium scale. A few typical results for nitrogen are given in Table 2.3. Here the

[6] Onnes, *Communs. Kamerlingh Onnes Lab. Univ. Leiden*, No. 71 (1901).

[7] Holborn and Otto, *Z. Physik*, **23**, 77 (1924); **30**, 320 (1924); **33**, 1 (1925); **38**, 366 (1926).

TABLE **2.3**

t, °C	A	$B \times 10^3$	$C \times 10^6$	$D \times 10^9$	$E \times 10^{12}$
200	1.73308	0.90133	1.5778		
100	1.36682	0.36057	3.1510		
0	1.00060	−0.60716	5.4056		
−100	0.63434	−3.04600	−3.0667	1.8603	
−130	0.52446	−4.68574	−24.4699	−20.2026	8.4248

unit of pressure is the meter of mercury, and the volume is relative to that occupied by the gas at 0°C and 1 meter of mercury. Under these standard conditions the volume is automatically unity. The other volumes may be interpreted as either relative volumes or *actual* volumes of a mass of gas that would occupy exactly a unit volume at 0°C and 1 meter of mercury (these units are usually referred to as Amagat units).

Each succeeding virial coefficient in the series decreases by a factor of about 10^{-3}. Consequently, the higher terms are negligible for low pressures, and often the first two terms are adequate. The blanks at certain temperatures in the table simply indicate lack of need for the corresponding terms. Although the A values *decrease* regularly with falling temperature, the higher terms become numerically larger as the temperature falls.

The important thing about Eq. 2.21 for the present purpose is that in the limit as $p \to 0$ we have a very simple result, that is,

$$\lim_{p \to 0} (pV)_t = A_t \tag{2.22}$$

where A_t is Boyle's constant. Since this applies for all temperatures, we may replace the limits in Eq. 2.20 by the proper first virial terms A_0, A_{100}, and A_t to give

$$t = t_{\lim} = 100 \frac{(A_t - A_0)}{(A_{100} - A_0)} \tag{2.23}$$

All indications as to whether the thermometer is a constant-volume or a constant-pressure device have disappeared.

One question still remains to be answered. Is the scale given by Eq. 2.23 the same for all gases? If we take the A values for a particular gas, we obtain the extrapolated scale for that gas, which is *defined* by saying that as $p \to 0$,

$$\lim_{p \to 0} (pV)_t = A_t$$

where A_t is to be a *linear* function of t. This is equivalent to saying that $A = X$, the thermometric property, whence

$$A_t = \alpha' + \beta' t$$

TABLE **2.4**

Observed Values of 100a

t, °C	Helium	Hydrogen	Neon	Nitrogen	Argon
400	0.36604		0.36604	0.36603	0.36603
300	.36604		.36603	.36603	.36604
200	.36607	0.36604	.36604	.36592	.36604
100	.36616	.36618	.36604	.36600	.366044
−100	.366044	.36604	.36604	.36602	.36604
−130	.36605				
−207.9		.36608	.36604		
−208				.36604	
−258	.36604				

or, more conveniently, simply

$$A_t = A_0(1 + at) \tag{2.24}$$

Here by definition $A_t \rightarrow A_0$ as $t \rightarrow 0$, and a is a constant defining the scale given as

$$a = \frac{A_t - A_0}{t A_0} \tag{2.25}$$

Values of $100a$ computed with this equation from the data of Holborn and Otto are given in Table 2.4. Constancy of the quantity $100a$ in the case of helium merely shows that the platinum thermometer correctly reproduces the extrapolated helium scale given by Eq. 2.24 over the range of the data from 400 to −258°C. The remarkably consistent behavior of the quantity for the other gases, however, is evidence for the conviction that *all* these gases *do really* give the same extrapolated scale. The quantity a thus appears to be experimentally the same for all gases.

2.9   The Absolute Gas Scale

Expanding Eq. 2.23 gives

$$t = \frac{100 A_t}{A_{100} - A_0} - \frac{100 A_0}{A_{100} - A_0} \tag{2.26}$$

where each of the terms on the right has the dimensions of temperature. The first is variable, whereas the second is a constant and may be transposed to the left, thus:

$$t + \frac{100 A_0}{A_{100} - A_0} = \frac{100 A_t}{A_{100} - A_0}$$

If we add the constant $100 A_0/(A_{100} - A_0)$ to the Celsius temperatures, we have a new scale directly proportional to A_t. If we call this constant T_0, define the new scale by $t + T_0$, and indicate temperatures on this scale by T, we have the so-called *absolute gas scale*, given by

$$T = t + T_0 = \frac{100A_t}{A_{100} - A_0} \qquad (2.27)$$

From the definition of a,

$$T_0 = \frac{100A_0}{A_{100} - A_0} = \frac{1}{a} \qquad (2.28)$$

Averaging the results for the five cases in Table 2.4 gives $a = 0.00366045$, and thus $T_0 = 273.19°C$.

A more accurate determination for the 0 to 100°C interval was made by Heuse and Otto,[8] who, taking into account earlier values, adopted 0.003660*8*, where the italicized digit is uncertain, as the most probable value for a to obtain

$$T_0 = 273.162$$

Revisions of the Reichsanstalt data in 1954 by Otto and by Van Dijk independently reduced the value to

$$T_0 = 273.149$$

As a result the zero for the absolute scale becomes $-273.149°C$.

Of course, such an important constant has been determined by different methods by many observers. Table 2.5 gives the results up to 1955.[9]

Using all the data from 1920 to 1941, Beattie gives as his recommended value

$$100a = 0.36608(\pm 2)$$

TABLE **2.5**

Laboratory	Dates	Number of points	T_0, °C
Bureau International, Paris	1887–1917	15	273.103
Physical Laboratory, Leiden	1900–1933	6	273.135
University College, London	1903–1914	10	273.132
Geophysical Laboratory, Washington	1908–1912	5	273.171
Reichsanstalt, Berlin	1911–1930	63	273.162
Tokyo University, Tokyo	1937	8	273.164
Massachusetts Institute of Technology, Cambridge, Mass.	1939	10	273.166
Reichsanstalt, Berlin (revised)	1954	63	273.149

[8] Heuse and Otto, *Ann. Physik*, **2**, 1022 (1929); **4**, 778 (1930).

[9] Roebuck and Murrel, *Symposium on Temperature, 1st*, New York, 1941, 62–3; and Beattie, *Symposium on Temperature, 1st*, New York, 1941, 74–5. See also Hall, *Symposium on Temperature, 3rd*, Wash., 1954 (1955), Chap. 8, 115–39.

where the italicized digit is uncertain by the quantity in parentheses, and hence, finally,

$$T_0 = 273.165(\pm.015) \tag{2.29}$$

This value is seen to be in agreement with the early value adopted by Heuse and Otto but distinctly higher than the 1954 value of Otto and Van Dijk.

Comparing Eq. 2.20 in its expanded form,

$$t = 100 \frac{\lim\limits_{p \to 0} (pV)_t}{\lim (pV)_{100} - \lim (pV)_0} - 100 \frac{\lim\limits_{p \to 0} (pV)_0}{\lim (pV)_{100} - \lim (pV)_0} \tag{2.20}$$

with Eq. 2.26,

$$t = \frac{100A_t}{A_{100} - A_0} - \frac{100A_0}{A_{100} - A_0} \tag{2.26}$$

and the definition of T from Eq. 2.27,

$$t = T - T_0$$

we have at once

$$T = \frac{100A_t}{A_{100} - A_0} = 100 \frac{\lim\limits_{p \to 0} (pV)_t}{\lim (pV)_{100} - \lim (pV)_0} \tag{2.30}$$

Lord Kelvin demonstrated the identity of the absolute gas scale with a universal temperature scale based on the second law of thermodynamics. As a result the absolute gas scale was renamed the *absolute thermodynamic* or *Kelvin* scale in his honor. Hereafter readings on this scale will be indicated by °K.

2.10   Correction of the Constant-Volume Gas Thermometer

We are now in a position to calculate the difference between $t_{\lim}$ and t_{gas}, where the latter is the reading obtained with an actual gas at any finite pressure. If we let Δt be given by

$$\Delta t = t_{\lim} - t_{gas}$$

then Δt is the correction to be added to t_{gas} to get the extrapolated reading $t_{\lim}$, the thermodynamic Celsius temperature.

To correct the constant-volume reading, we need to find

$$\Delta t_p = t_{\lim} - t_p$$

For this purpose we take $t_{\lim}$ from Eq. 2.23 and t_p from Eq. 2.19. The result is

$$\Delta t_p = 100 \left[\frac{(A_t - A_0)}{(A_{100} - A_0)} - \frac{(pV)_t - (pV)_0}{(pV)_{100} - (pV)_0} \right] \tag{2.31}$$

Since we are calculating a small correction for a gas at low pressure, we may use Onnes' equation (Eq. 2.21), neglecting all terms on the right after the first two. For the temperatures of 0, 100, and t, we have

$$\begin{aligned}
(pV)_0 &= A_0 + B_0 p_0 \\
(pV)_{100} &= A_{100} + B_{100} p_{100} \\
(pV)_t &= A_t + B_t p_t
\end{aligned} \tag{2.32}$$

On substitution in Eq. 2.31 the correction may be written

$$\Delta t_p = 100 \frac{(A_t - A_0)}{(A_{100} - A_0)} \left[1 - \frac{1 + \dfrac{(B_t p_t - B_0 p_0)}{(A_t - A_0)}}{1 + \dfrac{(B_{100} p_{100} - B_0 p_0)}{(A_{100} - A_0)}} \right] \tag{2.33}$$

where the function involving the A's has been taken out as a factor. Since the ratios in the brackets are quite small compared to unity, the expression in the denominator may be expanded by the binomial theorem, with squares and higher terms being neglected. This gives

$$\Delta t_p = \frac{(B_{100} p_{100} - B_0 p_0)}{(A_{100} - A_0)} t_{\lim} - 100 \frac{(B_t p_t - B_0 p_0)}{(A_{100} - A_0)} \tag{2.34}$$

where $t_{\lim}$ has been reintroduced from Eq. 2.23. To eliminate p_{100} and p_t, we may use the approximations from Eq. 2.32 and neglect the B's. Then, since V is a constant,

$$p_t = p_0 \frac{A_t}{A_0}$$

and

$$p_{100} = p_0 \frac{A_{100}}{A_0}$$

which on substitution in Eq. 2.34 give

$$\Delta t_p = \frac{p_0}{A_0} \left[\frac{B_{100} A_{100}}{A_{100} - A_0} t_{\lim} - \frac{B_0 A_0}{A_{100} - A_0} t_{\lim} - \frac{100 B_t A_t}{A_{100} - A_0} + \frac{100 B_0 A_0}{A_{100} - A_0} \right] \tag{2.35}$$

From the definition of the Kelvin scale, Eqs. 2.27 and 2.28, if T_s is the value of T at 100°C and T_i is the value of T at 0°C,

$$\frac{A_{100}}{A_{100} - A_0} = \frac{T_s}{100} = \frac{373}{100} = 3.73$$

$$\frac{A_0}{A_{100} - A_0} = \frac{T_i}{100} = \frac{273}{100} = 2.73$$

and

$$\frac{100 A_t}{A_{100} - A_0} = T = t + 273$$

Since A_0 is nearly unity, we may, for the precision needed in a correction formula, take it as exactly unity. Thus finally

$$\Delta t_p = p_0[3.73B_{100}t - 2.73B_0(t - 100) - (t + 273)B_t] \qquad (2.36)$$

where the unknown t can be replaced by t_p without serious error.

2.11   Correction of the Constant-Pressure Thermometer

First we shall obtain the correction Δt for the simple constant-pressure thermometer prototype illustrated in Fig. 2.3, and then we shall show that the same correction formula applies to observed readings from an actual thermometer.

We begin with the equations for $t_{\lim}$ and t_V, Eqs. 2.23 and 2.15, respectively.

$$t_{\lim} = 100 \frac{(A_t - A_0)}{(A_{100} - A_0} \qquad (2.23)$$

$$t_V = 100 \frac{(p_0 V_t - p_0 V_0)}{(p_0 V_{100} - p_0 V_0)} \qquad (2.15)$$

As before, we use Onnes' equation for the pV products on the right side of the latter equation, obtaining

$$
\begin{aligned}
p_0 V_0 &= A_0 + B_0 p_0 \\
p_0 V_{100} &= A_{100} + B_{100} p_0 \\
p_0 V_t &= A_t + B_t p_0
\end{aligned}
$$

On substitution of these relations, Eq. 2.15 becomes

$$t_V = 100 \left[\frac{A_t - A_0 + (B_t - B_0)p_0}{A_{100} - A_0 + (B_{100} - B_0)p_0} \right] \qquad (2.37)$$

Consequently, for the correction term,

$$\Delta t_V = t_{\lim} - t_V$$

Subtracting Eq. 2.37 from Eq. 2.23 gives

$$\Delta t_V = 100 \left[\frac{A_t - A_0}{A_{100} - A_0} - \frac{A_t - A_0 + (B_t - B_0)p_0}{A_{100} - A_0 + (B_{100} - B_0)p_0} \right] \qquad (2.38)$$

On taking $A_t - A_0$ out of the numerators and $A_{100} - A_0$ out of the denominators, this becomes

$$\Delta t_V = 100 \frac{(A_t - A_0)}{(A_{100} - A_0)} \left[1 - \frac{1 + \dfrac{(B_t - B_0)p_0}{(A_t - A_0)}}{1 + \dfrac{(B_{100} - B_0)p_0}{(A_{100} - A_0)}} \right] \qquad (2.39)$$

On expanding the denominator in the brackets by the binomial theorem and introducing $t_{\lim}$ from Eq. 2.23 as before, we obtain

$$\Delta t_V = p_0 \left[\frac{(B_{100} - B_0)}{(A_{100} - A_0)} t_{\lim} - 100 \frac{(B_t - B_0)}{(A_{100} - A_0)} \right] \tag{2.40}$$

Again using Eq. 2.28 with $A_0 = 1$,

$$\frac{1}{A_{100} - A_0} = \frac{273}{100} = 2.73$$

Finally, then,

$$\Delta t_V = 2.73 p_0 [(B_{100} - B_0)t - 100(B_t - B_0)] \tag{2.41}$$

This is the correction equation for the constant-pressure instrument. Both corrections are seen to vary directly with p_0, thus accounting for the linear behavior of the curves in Fig. 2.4.

We must now look at an actual working model of the constant-pressure thermometer (Fig. 2.5). As the gas in the main bulb, B_1, is heated to temperature t, it is allowed to overflow into a second bulb, B_2. The pressure is adjusted to a constant value by raising the mercury level in the open manometer tube, B_3, to a predetermined height, h_0, above the mercury level in B_2.

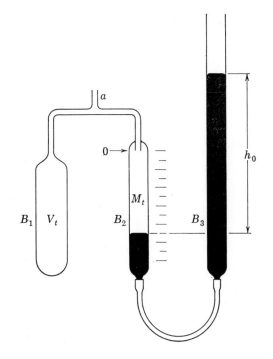

FIGURE **2.5**

At the start, gas is introduced through the side tube, a, until the mercury in B_3 has been forced to the desired height above the level in B_2. Then, with B_1, B_2, and B_3 at 0°C, a is sealed off. The volume of gas in B_2 is read as M_t under the constant operating pressure, $p_0 = p_{atm} + h_0$.

B_1 is then placed in a steam bath, the pressure is readjusted to p_0, and the overflow into B_2 is again read. This is the volume M_{100}. For any unknown temperature, t, the overflow into B_2 is M_t. The volume of main bulb, V_t, is at t, while the overflow, M_t, is always at 0°C. (The capillary is regarded as a part of the volume of B_1, and for this treatment expansion of the apparatus and any nonuniformity of heating in the capillary are neglected.)

Equation 2.2 serves as the starting point for setting up a constant-pressure temperature scale. For any arbitrary volume V of gas at a uniform temperature we write

$$V = \alpha' + \beta' t = \alpha' \left(1 + \frac{\beta'}{\alpha'} t\right) \tag{2.42}$$

Since $\alpha' = V_0$ and we may write $\beta'/\alpha' = b$ (another constant), the general result becomes

$$V = V_0(1 + bt)$$

For any mass of m grams of gas we may write $V_0 = mv_0$, where v_0 is the volume of 1 g at 0°C and p_0. Thus the general relation

$$V = mv_0(1 + bt) \tag{2.43}$$

is really the basis of the constant-pressure temperature scale.

Solving this equation for m gives

$$m = \frac{V}{v_0(1 + bt)} \tag{2.44}$$

If the same mass of gas is broken up into separate masses m_1 and m_2 with coordinates V_1 and t_1 and V_2 and t_2, respectively, and the pressure is p_0 as before, we have

$$m = m_1 + m_2 = \frac{V_1}{v_0(1 + bt_1)} + \frac{V_2}{v_0(1 + bt_2)} = \frac{V_{total}}{v_0(1 + bt_3)} \tag{2.45}$$

where V_{total} represents the sum of the volumes of the two separate masses when they are at some common temperature, t_3.

We now apply this general relation to the gas divided as in Fig. 2.5 with $V_1 = V_t$, $t_1 = t$, $V_2 = M_t$, $t_2 = t_3 = 0°C$, and $V_{total} = V_0 + M_0$ when

$$\frac{V_t}{1 + bt} + M_t = V_0 + M_0 \tag{2.46}$$

Since we are neglecting the expansion of bulb B_1, $V_t = V_0$. Solving Eq. 2.46 for t (which is really t_V) gives

$$t = t_V = \frac{1}{b}\left(\frac{\Delta M_t}{V_0 - \Delta M_t}\right) \tag{2.47}$$

where $\Delta M_t = M_t - M_0$. On setting $t_V = 100$ and $\Delta M_t = M_{100} - M_0 = \Delta M_{100}$,

$$\frac{1}{b} = 100 \left(\frac{V_0 - \Delta M_{100}}{\Delta M_{100}} \right)$$

and finally Eq. 2.47 becomes

$$t_V = 100 \left(\frac{V_0 - \Delta M_{100}}{\Delta M_{100}} \right) \left(\frac{\Delta M_t}{V_0 - \Delta M_t} \right) \tag{2.48}$$

To express this relation in terms of the virial constants, we return to Onnes' equation, retaining only the first two terms as before.

$$p_0 V_t = A_t + B_t p_0 \tag{2.49}$$

Here the constant A_t refers to that mass of gas occupying exactly unit volume at $p = p_0$. If we have k such mass units, we rewrite Eq. 2.49 to read

$$p_0 V = k(A_t + B_t p_0) \tag{2.50}$$

where V refers to k mass units of gas. Solving for k gives us

$$k = \frac{p_0 V}{A_t + B_t p_0} \tag{2.51}$$

which is the analog of Eq. 2.44. Now as before let the gas be divided into two separate masses k_1 and k_2 (the first in B_1 and the second in B_2), where $k_1 + k_2 = k$.

Then, under the same conditions as in Eq. 2.46, Eq. 2.51 becomes

$$\frac{p_0 V_t}{A_t + B_t p_0} + \frac{p_0 M_t}{A_0 + B_0 p_0} = \frac{p_0 (V_0 + M_0)}{A_0 + B_0 p_0} \tag{2.52}$$

which can readily be put in the form

$$\frac{V_0}{V_0 - \Delta M_t} = \frac{A_t + B_t p_0}{A_0 + B_0 p_0} \tag{2.53}$$

where V_t has been set equal to V_0 as before.

We can solve Eq. 2.53 to obtain the ratio $\Delta M_t / (V_0 - \Delta M_t)$ that occurs in Eq. 2.48.

$$\frac{\Delta M_t}{V_0 - \Delta M_t} = \frac{A_t - A_0 + (B_t - B_0) p_0}{A_0 + B_0 p_0} \tag{2.54}$$

Eq. 2.48 shows the left side of Eq. 2.54 to be directly proportional to t_V. To obtain the proportionality constant in Eq. 2.48, we have simply to set $t = 100°C$ and invert both sides of Eq. 2.54. The result is

$$\frac{V_0 - \Delta M_{100}}{\Delta M_{100}} = \frac{A_0 + B_0 p_0}{A_{100} - A_0 + (B_{100} - B_0) p_0} \tag{2.55}$$

Direct substitution of the last two relations in Eq. 2.48 gives

$$t_V = 100 \left[\frac{A_t - A_0 + (B_t - B_0) p_0}{A_{100} - A_0 + (B_{100} - B_0) p_0} \right] \tag{2.56}$$

This is precisely the relation we obtained earlier, in Eq. 2.37, for the simple prototype constant-pressure device. Hence the argument would carry on from this point as before, and we should arrive at the same final correction formula, Eq. 2.41, for the practical form of the constant-pressure thermometer.

2.12 Numerical Magnitudes of Corrections

The corrections calculated from Eqs. 2.36 and 2.41 contain only the second virial coefficients in a form that involves the difference between positive and negative terms of very nearly the same magnitude. As a result, the numerical corrections depend very much upon how the B values are determined. In order to obtain consistent and evenly varying results over a wide temperature range, Holborn and Otto found it necessary to smooth the original B values by using an analytical temperature function of the form

$$B \times 10^5 = a + b\frac{T}{100} + 10^2\frac{c}{T} + 10^6\frac{d}{T^3} \tag{2.57}$$

The coefficients a, b, c, and d were determined for each gas. Then smoothed B values for the desired temperatures were calculated from Eq. 2.57 and these only were used to obtain the final numerical corrections for the reduction of observed gas thermometer readings to the thermodynamic Celsius scale.

Table 2.6 gives corrections calculated from smoothed B values for the important thermometric gases helium, hydrogen, and nitrogen. Smoothed B values for these gases as well as for neon are given in Appendix 2.1.

On the whole, the corrections are least for the constant-volume thermometers. They increase very rapidly for the constant-pressure types as the temperatures approach the normal boiling points of the liquefied gases. It is not usually necessary to apply the corrections above 500°C since the normal uncertainties of measurement in that range are of the same order of magnitude as the corrections.

An independent method for calculating the corrections is furnished by the Joule-Kelvin effect (Chap. 12). Although the results are somewhat limited, they are in substantial agreement with those of Holborn and Otto.[10] A careful re-examination of the whole field has been made by Keyes,[11] who has represented the B value data by expanding the product $BT^{1/4}$ as a power series in $I/T^{1/4}$. Thus for helium and hydrogen

$$BT^{1/4} = a_0 - a_1\frac{1}{T^{1/2}} - a_2\frac{1}{T}$$

is adequate, whereas for nitrogen the best fit is obtained with

$$BT^{1/4} = a_0 - a_1\frac{1}{T^{3/4}} - a_2\frac{1}{T^{15/4}}$$

The agreement with the older correction data is very good, except perhaps for nitrogen.

---

[10] Roebuck and Osterburg, *Phys. Rev.*, **48,** 450 (1935).

[11] Keyes, *Symposium on Temperature, 1st,* New York, 1941, 45–59; and Roebuck and Murrell, *Symposium on Temperature, 1st,* New York, 1941, 60–73.

TABLE **2.6**

*Corrections for Gas Thermometers**

t, °C	Constant pressure			Constant volume		
	Helium	Hydrogen	Nitrogen	Helium	Hydrogen	Nitrogen
459	12		670	61		190
400	10		550	46		150
300	6		320	23		80
200	2	20	132	8	17	27
150	1	8	56	3	7	11
50	0	−3	−25	−1	−2	−4
−50	2	18	112	2	3	15
−100	6	82	399	9	15	52
−150	18	139		18	28	
−200	46	368		28	47	
−250	195			43		
−260	500			48		

* In units of 0.001°C; calculated from Eqs. 2.36 and 2.41 with the smoothed B values of Holborn and Otto, Z. *Physik*, **38**, 365 (1926) (data below 0°C), and **33**, 10 (1925) (data above 0°C). Corrections are positive unless otherwise indicated.

The best over-all indication of the reliability of the extrapolated gas scale is given by measurement with two thermometers employing different gases side by side in a temperature bath or by direct comparison of constant-volume and constant-pressure readings.[12] Such tests amply confirm the preceding arguments.

2.13 Primary and Secondary Thermometers

The use of gas thermometers for high-precision work requires time, patience, and many precautions and repetitions to reduce errors to a minimum. Care must, of course, be taken to ensure that all parts of the main bulb are at a uniform temperature and that the bulb does not suffer any permanent sag or volume change at high temperatures. Pure platinum is a better bulb material than porcelain. Errors that may be corrected for by calculation include these:

1. The error due to nonuniform heating of the gas in the capillary and in any "dead space." If these volumes are kept as small as possible compared with the main volume, the correction need not be more than 5° at 1000°C.

2. The error due to the expansion of the gas container. The coefficient of expansion of the bulb must be known to be below 1%, since otherwise this correction might amount to as much as 45° at 1000°C.

[12] Callendar, *Proc. Roy. Soc.* (*London*), **A83**, 106 (1910); and Eumorfopoulos, *Proc. Roy. Soc.* (*London*), **A90**, 189 (1914).

In spite of all precautions, the experimental uncertainties in gas thermometry with the conventional types of instruments increase rapidly above 500°C until they reach the order of $\pm 1°$ at 1000°C. The errors have been traced in part to variation in the actual amount of free gas in the system due to absorption and desorption as the temperature of the bulb is altered. A type of thermometer known as the constant-bulb-temperature gas thermometer reduces these effects so much that a precision of $\pm 0.1°$ at 1000°C is claimed for it.[13] In principle, the temperature of the bulb is calculated from the pressure drop when, with the bulb at T, the gas is allowed to overflow into a side vessel of known size and temperature. The desorption on pressure reduction at a high temperature is much less than that due, say, to heating the bulb from the ice point to T. (See Problem 2.9 for the first-order theory.)

As was emphasized earlier, the very size, cost, slowness of response, and difficulty in use of gas thermometers mean that they are suitable only for primary standards. For general laboratory use it is necessary to employ electrical thermometers calibrated either directly against a primary gas instrument or, more readily, by means of fixed points already so determined.

For the standardization of secondary thermometers a number of primary fixed points are available, the temperatures of which have been determined with great care on the thermodynamic Celsius scale. The General Conference on Weights and Measures adopted in 1927 and amended in 1948[14] a set of primary fixed points for the calibration of secondary thermometers. These points are the basis of the so-called International Temperature Scale. Values of the secondary temperatures are given in Table 2.7, for systems under standard atmospheric pressure of 76.0 cm of mercury with a standard gravity of 980.665 cm/sec².

TABLE **2.7**

Primary Fixed Points

System	$t,$ °C
Boiling oxygen	-182.97
Ice water (by definition)	(0.000)
Steam bath (by definition)	(100.000)
Boiling sulfur	444.60
Freezing silver	960.8
Freezing gold	1063.

[13] Moser, Otto, and Thomas, *Z. Physik,* **147**, 58, 76 (1957).

[14] *The International Temperature Scale of 1948*, National Physical Laboratory, Teddington, England, 1948; Wensel, *Symposium on Temperature, 1st*, New York, 1941, 21; Blaisdell and Kaye, *Symposium on Temperature, 1st*, New York, 1941, 135; A. L. Day and R. B. Sosman, *A Dictionary of Applied Physics*, Macmillan, London, 1922, Vol. I; and Day and Sosman, *Carnegie Inst. Wash. Publ.*, No. 137, 103 (1911).

TABLE **2.8**

Secondary Fixed Points

System	t, °C
Boiling helium	−268.93
Boiling hydrogen	−252.78
Boiling neon	−246.09
Boiling nitrogen	−195.81
Freezing mercury	−38.7
Condensing naphthalene	−218.0
Condensing mercury	365.58
Freezing antimony	630.5
Freezing palladium	1552.
Freezing platinum	1769.
Melting tungsten	3380.

The International Temperature Scale as realized by properly specified secondary instruments calibrated at the fixed points probably approximated the true thermodynamic scale as closely as possible when first adopted. Good evidence exists, however, that the normal boiling point of sulfur is 444.70 rather than 444.60°C,[15] the value adopted in 1948, and the melting point of gold is now reported as 1064.76(±.1) rather than 1063°C.

For many measurements it is useful to have other fixed points with temperatures referred to those of the primary points. These constitute the secondary fixed points[16] (see Table 2.8).

2.14   The Platinum Resistance Thermometer

A very satisfactory secondary thermometer is the platinum resistance thermometer. It consists essentially of a fine coil of pure platinum wire wound on a core, with special precautions being taken to prevent stressing the wire. To prevent contamination by furnace gases, the coil and assembly are placed in a suitable sealed tube, either evacuated or containing dry gas. To avoid errors due to the resistance of the leads to the coil itself, Callendar introduced a pair of dummy leads that follow the actual leads as closely as possible and are short-circuited at one end. Fig. 2.6 shows the coil and its leads in one arm of a Wheatstone bridge with the dummy leads in series with the variable resistance, X. Since R_1 and R_2 are the equal ratio arms of the bridge, X measures only the resistance, r, of the coil.

---

[15] Stimson, *J. Research Natl. Bur. Standards*, **42**, 216 (1949).

[16] For a selection of low-temperature fixed points, see Hoge and Brickwedde, *J. Research Natl. Bur. Standards*, **22**, 351 (1939); Hoge, *Symposium on Temperature, 1st*, New York, 1941, 141; and Scott, *Symposium on Temperature, 1st*, New York, 1941, 206.

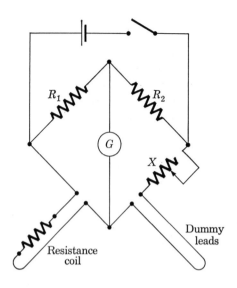

FIGURE **2.6**

Returning to the definition of the Celsius scale, with $X = r$ we have

$$t_{r,\text{Pt}} = t_{\text{Pt}} = 100\,\frac{(r_t - r_0)}{(r_{100} - r_0)} \tag{2.58}$$

For calibration, the resistance of the coil must be measured at 0 and 100°C (r_0 and r_{100}, respectively). Since a platinum scale agrees with the thermodynamic scale only at 0 and 100°C, a correction formula is needed for reducing the readings to the latter scale.

The easiest way to obtain this formula is by Callendar's method.[17] He has shown that the resistance, r, can be represented by a power series in t, of the form

$$r_t = r_0(1 + at + bt^2) \tag{2.59}$$

At 100°C this reduces to

$$r_{100} = r_0(1 + 100a + 100^2 b) \tag{2.60}$$

Substitution of these values in Eq. 2.58 gives

$$t_{\text{Pt}} = \frac{(at + bt^2)}{(a + 100b)} \tag{2.61}$$

The desired correction formula, $\Delta t = t - t_{\text{Pt}}$, then results on subtracting the right-hand term of Eq. 2.61 from t. After some rearrangement there results

$$\Delta t = \frac{(-b \times 10^4)}{(a + 100b)}\left[\left(\frac{t}{100}\right)^2 - \left(\frac{t}{100}\right)\right]$$

or

$$\Delta t = \delta\left[\left(\frac{t}{100}\right)^2 - \left(\frac{t}{100}\right)\right] \tag{2.62}$$

---

[17] Callendar, *Phil. Trans., Roy. Soc. London,* **A178,** 160 (1887).

where δ has been substituted for $(-b \times 10^4)/(a + 100b)$. The value of δ is very sensitive to the presence of impurities in the platinum, being $+1.50$ for the purest samples.

Since the correction formula involves the unknown value of t itself, it is necessary to use a process of successive approximations to find Δt. Thus t_{Pt} as calculated from Eq. 2.61 is substituted in Eq. 2.62 as a first approximation for t. This gives a first approximation to Δt, which gives a second approximation to t, and so on.

Once a platinum instrument with properly specified coil has been standardized, it reproduces the thermodynamic scale between 0 and 660°C within a few hundredths of a degree. The platinum thermometer has accordingly been taken as the legal definition for this range of the International scale.[18]

2.15   The Thermocouple

When two different metals, A and B, are arranged as shown in Fig. 2.7(a), with one junction at 0°C and the other at t, a thermal emf is produced that can be

FIGURE **2.7**

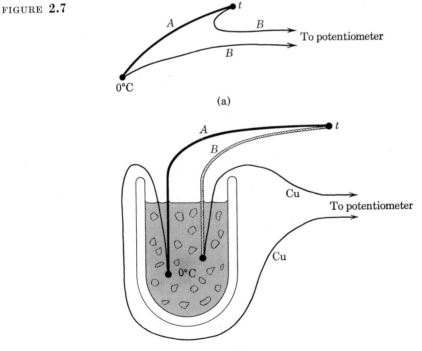

(a)

(b)

[18] E. Griffiths, *Methods of Measuring Temperature*, Griffin, London, 1925, Chap. 3, pp. 30–60; and Mueller, *Symposium on Temperature, 1st*, New York, 1941, 162–79. See Hoare, *Phil. Mag.*, (7)**7**, 384 (1929), for a short-cut in using Callendar's equation. For the use of a four-constant correction formula for temperatures below 0°C, see Henning and Heuse, *Z. Physik*, **23**, 95 (1924); Van Dusen, *J. Am. Chem. Soc.*, **47**, 326 (1925); and Moser, *Ann. Physik*, **6**, 852 (1930).

TABLE **2.9**

Useful Thermocouples

Pair	Typical emf, mv	Max t, °C	Usual t, °C
Copper-constantan	4.3	600	−200 to + 300
Iron-constantan	5.3	1000	−200 to + 750
Chrome P-alumel	4.1	1350	−200 to +1200
Platinum-(10% rhodium + 90% platinum)	0.64	1700	−200 to +1450

measured on a potentiometer. When the second metal, *B*, is *not* copper, the arrangement of Fig. 2.7(a) must be modified as shown in Fig. 2.7(b), where the junctions of both *A* with copper and *B* with copper are placed side by side in an ice bath. This modification effectively prevents unknown emf's at the other metallic junctions in the circuit, which would otherwise be at variable or unknown temperatures. Precaution must also be taken to avoid stressing the wires of the thermocouple in any way, as stressing alters the emf observed.

Many metallic combinations are available as thermocouples, and a few of the more common ones are listed in Table 2.9. The first column gives the combination of metals, the second typical emf's (in millivolts) developed when one junction is at 0 and the other at 100°C, and the last two the maximum temperature and the usual operating temperature range, respectively.

Since the behavior of a given pair of metals or alloys depends upon the exact composition and past history of the sample, each must be calibrated if possible in the position in which it is to be used.

The emf, *E*, of a thermocouple can be represented by a relation of the form

$$E = a_0 + a_1 t + a_2 t^2 + a_3 t^3 + \cdots \tag{2.63}$$

where the last term is unnecessary for limited ranges. Since these constants may not with safety be taken from standard tables, it is necessary either to determine the departure of the given couple from the behavior of average samples as published in tables[19] or to determine the constants by direct calibration at a suitable number of points.

2.16   New Basis for the Thermodynamic Scale

Lord Kelvin defined the thermodynamic scale in 1854 but pointed out that ultimately it would be necessary to base the degree size not on the ice-steam

---

[19] Adams, Session on Pyrometry, American Institute of Mining and Metallurgical Engineers, Chicago, Sept., 1919; *J. Am. Chem. Soc.*, **36**, 65 (1914); and Roaser, *J. Research Natl. Bur. Standards*, **3**, 343 (1929). Excellent general accounts appear in Roaser, *Symposium on Temperature, 1st*, New York, 1941, 162–205 (use and theory), 284–313 (testing.)

interval but rather on the absolute zero-ice point interval. This adjustment was later recommended by Mendeleev and by Giaque.[20] Finally the Tenth General Conference on Weights and Measures[21] in 1954 adopted the proposal by defining the triple point of water as 273.16°K (or the ice point as 273.15°K). On this basis the *size* of the degree does not alter owing to newer and better measurements; rather the boiling point of water, instead of being 373.15°K by definition, may vary in the last place. Since this variation will represent at most a few parts in 37,000, it is insignificant for most purposes. The result of having the ice-steam interval an experimental number rather than 100° by definition is a small price to pay for the advantages gained.

There are two principal advantages. Since most thermodynamic formulas involve T (and $T = T_i + t$), any revision of the value of T_i at once necessitates small changes in every thermodynamic table. Adoption of a fixed value for T_i eliminates this necessity. Further, in low-temperature work the new scale is much preferable to the old one. Suppose an experimental temperature of $-272.00°C$ is reported. Conversion of this to the Kelvin scale requires selection of a value for T_i. The uncertainty in $T_i - 272.00$ may well be a hundred times as great as that in the original experimental number, $t = -272.00°C$. The newly redefined Kelvin scale avoids this difficulty.

Problems

2.1　Find the diameter of bore necessary to give a thermometer with 1°C marks 1 cm apart when 30 g of mercury is used in the bulb. Use Jena 59III (so-called Jena normal) glass. Neglect the expansion of the capillary.

2.2　What is the effect of the expansion of the capillary neglected in Problem 2.1? Obtain an algebraic expression for the correction necessary to reduce the apparent temperature, t_a, as read off the stem, to the actual Celsius temperature, t. Compute the actual temperature when $t_a = 50.00°C$. The thermometer is assumed to read correctly at the 0 and 100°C marks.

2.3　When the thermometer of Problem 2.1 is heated to 200°C and cooled in an ice bath, it shows a freezing point depression of 0.01°. If a constant-volume gas thermometer using nitrogen is subject to the same treatment, what would you expect its freezing point depression to be?

2.4　Work through the algebra leading to Eq. 2.41, which gives the correction, Δt, required to reduce the actual gas scale readings for a constant-pressure thermometer at pressure p_0 to the ideal gas scale readings. If such a thermometer containing pure nitrogen at $p_0 = 1$ meter of mercury gives a reading of 150.000°C, what is the true ideal gas scale reading? See Appendix 2.1 for values of the second virial coefficient, B.

2.5　Given a platinum resistance thermometer of metal of purity such that $\delta = +1.50$, compute the ideal gas scale temperature when the observed platinum temperature, t_{Pt}, is 350.00°C.

[20] Giaque, *Nature*, **143**, 623 (1939).

[21] Stimson, *Am. J. Phys.*, **23**, 614 (1955).

2.6 Assume that the emf produced by a given thermocouple, with one junction at 0°C and the other at t, can be represented by

$$E = a_0 + a_1t + a_2t^2$$

Taking $E = X$, the thermometric property, define a Celsius scale in terms of thermal emf's, and obtain a formula for calculating the correction $\Delta t = t - t_E$, t_E being the value of the temperature calculated from the definition.

2.7 Verify the statement made in Sec. 2.3 that the readings of Celsius thermometers based on the change in length of copper and tungsten rods will differ by about 4° when the copper rod thermometer reads 50°C.

2.8 Calculate the correction, Δt, for reducing an observed reading of 300°C on a constant-volume helium thermometer with $p_0 = 1$ meter of mercury to the actual Celsius temperature. (See Appendix 2.1.)

2.9 In the new constant-bulb-temperature gas thermometer of Moser, Otto, and Thomas,[13] each absolute temperature is calculated from the drop in pressure as the hot gas is allowed to expand into and cool in a known outside volume. Thus, in Fig. 2.5 with bulb B_1 at T, the mercury in B_2 is adjusted to the zero mark, and the pressure is read as p_i. Then with B_1 at the *same temperature*, the gas is allowed to expand into B_2 and cool to, say, T_0. Call the outside volume M_t as in the figure and the end pressure p_e. Show that to a first approximation the equivalent of the constant mass relation, Eq. 2.45, may be written for this case as

$$m = m_1 + m_2 = \frac{p_e V_t}{rT} + \frac{p_e M_t}{rT_0} = \frac{p_i V_t}{rT}$$

where r is the gas constant per unit mass of gas, so that the temperature of the bulb becomes

$$T = T_0 \left(\frac{p_i - p_e}{p_e}\right)\left(\frac{V_t}{M_t}\right)$$

(The expansion of the gas from p_i to p_e with the bulb at constant temperature produces very small desorption of gas compared with that caused by heating the bulb from the ice point to T when T is high.)

CHAPTER THREE

The Equation of State

3.1 The Ideal Gas

Since the equation of state is needed in most discussions of a system, the form and properties of this important function must be considered in some detail. The special case of gases merits most of our attention, beginning with gases in the ideal state. The case of solids and liquids is reserved for a brief discussion at the end of the chapter.

The empirical equation of state of Onnes was used in Chap. 2 in arriving at the absolute gas scale. In the form there used (Eq. 2.21), but with V' replacing V,

$$pV' = A + Bp + Cp^2 + Dp^3 + Ep^4 + \cdots \tag{3.1}$$

This equation has one serious drawback for the present purpose: the mass of gas in question is not fixed. This limitation arises from the use of relative volume or Amagat units, in which the unit volume is taken as that volume occupied by the system at 0°C and 1 unit of pressure. If pressure is, for example, in meters of mercury, the equation may be interpreted as referring to that mass of gas which actually does occupy a unit volume, say, 1 cm³, under these standard conditions. Since the volume is unity, the mass and the mass density, say, ρ_{01}, of the gas, become numerically alike. If we multiply both sides of the equation by the ratio of the molecular weight (really a mass), M, to ρ_{01}, it will refer to a gram-mole of gas. Writing V for $V'M/\rho_{01}$, we have

$$pV = \frac{M}{\rho_{01}} (A + Bp + Cp^2 + Dp^3 + \cdots) \tag{3.2}$$

as Onnes' equation of state referred to 1 g-mole.

In Chap. 2 we saw that the absolute temperature was directly proportional to A. If both sides of Eq. 3.2 are divided by T and the limit is taken as $p \to 0$, then

$$\lim_{p \to 0} \frac{pV}{T} = \lim_{p \to 0} \frac{M}{\rho_{01}T} (A + Bp + Cp^2 + \cdots) = \frac{MA}{\rho_{01}T} \tag{3.3}$$

must in effect be independent of T and the same for all gases. For this reason it is called the universal gas constant, usually designated by R. Fig. 3.1 shows the characteristic behavior for nitrogen when the ratio pV/T (in liter-atmospheres per mole-degree) is plotted vertically versus p. The isotherms, although curved, straighten out at low pressures and converge at a common point, the value of R in these units.

We may write for 1 mole of gas in the ideal state, when the higher terms in Eq. 3.2 vanish,

$$pV = RT \qquad (3.4)$$

or

$$pV = \nu RT \qquad (3.5)$$

where $\nu = m/M =$ the number of gram-moles of gas. Hereafter all equations dealing with gases will refer to gram-molar quantities unless otherwise indicated. When a unit mass of gas is used, lower-case letters will represent specific quantities such as volume per gram. Thus Eq. 3.4 will become

$$pv = \frac{RT}{M} = r_x T \qquad (3.6)$$

where r_x is used to indicate the gas constant per gram for gas x. Since this value varies from gas to gas, the gas in question must be indicated.

The ideal gas law as given here summarizes in a single relation the following information:

1. Boyle's law, since $pV =$ constant when T is fixed,

2. Charles's and Gay-Lussac's laws. A gas heated at constant volume has an average coefficient, $\overline{\alpha_V}$, of pressure increase at constant volume and an average coefficient, $\overline{\beta_p}$, of volume increase at constant pressure, which are both

FIGURE **3.1**

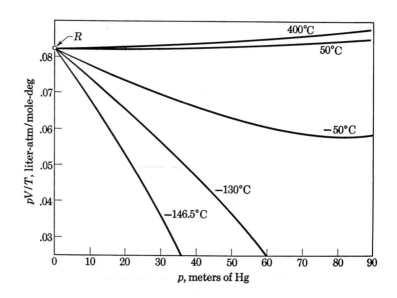

constant and the same for all gases. Here $\overline{\alpha_V}$ and $\overline{\beta_p}$ are defined by the relations

$$\overline{\alpha_V} = \frac{p_t - p_0}{p_0 t}$$

$$\overline{\beta_p} = \frac{V_t - V_0}{V_0 t} \tag{3.7}$$

Use of Eq. 3.4 or Eq. 3.5 shows at once that

$$\overline{\alpha_V} = \overline{\beta_p} = \frac{T - T_0}{T_0 t} = \frac{1}{T_0} \tag{3.8}$$

3. The truth of Avogadro's law. "Equal volumes of all gases at the same temperature and pressure contain equal numbers of molecules." If we have molar quantities of two gases, for which the pressures, volumes, and temperatures are p_1, V_1, and T_1 and p_2, V_2, and T_2, respectively, then from Eq. 3.6

$$\frac{p_1 V_1}{T_1} M_1 r_1 = \frac{p_2 V_2}{T_2} M_2 r_2 = R$$

Therefore, for any two ideal gases,

$$M_1 r_1 = M_2 r_2$$

But $M_1 = N_1 m_1$ and $M_2 = N_2 m_2$, where N stands for the number of molecules of gas and m for the mass. We cannot prove from the perfect gas law alone that $N_1 = N_2$, but this assumption leads to

$$\frac{r_1}{r_2} = \frac{m_2}{m_1} = \frac{M_2}{M_1} \tag{3.9}$$

which is in complete agreement with physical and chemical methods of measuring the relative and absolute masses of molecules.

3.2   The Universal Gas Constant

The value of the gas constant is so important that great care has been devoted to its determination. Since at 0°C $T = T_i = T_0$, where T_0 is the absolute value of the ice point, Eq. 3.3 gives

$$R = \frac{M A_0}{\rho_{01} T_0}$$

Therefore, accurate determination of R depends on a precision measurement of the gas density, ρ_{01}, at 0°C and 1 atm. Since the result also depends on the molecular weight, oxygen is chosen as the standard gas since M is then exactly 32 by definition. Cragoe[1] examined available data very carefully, and Dumond

---

[1] Cragoe, *J. Research Natl. Bur. Standards.*, **26**, 495 (1941).

and Cohen[2] reviewed the pertinent measurements and gave as their best estimate

$$\lim_{p \to 0} (pV)_0 = RT_0 = \frac{MA_0}{\rho_{01}} = 22.4207(\pm 6) \text{ liter-atm}$$

(for the standard acceleration of gravity, g_0, taken as 980.655 cm/sec^2). Since for an ideal gas the pV product at constant temperature is the same for all pressures, this number represents the volume in liters of 1 g-mole of ideal gas at 0°C and 1 atm pressure, the so-called normal molecular volume. The normal molecular volume is therefore 22.4207 liters.

Once this value is obtained, R results on division by T_0. With $T_0 = 273.165°K$, Dumond and Cohen's value for R results (here given in three different units):

$$R = 8.2077(\pm 4) \times 10^{-2} \text{ liter-atm/mole-deg}$$
$$= 8.2079(\pm 4) \times 10^1 \text{ cm}^3\text{-atm/mole-deg}$$
$$= 8.3166(\pm 4) \times 10^7 \text{ erg/mole-deg}$$

The data required for conversion is given in the next section.

3.3 Units

We have already had occasion to use various common sets of units. It is desirable at this point to collect a few of the more important ones.

Since the equations to be developed will in all cases be *complete* equations, that is, equations in which any consistent system of units may be used, no single system will be adhered to. It will therefore be necessary here and in references to the literature to change units frequently. The changes will be facilitated by the following standard conventions and accepted values.

Volume.   Volume is usually measured in cubic meters (meters^3 or m^3), cubic centimeters (cm^3), or liters, where by definition 1 liter = volume of 1 kg of air-free water at the temperature of maximum density. The maximum density of air-free water is 0.999972(± 2) g/cm^3 and hence

$$1 \text{ liter} = \frac{1000}{0.999972} = 1000.028(\pm 2) \text{ cm}^3$$

The thousandth part of a liter, the milliliter (ml), is therefore not exactly the same as 1 cm^3, although the difference is quite negligible for most purposes.

From the preceding definitions

$$1 \text{ meter}^3 = 10^6 \text{ cm}^3 = 0.999972(\pm 2) \times 10^3 \text{ liters}$$

Pressure.   Pressure, as force per unit area, may be in the cgs unit of the dyne per square centimeter or the mks unit of the newton per square meter

---

[2] See Birge, *Repts. Progr. in Phys.*, **8**(1941), 90, where references are given; also Dumond and Cohen, *Am. Scientist*, **40**, 447 (1952).

(new/meter²). Both of these are rather small for the range of pressures important here, and larger units are usually employed. These include the meter of
mercury already used and the standard atmosphere. Each is defined in terms
of the height of a column of mercury of standard density, ρ_0, at 0°C and at a
point where the acceleration of gravity has the conventional or normal value,
g_0. If the size of the standard atmosphere is designated by 1 atm,

$$1 \text{ atm} = h_0 g_0 \rho_0$$

where $h_0 = 76.000$ cm of mercury, $\rho_0 = 13.59504(\pm 5)$ g/cm³, and $g_0 = 980.665$
cm/sec², so that

$$1 \text{ atm} = 1.013246(\pm 4) \times 10^6 \text{ dynes/cm}^2$$

The meter of mercury being 1/0.76 times as large as the atmosphere by
definition,

$$1 \text{ meter of mercury} = 1.315789 \text{ atm} = 1.333218(\pm 5) \times 10^6 \text{ dynes/cm}^2$$

The shift to newtons per square meter is readily made, since 1 new/meter² = 10
dyne/cm².

Pressure-Volume (pV).   Since the pV product is essentially a force times
a distance, it has the units of energy. The corresponding energy units include
the liter-atmosphere and the cubic centimeter-atmosphere. The following
relationships exist:

$$1 \text{ liter-atm} = 1.000028(\pm 2) \times 10^3 \text{ cm}^3\text{-atm}$$
$$= 1.013274(\pm 6) \times 10^9 \text{ ergs} = 1.013274(\pm 6) \times 10^2 \text{ joules}$$

For most purposes these values can be considerably rounded off, with a liter
being taken as 1000 cm³, etc.

3.4   The p-V-T Surface

Since we shall use the equation of state a great deal, let us examine the general
nature of the geometric locus or surface defined by the relation

$$p = p(V, T) \quad \text{or} \quad F(p, V, T) = 0$$

when p, V, and T are measured along mutually perpendicular axes.

For the ideal gas the surface is a simple one with important general properties. A section of this surface is sketched in Fig. 3.2. The intersections of this
surface with planes drawn perpendicularly to the temperature axis give the
isotherms (indicated by T_1, T_2, etc.). These curves are equilateral hyperbolas.
For comparison they are projected on the pV plane in Fig. 3.3, which is what
one would see by viewing the surface from a point at the lower left of Fig. 3.2
and looking along the T axis. Planes perpendicular to the volume axis at V_1,
V_2, etc., intersect the surface in a series of isochores (A_1B_1, A_2B_2, etc.). Despite
the curvature of the surface, these are always straight lines. They indicate the

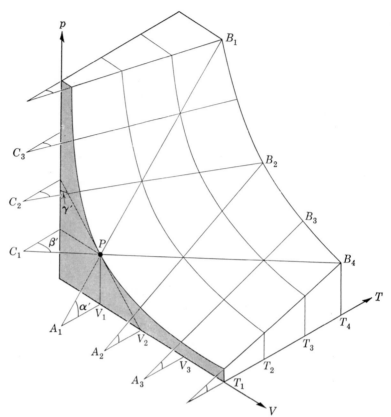

FIGURE **3.2**

linear rise of pressure with temperature at constant volume. If the angle between these isochores and a line parallel to the temperature axis is called α', then α' decreases as the volume is increased. The partial derivative $(\partial p/\partial T)_V$ is the slope of an isochore or the *isochoric rate of pressure increase per degree*, and therefore, if equal scales on the three axes are assumed,

$$\left(\frac{\partial p}{\partial T}\right)_V = \tan \alpha'$$

In a similar way planes perpendicular to the p axis intersect the surface in another set of straight lines (C_1B_4, C_2B_2, etc.), which are *isobars*. The angle between these isobars and a line parallel to the temperature axis is indicated by β'. Here the partial derivative $(\partial V/\partial T)_p$, or the *isobaric volume expansion per degree*, is given by

$$\left(\frac{\partial V}{\partial T}\right)_p = \tan \beta'$$

Finally, if we draw a tangent to an isotherm (as at the point P in Fig. 3.2) and call the angle this makes with the p axis γ', the final partial derivative

$(\partial V/\partial p)_T$ is given by

$$\left(\frac{\partial V}{\partial p}\right)_T = -\tan \gamma'$$

This is the *isothermal volume change per unit pressure rise*. It is *negative* here and, in fact, in general. Thus all stable hydrostatic systems respond with a pressure *rise* when the volume is *diminished*.

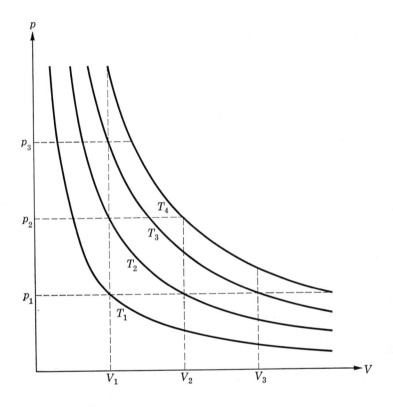

FIGURE **3.3**

The product of these three derivatives at any single point, say, P, is invariably negative.[3] Since $(\partial V/\partial p)_T$ must be negative, the other two must be of the same sign. This sign is normally positive, since most substances expand on heating.

The preceding discussion illustrates a general theorem needed so often that its proof at this point is desirable. Its proof involves the establishment of another result that will also be of frequent use—the reciprocal theorem.

---

[3] This happens to be a specially situated point at which the actual values of the slopes are, in order, $+1$, $+1$, and -1, but the sign condition holds at any point of the surface.

3.5   The Reciprocal and the Reciprocity Theorems

Suppose we have three variables connected by a general relation of the form

$$F(x, y, z) = 0$$

which is assumed to be solvable for any of the three as a dependent variable. If we choose x,

$$x = x(y, z)$$

From the fundamental theorem of the calculus for the differentiation of a function of two variables, dx is given as

$$dx = \left(\frac{\partial x}{\partial y}\right)_z dy + \left(\frac{\partial x}{\partial z}\right)_y dz \tag{3.10}$$

With z regarded as a function of x and y,

$$dz = \left(\frac{\partial z}{\partial x}\right)_y dx + \left(\frac{\partial z}{\partial y}\right)_x dy$$

On substitution of this value of dz in Eq. 3.10 and collection of the terms in dx and dy,

$$dx = \left(\frac{\partial x}{\partial z}\right)_y \left(\frac{\partial z}{\partial x}\right)_y dx + \left[\left(\frac{\partial x}{\partial y}\right)_z + \left(\frac{\partial x}{\partial z}\right)_y \left(\frac{\partial z}{\partial y}\right)_x\right] dy$$

This last result must be true, whatever variables are chosen as independent. If we choose, say, x and y, then it must be true, whatever independent values are assigned to dx and dy. If, in particular, $dy = 0$ and $dx \neq 0$, then the second term on the right drops out and

$$\left(\frac{\partial x}{\partial z}\right)_y \left(\frac{\partial z}{\partial x}\right)_y = 1$$

or

$$\boxed{\left(\frac{\partial x}{\partial z}\right)_y = \frac{1}{\left(\dfrac{\partial z}{\partial x}\right)_y}} \tag{3.11}$$

Eq. 3.11 is the *reciprocal theorem*, which enables us to replace any partial derivative by the reciprocal of the inverted derivative, *provided the same variable is held constant in each case.*

Similarly, with $dx = 0$ and $dy \neq 0$, the coefficient of dy must vanish, and therefore

$$\left(\frac{\partial x}{\partial z}\right)_y \left(\frac{\partial z}{\partial y}\right)_x = -\left(\frac{\partial x}{\partial y}\right)_z$$

or, with application of the reciprocal theorem to the term on the right,

$$\left(\frac{\partial x}{\partial z}\right)_y \left(\frac{\partial y}{\partial x}\right)_z \left(\frac{\partial z}{\partial y}\right)_x = -1 \tag{3.12}$$

This is the *reciprocity theorem*. It can always be written by starting with any of the three derivatives or their reciprocals and permuting the variables in cyclical order clockwise or anticlockwise.

3.6 Thermodynamic Coefficients

The reciprocity theorem applied to the equation of state or p-V-T function gives us

$$\left(\frac{\partial p}{\partial T}\right)_V \left(\frac{\partial V}{\partial p}\right)_T \left(\frac{\partial T}{\partial V}\right)_p = -1 \tag{3.13}$$

In practice, the measured values of these derivatives are not recorded as such in tables of physical constants. The first is hard to measure directly since it is very difficult to heat a body at exactly constant volume. The other two are readily measured but naturally change with the volume considered.

If, however, $(\partial V/\partial p)_T$ is divided by V, the result is independent of the size of the body. This quantity with sign reversed is taken as the definition of the *isothermal compressibility*, κ_T.

$$\kappa_T = -\frac{1}{V}\left(\frac{\partial V}{\partial p}\right)_T \tag{3.14}$$

Division of $(\partial V/\partial T)_p$ by the volume gives the *isobaric coefficient of thermal expansion*, β_p (again independent of V), and

$$\beta_p = \frac{1}{V}\left(\frac{\partial V}{\partial T}\right)_p \tag{3.15}$$

Finally it is convenient to divide $(\partial p/\partial T)_V$ by the pressure to obtain the so-called *isochoric coefficient of pressure rise with temperature*, α_V. Then

$$\alpha_V = \frac{1}{p}\left(\frac{\partial p}{\partial T}\right)_V \tag{3.16}$$

Substitution of the last three equations in Eq. 3.13 gives

$$p\alpha_V\kappa_T = \beta_p \tag{3.17}$$

whence any one coefficient can be found from the other two. The quantities $\alpha_V, \beta_p,$ and κ_T or the corresponding derivatives are often called *thermodynamic coefficients*.

When no equation of state is known, it is convenient experimentally to define *average* coefficients, such as were used in the discussion of the behavior of an ideal gas in Sec. 3.1.

3.7 The *p-V-T* Relation for a Pure Substance

The *p-V-T* surface for a real substance differs markedly from that of an ideal gas. If we begin with a pure substance in the gaseous state and draw the isotherms on the *p-V-T* surface, as the temperature is reduced, we have the general result sketched in Fig. 3.4. The isotherms become more distorted as the critical isotherm is approached. In the figure the equilateral hyperbola *AE* changes to *BCD*, where *C* is the critical point. For temperatures above this critical temperature, no pressure, however large, will liquefy the substance, and we may properly call it a gas. The *ABCDE* portion of the surface therefore represents the gaseous domain. Just below the critical isotherm are three new regions: a liquid domain, *BHGC*; a two-phase region, *CGF*; and a gaseous region, *CFD*. The last region, although continuous with the first gaseous region, represents material that can always be condensed by sufficient increase of pressure and is appropriately called the *vapor* domain. In the two-phase region, liquid and vapor can exist in all proportions, one boundary, *CG*, corresponding

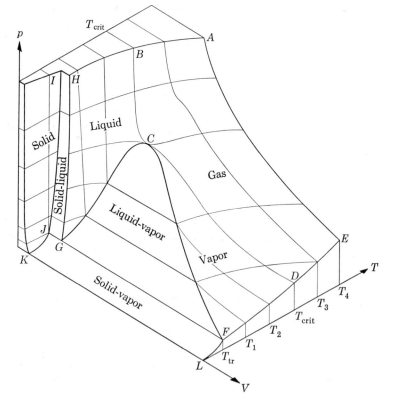

FIGURE **3.4**

to pure saturated liquid, and the other, CF, to pure saturated vapor. The isotherm JGF is the *triple*-line isotherm, since here all the phases—solid, liquid, and vapor—coexist. Above it is the narrow strip, $IJGH$, where solid and liquid coexist, and below it is the solid-vapor region, $JKLF$. The three surfaces of two-phase existence are so-called *ruled* surfaces, made up of straight lines that are isobars.

Since it is important to be able to visualize the surface of Fig. 3.4 as it would appear if projected against either the p-T or the p-V plane, such a projection is represented in Fig. 3.5. The three ruled surfaces of two-phase coexistence are indicated as shaded regions. The two projections are redrawn side by side in Fig. 3.6. In the p-T projection, Fig. 3.6(a), the three ruled surfaces are seen edge on and produce three curves intersecting at the triple point G of temperature T_{tr}. Thus the curves CG and CF of Fig. 3.4 become the liquid-vapor equilibrium curve (or the vapor pressure curve) CG of Fig. 3.6(a). Similarly curves IJ and HG coincide as HG of the new figure, a portion of the solid-liquid equilibrium (or melting) curve. Whereas the vapor pressure curve definitely ends at the critical point, the melting curve extends upward indefinitely (or until another triple point is reached, if more than one solid modification exists). Finally the surface $JKLF$ projects in the new figure into GL, the solid-vapor equilibrium (or sublimation) curve. This latter curve falls as the temperature is lowered either directly or through one or more other triple points to the origin, $p = 0$ and $T = 0°K$. The solid and vapor regions are thus separated into mutually exclusive domains of existence. This is not true for the

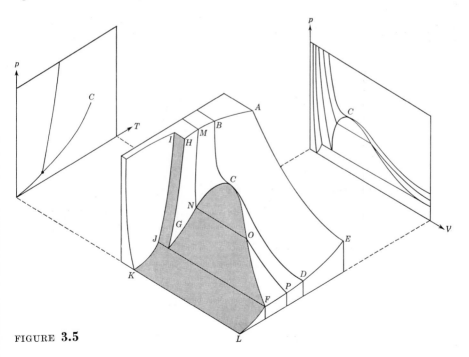

FIGURE **3.5**

liquid and vapor except below the critical temperature, T_c. Above T_c the gas at, say, A in Fig. 3.6(a) may pass to the liquid state, B, with no discontinuous change in any properties ensuing.

In Fig. 3.6(b) the p-V projection exhibits six domains, three of single-phase and three of two-phase existence. The triple line JGF, which projects into the triple point G in Fig. 3.6(a), is the single isotherm common to the three two-phase areas.

The p-V-T surfaces in Fig. 3.4 and Fig. 3.5 were drawn for a substance that expands on melting. For abnormal substances such as water, which contract on melting, the p-V-T surface must be modified as in Fig. 3.7. The solid-liquid domain $GJIH$ is now behind a shoulder of the main surface.

The corresponding projections in the p-T and p-V planes are shown in Fig. 3.8. The melting curve slopes upward to the *left* rather than to the right as in Fig. 3.6. As we shall see in Chap. 11, sloping to the left always accompanies *shrinking* on *melting*, whereas sloping to the right is a necessary result of expanding on melting.

Below the critical temperature each isotherm breaks up into three distinct portions, as we have seen, and no single analytical expression can hope to represent such behavior (see, for example, $MNOP$ in Fig. 3.7). James Thomson, however, suggested that the two end portions of each isotherm might in fact be connected by a continuous curve [see *abcde* for the isotherm in Fig. 3.6(b)]. He found that, although the region between b and d is basically unstable, it is always possible to move from a toward b (and from e toward d) without the appearance of a second phase.

Although the critical point retains its precise meaning as the point at which the densities of the liquid and vapor phases become identical, later work

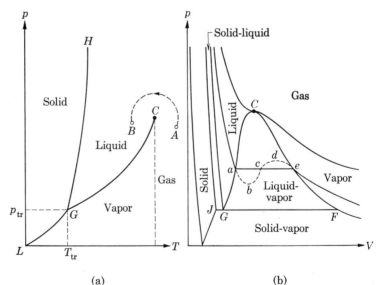

FIGURE **3.6**   (a)   (b)

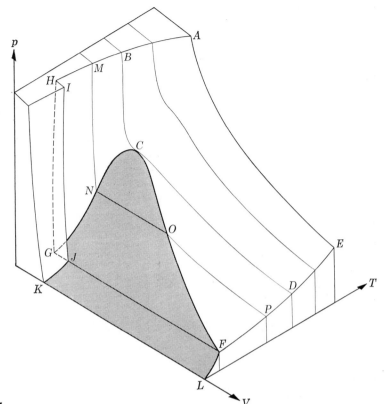

FIGURE **3.7**

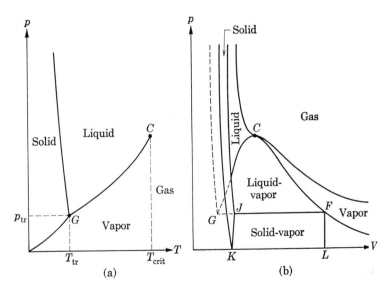

FIGURE **3.8**

indicates that there is a finite *critical region* in which the two phases have almost identical properties. The high-precision measurements of Maas and his co-workers suggest that the early method of taking a disappearing miniscus as the criterion for the critical temperature is not justified. The miniscus may disappear as much as 5 or 6°C *below* the true critical temperature. In this large temperature interval the two phases have almost identical properties.[4]

The problem of representing the complex relationships embodied in the p-V-T surface by analytical functions is a fascinating one, and for the gaseous region alone many equations of state have been proposed. Familiarity with the general properties of a few of these is useful.

3.8   The Kamerlingh Onnes Equation

We have already used the Kamerlingh Onnes equation as a means of extrapolation to the condition of zero pressure. Returning to the discussion of Sec. 3.1 and Eq. 3.2, we must now write this equation in a standard form. Thus MA/ρ_{01} is RT, whereas $MB/\rho_{01}, MC/\rho_{01}$, etc., are simply new coefficients. Designating them as B_1, B_2, etc., gives us

$$pV = RT + B_1p + B_2p^2 + B_3p^3 + \cdots \tag{3.18}$$

Here V refers to the volume of a mole of gas, and B_1, B_2, etc., are the second, third, etc., virial coefficients.

Let us now study the behavior of the pV product for an actual case. The results for carbon dioxide are shown in Fig. 3.9, with the pV product, in Amagat units, plotted vertically versus the pressure. A portion of the critical isotherm has been drawn as a broken line. The departure from ideal gas behavior is obvious, since for an ideal gas all the isotherms would be horizontal. The pronounced minima in the isotherms become more marked as the temperature is lowered, and when the critical isotherm is reached, a vertical tangent occurs at the critical pressure. The critical isotherm is also tangent to the curve (dashed in the figure) outlining the liquid-vapor domains. It is apparent that a power series is ill adapted to represent such behavior, and in fact the Onnes-type equation is useful neither at temperatures near the critical temperature nor for high pressures.[5]

The pronounced minima in these isotherms fall on a smooth curve (dotted in Fig. 3.9) which would strike the $p = 0$ axis at two points, one beyond the

---

[4] Naldrett and Maas, *Can. J. Research*, **B18**, 103 (1940).

[5] The Michels found that their extensive data on carbon dioxide could not be fitted exactly to such a series. Their data, which went to pressures of 3000 atm, showed systematic deviations even when terms in the tenth power of p were used. See *Proc. Roy. Soc. (London)*, **A160**, 348 (1937). Actually they needed no odd powers beyond the third, but the principle remains the same.

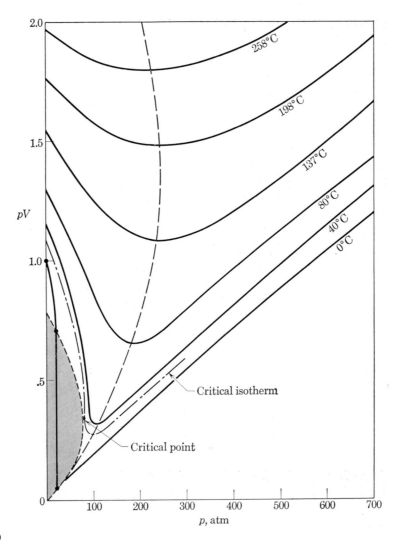

FIGURE **3.9**

present data. If we differentiate Eq. 3.18 with respect to p at constant T, we have

$$\left(\frac{\partial pV}{\partial p}\right)_T = B_1 + 2B_2p + 3B_3p^2 + \cdots$$

The limit of this derivative as $p \to 0$ becomes

$$\lim_{p \to 0}\left(\frac{\partial pV}{\partial p}\right)_T = B_1$$

and the second virial coefficient therefore gives the initial slope of each isotherm at $p = 0$. Consequently, B_1 is negative at low temperatures, rises slowly to zero, and eventually becomes positive for all higher temperatures.

For carbon dioxide the B_1 value remains negative until beyond the range of the data of Fig. 3.9. For nitrogen, however, B_1 changes sign between 0 and 100°C (see Table 2.3, where B is proportional to the present B_1). The temperature at which B_1 vanishes is called the *Boyle temperature*. At this temperature the pV product differs from RT only by the square terms in p and higher, and hence Boyle's law is obeyed to higher pressures than at any other temperature. For nitrogen B_1 is equal to zero at slightly above 50°C, and at this temperature Boyle's law is obeyed to within two parts per thousand up to 40 atm. This behavior is illustrated by Fig. 3.1 (where pV/T rather than pV is plotted vertically; this modification does not affect the near horizontalness of the 50°C isotherm).

It has been found experimentally that if the pV product is expanded as a power series in $1/V$, *fewer virial terms* are required to attain a given precision than when powers of p are used (Eq. 3.18). Onnes' equation thus becomes

$$pV = RT + \mathcal{B}_1 \frac{1}{V} + \mathcal{B}_2 \frac{1}{V^2} + \mathcal{B}_3 \frac{1}{V^3} + \cdots \tag{3.19}$$

where $\mathcal{B}_1, \mathcal{B}_2, \mathcal{B}_3$, etc., are the new virial coefficients for the series in $1/V$. It can be shown (see Problem 3.4) with a little algebra that the new coefficients of Eq. 3.19 are related to those of Eq. 3.18 as follows:

$$\mathcal{B}_1 = B_1 RT$$
$$\mathcal{B}_2 = RT(B_1{}^2 + B_2 RT)$$
$$\mathcal{B}_3 = RT(B_1{}^3 + 3B_1 B_2 RT + B_3 R^2 T^2)$$
$$\cdots \cdots \tag{3.20}$$

Any other equation for pV in the virial form in powers of p can be converted to the form in powers of $1/V$ (or vice versa) by means of Eq. 3.20.

3.9   Van der Waals' Equation

Van der Waals[6] attributed the departure of real gases from ideal gas behavior, as pressure is raised and temperature is lowered, to the growing importance of the *attractive forces* between the molecules and to their *finite volume*. As a result of an approximate theoretical treatment, he proposed the now well-known equation

$$\left(p + \frac{a}{V^2} \right)(V - b) = RT \tag{3.21}$$

The molecules are treated as hard attracting spheres, and the term a/V^2 arises from this intermolecular attraction. It is seen to become rapidly smaller

---

[6] Van der Waals, Dissertation, Leiden, 1873.

as the gas expands and the molecules on the average become farther apart. If we solve Eq. 3.21 for p,

$$p = \frac{RT}{V - b} - \frac{a}{V^2}$$

The pressure increases indefinitely as the volume approaches b, when the molecules may be thought of as essentially in contact. Actually the terms a/V^2 and b are both first approximations only and were never intended to be used to give other than first-order departures from the ideal gas law. Despite

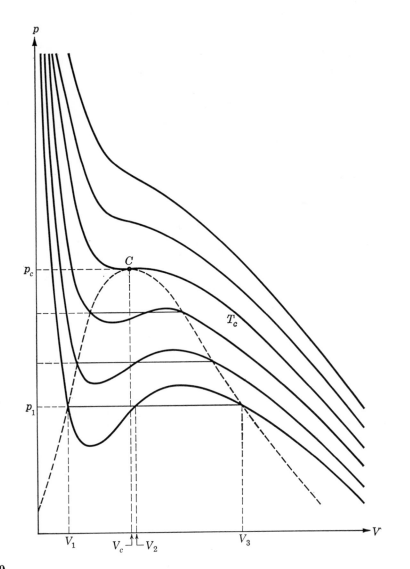

FIGURE **3.10**

this fact, van der Waals' equation has been found to provide a very satisfactory *qualitative* description of the behavior of real gases at high pressures, including the continuous passage from the vapor region to the liquid region mentioned in Sec. 3.7.

A few isotherms, as given by van der Waals' equation, are plotted in Fig. 3.10. Since this equation, when multiplied out, is seen to be a cubic in V, it must have *three* roots for every fixed value of p and T. With three roots we may have one real and two imaginary, three real and different, or three real and coincident. The first case corresponds to the region *above* the critical isotherm (T_c in the figure), the second to the region *below*, and the case of the three identical roots to the critical isotherm itself. Below the critical temperature the isobars are drawn at the vapor pressures proper to the temperatures[7] and intersect the cubic in three places. Thus at $p = p_1$ there are three roots, V_1, V_2, and V_3. V_1 represents the actual volume of the saturated liquid, and V_3 that of the saturated vapor. V_2 is not physically realizable. These roots draw together toward the critical temperature and become identical at the critical point C, where $V = V_c$, the critical volume. Since the equation must have identical roots at this point, we can write

$$(V - V_c)^3 = 0$$

If this is expanded and compared with Eq. 3.21 similarly expanded, we have

$$V^3 - 3V_cV^2 + 3V_c^2V - V_c^3 = 0$$

and

$$V^3 - \left(\frac{RT_c}{p_c} + b\right)V^2 + \frac{a}{p_c}V - \frac{ab}{p_c} = 0$$

where p_c and T_c are written in place of p and T. Equating coefficients of like powers of V after some reduction gives

$$V_c = 3b$$

$$p_c = \frac{a}{27b^2}$$

$$T_c = \frac{8a}{27Rb} \qquad (3.22)$$

or

$$a = \frac{27}{64}\frac{R^2T_c^2}{p_c}$$

$$b = \frac{RT_c}{8p_c} \qquad (3.23)$$

---

[7] The proper places for these isobars is, of course, not given by van der Waals' equation. They are drawn, for thermodynamic reasons, so that the loops above and below them have equal areas.

TABLE **3.1**

Critical Constants of Gases

Gas	p_c, atm	T_c, °K	V_c, cm³/g-mole	p_cV_c/RT_c
Helium	2.25	5.2	61.55	0.3245
Neon	26.86	44.75	44.30	.3240
Argon	47.996	150.66	77.07	.2984
Hydrogen	12.8	33.2	69.68	.3284
Oxygen	49.713	154.28	74.42	.2921
Nitrogen	33.49	125.97	90.03	.2922
CO_2	72.83	304.16	94.23	.2748
H_2O	218.85	647.3	55.44	.2281
NH_3	111.3	405.5	72.02	.2428
CO	34.6	134.4	90.03	.2825
CCl_4	44.98	556.25	275.8	.2717
C_2H_5OH	63.1	516.2	172.0	.2545

In the latter equations a and b are expressed entirely in terms of T_c and p_c, since these are much more accurately determinable experimentally than V_c.

From the quantative standpoint van der Waals' equation fails on a number of counts:

1. The values of a and b producing the best fit for measurements at one temperature are different from those producing the best fit at another temperature. Thus a and b are only approximately constant, and compromise values must be adopted.

2. The empirical values of a and b are not the same as those calculated from p_c and T_c in Eq. 3.23. The differences may be as great as 50% but average 20 to 30%.[8]

3. Replacing b by $V_c/3$ in the second relation of Eq. 3.23 gives us

$$\frac{p_cV_c}{RT_c} = \frac{3}{8} = 0.375$$

The experimental values are generally lower and average around 0.270 to 0.280 (see Table 3.1, where values of the critical constants for a few typical gases are given together with this ratio).

The difference between 0.375 and the measured value is not to be wondered at, since such a comparison with experimental results is a test to which van der Waals' equation should hardly be subjected. Nevertheless, all the values of a and b given in published handbooks of physical constants are those

[8] See J. H. Jeans, *Dynamical Theory of Gases*, 3rd ed., Cambridge Univ. Press, Cambridge, 1921, p. 13 and tables on p. 148. See also Guye and Frederick, *Arch. sci. phys. et nat.*, **13**, 559 (1902); and van Lahr, *Koninkl. Ned. Akad. Wetenschap. Proc.*, **21**, 1, 16 (1918).

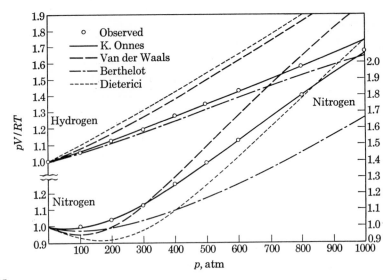

FIGURE **3.11**

computed from Eq. 3.23. They are thus not those determined empirically to give the best fit but those consistent with taking the ratio as 0.375. Pickering[9] compared the computed pV values of some eighteen gases at 0°C with the observed data. Fig. 3.11 gives the comparison for hydrogen and nitrogen and shows that the agreement of van der Waals' predictions is limited to very low pressures (where, of course, a much better fit could be obtained by choosing a and b values for the 0°C isotherm). The observed data fit the Onnes equation very closely. Predictions from the two other two-constant equations (Berthelot and Dieterici) have been included. These equations will be considered next.

3.10   Berthelot's Equation

To take account of the marked diminution of van der Waals' a with tempera-ture, Berthelot[10] introduced the term a'/TV^2 in place of a/V^2. The result is

$$\left(p + \frac{a'}{TV^2}\right)(V - b') = RT \tag{3.24}$$

where a' and b' are new constants, determined in terms of the critical constants by the same algebraic process as was used with van der Waals' equation. The result is

$$a' = 3p_c V_c^2 T_c$$

$$b' = \frac{V_c}{3}$$

$$p_c V_c = \tfrac{3}{8} RT_c \tag{3.25}$$

[9] Pickering, *Natl. Bur. Standards (U. S.) Circ.,* No. 279 (1932).
[10] Berthelot, *Trav. et mem. bur. intern. poids et mesures.,* **13** (1906).

or

$$a' = \frac{27}{64} \frac{R^2 T_c^3}{p_c}$$

$$b' = \frac{1}{8} \frac{RT_c}{p_c} \qquad (3.26)$$

Berthelot then set out to modify this result so that it would give better agreement with experiment at moderate pressures. Solving Eq. 3.24 for pV gives

$$pV = RT + pb' - \frac{a'}{TV} + \cdots \qquad (3.27)$$

where the small term in $a'b'$ has been neglected. Since the a'/TV term is a small correction term, the V is replaced by RT/p from the ideal gas law, and we have

$$pV = RT \left[1 + \left(b' - \frac{a'}{RT^2} \right) \frac{p}{RT} + \cdots \right] \qquad (3.28)$$

This is Berthelot's equation in the virial form, with the series terminated with the first term in p. In practice the values of a' seem satisfactory, whereas those of b' are too large.

Berthelot then made two empirical changes to produce results more in line with experiment.

1. Since the observed values of V_c are larger than $3b'$ and closer to $4b'$, he wrote $V_c = 4b'$.

2. The observed ratios of $p_c V_c / RT$ are always less than $3/8 = 0.375$ but seem to average near 0.28. The nearest simple fraction that lies in this region is taken for the ratio. He chose $9/32 = 0.28125$.

These changes, of course, make Eqs. 3.25 and 3.26 no longer compatible. Algebraic examination shows that, to retain the satisfactory value of a', the factor of 3 in the first of Eqs. 3.25 must be replaced by 16/3 so that

$$a' = {}^{16}\!/_3 p_c V_c^2 T_c$$

$$b' = \frac{V_c}{4}$$

$$p_c V_c = {}^9\!/_{32} RT_c$$

or

$$a' = \frac{27}{64} \frac{R^2 T_c^3}{p_c} \qquad (3.29)$$

$$b' = \frac{9}{128} \frac{RT_c}{p_c} \qquad (3.30)$$

Thus a' and b' may be obtained directly from van der Waals' a and b by the relations

$$a' = aT_c$$

and

$$b' = \tfrac{9}{16}b \tag{3.31}$$

where a and b are, of course, computed from Eq. 3.23.

On substitution of Eq. 3.30 in Eq. 3.28, we have

$$pV = RT \left[1 + \frac{9pT_c}{128p_cT} \left(1 - \frac{6T_c^2}{T^2} \right) \right] \tag{3.32}$$

which is the conventional form of Berthelot's equation. Berthelot's equation in the (modified) virial form of Eq. 3.28 or Eq. 3.32 is not applicable for pressures near the critical value, but for low pressures, especially when wide temperature ranges are involved, it is better than van der Waals' equation.

3.11 Dieterici's Equation

In an attempt to represent the behavior of gases at the critical isotherm and above, Dieterici[11] proposed the equation of state

$$p(V - b'') = RT \exp - \frac{a''}{T^nV} \tag{3.33}$$

Here a'' and b'' play the same roles as in the other equations. Although n was originally taken as unity, later results indicated better agreement for $n = 1.27$.

For finding a'' and b'' in terms of the critical constants, the algebraic device previously employed is not applicable. We use instead the fact that in the p-V plane the critical isotherm has a point of horizontal inflection at the critical point. (See Problem 3.3.) Thus we must set

$$\left(\frac{\partial p}{\partial V} \right)_T = \left(\frac{\partial^2 p}{\partial V^2} \right)_T = 0$$

It can readily be shown that these conditions lead to

$$b'' = \frac{V_c}{2}$$
$$a'' = 4b''T_c^n$$
$$p_cV_c = \frac{2}{e^2} TR_c \tag{3.34}$$

---

[11] Dieterici, *Ann. Physik*, **69**, 685 (1899); **5**, 51 (1901).

where e is the base of Naperian logarithms. The value of V_c, here only $2b''$, is farther out of line than van der Waals' $3b$, although the virial ratio $p_c V_c / R T_c$ = $2/e^2 = 2/7.389 = 0.2707$ is much nearer the general average. On the whole, Dieterici's equation has as sound a theoretical basis as has van der Waals' and is more satisfactory where wide temperature variations or temperatures near the critical point are involved.

3.12   The Beattie-Bridgeman Equation

Another equation of state, essentially an empirical modification of van der Waals' equation, was proposed by Beattie and Bridgeman[12] and takes the form

$$pV = \frac{RT(1 - \epsilon)(V + B)}{V} - \frac{A}{V} \tag{3.35}$$

where $A = A_0(1 - a/V)$, $B = B_0(1 - b/V)$, and $\epsilon = c/VT^3$. The five constants A_0, a, B_0, b, and c must be obtained by experiment for each gas. Beattie and Stockmayer[13] have given the values of these constants for a large number of gases. This equation of state with its five adjustable constants is much more accurate than the two- and three-constant equations. It gives a good account of the behavior of nonpolar gases and a somewhat less good description of that of polar gases up to about the critical density, $p_c = M/V_c$, and from low temperatures to well above the Boyle temperature, usually with a precision of a few tenths of a per cent.

3.13   The Equation of State in Virial Form

It is frequently desirable to have a given equation of state expressed in the virial form either as a function of $1/V$ or of p as in the empirical Onnes equations. To throw van der Waals' equation into the virial form in $1/V$, we first solve for p to get

$$p = \frac{RT}{V - b} - \frac{a}{V^2}$$

This can be rewritten as

$$pV = RT \left(1 - \frac{b}{V}\right)^{-1} - \frac{a}{V}$$

On expanding the factor $(1 - b/V)^{-1}$ by the binomial theorem and collecting terms, we obtain

$$pV = RT + (RTb - a)\frac{1}{V} + b^2\frac{RT}{V^2} + b^3\frac{RT}{V^3} + \cdots \tag{3.36}$$

[12] Beattie and Bridgeman, *J. Am. Chem. Soc.*, **49**, 1665 (1927); **50**, 3151 (1928); *Proc. Am. Acad. Arts Sci.*, **63**, 229 (1928).

[13] Beattie and Stockmayer, *Repts. Progr. in Phys.* 8(1941), 206, which see also for other references to data on this equation.

which is of the standard form

$$pV = RT + \mathcal{B}_1 \frac{1}{V} + \mathcal{B}_2 \frac{1}{V^2} + \mathcal{B}_3 \frac{1}{V^3} + \cdots \qquad (3.19)$$

of Sec. 3.8, with $\mathcal{B}_1 = (RTb - a)$, $\mathcal{B}_2 = b^2 RT$, $\mathcal{B}_3 = b^3 RT$, etc. To convert Eq. 3.36 into the other standard form

$$pV = RT + B_1 p + B_2 p^2 + B_3 p^3 + \cdots \qquad (3.18)$$

it is merely necessary that we use the coefficient equations given in Eq. 3.20 to express the B's in terms of the $\mathcal{B}$'s. The result of this inversion is

$$B_1 = \frac{\mathcal{B}_1}{RT}$$

$$B_2 = \frac{1}{R^2 T^2}\left(\mathcal{B}_2 - \frac{\mathcal{B}_1{}^2}{RT}\right)$$

$$B_3 = \frac{1}{R^3 T^3}\left(\mathcal{B}_3 - \frac{3\mathcal{B}_1 \mathcal{B}_2}{RT} + \frac{2\mathcal{B}_1{}^3}{R^2 T^2}\right)$$

$$\cdot \; \cdot \; \cdot \; \cdot \; \cdot \qquad (3.37)$$

Returning to Eq. 3.36, $B_1 = (b - a/RT)$ with similar results for the higher terms. Table 3.2 lists the $\mathcal{B}$ coefficients (which most equations of state give fairly directly) for the four equations of state so far discussed and for the state equation of Wohl.[14] This has the form

$$p = \frac{RT}{V - b} - \frac{a}{TV(V - b)} + \frac{c}{T^n V^3} \qquad (3.38)$$

where $n = \frac{4}{3}$, and is thus a three-constant equation of considerable interest. (See Problem 3.11.)

TABLE **3.2**

Virial Coefficients for Various Equations of State Expanded in Powers of $1/V$

Equation	$\mathcal{B}_1$	$\mathcal{B}_2$	$\mathcal{B}_3$
Van der Waals	$RTb - a$	RTb^2	
Berthelot	$RTb' - \dfrac{a'}{T}$	RTb'^2	
Dieterici*	$RT\left(b'' - \dfrac{a''}{T^n}\right)$	$RT\left(b''^2 - \dfrac{a''b''}{T^n} + \dfrac{a''^2}{2T^{2n}}\right)$	
Wohl†	$RTb - \dfrac{a}{T}$	$RTb^2 - \dfrac{ab}{T} + \dfrac{c}{T^n}$	$RTb^3 - \dfrac{ab^2}{T}$
Beattie-Bridgeman	$RT\left(B_0 - \dfrac{A_0}{RT} - \dfrac{c}{T^3}\right)$	$RT\left(-B_0 b + \dfrac{A_0 a}{RT} - \dfrac{B_0 c}{T^3}\right)$	$RB_0 \dfrac{bc}{T^2}$

*$n = 1.27$.   †$n = \frac{4}{3}$.

[14] Wohl, *Z. physik. Chem.*, **133**, 305 (1928).

The a, b, and c, of course, have different values for each equation. For the two-constant equations (van der Waals, Berthelot, and Dieterici) the use of the third virial coefficient is seldom justified.

3.14 Solid and Liquid States

The portions of the general p-V-T surface of Fig. 3.4 that represent the domains of existence of the solid and liquid states depart only slightly from plane surfaces and are nearly perpendicular to the volume axis, emphasizing that the volumes of liquids and solids are fairly insensitive to pressure and temperature changes. If, therefore, for these so-called condensed phases we regard V as a function of p and T,

$$V = V(p, T)$$

we can always write for a differential change dV

$$dV = \left(\frac{\partial V}{\partial T}\right)_p dT + \left(\frac{\partial V}{\partial p}\right)_T dp$$

or, introducing the coefficients of thermal expansion and compressibility, β_p and κ_T, respectively,

$$dV = V\beta_p dT - V\kappa_T dp$$

To obtain the change in volume for any change of the system from p_0 and T_0, say, to p and T, we have

$$V - V_0 = \int_{T_0, p_0}^{T, p} V\beta_p dT - \int_{T_0, p_0}^{T, p} V\kappa_T dp$$

Since V, β_p, and κ_T are relatively insensitive to changes in T and p, these quantities may be taken outside the integrals as averages to give the useful result

$$V - V_0 = \overline{V\beta_p}(T - T_0) + \overline{V\kappa_T}(p - p_0)$$

where, provided the ranges of integration are not large, the values of V, β_p, and κ_T at any point of the range may be substituted for the average values.

When wide intervals of change are involved, of course, the actual variations of β_p and κ_T must be considered. As an indication of the behavior to be expected, the coefficients of thermal expansion of the solids copper and iron are shown in Fig. 3.12, and that of water in Fig. 3.13.

The coefficients of thermal expansion of all solids decrease with temperature to vanish at the absolute zero. This, we shall find later, is confirmation of the third law of thermodynamics.

In general, solids become more rigid and therefore less compressible as the temperature is reduced. Accordingly, κ_T falls with temperature, although it

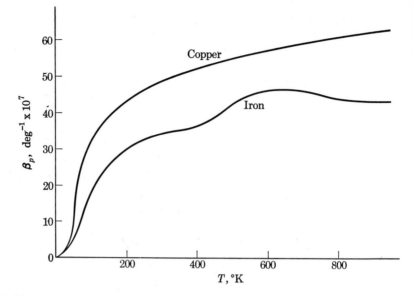

FIGURE **3.12**

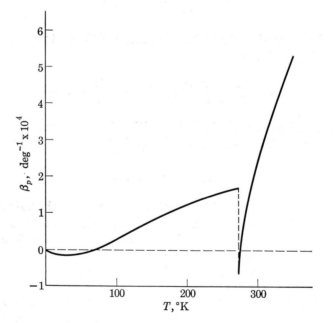

FIGURE **3.13**

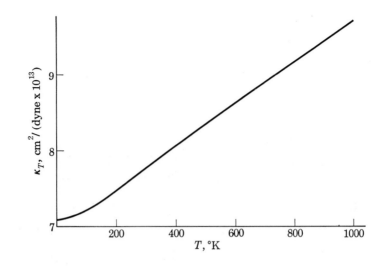

FIGURE **3.14**

never vanishes. For copper the fall of κ_T with temperature is almost exactly linear down to nearly 100°K. (See Fig. 3.14.)

Problems

3.1 A general mathematical theorem states that the necessary and sufficient condition for a function $f(x)$ to have n identical roots at x_1 is that the first $(n-1)$ derivatives shall vanish at this point, that is,

$$f'(x_1) = f''(x_1) = \cdots = f^{n-1}(x_1) = 0$$

but that
$$f^n(x_1) \neq 0$$

Solve van der Waals' equation for p, and setting $(\partial p/\partial V)_T$ and $(\partial^2 p/\partial V^2)_T$ equal to zero at the critical point, show that the results in Eq. 3.23 are obtained; that is,

$$a = \frac{27}{64}\frac{R^2 T_c^2}{p_c}$$

$$b = \frac{RT_c}{8p_c}$$

Also verify that $(\partial^3 p/\partial V^3)_T \neq 0$ at this point.

3.2 What is the value of the gas constant R when p is in atmospheres, volume is in Amagat units, and temperature is expressed as a multiple of $T_0 = 273°C$?

3.3 Apply the method of Problem 3.1 to Dieterici's equation,

$$p(V - b'') = RT \exp - \frac{a''}{T^n V}$$

to show that

$$b'' = \frac{V_c}{2}$$

$$a'' = 4b'' T_c{}^n$$

$$p_c V_c = \frac{2}{e^2} R T_c$$

the results given in Eq. 3.34.

3.4 Verify the expressions given for the virial coefficients $\mathcal{B}_1$, $\mathcal{B}_2$, and $\mathcal{B}_3$ for the Beattie-Bridgeman equation in Table 3.2. Also verify the general results in Eq. 3.20.

3.5 How would you convert Onnes' equation of state,

$$pV = RT + B_1p + B_2p^2 + B_3p^3 + \cdots$$

where pressure is in meters of mercury, to a form satisfactory for pressure in atmospheres?

3.6 Calculate the values of the critical temperature and pressure of, say, oxygen and nitrogen from the values of van der Waals' a and b given in handbooks of physical constants. Compare these with the results given in Table 3.1. What is your conclusion?

3.7 A 500 g mass of copper is heated from 0 to 100°C and compressed from $p = 1$ atm to $p = 1000$ atm. What is the approximate change in volume you would expect?

3.8 Heuse and Otto [*Ann. Physik*, **2**, 1012 (1929); **4**, 778 (1930)] determined the absolute value of the ice point, T_0, by extrapolating to $p = 0$ the coefficient of thermal expansion, β_p, and the coefficient of pressure rise, α_V. Show analytically that for any gas, whatever the equation of state we employ to represent its behavior,

$$\lim_{p \to 0} \frac{1}{\alpha_V} = \lim_{p \to 0} \frac{1}{\beta_p} = T_0$$

The data of Heuse and Otto are

Gas	$\alpha_V \times 10^8$	$\beta_p \times 10^8$
Helium	366072	366079
Hydrogen	366110	366103
Nitrogen	366093	366076
Neon	366092	366104

Obtain a probable value of T_0 from these results (the last figure is uncertain in each case).

3.9 Show that if we define the reduced pressure, π, reduced temperature, θ, and the reduced volume, ϕ, by the ratios $\pi = p/p_c$, $\theta = T/T_c$, and $\phi = V/V_c$, with the use of Eq. 3.23 for a and b, van der Waals' equation takes on the *reduced* form

$$\left(\pi + \frac{3}{\phi^2}\right)(3\phi - 1) = 8\theta$$

where all properties of a particular gas have disappeared.

3.10 Follow the same procedure as in Problem 3.9 to obtain the reduced forms of the modified Berthelot and Dieterici equations as

$$\pi\phi = \frac{32}{9}\theta\left[1 + \frac{9}{128}\frac{\pi}{\theta}\left(1 - \frac{6}{\theta^2}\right) + \cdots\right]$$

and

$$\pi(2\phi - 1) = \theta\exp\left[2\left(1 - \frac{1}{\theta^n\phi}\right)\right]$$

3.11 Show that for Wohl's equation of state,

$$p = \frac{RT}{V - b} - \frac{a}{TV(V - b)} + \frac{c}{T^nV^3}$$

the critical point conditions analogous to, say, Eq. 3.23 (with $n = \frac{2}{3}$), are

$$a = \frac{32}{75}\frac{R^2T_c^3}{p_c}$$

$$b = \frac{1}{15}\frac{RT_c}{p_c} = \frac{V_c}{4}$$

$$c = \frac{8}{3}abT_c^{1/3} = 4V_c^3p_cT_c^{4/3}$$

and so

$$p_cV_c = \frac{4}{15}RT_c = 0.2667RT_c$$

3.12 With the results of Problem 3.11, show that the reduced form of Wohl's equation is

$$\pi\left(\phi - \frac{1}{4}\right) = \frac{15\theta}{4} - \frac{6}{\theta\phi} + \frac{4(\phi - \frac{1}{4})}{\theta^{2/3}\phi^3}$$

CHAPTER FOUR

The First Law
of Thermodynamics

4.1 Measurement of Heat

During the eighteenth and early nineteenth centuries the observed thermal behavior of matter was interpreted in terms of a fluid, called *caloric*, the flow of which into a body caused its temperature to rise and the loss of which from a body caused its temperature to fall. Caloric was, of necessity, a very subtle, tenuous fluid since it was both invisible and weightless; it betrayed its presence to the sense of touch as "sensible heat." The caloric added to a liquid in evaporation was thought of as filling the spaces between the ultimate particles, where it remained in a *latent* or "insensible" form until condensation released it once more in a sensible form. When a hot body and a cold body were put together in a calorimeter, caloric flowed from the hotter body to the colder one until both attained a common temperature. This picture of a fluid constant in amount and detectable only indirectly by the effects it produced was very useful in explaining many thermal phenomena. It met unsurmountable difficulties, however, when confronted with the thermal effects of friction and the mechanical effects of thermal expansion.

Consideration of these latter phenomena led directly to the mechanical theory of heat and to the ultimate overthrow of the caloric idea. But as long as we are concerned with the purely calorimetric properties of heat, that is, with the heat *interchanges* between bodies contained in well-insulated calorimeters, we employ, with only a slight change of vocabulary, concepts inherited directly from the fluid theory of heat. We still speak of the "flow" of heat and measure the quantity or amount of this invisible agent indirectly through its effect in raising some body's temperature.

It is important to list here the fundamental postulates or axioms regarding the purely empirical behavior of heat. These form the basis of the modern science of calorimetry or heat measurement and are independent of any theory of the nature of heat. They may be stated as follows:

1. When two bodies at different temperatures are brought together in

a calorimeter, the heat *lost* by one is equal to that *gained* by the other.

2. When a body is warmed through a given temperature interval, it always absorbs the *same* quantity of heat.

3. The quantity of heat *evolved* by a body cooling from t_1 to $t_2(t_1 > t_2)$ is the same as that *absorbed* when it is warmed from t_2 to t_1.

4. The quantity of heat required to raise a body from t_1 to t_3 is equal to that required to raise it from t_1 to t_2 and then from t_2 to $t_3(t_1 < t_2 < t_3)$.

5. The quantity of heat necessary to raise a mass of m grams of a substance through any interval is m times that required to raise 1 g through the same interval.

6. Two quantities of heat (from different bodies) are equal when they produce the same temperature change in a third body.

The first of these statements is the general postulate of heat conservation and naturally is satisfied only when the greatest precautions are taken in the design of calorimeters to prevent the flow of heat through the walls or to ensure that heat losses are balanced by gains during the experiment. The second is the definition of thermal constancy; a body for which it does not hold is always found to have undergone some irreversible physical or chemical change so that it is not really the same body as at the beginning. The third, fourth, and fifth may be said to establish the *algebraic scalar* nature of heat. The last postulate is the essential definition of equality: two quantities of heat are equal in amount when they produce equal effects in a test body.

A further assumption (number 7) is usually made, namely, that the heat required to warm a body through an interval $t - t_0$ is $(t - t_0)$ times as great as that required to warm it through 1°. This statement is not rigorously true, as we shall see, but it is convenient at the start.

4.2 Heat Capacity and the Unit of Heat

According to postulates 5, 6, and 7, we agree to measure quantity of heat in terms of the total temperature rise, say, $t - t_0$, and the total mass, m, of the body warmed. If Q is this quantity of heat, then we set

$$Q \propto m(t - t_0)$$

or
$$Q = cm(t - t_0) \tag{4.1}$$

where c is simply an arbitrary proportionality constant. For a temperature rise from t to $t + \Delta t$, a further increment of heat, ΔQ, is needed, and we have

$$Q + \Delta Q = cm(t + \Delta t - t_0)$$

or
$$\Delta Q = cm \, \Delta t$$

whence
$$c = \frac{\Delta Q}{m \, \Delta t} \tag{4.2}$$

Thus c is a measure of the heat absorbed per unit mass per degree rise in temperature. It gives a measure of the body's ability to absorb heat and is called, therefore, the *specific heat capacity* or simply the *specific heat* of the body. Since the heat absorbed depends on the exact conditions under which it was absorbed, we must indicate these. When the volume is held constant, we have the specific heat at *constant volume,* indicated by c_V; when the pressure is held constant, we have the specific heat at *constant pressure,* with the symbol c_p; etc.

Since the usual calorimetric conditions are those of constant pressure, it is convenient in Eqs. 4.1 and 4.2 to write Q_p for Q and substitute c_p for c. Thus we have

$$Q_p = c_p m(t - t_0)$$

and

$$c_p = \frac{\Delta Q_p}{m \, \Delta t} \tag{4.3}$$

With this definition of c_p, however, we find that c_p varies with the size of the interval Δt and is therefore strictly an *average* specific heat over the interval, which should be written $\overline{c_p}$. If we allow the interval Δt to shrink to zero,

$$c_p = \lim_{\Delta t \to 0} \frac{1}{m} \frac{\Delta Q_p}{\Delta t} = \frac{1}{m} \frac{dQ_p}{dt}$$

or

$$dQ_p = mc_p dt \tag{4.4}$$

where c_p is now the actual or *instantaneous* specific heat at the temperature t. It is simply the fact that the instantaneous value of c_p varies with temperature that renders postulate 7 not quite true.[1] For most purposes the differences between the values given by Eqs. 4.3 and 4.4 are not large. Thus if $\Delta t = 1°$, we may usually take the average value of c_p for this interval to be identical with the instantaneous value at the mid-point of the interval.

We then may rewrite Eq. 4.3 as

$$\Delta Q_p = c_p m \, \Delta t$$

and use this relation to define our *unit* of heat in terms of a convenient standard body. For this purpose water is an ideal choice. Thus we say that ΔQ_p represents a unit quantity of heat when m refers to a unit mass of water warmed through $1°$. This means, of course, that the specific heat of water at constant pressure has been defined as unity.

In the cgs system the unit of heat, the *calorie,* is the heat required to warm 1 g of water 1°C. In the mks system the unit becomes the mks calorie (or the large calorie), the heat required to warm 1 kg of water 1°C. The British thermal unit (the Btu) is the heat required to warm 1 lb of water 1°F.

Of course, since the specific heat of water itself changes with temperature, different heat units result when the 1° interval is taken at different parts of the scale. Hence we may have a 20° calorie defined for the interval 19.5 to 20.5°C, a 15° calorie defined for the interval 14.5 to 15.5°C, etc. In what follows the

---

[1] For example, when two equal masses of water at different temperatures are mixed, they do *not* come to a final temperature exactly midway between the two initial temperatures, although the differences are small.

15° calorie will always be implied and understood when the calorie is used without qualification. Since the *instantaneous* 15° calorie defined by dQ_p/dt at 15°C and the *average* 15° calorie defined by $\Delta Q_p/\Delta t$ with $\Delta t = 15.5 - 14.5°$ are so close together, the 15° calorie will hereafter be taken in either sense.

To measure the amount of heat in 15° calories necessary to warm m grams of water over a finite interval, say, from t_0 to t, we must integrate Eq. 4.4 when

$$Q_p = \int_{t_0}^{t} dQ_p = \int_{t_0}^{t} mc_p\, dt = m\overline{c_p}(t - t_0) \qquad (4.5)$$

where $\overline{c_p}$ is the average specific heat of water in 15° calories over the interval t_0 to t; for rough purposes it may be assumed to be unity.

For m grams of some other substance the same quantity of heat, dQ_p, produces a different rise of temperature, say, dt'. Then

$$dQ_p = mc_p\, dt = mc_p{}'\, dt_V{}'$$

or

$$c_p{}' = c_p \frac{dt}{dt'}$$

where $c_p{}'$ is the specific heat of the new substance. Since the masses cancel and the ratio dt/dt' is independent of the system of units, $c_p{}'$ takes on the same numerical value, *whatever the system of units*, as soon as c_p is referred to water at 15°C. This does not mean that specific heat is dimensionless (as is specific gravity). By Eq. 4.3 the dimensions of c_p are given as

$$[c_p] = \left[\frac{\text{heat unit}}{\text{mass} \cdot \text{degree}} \right]$$

In the cgs system c_p is in *calories* per gram-degree. When we change to a new system, we change the *size* of the heat unit in direct proportion to the change in the *product* of mass unit by degree unit.

It is often convenient to define the product mc_p as the heat capacity, C_p, of the body or system. Then

$$dQ_p = C_p\, dt = mc_p\, dt$$

and

$$Q_p = \int_{t_0}^{t} dQ_p = \int_{t_0}^{t} C_p\, dt = m \int_{t_0}^{t} c_p\, dt$$

become the relations for differential and finite heat absorptions, respectively.

4.3   Method of Mixtures

In the usual elementary method for measuring the specific heat of an unknown substance, we proceed by the *method of mixtures*.

The specimen to be studied is heated to a certain temperature, say, t', and dropped into a quantity of colder water at temperature t in a calorimeter. The whole system, after being stirred, comes to a final or mixture temperature, t_m.

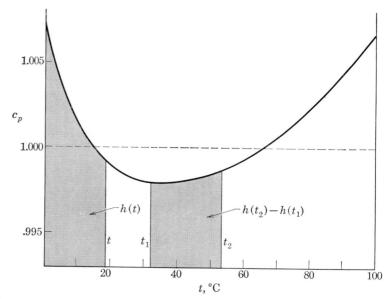

FIGURE **4.1**

Then from the calorimetric postulates we have (omitting the calorimeter's finite mass),

heat lost by sample = heat gained by water

$$\left(\begin{array}{c}\text{heat lost by } m' \\ \text{grams of sample cool-} \\ \text{ing from } t' \text{ to } t_m\end{array}\right) = \left(\begin{array}{c}\text{heat required to} \\ \text{warm } m' \text{ grams of} \\ \text{sample from } t_m \text{ to } t'\end{array}\right) = \left(\begin{array}{c}\text{heat required to} \\ \text{warm } m \text{ grams of} \\ \text{water from } t \text{ to } t_m\end{array}\right)$$

and using the integrals from the last section with $t' > t_m > t$

$$m' \int_{t_m}^{t'} c_p' \, dt = m \int_{t}^{t_m} c_p \, dt$$

or

$$m' \overline{c_p'}(t' - t_m) = m \overline{c_p}(t_m - t) \tag{4.6}$$

where $\overline{c_p'}$, and $\overline{c_p}$, are integral averages of the specific heats of the substance and of water, taken over *nonoverlapping* intervals. Of course, we may set $\overline{c_p} = 1$ and obtain a number for the average specific heat of our substance, but it will not be in 15° calories (or any other known unit).

To evaluate the right side of Eq. 4.6, we must have c_p for water determined over the necessary interval in 15° calories. This information is difficult to obtain with precision by other than electrical means, the study of which we must postpone until later.[2] The results of such measurements are, however, given in Fig. 4.1 for the 0 to 100°C interval under normal atmospheric pressure.

---

[2] See Osborne, Stimson, and Ginnings, *J. Research Natl. Bur. Standards*, **23**, 238 (1939). Their data have been reduced from international steam table (IT) calories to 15° calories and are so plotted in Fig. 4.1. See also Appendix 4.1.

The value of c_p, far from being constant, starts above unity, drops below it to a minimum near 32°, and rises at 100° to almost as large a value as at 0°.

As a means of utilizing the information given by such data, it is convenient to define a new function, often called the "heat of the liquid" or, better, the *enthalpy*. This is given by the relation

$$h = \int_0^t c_p \, dt \tag{4.7}$$

and thus represents the heat absorbed in 15° calories by 1 g of water in warming from 0°C to any temperature t. Since pressure is constant and only the upper limit of the integral is variable, h is a function of t only

$$h = h(t)$$

and values of the integral may be tabulated at 1° intervals through the range 0 to 100°C. To determine the heat required to warm 1 g between any two temperatures t_1 and t_2, we have

$$\text{heat required} = \int_{t_1}^{t_2} c_p \, dt = \int_0^{t_2} c_p \, dt - \int_0^{t_1} c_p \, dt$$
$$= h(t_2) - h(t_1) = h_2 - h_1 \tag{4.8}$$

The required heat is found by substituting the appropriate values of h from tables of $h(t)$. Graphically $h(t)$ is the area under the c_p curve of Fig. 4.1 between 0 and t, and $h_2 - h_1$ is simply the area under the curve and between the verticals at t_1 and t_2.

To find the heat involved, Q_p, with m grams of water, we have merely to multiply the result by m.

$$Q_p = m[h(t_2) - h(t_1)]$$

With this new function for the right-hand term of Eq. 4.6,

$$m'\overline{c_p}'(t' - t_m) = m[h(t_m - h(t)]$$

or
$$\overline{c_p}' = \frac{m[h(t_m) - h(t)]}{m'(t' - t_m)} \tag{4.9}$$

This relation gives a precise value of $\overline{c_p}'$ in 15° calories per gram-degree over the interval t_m to t'. By choosing a mass of substance sufficiently large to render $t' - t_m$ small, we may take the average value, $\overline{c_p}'$, as a good measure of the instantaneous value, c_p', at the mid-point of the interval.

For convenience of reference the calculated values of the enthalpy of water at atmospheric pressure have been tabulated along with the values of c_p in Appendix 4.1.

4.4   Mechanical Nature of Heat

The mechanical interpretation of heat gradually triumphed over the caloric theory as a result of the labors of Rumford, Mayer, Davy, and Helmholtz and the lifetime of effort devoted to the subject by James Joule.

With the caloric theory friction was interpreted as a dislodging of part of the caloric inherent in the body so that the body perforce contained *less* caloric after rubbing than before. But Rumford, far from being able to remove all of the caloric by protracted rubbing, found that the "source of heat generated by friction in these experiments appeared evidently to be inexhaustible."[3]

At about the same time (1799) Davy showed that two pieces of ice could be melted by rubbing them together. According to the calorists, rubbing *reduced* the caloric content, and the liquid must then have *less* caloric than the ice. As early as 1761, however, Joseph Black had measured the heat absorbed by melting ice and shown that the liquid must contain *more* heat than the solid. These results we now recognize as crucial (although they were not so recognized at the time.[4] The liquid could not have both *more* and *less* caloric than the ice. It became, therefore, necessary to realize that heat was not always conserved but could be *increased* in amount when mechanical energy was dissipated through friction, or *diminished* as when an expanding system performed mechanical work.

Historically, Mayer (1814–1878) was the first to suggest the general conservation of energy principle and the equivalence of the different types of energy. Although his results were largely speculative, he did obtain a numerical value for the mechanical equivalent of heat by regarding the difference between the specific heat of a gas at constant pressure and that at constant volume as being due to the external work performed by the gas heated at constant pressure.

James Joule (1818–1889) was the first to devote himself to the quantitative aspects of the problem. He took extreme pains and exhibited great ingenuity in collecting and measuring all of the heat produced in his experiments, the most famous of which were performed with his paddle-wheel apparatus. In this apparatus weights descending under gravity rotated a paddle wheel in a mass of water contained in a calorimeter. The heat produced by the frictional dissipation of the mechanical energy was measured by the rise in temperature of the calorimeter and its contents. As a result of a large number of such experiments, Joule concluded that a standard mass of 1 lb had to descend 722 ft to produce 1 Btu. He extended his labors to the study of the friction between iron rings under mercury, the compression and expansion of air, the electrical energy expended when a current passes through a wire, etc. His body of results essentially established the accurate proportionality of work dissipated, W, to heat produced, Q. This relation may be written

$$W = JQ$$

---

[3] Count Rumford, *Collected Works*, American Academy of Arts and Sciences, Boston, 1870, Vol. 1, p. 490.

[4] Black's finding was not published until 1803, four years after his death. Whether Davy actually had access to it is not clear.

Here the constant of proportionality, J, so designated in his honor, represents in a very literal sense the *mechanical equivalent* of heat. When Q is unity, J is numerically the work required to produce the same thermal effects as the unit of heat.

Although the quantitative experimental results of Joule were most significant, the general extension of the principle of conservation to include not only mechanics and heat but also electricity, magnetism, physical chemistry, and astronomy must be ascribed to the brilliant efforts of Helmholtz (1821–1894). He demonstrated by a general mathematical analysis the exact way in which the new results were to be applied in the new fields and thus provided the greatest single step in unifying the exact sciences since the time of Newton. It now became possible to regard energy as a universal entity of which the sum total in a closed system was unalterable. Energy could be transformed by various means into different forms, but the total quantity remained unchanged. The conservation of energy principle was thus extended from the rather artificial realm of idealized mechanical and electrical processes without friction to include the most diverse types of operations in a real world.

4.5 Mechanical Equivalent of Heat

Since Joule's work belonged to an earlier age of experimentation, it is impossible to evaluate his final results in terms of modern units. Accordingly, some of the most dependable later determinations of the accurate numerical value of J must be considered. As is evident from Joule's work, there are two main methods for measuring J, the mechanical and the electrical. In the mechanical method, a definite quantity of work measured as the product of a force, F, through a distance, L, is converted into heat, and the quantity, Q, is measured as accurately as possible. Thus

$$FL = JQ$$

In the electrical method a definite amount of electrical energy is dissipated in a calorimeter. This is measured, say, by the product of the electric current, i, through a resistor, the potential drop, E, across the resistor, and the time of flow, τ. Then

$$Ei\tau = Ez = JQ$$

where z is the total charge that passes through the resistor.

For the purposes of this discussion it will be assumed that Q is in 15° calories and that W is expressed in absolute mechanical joules, where 1 mechanical joule $= 10^7$ ergs $= 1$ new-meter. The electrical quantities are often given in terms of the international electrical joule (a "defined" or legal electrical unit), which is defined in terms of agreed-upon international coulombs and international volts. The precise value of an international electrical joule in absolute mechanical joules must be determined by careful experimentation.

Here[5] the relation will be taken as 1 international electrical joule = 1 international v-amp = 1.00020($\pm$4) absolute mechanical joules.

Direct Mechanical Determinations.   Of the direct mechanical determinations three should be mentioned: those of Rowland, Reynolds and Moorby, and Laby and Hercus.

Rowland used an elaboration and refinement of Joule's paddle-wheel apparatus.[6] His value for J was 4.189 absolute joules per 15° calorie. Rowland's observations were recorded so carefully and completely that nineteen years later a revision was possible, in which the original thermometers were compared with the Paris standard (the international hydrogen scale). This painstaking revision altered Rowland's value to 4.188, a change of only 1 part in the fourth place (see Table 4.1).

Reynolds and Moorby[7] used a hydraulic brake driven by a steam engine. Water entered the brake at about 1.3°C and left near 100°C. Large masses of water were used (up to 65 hp was dissipated). Their final result of $J = 4.1832$ is in terms of the *mean* calorie and not, therefore, directly comparable with the other entries of Table 4.1.

Laby and Hercus[8] used a continuous-flow calorimeter in which the mechanical energy was dissipated as heat in an induction dynamometer. Their original value was reappraised in 1935 to give $J = 4.1852$.

Electrical Methods.   Electrical methods offer the same two variations as mechanical methods. These may be designated as *cumulative* and *continuous-flow* methods. In the cumulative method the electrical energy is dissipated in a resistance wire in the calorimeter, and the equivalent heat production is measured in terms of the total temperature rise produced. The water equivalent of the calorimeter proper must be determined very carefully from observations taken first with a small amount of water in the calorimeter and then with the calorimeter nearly full.

In the continuous-flow method purified air-free water flows into the system, is warmed as it flows past the electrical resistance wire, and leaves the system at a higher temperature. The mass rate of flow is accurately measured by weighing, and this value and the temperature rise determine the equivalent rate of heat production. The great advantages of this method are that, if completely steady conditions are maintained, the heat capacity of the apparatus disappears from the problem and all errors due to thermometer lag are eliminated.

Both electrical methods require the utmost care in insulating the calorimetric vessel (generally an evacuated jacket is used), and corrections are made for heat exchanges along all mechanical connections to the internal or insulated part of the apparatus.

---

[5] See Birge, *Revs. Modern Phys.*, **13**, 233 (1941); and Stimson, *Am. J. Phys.*, **23**, 614 (1955).

[6] Rowland, *Proc. Am. Acad. Arts Sci.*, **15**, 75 (1879/80).

[7] Reynolds and Moorby, *Phil. Trans. Roy. Soc. London*, **A190**, 301 (1897).

[8] Laby and Hercus, *Phil. Trans. Roy. Soc. London*, **A227**, 63 (1927); *Proc. Phys. Soc. (London)*, **47**, 1003 (1935).

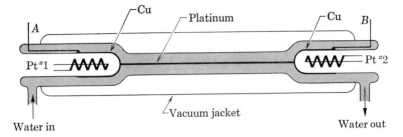

FIGURE **4.2**

Of the three electrical determinations to be mentioned, that of Callendar and Barnes[9] used the continuous-flow method, which they developed. The apparatus (Fig. 4.2) consists essentially of a small glass tube with a platinum resistance wire down its center. Water enters at the left and leaves at the right. The wire, which carries the heating current, terminates at the ends in heavy copper sheaths into which platinum resistance thermometers (#1 and #2) are inserted. This arrangement provides immediate thermal contact of the thermometers with the entering and leaving water streams. The great electrical conductivity of the copper at the same time effectively restricts the heat production to the high-resistance part of the circuit formed by the platinum wire. The potential drop across the wire is measured by a potentiometer connected between A and B. The critical part of the apparatus is sheathed by a vacuum jacket.

The remaining two electrical determinations were carried out by Jaeger and von Steinwehr[10] and by Osborn, Stimson, and Ginnings.[11] Each group used the cumulative method, and both determinations were characterized by great care in the design of the apparatus and careful correction for heat interchanges with the surroundings. A schematic diagram of the calorimeter used by Osborn *et al.* (Fig. 4.3) illustrates the main features of the method.

Purified water was introduced from a reservoir (detachable for weighing) into the calorimeter through a valve, V_2. Here the water was heated by resistance coils, with stirring adequate to produce temperature uniformity. The gold-plated copper calorimeter itself was insulated by a vacuum jacket from an outer steam jacket filled with water vapor at the same temperature as the water in the calorimeter. All temperatures were determined by means of thermocouples having one junction in a heavy reference block, the absolute temperature of which was measured by a platinum resistance thermometer. In all, sixteen thermal elements were attached to the body of the calorimeter to ensure that uniformity of temperature was maintained. After a run the

[9] Barnes, *Proc. Roy. Soc. (London)*, **A82**, 390 (1909); and Callendar, *Phil. Trans. Roy. Soc. London*, **A212**, 1 (1912).

[10] Jaeger and von Steinwehr, *Ann. Physik*, **64**, 305 (1921).

[11] Osborn, Stimson, and Ginnings, *J. Research Natl. Bur. Standards*, **23**, 197 (1939).

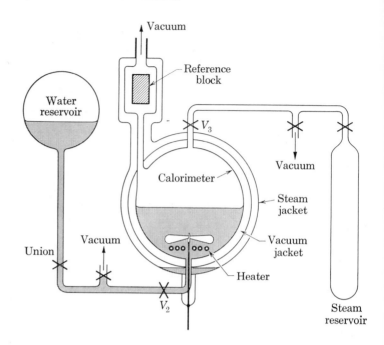

FIGURE **4.3**

water was pumped out through another valve, V_3, and condensed into a steam reservoir, which was also weighable. The electrical energy was measured in international volt-amperes and reduced to absolute joules.

The final results of all these observations are collected in Table 4.1. The remarkable consistency of the findings, which were accumulated by such a diversity of methods over such a long time, is striking. Birge,[12] after a careful analysis of all the data, has given as his final average value

$$J = 4.1855(\pm 4) \frac{\text{absolute joules}}{15° \text{ calorie}}$$

or
$$J' = 4.1847(\pm 3) \frac{\text{international joules}}{15° \text{ calorie}}$$

He has adopted the equivalents

$$1 \text{ international joule} = 1.00020(\pm 4) \text{ absolute joules}$$

In what follows the absolute joule will be understood, although the differences between it and the international joule are negligible for most purposes.

---

[12] Birge, *Repts. Progr. in Phys.*, **8**(1941), 112.

For convenience the reciprocal of J is also given, as

$$\frac{1}{J} = \frac{1}{4.1855} = 0.23892(\pm 2)\; \frac{15°\text{ calorie}}{\text{absolute joule}}$$

4.6 The System as a Reservoir of Energy

Although we might regard the relation

$$W = JQ$$

as basically a statement of the conservation of energy principle and hence of the first law of thermodynamics, it is highly desirable to express its essential truth in a more flexible form.

This becomes possible if we agree to regard the thermodynamic system as simply a *reservoir of energy*. From this point of view any energy that flows across the boundaries of the system increases the *total amount* present whether it enters as heat or in mechanical or electrical form. In fact, we may now speak of *heat* only as *thermal energy* in *transit* to or from the system. We shall no longer speak of "heat in the system" but merely refer to the internal energy. We need not try to separate energy inside the system into potential and kinetic and chemical and other forms. It is simply *internal energy* of the system.

TABLE **4.1**

Determination of the Mechanical Equivalent of Heat

Observer	Method	J, absolute joules/15° calorie
Rowland, 1879 (revised by Day, 1898)	Elaboration of Joule's paddle wheel	4.188
Reynolds and Moorby, 1897	Hydraulic brake and steam engine	(4.1832)*
Barnes (revised, 1909)	Continuous-flow electrical calorimeter	4.1842
Callendar (revised, 1925)	Continuous-flow electrical calorimeter	4.1831†
Jaeger and von Steinwehr, 1921	Electrical heating	4.1850
Laby and Hercus, 1927 (reappraised, 1935)	Induction dynamometer and continuous-flow calorimeter	4.1852
Osborn, Stimson, and Ginnings, 1939	Electrical heating	4.1858

* Mean calories (1.3 to 100°C).
† Reduced from Callendar's value in 20° calories by the use of his specific heat values of 1912.

When energy is added to a system, it always produces certain changes in the thermodynamic variables describing the status of the system. If these variables remain unchanged, we conclude that no net energy of any form or forms has passed into or out of the system. A rise in temperature or pressure is a direct indication that the store of internal energy in the system has been altered by the addition of some energy from without. On the withdrawal of an equivalent amount of energy, the system returns to its original temperature and pressure. We conclude that if energy is really indestructible and uncreatable, then the internal energy of the system must have returned to its original value, also.

This concept leads to the view that the internal energy of a system is a *quantity that cannot be altered without producing some change in at least one physical property of the system.* When heat is added to ice, some of the ice melts, and the appearance of a new phase (as well as the reduction of the amount of ice) at once betrays the change in internal energy, even though pressure and temperature remain fixed. Were there no change in the amount, temperature, or pressure of the ice, we should conclude that there was no change in internal energy. Considerations of this type lead to a statement of what we may term the *fundamental hypothesis:* "There exists a quantity, the internal energy, U, of a system, that takes on a unique value for every configuration of the system." Or, in a slightly different form: "There exists a function, U, the *internal energy* function, such that U is a single-valued function of the independent variables fixing the thermodynamic state of the system."

If a system has the three independent variables x, y, and z, then

$$U = U(x, y, z)$$

Any changes in one or more of these variables will correspond to a change in U, and, conversely, any change in U will be reflected by a change in one or more of the set x, y, and z. Further, if the system, starting in some state given by x_1, y_1, z_1, is taken through a series of changes of whatever nature and eventually left with the variables having their original values (x_1, y_1, and z_1), then U must have been returned to its original value, say,

$$U_1 = U(x_1, y_1, z_1)$$

The fundamental hypothesis cannot be proved directly by experiment for the simple reason that we cannot measure the actual value of U but can only observe the *changes* in U that additions or withdrawals of energy produce. We can only infer the truth of the fundamental hypothesis by the consistency of experimental results interpreted in its light.

It is instructive to regard the internal energy of a system as being very much like the total volume, V, of water in a well. Although we cannot measure the actual instantaneous value of V, but only changes in V, none the less we hardly doubt the existence of such a quantity! We infer changes in V through variations in the height, h, of the water surface, measured from the well curb. If h varies, we can infer an increase or decrease in V without regard to the *source* of the water. Rain, hail, snow, mist, surface water, ground water—all may contribute to changes in V. Once inside the well, water is water, and V is its measure.

Stated more briefly, V is a function of h,

$$V = V(h)$$

where the nature of the function is determined by the size and shape of the well and not by the source or original form of the water.

4.7   Formulation of the First Law of Thermodynamics

We are now in a position to formulate the first law of thermodynamics in terms of the concept of internal energy. Since we cannot measure the absolute value of U but only changes in U as the system passes from one state to another, let two states of the system have energies U_1 and U_2, respectively. Let the system pass from the first to the second state by a flow of energy across the boundaries from outside. Then

$$\begin{pmatrix} \text{change in} \\ \text{internal energy} \end{pmatrix} = U_2 - U_1 = \begin{pmatrix} \text{net energy flow} \\ \text{across the boundaries} \\ \text{from outside} \end{pmatrix}$$

To be more specific, let the change be brought about by performing both mechanical and electrical work on the system while at the same time adding heat. Then with U in joules we have

$$\begin{bmatrix} U_2 - U_1 \\ \text{(joules)} \end{bmatrix} = \begin{bmatrix} \text{mechanical work} \\ \text{done on system} \\ \text{(joules)} \end{bmatrix} + \begin{bmatrix} \text{electrical work} \\ \text{done on system} \\ \text{(joules)} \end{bmatrix} + J \begin{bmatrix} \text{heat added} \\ \text{to system} \\ \text{(calories)} \end{bmatrix}$$

Since mechanical work and electrical work are in the same units, they may be lumped together as *work added*. Therefore

$$U_2 - U_1 = \text{work added} + J(\text{heat added})$$

Historically, the subject of thermodynamics developed from a study of heat engines, that is, devices for producing useful external work. Systems were regarded as sources of *external* work rather than as reservoirs to which work was added. As a result, work as indicated by W was normally taken as *positive* when it represented external work performed at the expense of the system. In this book the same sign convention will be used for both heat and work; that is, W and Q will be taken as *positive* when they represent energy *added* to the system and *negative* when they represent a *loss* to the system. We shall use work *gain* to mean work *done on* the system by the outside world and work *loss* to refer to work performed *by* the system on the outside world (so-called external work). With these sign conventions we may write

$$U_2 - U_1 = JQ + W$$

There are no advantages in retaining *two* different *primary* energy units, the joule and the calorie. It is desirable to settle on one or the other. If the joule is chosen as the universal unit of energy, then we define, for convenience, a 15° calorie as 4.1855 joules and convert all heat quantities to this unit before inserting them in the statement of the first law. This would then read

$$U_2 - U_1 = Q + W \qquad (4.10)$$

On the other hand, we might agree to measure everthing in 15° calories at the rate of 1 joule = 0.23892 cal and thus express everything in Eq. 4.10 in heat units.

The Advisory Committee on Thermometry in 1948[13] proposed the joule as the unit for heat measurements, with the calorie thereafter to be simply a defined unit. Since, even with the adoption of this proposal for future work, all past data in the literature are in calories, it is convenient to retain Eq. 4.10 as the general formulation of the first law. *Any consistent energy units may then be used*, necessary conversions being carried out *before* numerical values are substituted in the equation.

The statement of the first law in Eq. 4.10 represents, of course, a considerable generalization from experiment. What Joule actually did was to show that when work was dissipated in the system, a change in internal energy occurred that could always be reproduced by the addition of an *equivalent* amount of heat (no work being involved). What Eq. 4.10 states is that a given change in internal energy can be brought about not only in these two special ways but also by having heat *and* work added *in any relative amounts we desire*. This behavior is, of course, not demonstrable directly by experiment. We can only attempt to deduce a wide variety of results from Eq. 4.10 and subject these to careful experimentation. Their verification will then serve as an indirect proof of the validity of the relation from which they were deduced. So many and varied have been these indirect proofs, however, that this general statement of the first law is now accepted as almost axiomatic in the exact sciences.

It should be noted in passing that no special terms need be added to Eq. 4.10 to represent, for example, chemical energy. Chemical energy, as such, does not flow across the boundaries of the system unless mass flow occurs. In this case the material arriving from the outside brings its own specific internal energy with every unit mass added, and we need not inquire how this energy is apportioned among the various types present.

The internal energy, U, is always taken as the *energy of the system at rest.* When motion of the system as a whole is concerned, it is always possible to add

---

[13] *Compt. rend. neuvieme conf. gen. poids et mesures* (1948); and Simpson, *Am. J. Phys.*, **23**, 604 (1955).

the large-scale kinetic and potential energies to U to obtain the *total energy* of the system. (See Sec. 4.14.)

4.8   Relative and Absolute Internal Energy

Consider a system with two degrees of freedom, and let x and y be a suitable pair of independent variables. (See Fig. 4.4.) Then for any equilibrium state of the system we write

$$U = U(x, y)$$

If we envisage a process whereby the system is changed from an initial state, represented by x_i, y_i, to a final state, x_e, y_e, then the internal energies for these two states, U_i and U_e, are given as

$$U_i = U(x_i, y_i)$$
$$U_e = U(x_e, y_e)$$

and the first law becomes

$$U_e - U_i = U(x_e, y_e) - U(x_i, y_i) = Q + W$$

where Q and W are the work and heat added during the process. This result holds true whatever the process—whether it be reversible or irreversible, quasistatic or nonquasistatic. A quasistatic process (path C in the figure) ensures the existence of thermodynamic coordinates and hence the internal energy function, $U(x, y)$, at all points of the curve C from i to e. A quasistatic and frictionless (and thus reversible) process further ensures that the work lost by the system, for example, is delivered to the external world as work, with none dissipated as heat on the way. When the process is irreversible owing to the finite rate of the process (hatched path), whether friction is present or absent, no proper thermodynamic coordinates exist. Although there is no

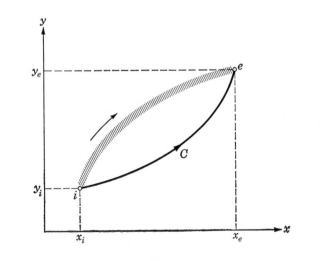

FIGURE **4.4**

doubt as to the validity of the conservation of energy principle for an irreversible process, the internal energy function as here defined, $U(x, y)$, does not exist except at i and e.

The first law applies to the over-all change *whatever the details of the process*, whether it be quasistatic or nonquasistatic. The change in U is given from Eq. 4.10 as

$$U_e - U_i = Q \left]_i^e + W \right]_i^e$$

where the symbols $Q \left]_i^e\right.$ and $W \left]_i^e\right.$ represent the net heat and work, respectively, for the actual process involved. They must be estimated from appropriate measurements made on the *sources* of heat and mechanical or electrical energy outside the system.

Since only differences in U may be measured, it is convenient to take some easily reproduced state as a *standard reference state* for the system. If this state is designated by 0 and the coordinates and internal energy by x_0, y_0, and U_0, then

$$U_0 = U(x_0, y_0)$$

If the system is taken from 0 to i, the change in internal energy, $U_i - U_0$, is measured by $Q + W$ evaluated for this process. Likewise, the change in U, $U_e - U_0$, between the points 0 and e is measured by $Q + W$ for that process. On subtraction of the first difference from the second, U_0 cancels, and

$$U_e - U_i = \Delta U$$

where ΔU is the difference between two experimentally found numbers, just as in Eq. 4.10. The value of U_0, which cannot in fact be determined by thermal or mechanical measurements, may therefore be taken arbitrarily as zero. Accordingly, internal energies are always *relative* and are never known in an *absolute* sense.

4.9   The First Law for Differential Processes

Although the first law holds equally for quasistatic and nonquasistatic processes, the former have a particular importance in thermodynamics. Since in a quasistatic process the system possesses thermodynamic coordinates at all times, we can envisage small increments in these coordinates. As these increments become smaller and smaller in the limit they become *infinitesimal*, and differential processes result.

Let us examine the form taken by the first law for such differential processes. For this purpose we return to Eq. 4.10 and rewrite it with an initial point, now a fixed reference point, 0, and an end point, any variable point, say, P. (See Fig. 4.5.) The first law becomes

$$U - U_0 = U(x, y) - U(x_0, y_0) = Q \left]_0^P + W \right]_0^P \tag{4.11}$$

where x and y are the coordinates of the variable point, P, and x_0 and y_0 those of the fixed reference point, 0. The symbols $Q \left.\right]_0^P_C$ and $W \left.\right]_0^P_C$ represent heat and work for the change from 0 to P along this *particular* curve C (and would in general be quite different for any other curve).

Now imagine a differential change along C' from the point P to P', where the coordinates are $x + dx$ and $y + dy$. The change in U is, of course, given by

$$dU = U(x + dx, y + dy) - U(x, y)$$

where dU may be calculated by the general formula for the differentiation of a function of two variables. Thus

$$dU = \left(\frac{\partial U}{\partial x}\right)_y dx + \left(\frac{\partial U}{\partial y}\right)_x dy \qquad (4.12)$$

The change dU is independent of *how* the system gets from P to P'. We could use the curve C' or the direct extension of C to P', and the change in U would remain differential as long as the differences in the coordinates of P and P' remained differential.

We can formally differentiate the left side of Eq. 4.11 directly since $U(x_0, y_0) = U_0$ is a constant and its differential is zero. The right side of the equation is, however, another matter. If we could treat Q and W in the same way, we might (as is all too often done) simply write

$$dU = dQ + dW \qquad (4.13)$$

But, of course, placing a d in front of a symbol does not make it a differential. We must know what variables Q and W depend on before we can calculate the differential heat and work corresponding to the assumed differential process.

Common sense tells us that when we perform operations of such magnitude as to change the thermodynamic state by only a small amount, both Q and W

FIGURE **4.5**

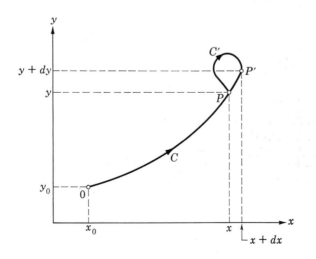

and their sums will be small. In this case Eq. 4.13 properly interpreted might describe the situation, provided we were careful to indicate that P' is reached from P along C extended and not some other curve, say, C'. For we find experimentally that the heat and work absorbed along a given path may be finite and quite large unless the *length* of path involved is small. In particular, both Q and W vanish as P' approaches P *along* the direct extension of C because the length of the path also vanishes. However, if the path from P to P' is C', then Q and W remain *finite* even though dU is differential (and vanishes as $P' \to P$). In this case we should have to write

$$dU = Q + W \tag{4.14}$$

To understand this rather paradoxical situation, we must study work performance and heat absorption in more detail.

4.10   Work in Quasistatic Processes

Consider a system acted on by a force of magnitude F. Let the force act through distance L. Then W, the work added to the system, is

$$W = FL$$

If F varies with L, we have to consider an average value, say, $\bar{F}$, over some increment, ΔL, of L, and the incremental work, ΔW, will be

$$\Delta W = \bar{F} \Delta L$$

As ΔL becomes differential, we have

$$dW = F \, dL \tag{4.15}$$

If F depends on L alone,

$$F = F(L)$$

and integration of Eq. 4.15 from L_0 to L gives the total external work, W, as

$$W = \int_{L_0}^{L} dW = \int_{L_0}^{L} F(L) \, dL \tag{4.16}$$

Since an integral with a variable upper limit is a function of that upper limit,

$$W = W(L) = \int_{L_0}^{L} F(L) \, dL \tag{4.17}$$

The quantity $W = W(L)$ we may call the *work* function for the particular problem. A formal differentiation of the work function as given by Eq. 4.17 leads us at once back to Eq. 4.15.

Suppose, however, that although F varies with L, it also depends on *some other variable* (such as the temperature, T). We must then write

$$F = F(L, T)$$

$$W = \int_{L_0, T_0}^{L, T} F(L, T) \, dL \tag{4.18}$$

This last type of integral is a so-called curve or *line* integral, since its value depends upon the precise curve along which we presume our system to move as it passes from L_0, T_0 to L, T. Integration cannot be carried out until we *know the curve*, that is, just how T varies with L.

If T is given as a specific function of L, say, $T'(L)$, then

$$F(L, T) = F[L, T'(L)] = F'(L)$$

and the force becomes a special function of L *for the particular curve* of integration indicated by $F'(L)$. If $F'(L)$ is plotted in the $F\text{-}L$ plane, the particular curve along which we integrate (or along which the image point moves) is marked C' (Fig. 4.6). Rewriting Eq. 4.18 with $F'(L)$ replacing $F(L, T)$ gives the term indicated in the general result of Eq. 4.11 by the rather awkward symbol $W \left. \right]_0^P$. For the path C' this becomes

$$W \left. \right]_0^P_{C'} = \int_{L_0}^L F'(L)\, dL = W'(L)$$

The work added along this particular path, C', is expressed as an integral with a *single* variable as the upper limit and is therefore a function of L, written as $W'(L)$. This we call the work function for path C'. If we had chosen path C'' or C''', the work functions would have been quite different, say, $W''(L)$ or $W'''(L)$, *a different one for each path.*

It becomes clear, therefore, that in thermodynamics we do not have a general work function analogous to the internal energy function. There is no general relation of the form $W(F, L)$, and we must not use mathematical methods that presume its existence. (See, for example, Eq. 4.13.) There are as many work functions as there are curves of integration, a different one for each curve. To emphasize the dependence of the work function on the curve C, we

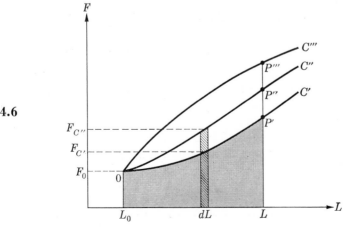

FIGURE **4.6**

shall use the subscript C and write

$$W \left.\right]_0^P = W_C = W_C(L) = \int_{L_0}^L F_C(L)\, dL = \int_{L_0}^L F_C\, dL \qquad (4.19)$$

Here $F_C(L)$ is the particular force relation determined by the curve C. In Fig. 4.6 the area of the strip that is shaded darker is given by $F_{C'}\,dL$. Integration of this term from 0 to P' along the curve C' sums the areas of all such strips beneath the curve. Thus the work added is the area below the curve C' and between the uprights at L_0 and L. Naturally integration along C'' from 0 to P'' involves a different work element, $F_{C''}\,dL$, and a quite different area for the added work.

In general, the proper expression for the differential work results from formal differentiation of Eq. 4.19:

$$dW_C = F_C\, dL = F\, dL \qquad (4.20)$$

In this equation dW_C is the element of work added for the differential change along C and may appropriately be called a *curve* differential.[14]

Although F is usually written for $F_C(L)$, we must remember that F is always the force fixed by the particular curve C. Thus neither $W = W(F, L)$ nor dW has any significance, whereas $W_C(L)$ is a continuous function of a single variable and dW_C is an *ordinary differential* of this function. Of course, W_C need not be expressed as a function of L. We may employ any convenient independent variable. In general, the same symbol, W_C, will always be used for the work function, and the particular independent variable will be read from the context.

4.11   Heat Absorbed in Quasistatic Processes

The preceding argument leads to a very simple and direct proof that a general heat function is nonexistent. Suppose that the path of a process is a closed one, as in Fig. 4.7. If we integrate

$$dW_C = F_C\, dL$$

around this curve in a counterclockwise direction, the work added is

$$W_C = \oint F_C\, dL = \int_1^2 F_{C'}\, dL + \int_2^1 F_{C''}\, dL$$

where the integral is broken into two parts, the first from 1 to 2 along C' and the second from 2 to 1 along C'', the upper of the two sections of the loop. Graphically the first integral is represented by the darker shaded area (which is positive, since the system gains work), whereas the second, which is negative, is given by both shaded areas. The difference, equal to the net area of the loop itself, is therefore negative and represents a net loss of work by the system.[15]

---

[14] See Crawford, *Am. J. Phys.*, **19**, 284 (1951).

[15] This result is in agreement with the earlier statement that no function of the sort $W = W(F, L)$ exists; if it did, it would suffer a zero change as does U in a cyclic process.

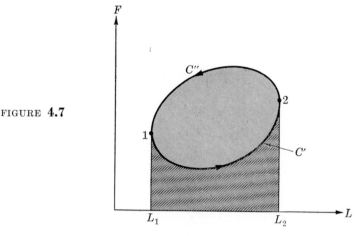

FIGURE **4.7**

Since the system returns to its starting point, no net change in U occurs. Hence, if Q_C is the heat added, or the heat function along curve C,

$$\oint dU = 0 = Q_C + W_C$$

or

$$Q_C = -W_C > 0$$

Thus $Q_C > 0$, and external work is done only at the expense of heat gained.

Since $Q \neq 0$, we know that $Q \neq Q(F, L)$. Therefore, neither general heat functions nor general work functions exist, and only the curve functions Q_C and W_C have meaning.

These heat and work functions are single-valued functions of a single variable as long as we confine ourselves to nonreentrant curves or paths without loops.[16] The curves C', C'', and C'''' of Fig. 4.6 are such curves, and along each of them we may define $Q_{C'}$ and $W_{C'}$, $Q_{C''}$ and $W_{C''}$, etc.

4.12   The First Law in Differential and Integral Forms

We are now in a position to write the proper differential form of the first law, as well as to understand the rather paradoxical situation presented by Eqs. 4.13 and 4.14. The first of these applies to the differential change from point P to P' along the curve C (Fig. 4.8). We rewrite this equation in terms of curve differentials as

$$dU = dQ_C + dW_C \tag{4.21}$$

---

[16] In the case of closed cycles, both W_C and Q_C take on multiple values, depending on the number of times a circuit of the loop is completed. For a more complete discussion of this problem, see Crawford, *Am. J. Phys.*, **19**, 284 (1951).

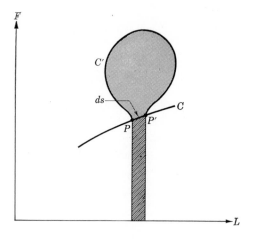

FIGURE **4.8**

Here dU is the difference between U at P and U at P', whereas dW_C and dQ_C refer to the differential element, ds, of the curve C, which connects P and P'. All the terms of Eq. 4.21 vanish as P approaches P' along C.

We now write Eq. 4.14 as

$$dU = Q_{C'} + W_{C'}$$

where dU is, as before, a differential and the other two terms are finite. $W_{C'}$ is the finite area of the loop formed by C' and the arc ds (lighter shading) plus the differential area $F\,dL$ (darker shading). Similarly, $Q_{C'}$ is the finite heat absorption along the finite length of C' and between P and P'.

We take Eq. 4.21 and its general integral between any two points, i and e,

$$\int_i^e dU = \int_i^e dQ_C + \int_i^e dW_C \qquad (4.22)$$

as the respective differential and integral forms of the first law, suitable for all quasistatic processes.

4.13   Cyclic Processes and Perpetual Motion

Since cyclic processes will be very important in what follows, it is worthwhile to emphasize some of their properties from the standpoint of the first law. It is convenient to divide cyclic processes into what we call *collapsed* and *noncollapsed* or loop cycles. Fig. 4.9(a) represents a collapsed cycle in which the system is taken from i to P along a curve, C, and returned to i along the *same* curve. The shaded area represents the work done by the surroundings from i

to P; an exactly equivalent amount is done by the system on the backward passage. Collapsed cycles produce *no net work*. Since U returns to its original value, there is no net absorption of heat either, the finite heat gained on the trip from i to P canceling that lost from P to i.

Fig. 4.9(b) represents a noncollapsed counterclockwise cycle in which the return curve, C', from P to i lies above the other curve, C. The area under C' represents work done by the system, of which the part represented by the darker shaded area under C is done on the system by the surroundings. Thus the net external work is positive and numerically equal to the area of the cycle. Calling the area A (where $A > 0$), we have (since $dU = 0$),

$$\oint dW_C = A = \oint dQ_C > 0$$

But this means that an external source must supply heat in order for the system to do work. A device using such a cycle is called a *heat engine*.

When, as in Fig. 4.9(c), the noncollapsed cycle is executed in a clockwise direction, the signs of all the quantities are altered. The area enclosed becomes negative, say, $-A$, and we must write

$$\oint dW_C = -A = \oint dQ_C < 0$$

The system has work done on it by the surroundings and rejects more heat than it absorbs. Any device using such a cycle represents a *refrigerator* or *heat pump* and of course requires for its operation an external source of mechanical energy.

For most substances a closed curve in the F-L plane executed in a *counter-clockwise* direction is the cycle of a heat engine, whereas the reverse produces a refrigerator. Refrigerators and heat engines will be examined in more satis-

FIGURE **4.9**

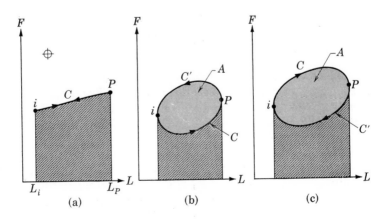

(a)   (b)   (c)

factory detail later, but this cursory account will serve to clarify the first law in its connection with perpetual motion.

The dream of inventors of constructing some device that could produce useful external work without an outside source of energy has persisted long after the first law rested on a secure experimental basis. It is important to realize that a perpetual motion machine is one that must have some sort of cyclic operation and therefore be capable of repeating its process indefinitely, producing useful external work each cycle. The early devices depended largely upon the attempt to extract mechanical work from isolated mechanical or electromechanical systems. The principle of the conservation of energy was sufficiently well established for these two forms of energy in 1760 for the French Academy to announce that from that time onward they would examine no more perpetual motion schemes. In our terms, if we insulate a system thermally, $dQ_C = 0$ for all parts of a cycle. Therefore, the cycle is essentially an adiabatic one for which $dU = dW_C$, and

$$\oint dU = 0 = \oint dW_C$$

Since external work can be performed only at the expense of internal energy, no net work can result from a cyclic process in an adiabatic electromechanical system, whatever its details may be.

The extension of the energy principle to heat and other forms of energy was carried out in the nineteenth century. For cyclic devices based on the extended first law

$$\oint dU = \oint dQ_C + \oint dW_C$$

and therefore

$$-\oint dW_C = \oint dQ_C$$

Hence net external work is possible only when the net heat absorbed is finite; when the system is shut off from outside heat sources, we have the same result as before; no external work is possible for adiabatic cycles. These results are categorical denials of the possibility of perpetual motion, whatever the principle of operation or the details of the processes may be.

4.14 Mechanics and the First Law

The difficulties of thermodynamics are usually sufficient without complications. It should be recognized, however, that the first law is readily stated in a general form such that it includes the energy principles of mechanics as well as the restricted formulation of the first law for a system assumed to be at rest.

For a given system we let E^{kin} = large-scale mechanical energy, E^{pot} = large-scale potential energy, and E^{tot} = total energy. The first two quantities are specifiable in terms of appropriate mechanical variables, and by definition

$$E^{\text{tot}} = E^{\text{kin}} + E^{\text{pot}} + U$$

For any finite process, whether reversible or irreversible,

$$\Delta E^{\mathrm{tot}} = \Delta E^{\mathrm{kin}} + \Delta E^{\mathrm{pot}} + \Delta U \tag{4.23}$$

The first law in a form that involves the principle of the conservation of energy more generally is

$$\boxed{\Delta E^{\mathrm{tot}} = Q + W} \tag{4.24}$$

Here Q and W are heat and work added, with no restrictions as to whether the process is reversible, quasistatic, or irreversible.[17]

As a simple example consider a block, B, of mass m sliding down an incline of height h, with the speeds at the top and bottom the same. First take the *block* as the system. Then

$$\Delta E_B^{\mathrm{kin}} = 0$$
$$\Delta E_B^{\mathrm{pot}} = -mgh$$

and for the work done on the block by friction

$$W = -mgh$$

Therefore, Eq. 4.24 becomes

$$\Delta U_B - mgh = Q_B - mgh$$

and any increase in the internal energy of the block, ΔU_B, is caused by the heat, Q_B, that flows across the block's surface into its interior. Similar reasoning indicates a parallel result when the plane is the system. Finally, if the block and plane together form the system, friction becomes a purely *internal* force, and $W = 0$. If the block and plane are assumed to be thermally insulated from their surroundings, $Q = 0$, and Eq. 4.24 gives

$$\Delta U_{B+P} - mgh = 0$$

In other words, the gain, ΔU_{B+P}, in the internal energy of the combined system is just the loss in potential energy of the block. A more detailed formulation of this general statement will be given in Sec. 7.16. (See Problem 4.6.)

Problems

4.1   When 250 g of water at 30°C is poured into a massive copper calorimeter of mass 3000 g at 0°C, a final equilibrium temperature of 11.90°C is observed. Calculate the average specific heat of the copper,
(a) taking the specific heat of the water as constant and equal to unity, and
(b) using the enthalpy values for water at atmospheric pressure (Appendix 4.1).

---

[17] Warner, *Am. J. Phys.*, **29**, 124 (1961).

4.2   From the definition of an international steam table (or IT) calorie as 1/860 of an international watt-hour, determine the IT calorie in terms of the absolute joule and hence in terms of the 15° calorie.

4.3   Using the enthalpy table (Appendix 4.1), determine the value of the so-called *mean* calorie in 15° calories. The mean calorie is defined as 1/100 of the heat required to warm 1 g of water from 0 to 100°C. Using a similar relation, express the value of J obtained by Reynolds and Moorby (Table 4.1) in terms of the 15° calorie.

4.4   In designing a model of Joule's paddle-wheel apparatus, it is desired to use a copper calorimeter, which together with the paddle wheel and fixed fins is to weigh about 1 kg. Two kg of water is to be used. How far must a 200 kg weight descend to produce a temperature rise of 2°C?

4.5   Examine the following processes and show clearly why each is thermodynamically irreversible:
(a) a heavy body falls to the ground,
(b) a gas expands into an evacuated region,
(c) a hot body and a cold one come to equilibrium, and
(d) a steel ball rolls down an incline.

4.6   Examine each of the situations in Problem 4.5 from the standpoint of the extended first law as stated in Eq. 4.24.

CHAPTER FIVE

Work and Heat in Various Systems

5.1 Introduction

In Chap. 4 the first law was obtained in the general form,

$$U_e - U_i = Q + W \tag{5.1}$$

suitable for all types of processes, and the differential form,

$$dU = dQ_C + dW_C \tag{5.2}$$

applicable only to quasistatic and reversible processes. We must now examine the various forms that Eq. 5.2 assumes for particular systems.

In all cases in which a single type of work, whether electrical or mechanical, is involved, we have the simple problem of interpreting

$$dW_C = F\,dL \tag{5.3}$$

for the particular system. Where more than one type of force is involved, a more general relation including a sum of such terms is needed.

After a discussion of these problems the first law will be solved for dQ_C and used to interpret the heat capacities and specific heats of systems made up of a single pure substance.

5.2 Systems under Uniform Hydrostatic Pressure

Systems under hydrostatic pressure have played a unique role in the development of thermodynamics and must, therefore, receive a large share of our attention. Let us rewrite Eq. 5.3, and then Eq. 5.2, in a form suitable for such systems.

Consider a fluid in a cylinder with a tight but frictionless piston as described in Chap. 1 (Fig. 5.1). Let the area of the piston be A. We suppose the fluid to be under uniform hydrostatic pressure, p. We shall use p as the size of the force per unit area whether we are talking of the force exerted on the fluid *by* the container or the oppositely directed force exerted by the fluid *on* the container. With large systems the effect of gravity is to cause p to vary with height in the system. In the relatively small systems we shall be considering, this variation may be neglected.

If the fluid is caused to expand and move the piston through a distance dL, it does work on the outside world, and the system loses work. If the force, F, of Eq. 5.3 is directed in the direction of increasing L,

$$dW_C = -F\,dL$$

and since $F = pA$ and $A\,dL = dV$, dV being the expansion in volume due to the piston's motion,

$$dW_C = -p\,dV \tag{5.4}$$

To find the work involved in any finite volume expansion, we must integrate dW_C along the appropriate curve of change. Thus for a constant-pressure or *isobaric* process, Fig. 5.2(a), the total work, W_p, is

$$W_p = -\int_i^e p\,dV = -p_i \int_i^e dV = -p_i(V_e - V_i)$$

a magnitude represented by the shaded area. For any other process, such as the general case of Fig. 5.2(b), we have formally

$$W_C = -\int_i^e p\,dV = -\int_{V_i}^{V_e} p_C(V)\,dV$$

a magnitude represented by the area under the curve of change, but one which cannot be explicitly evaluated until the equation of the curve, $p = p_C(V)$, is given.

To transfer a uniform pressure from a solid to a piston, we need an auxiliary fluid to surround the solid and act as the mechanical link between it and the external piston. Suppose the solid expands from its original volume to a new

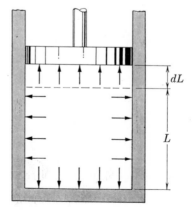

FIGURE **5.1**

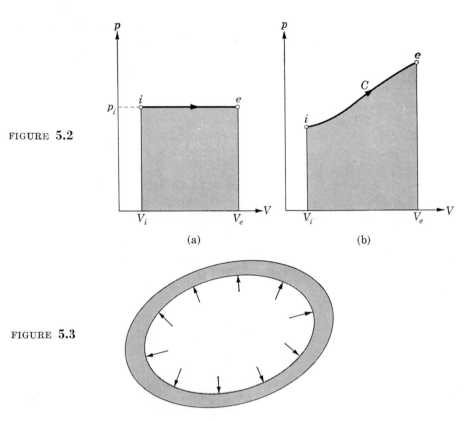

FIGURE **5.2**

(a)   (b)

FIGURE **5.3**

volume greater by the amount of the shaded region in Fig. 5.3. Then the total external work performed can be represented as a sum over the surface of the form

$$\sum_i \overline{p}_i \Delta A_i \Delta L_i$$

where $\overline{p}_i \Delta A_i$ is the average force on a small area of the surface, ΔA_i, that is pushed a distance, ΔL_i, by an average pressure, $\overline{p}_i$. If we allow ΔA_i and ΔL_i to become infinitesimal, the average pressure becomes the instantaneous (and uniform) pressure at any point in the auxiliary fluid. Thus

$$p \lim_{\substack{\Delta A \to 0 \\ \Delta L \to 0}} \Sigma \, \Delta A_i \Delta L_i = p \, dV = -dW_c$$

where dV is the volume expansion of the solid. Whether the system is gaseous, liquid, or solid, dW_c is of the same form, and the first law becomes

$$dU = dQ_c - p \, dV \tag{5.5}$$

for all systems under a uniform hydrostatic pressure. Only when there is an actual shrinkage in volume does the system gain work.

5.3   Other Mechanical Systems

In many other systems a simple interpretation of the original expression (Eq. 5.3) with no change in sign is possible. These will be considered briefly with reference to the appropriate figures in Chap. 1.

Thin Uniform Filament under Stretching Force. In Sec. 1.13 it was shown that a thin uniform filament under the action of a stretching force, F (Fig. 1.9), could be considered as a system having two degrees of freedom. If the stretching force, F, acts through an elongation, dL, the system gains work, $F\,dL$, and Eq. 5.3 applies directly. Neglecting any contributions due to atmospheric pressure, the first law for this system takes the form

$$dU = dQ_c + F\,dL \qquad (5.6)$$

Systems with Surface Tension. In the case of the thin film in the wire frame (Fig. 1.10), an increase of L by dL and of the film area, A, by dA requires that the external force, F, perform work of amount $F\,dL$ on the system. But since the film is double-sided, $F = 2B\mathscr{S}$, where $\mathscr{S}$ is the surface tension and $dA = 2B\,dL$. Consequently,

$$dW_c = F\,dL = 2B\mathscr{S}\,dL = \mathscr{S}\,dA$$

and

$$dU = dQ_c + \mathscr{S}\,dA \qquad (5.7)$$

Here $\mathscr{S}$ is usually dependent on the temperature only, so that as long as T is fixed, $\mathscr{S}$ is independent of A over wide limits.

5.4   Electrical Systems

We have already considered the dissipation of electrical energy as heat, along with the analogous case of mechanical dissipation. Strictly speaking, of course, neither of these processes is reversible. The charging of a condenser can, however, in principle at least, be carried out in a strictly reversible fashion. Consider a parallel plate condenser attached to a potentiometer as illustrated in Fig. 1.13 (Problem 1.8). As long as the potentiometer is adjusted so that the difference of potential, E, between the plates of the condenser is exactly balanced by the drop in potential along the resistance wire, no current flows, and the system with charge z is in equilibrium. To increase this charge, we must move the slider of the potentiometer to the right. If a current, i, flows for a time, $d\tau$, then

$$dW_c = Ei\,d\tau = E\frac{dz}{d\tau}d\tau = E\,dz \qquad (5.8)$$

Since the time cancels from the result, we are free to choose as small a current, i, as we like and to take as long a time as is needed to allow the charge, z, to flow into the condenser. In the limit of infinitely slow charging, we may regard the process as essentially quasistatic. It also becomes dissipationless in the limit and hence reversible also, as the following considerations show.

In general, when an electric current flows, heat is dissipated in all conducting elements owing to their ohmic resistance. If the combined resistance of these is r, the *Joulian heat production* in time $d\tau$ is given by

$$ri^2\,d\tau = ri\frac{dz}{d\tau}\,d\tau = ri\,dz$$

Since r may be taken as a constant, the heat dissipated for a given charge passed varies with i. In the limit of infinitely small currents, this term vanishes. Hence, in all strictly quasistatic charging processes, the Joulian heating term may be neglected in comparison with other effects from which the factor i is missing. Such processes may therefore be regarded as reversible.

A similar situation arises in the charging of certain types of storage cells. The storage cell must be of the type in which reversal of the current exactly reverses the chemical process taking place in the cell. Then, on recharge, the state of the cell is exactly the same as before the discharge. In such a case we may describe the state of the cell in terms of the total charge that has passed, the temperature, and the pressure. Usually the changes of volume involved may be neglected unless there is evolution of gas. Assuming no gas to be evolved, work is entirely electrical, and by suitable shifting of the potentiometer, charge or discharge may be made quasistatic and reversible. A positive dz represents plus charges flowing *into* the cell, causing the chemical reaction to proceed in such a direction as to increase the internal energy. Thus work is added when dz is positive, and Eq. 5.8 applies as in the case of the condenser.

The first law in its general form, Eq. 4.10,

$$U_e - U_i = Q + W$$

applies in particular to a conductor in which a finite current flows for a time, τ, when

$$U_e - U_i = Q + Ei\tau \tag{5.9}$$

With most metallic conductors the thermal conductivity is sufficiently high for the heat generated by Joulian dissipation to diffuse rapidly through the system. If the heat, Q, added from the outside is likewise rapidly diffused, temperature and pressure may be regarded as essentially uniform at all instants, and the system may be treated as essentially changing along a quasistatic path. Replacing Q by Q_C and $U_e - U_i$ by $U - U_0$ gives

$$U - U_0 = Q_C + Ei\tau \tag{5.10}$$

Regarding U_0, E, and i as constant, we have, on formal differentation,

$$dU = dQ_C + Ei\,d\tau$$
or
$$dU = dQ_C + E\,dz \tag{5.11}$$

Within the limitations imposed we have formal agreement with the two reversible cases—that is, electrical work is given by the term $E\,dz$—and the first law takes the form of Eq. 5.11.

The situations are, however, not actually parallel. Joulian heating is always a dissipative process, and U can never be *decreased* by such a current. Whichever way it flows, U always increases. Strictly speaking, therefore, Eqs. 5.10 and 5.11 should be replaced by

$$U - U_0 = Q_C + E|i|\tau$$

and

$$dU = dQ_C + E\,|dz|$$

where the absolute value signs indicate the irreversible nature of the quasistatic process. We shall return in Chap. 9 to a more general account of processes that by their very nature are inherently irreversible.

5.5 Magnetic Systems

A further interesting example of work performance is afforded by the magnetization of certain types of magnetic materials. As is well known, a very important class of magnetic substances called *ferromagnetic* exhibits the phenomenon of hysteresis. If we place a sample of such a material in a coil and gradually increase the current in the coil, the corresponding magnetic induction, B, when plotted against the magnetizing field, $\mathcal{H}$, gives the familiar hysteresis loop, shown in Fig. 5.4. If we pass from O to a and b, we find that

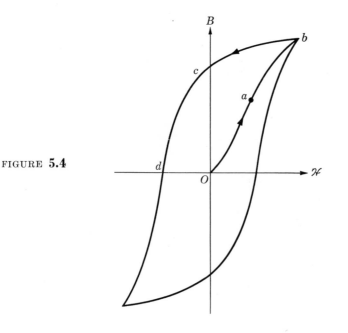

FIGURE **5.4**

decreasing $\mathscr{H}$ does *not* permit us to retrace this curve, but rather that we move along b, c, d, etc. The magnetization is thus not a *reversible* process. The true status of the system at point a, for example, is not determined solely by the values of B, T, and $\mathscr{H}$ corresponding to this point but depends also on just how the system got to this point. Thus the state of the system depends not on present conditions alone but also on the past history of the system. Such systems are not describable in terms of any (as yet known) set of thermodynamic variables and are, therefore, not amenable to detailed thermodynamic analysis.

Fortunately there is another class of magnetic substances called *paramagnetic* in which the magnetic effects, although less marked than in the ferromagnetic materials, are reversible. In these substances, even though the change of B with $\mathscr{H}$ is seldom linear, the curve is exactly retraceable, and no hysteretic effects are observed. The true state of the system can be described in terms of a few thermodynamic variables. If we choose to keep the pressure constant and neglect the small change in volume caused by the field (so-called *magnetostriction*), we may describe such systems adequately in terms of two independent variables, say, T and $\mathscr{H}$ or T and $\mathbf{M}$, the total magnetic moment of the system.

Consider now the reversible magnetization of a paramagnetic material, which, for simplicity, we form into a toroid of uniform cross section, A (Fig. 5.5). Suppose that the material is magnetized by a current from a battery that flows through a toroidal winding of N turns so closely wound as to produce an essentially uniform field, $\mathscr{H}$, at all points in the specimen. If the toroid can be regarded as thin compared with the radius, r, we may write the length, L, of the sample as $L = 2\pi r$ and its volume, V, as $2\pi A L$. Then the field within the

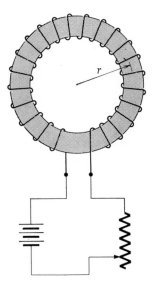

FIGURE **5.5**

toroid is given by

$$\mathcal{H} = \frac{4\pi N A i}{V} \tag{5.12}$$

By Faraday's principle of electromagnetic induction, the magnetic field produces an induction, B, having a rate of change, $dB/d\tau$, that determines the back emf, E, where

$$E = NA\frac{dB}{d\tau}$$

Any charge increment, dz, passing through the coil must perform work against this emf, and

$$dW_C = E\,dz = NA\,dz\frac{dB}{d\tau}$$

Since $dz/d\tau = i$,

$$dW_C = NAi\,dB \tag{5.13}$$

Combining Eqs. 5.12 and 5.13 gives at once

$$dW_C = \frac{V\mathcal{H}}{4\pi}\,dB \tag{5.14}$$

In any region where no free magnetic poles are present, $\mathcal{H}$, B, and $\mathbf{M}$ are connected by

$$B = \mathcal{H} + \frac{4\pi\mathbf{M}}{V}$$

or

$$dB = d\mathcal{H} + \frac{4\pi}{V}d\mathbf{M} \tag{5.15}$$

the small changes in V being neglected. On combining this result with Eq. 5.14, we have

$$dW_C = \frac{V\mathcal{H}}{4\pi}d\mathcal{H} + \mathcal{H}\,d\mathbf{M}$$

This relation contains two terms, of which the first holds for a vacuum whereas the second vanishes. Integration of the first term gives $V\mathcal{H}^2/8\pi$ as the energy stored in the magnetic field in a vacuum. It is reasonable, therefore, to regard the second term as the magnetic energy stored in the magnetized substance itself. As far as the system proper is concerned, this represents the only addition to *its* internal energy. We therefore drop out the first term and have finally

$$dW_C = \mathcal{H}\,d\mathbf{M}$$

and

$$\boxed{dU = dQ_C + \mathcal{H}\,d\mathbf{M}} \tag{5.16}$$

as the proper relation for paramagnetic materials in uniform magnetic fields.

5.6   The General Case

We may now with profit define a *generalized* force, F, such that its product by the differential of an appropriate generalized geometric variable, say, θ, represents work. Then

$$dW_C = F\,d\theta \tag{5.17}$$

is the general work expression. The values of F and θ for the special cases of the last four sections are summarized in Table 5.1. In the last two columns appropriate units of F and θ are given for the cgs and the mks systems. When the rationalized mks units are used for magnetic systems, $\mathscr{H}$ must be in ampere-turns per meter, and $\mathbf{M}$ in weber-meters, so that the product is in joules.

When several independent generalized forces are involved, we must write

$$dW_C = F_1\,d\theta_1 + F_2\,d\theta_2 + F_3\,d\theta_3 + \cdots$$

or

$$dW_C = \sum_i F_i\,d\theta_i \tag{5.18}$$

Here the summation extends over all the independent work terms. The first law now becomes

$$dU = dQ_C + \sum_i F_i\,d\theta_i \tag{5.19}$$

In practice a number of interesting cases arise in which only *two* work terms are involved. When both pressure and surface tension perform work, we have

$$dW_C = -p\,dV + \mathscr{S}\,dA$$

and

$$dU = dQ_C - p\,dV + \mathscr{S}\,dA \tag{5.20}$$

TABLE **5.1**

Differential Work in Various Systems

System	F	θ	Work units cgs	mks
Hydrostatic	$-p$	V	$\dfrac{\text{dyne}}{\text{cm}^2}\cdot\text{cm}^3$	$\dfrac{\text{new}}{\text{meter}^2}\cdot\text{meter}^3$
Tensed filament	$+F$	L	dyne $\cdot$ cm	new $\cdot$ meter
Surface film	$+\mathscr{S}$	A	$\dfrac{\text{dyne}}{\text{cm}}\cdot\text{cm}^2$	$\dfrac{\text{new}}{\text{meter}}\cdot\text{meter}^2$
Reversible cell, charged condenser, quasistatic electrical heating	$+E$	z		v $\cdot$ coul
Paramagnetic salt	$+\mathscr{H}$	$\mathbf{M}$	oersted $\cdot$ pole $\cdot$ cm (emu)	$\dfrac{\text{amp-turns}}{\text{meter}}\cdot$ weber-meter*

* In Kennelly's rationalized mks units.

For the case of the quasistatic electrical heating of a hydrostatic system (that is, when the resistance coils are *inside* the system so that the energy to be dissipated enters in electrical form and not as heat),

$$dW_C = - p\,dV + E\,|dz|$$

and
$$dU = dQ_C - p\,dV + E\,|dz| \tag{5.21}$$

Equation 5.21 is of importance in many types of electrical calorimeters.

5.7   Heat Capacities of a Pure Substance

Let us now return to the important case of systems under hydrostatic pressure and Eq. 5.5,

$$dU = dQ_C - p\,dV \tag{5.5}$$

The systems to which this equation applies may be gaseous, liquid, or solid. Although they might consist of homogeneous mixtures, a single pure substance will normally be assumed.

Our immediate problem is to examine the general thermal properties of pure substances in the light of Eq. 5.5. Solving for dQ_C, the heat absorbed along a curve, C, we have

$$dQ_C = dU + p\,dV \tag{5.22}$$

Since single-phase systems have two degrees of freedom, there are a number of possible independent variable sets, of which T and p, T and V, and p and V are the most useful.

Using the definition of heat capacity as the ratio of the heat absorbed per unit change of a suitable variable, x, along a given path, C, we now define a general heat capacity as

$$\frac{dQ_C}{dx}$$

where Q_C is to be regarded as a function of x alone. Actually the most useful curves are those along which some other single variable, say, y, is held constant. Indicating this relationship by placing y as a subscript to Q, we have

$$\text{general heat capacity} = \frac{dQ_y}{dx} \tag{5.23}$$

When $y = p$ and $x = T$, we have the heat absorbed along an isobar per unit rise in temperature. This was the definition used in Chap. 4 for C_p, the heat capacity at constant pressure. With x and y chosen in pairs from the set T, p, and V, there are in all six possibilities and thus six heat capacities. These may all be calculated from Eq. 5.22.

5.8   Heat Capacities with the Variables T and p

With T and p as the independent variables we must write

$$U = U(T,p)$$

and
$$V = V(T,p)$$

Then by the general theorem

$$dU = \left(\frac{\partial U}{\partial T}\right)_p dT + \left(\frac{\partial U}{\partial p}\right)_T dp$$

and
$$dV = \left(\frac{\partial V}{\partial T}\right)_p dT + \left(\frac{\partial V}{\partial p}\right)_T dp$$

On substitution of these relations in Eq. 5.22 and collection of terms,

$$dQ_c = \left[\left(\frac{\partial U}{\partial T}\right)_p + p\left(\frac{\partial V}{\partial T}\right)_p\right]dT + \left[\left(\frac{\partial U}{\partial p}\right)_T + p\left(\frac{\partial V}{\partial p}\right)_T\right]dp \qquad (5.24)$$

For an isobaric path
$$dQ_c \equiv dQ_p$$

and the last term of Eq. 5.24 falls out, leaving

$$dQ_p = \left[\left(\frac{\partial U}{\partial T}\right)_p + p\left(\frac{\partial V}{\partial T}\right)_p\right]dT \qquad (5.25)$$

On division by dT, we have dQ_p/dT, which is C_p, and therefore

$$C_p = \left(\frac{\partial U}{\partial T}\right)_p + p\left(\frac{\partial V}{\partial T}\right)_p \qquad (5.26)$$

For an isothermal change
$$dQ_c \equiv dQ_T$$

and the first term on the right of Eq. 5.24 falls out, leaving

$$dQ_T = \left[\left(\frac{\partial U}{\partial p}\right)_T + p\left(\frac{\partial V}{\partial p}\right)_T\right]dp \qquad (5.27)$$

Then dQ_T/dp is a new kind of heat capacity, the heat absorbed *along an isotherm per unit pressure rise*. Since the temperature remains constant during this addition, dQ_T/dp represents a sort of *latent heat*. It is accordingly called the *latent heat of pressure rise* and given the symbol L_p. Therefore,

$$L_p = \left(\frac{\partial U}{\partial p}\right)_T + p\left(\frac{\partial V}{\partial p}\right)_T \tag{5.28}$$

It is important to recognize that $L_p \equiv dQ_T/dp$ by definition (that is, is *identically* equal), whereas L_p is equal to the sum of the two quantities in the square bracket as a result of the first law. The relations in Eqs. 5.26 and 5.28 may therefore be taken as interpretations of the meanings of C_p and L_p in the light of the first law. Each is made up of two terms, the first representing heat used to increase the internal energy and the second representing heat that goes directly into performing external hydrostatic work.

In terms of the heat capacities C_p and L_p, we are able to rewrite Eq. 5.24 as

$$dQ_C = C_p\,dT + L_p\,dp \tag{5.29}$$

This important relation we shall refer to as the *first dQ_C* expression.

5.9   Heat Capacities with the Variables *T* and *V*

Since dV is already an independent increment, we have only to express dU in terms of dT and dV and substitute the result in Eq. 5.22. This procedure gives

$$dQ_C = \left(\frac{\partial U}{\partial T}\right)_V dT + \left[\left(\frac{\partial U}{\partial V}\right)_T + p\right]dV \tag{5.30}$$

For a constant volume change

$$dQ_C \equiv dQ_V$$

and

$$\frac{dQ_V}{dT} = \left(\frac{\partial U}{\partial T}\right)_V$$

Since dQ_V/dT is the heat absorbed per degree rise of temperature along an isochore, it represents the *heat capacity at constant volume*, or the *isochoric* heat capacity, C_V. Thus

$$C_V \equiv \frac{dQ_V}{dT} = \left(\frac{\partial U}{\partial T}\right)_V \tag{5.31}$$

The heat capacity at constant volume is simpler than that at constant pressure and gives directly the isochoric rate of rise of the internal energy of the sample with temperature. The work term is missing because no hydrostatic work can be performed when the volume is constant. Since for all physical systems U increases with T, $(\partial U/\partial T)_V > 0$, and C_V is a positive quantity.

When, in Eq. 5.30, we set $dT = 0$, an isothermal change results, and

$$\frac{dQ_T}{dV} = \left(\frac{\partial U}{\partial V}\right)_T + p \tag{5.32}$$

Here the ratio dQ_T/dV represents another type of latent heat. It is called the *latent heat of expansion* and is represented by L_V, where

$$L_V \equiv \frac{dQ_T}{dV} = \left(\frac{\partial U}{\partial V}\right)_T + p \tag{5.33}$$

The latent heat of expansion gives directly the rate of increase of U with volume (T constant) only when the pressure, p, is vanishingly small.[1] On rewriting Eq. 5.30 in terms of C_V and L_V, we have the important result

$$dQ_c = C_V \, dT + L_V \, dV \tag{5.34}$$

This is the *second dQ_c equation*. A third dQ_c equation may be obtained for the variable pair p and V, but it is not really needed and will be omitted.

5.10   Heat Absorbed along Certain Curves

The physical meaning of the four heat capacities just discussed is best seen by consideration of differential changes in, say, the p-V plane (Fig. 5.6). Consider

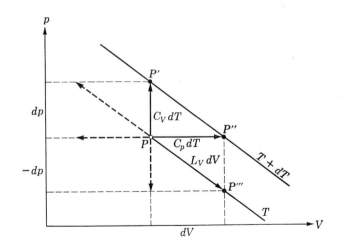

FIGURE **5.6**

---

[1] The use of L_p and L_V for the heats of pressure rise and expansion represents a departure from the usual rule that any subscript indicates a variable held constant. It can be defended only on the ground that a two-letter symbol is much more convenient to write, even if less explicit, than a three-letter one.

TABLE **5.2**

Four Heat Capacities

Independent variables	Curve	Heat capacity		Heat absorption, $dQ_y{}^{(x)}$	Interpretation from first law
		Common symbol	3-letter symbol		
T, p	Isobar	C_p	$C_p{}^{(T)}$	$dQ_p = C_p\,dT$	$C_p = \left(\dfrac{\partial U}{\partial T}\right)_p + p\left(\dfrac{\partial V}{\partial T}\right)_p$
	Isotherm	L_p	$C_T{}^{(p)}$	$dQ_T = L_p\,dp$	$L_p = \left(\dfrac{\partial U}{\partial p}\right)_T + p\left(\dfrac{\partial V}{\partial p}\right)_T$
T, V	Isochore	C_V	$C_V{}^{(T)}$	$dQ_V = C_V\,dT$	$C_V = \left(\dfrac{\partial U}{\partial T}\right)_V$
	Isotherm	L_V	$C_T{}^{(V)}$	$dQ_T = L_V\,dV$	$L_V = \left(\dfrac{\partial U}{\partial V}\right)_T + p$

two isotherms (drawn as straight lines since only differential changes are contemplated), one for T and the other for $T + dT$. From any point, P, on the first one, we can pass to the other in two simple ways.

Along the isochore ($P \to P'$) the volume is constant, and T and p increase by dT and dp. With T and V as our independent variables, and using the *second* expression for dQ_C (Eq. 5.34), we obtain

$$dQ_V = C_V\,dT$$

For the isobaric change ($P \to P''$), use of the *first* expression (Eq. 5.29) gives

$$dQ_p = C_p\,dT$$

Finally, for the isothermal change ($P \to P'''$), use of the first and second dQ_C expressions gives

$$dQ_T = L_p\,dp$$

or

$$dQ_T = L_V\,dV$$

In the last expression, since a change of $+dV$ must correspond to a change of $-dp$, L_p and L_V must have *opposite* signs. In Fig. 5.6 dQ_V, dQ_p, and dQ_T are indicated. Since dT, dV, and dp all reverse their signs when we move in the opposite directions from P (dashed arrows), the heat transfers all reverse in sign.

For convenience of reference the results of the last three sections are summarized in Table 5.2. In particular, column 5 gives the general heat absorption, $dQ_y(x)$, along a curve at constant y (with x as an independent variable) in the form

$$dQ_y(x) = C_y{}^{(x)}\,dx$$

and column 6 gives the interpretation of each heat capacity in terms of the first law from Eqs. 5.26, 5.28, 5.31, and 5.33.

5.11   Relations among the Heat Capacities; Specific Heats

Although certain important relationships can be read directly out of the fifth column of Table 5.2, care in interpretation is needed. A more general approach that gives all the relations we seek is therefore used. We start with the first and second dQc expressions

$$dQ_C = C_p dT + L_p dp \tag{5.29}$$

and
$$dQ_C = C_V dT + L_V dV \tag{5.34}$$

Since these are completely equivalent expressions in terms of different variables, they can be made identical by a suitable change of variable. If in the second one dV is expressed in terms of dT and dp, two equations for dQ_C in terms of the *same* variables result, and the coefficients of dT and dp may be equated.

With $V = V(T, p)$

$$dV = \left(\frac{\partial V}{\partial T}\right)_p dT + \left(\frac{\partial V}{\partial p}\right)_T dp$$

and Eq. 5.34 becomes

$$dQ_C = \left[C_V + L_V \left(\frac{\partial V}{\partial T}\right)_p\right] dT + L_V \left(\frac{\partial V}{\partial p}\right)_T dp \tag{5.35}$$

Equating coefficients in Eqs. 5.35 and 5.29 gives us

$$\boxed{C_p = C_V + L_V \left(\frac{\partial V}{\partial T}\right)_p} \tag{5.36}$$

and

$$\boxed{L_p = L_V \left(\frac{\partial V}{\partial p}\right)_T} \tag{5.37}$$

The relations given in Eqs. 5.36 and 5.37 enable us to determine two of the four heat capacities in terms of a given pair, C_V and L_V. In addition, certain derivatives that can be measured directly or calculated from the equation of state, when that is known, are needed. Since by the reciprocity relation

$$\left(\frac{\partial V}{\partial T}\right)_p \left(\frac{\partial p}{\partial V}\right)_T \left(\frac{\partial T}{\partial p}\right)_V = -1$$

only two of these derivatives are needed to determine the third.

It is often convenient to express the first law in a form applicable to systems of *unit* mass by dividing all extensive variables by the mass of the system and using the corresponding *specific* quantities throughout. Thus we set $U = mu$,

$V = mv$, $dQ_C = m\,dq_C$, and $dW_C = mp\,dv$, where u is the specific internal energy, v the specific volume, dq_C the heat added to the unit mass system, etc. This usage conforms to the convention of using capital letters to refer to *extensive* properties (which vary with mass) and lower-case letters for all corresponding *intensive* or specific properties. Since the specific properties are inherently independent of the mass or scale of the system, they are characteristic properties of the substance itself. With these substitutions the first law for a system of unit mass becomes

$$du = dq_C - p\,dv \tag{5.38}$$

We now examine the heat capacities in these terms. The general heat capacity is given by

$$C_y{}^{(x)} = \frac{dQ_y}{dx} = m\frac{dq_y}{dx} \tag{5.39}$$

When x is an *intensive* variable, this last ratio is *intensive*,

$$\frac{dq_y}{dx} = c_y{}^{(x)}$$

Thus $c_y{}^{(x)}$ is a *specific* heat for a change at constant y. Of the four heat capacities mentioned, three may be expressed this way, as we see on writing out their definitions. Hence $C_p = mc_p$, $C_V = mc_V$, and $L_p = ml_p$.

The remaining one is

$$C_y{}^{(V)} = \frac{dQ_y}{dV} = m\frac{dq_y}{m\,dV} = \frac{dq_y}{dv} = L_v$$

Since V is an *extensive* variable, $dV = m\,dv$. This mass in the denominator cancels that in the numerator. Thus L_v is inherently an intensive or specific property of the substance considered, and we might logically adopt the lower-case equivalent, $L_v \equiv l_v$.

Although in many cases the unit of mass may be the gram, it might equally well be, for example, the gram-mole. In what follows, however, the symbol for mass, m will *always* refer to the gram, kilogram, etc. Capital letters will be used for *all nonunit mass systems*, chiefly because symbols with capital letters are more clearly and easily written by hand (especially with subscripts) and the possibility of confusion or errors from different-sized symbols is avoided.

5.12   Heat Capacities for Other Systems

The definitions of these four heat capacities as well as of the relations connecting them are general and apply equally to a solid, a liquid, or a gas, provided that the only force variable involved is a hydrostatic pressure. Similar discussions are, of course, possible for the other simple systems treated earlier, such as the thin filament under uniform tension. Comparing the forms of the first law written for the hydrostatic system and the thin filament, we have

$$dU = dQ_c - p\,dV$$
$$dU = dQ_c + F\,dL$$

With temperature a common variable in the two systems, it is apparent that p corresponds to $-F$ and V to L. Thus in one case $V = V(T, p)$, and in the other $L = (T, F)$. Accordingly, the results of the last five sections can be translated at once from the hydrostatic system to the thin filament. As an example, take Eq. 5.26:

$$C_p = \left(\frac{\partial U}{\partial T}\right)_p + p\left(\frac{\partial V}{\partial T}\right)_p \qquad (5.26)$$

This becomes
$$C_F = \left(\frac{\partial U}{\partial T}\right)_F - F\left(\frac{\partial L}{\partial T}\right)_F \qquad (5.40)$$

Here, of course, we do not need to write $-F$ as a subscript to indicate constancy.

Since the ordinary coefficient of linear expansion, α_p, is given by

$$\alpha_p = \frac{1}{L}\left(\frac{\partial L}{\partial T}\right)_p$$

the coefficient involved here is α_F, the coefficient measured at *constant force*, and

$$\alpha_F = \frac{1}{L}\left(\frac{\partial L}{\partial T}\right)_F$$

These two coefficients are generally different, although the difference is negligible as long as the tensions and pressures are small.

The translation of the hydrostatic relations to the proper forms for other simple systems can be carried out in the same way as for the thin filament.

When more than two independent variables are involved, we may proceed much as just demonstrated. Thus for a surface film under hydrostatic pressure Eq. 5.20 is rewritten as

$$dQ_c = dU + p\,dV - \mathscr{S}\,dA$$

Then with the independent variables T, p, and A, for example, dQ_c may be written

$$dQ_c = C_{pA}^{(T)}\,dT + C_{TA}^{(p)}\,dp + C_{Tp}^{(A)}\,dA$$

where
$$C_{pA}^{(T)} = \left(\frac{\partial U}{\partial T}\right)_{pA} + p\left(\frac{\partial V}{\partial T}\right)_{pA}$$

$$C_{TA}^{(p)} = \left(\frac{\partial U}{\partial p}\right)_{TA} + p\left(\frac{\partial V}{\partial p}\right)_{TA}$$

and
$$C_{Tp}^{(A)} = \left(\frac{\partial U}{\partial A}\right)_{Tp} + p\left(\frac{\partial V}{\partial A}\right)_{Tp} - \mathscr{S} \qquad (5.41)$$

The heat capacities $C_{pA}^{(T)}$ and $C_{TA}^{(p)}$ are generalizations of C_p and $C_{T}{}^{(p)}$ (or L_p), respectively. The heat capacity $C_{Tp}^{(A)}$ is a new type, the latent heat absorption at constant pressure per unit increase in area. It represents the heat absorbed at constant T and p as the surface area is increased a unit amount.

5.13   Internal Energy of a Gas

Because of the many simple properties of gases as compared with matter in more condensed forms, the study of gases has contributed greatly to the growth of ideas in thermodynamics. Let us, for example, examine the internal energy of a gas. We may do this experimentally in a number of ways.

When a gas is allowed to expand against a piston or against the atmosphere, it performs external work, and if we are to keep its internal energy constant, an equivalent of heat must be added. If, however, we insulate the gas and permit its expansion into a vacuum, a so-called *adiabatic free expansion*, then, since both Q and W are zero, the internal energy must remain unchanged.

With the variables T and V

$$U = U(T, V) = \text{constant} \tag{5.42}$$

and the gas at constant internal energy can cool, warm, or remain at the same temperature as V increases. Thus adiabatic free expansion offers a direct method of obtaining information about the internal energy function of a particular gas.

Using the reciprocity relation for the three variables U, T, and V, we have

$$\left(\frac{\partial U}{\partial T}\right)_V \left(\frac{\partial V}{\partial U}\right)_T \left(\frac{\partial T}{\partial V}\right)_U = -1$$

or

$$\left(\frac{\partial T}{\partial V}\right)_U = -\frac{\left(\frac{\partial U}{\partial V}\right)_T}{\left(\frac{\partial U}{\partial T}\right)_V} = -\frac{\left(\frac{\partial U}{\partial V}\right)_T}{C_V} \tag{5.43}$$

where $(\partial T/\partial V)_U$ is the change in temperature per unit change in V at constant U. Since $C_V > 0$, this derivative depends for its sign on $(\partial U/\partial V)_T$. When U increases with volume (T constant), then $(\partial T/\partial V)_U$ should be negative, that is, the gas should *cool* on free expansion, whereas if the reverse is true, the gas should be warmed. Only in the special case that $(\partial U/\partial V)_T = 0$ can we expect no temperature change whatever. Then, of course, U is independent of V. However, since

$$\left(\frac{\partial U}{\partial p}\right)_T = \left(\frac{\partial U}{\partial V}\right)_T \left(\frac{\partial V}{\partial p}\right)_T$$

and since $(\partial V/\partial p)_T \neq 0$, U must also be independent of p and hence *can depend on T only*. A gas for which $U = U(T)$ is known as an *ideal* gas.

To see more fully what this means, return to the definition of L_V, the latent heat of expansion:

$$L_V \equiv \frac{dQ_T}{dV} = \left(\frac{\partial U}{\partial V}\right)_T + p \tag{5.33}$$

where each term has the dimensions of a pressure. Since L_V is the sum of two terms, we may regard it as a sort of "total pressure" made up of the external pressure exerted by the container, which we now write p_{ext}, and the internal pressure, $p_{int} = (\partial U/\partial V)_T$. Then

$$L_V = p_{int} + p_{ext}$$

With an isothermal volume expansion dV,

$$dQ_T = L_V dV = p_{int} dV + p_{ext} dV$$

and the heat absorbed goes partly into doing work against the external pressure, the rest being used to do work against the internal pressure. The latter amount is

$$p_{int} dV = \left(\frac{\partial U}{\partial V}\right)_T dV = dU_T$$

or the isothermal increase in U. This internal work may be positive, negative, or zero. When it is positive, we interpret it as work done *against* the attractive forces between the molecules. When it is negative, net repulsion between the molecules causes the performance of external work. Finally, when the gas is so expanded that $p_{int} = (\partial U/\partial V)_T = 0$, the gas has reached the ideal state. We interpret the vanishing of p_{int} as indication of the complete absence of attractive forces between the molecules.

In effect, then, we adopt as the thermodynamic definition of an ideal gas the two relations

$$pV = RT$$

and
$$p_{int} = \left(\frac{\partial U}{\partial V}\right)_T = 0 \tag{5.44}$$

5.14   Internal Energy of a Gas from Experiment

Direct attempts to study the free expansion of gases were first made by Joule in 1843, and $(\partial T/\partial V)_U$ and other similar coefficients characteristic of adiabatic expansion are usually referred to as *Joule* or *Joule-Kelvin coefficients*. Joule originally used two large vessels connected by a valve (Fig. 5.7) and placed together in a tank of water. One vessel was evacuated, and the other filled with gas. When the valve was opened, the gas expanded, and any change in temperature was determined by measurement of the water temperature. Since the heat capacities of the water and the containers were many times as great as the heat capacity of the gas, it is probably not surprising that Joule was able to detect no temperature change.

Later Kelvin devised and carried out with Joule[2] a more delicate experiment in which the gas was allowed to flow through a porous plug from a high pressure (p) to a low pressure (p_0). We may think of this streaming process as maintained by a pair of pistons, #1 and #2 of Fig. 5.8. Piston #1 keeps the gas compressed to the high pressure, p, and moves to the right as the gas streams through the plug, where it undergoes a pressure drop to p_0. This lower pressure is kept constant by having piston #2 also move to the right but at a faster rate than

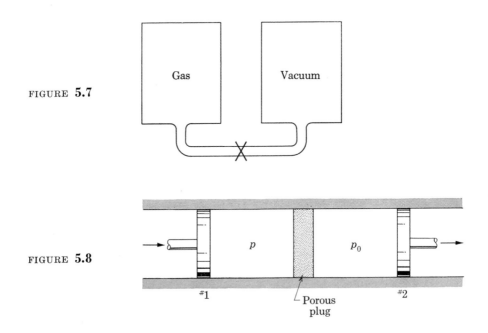

FIGURE **5.7**

FIGURE **5.8**

piston #1. In the actual experiment the system was insulated around the region of the plug, the temperature of the gas being measured as it came out at the lower pressure, p_0. Joule and Kelvin found in general that the cooling effect depended on the departure of the gas from Boyle's law and in particular that $\Delta T/\Delta p$, where $\Delta p = p - p_0$, was independent of p up to 5 or 6 atm.

Many later attempts were made to obtain more accurate data on the temperature drop in such Joule-Kelvin expansions; in fact, a large literature has grown up on the subject. Unfortunately, however, systematic errors are unavoidable, owing to the flow of heat into the cooled gas from the other parts of the apparatus. For the most reliable results, therefore, it seems advisable to abandon efforts to measure the temperature drop directly and to attempt rather to compensate by carefully controlled electrical heating for the drop that would otherwise be produced. In other words, the gas is allowed to undergo an isothermal expansion from a high pressure, p, to, say, atmospheric pressure, p_0.

[2] Joule and Thompson, *Phil. Trans. Roy. Soc. London*, **152**(1862); and earlier papers.

During this expansion external mechanical work is performed, and electrical heating of a surrounding water bath supplies the necessary energy to keep the temperature exactly constant.

This method has been employed by Rossini and Frandsen[3] for air, oxygen, and mixtures of carbon monoxide and oxygen. Their apparatus is shown in Fig. 5.9. The gas, contained in a steel bomb, B, at pressure p, is allowed to expand very slowly through a valve into a copper tube, which spirals through the surrounding water bath and out to the atmosphere. An electric heater at A is adjusted to maintain the gas at the exact temperature of the bath (and the original temperature of the gas in the bomb). Then the electrical work in time $d\tau$, $Ei\,d\tau$, provides the heat absorbed by the gas as it expands, and

$$dU' = dQ'_T - p_0 dV' = Ei\,d\tau - p_0 dV'$$

where it is assumed that the gas streams out at essentially the atmospheric pressure, p_0, with a negligible kinetic energy. Primes are used to indicate that the mass of gas involved is not 1 mole but, say, ν moles.

The flow is allowed to continue until the gas originally at pressure p has expanded to the atmospheric pressure, p_0. Then integration of dU' from the initial to the final state of the gas gives at once

$$U'_e - U'_i = Ei\tau' - p_0(V'_e - V'_i) \qquad (5.45)$$

where τ' is the total time of flow. If we divide through by the total number of

FIGURE **5.9**

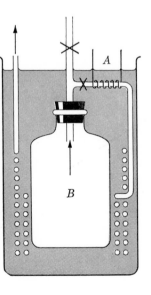

[3] Rossini and Frandsen, *J. Research Natl. Bur. Standards*, **9**, 733 (1932).

moles of gas, ν, originally in vessel B, we obtain

$$\Delta U = U_e - U_i = Ei\tau - p_0(V_e - V_i)$$

where the unprimed quantities refer to a gram-mole of gas. If we write

$$\Delta U = U_e - U_i = U(p, T) - U(p_0, T) \tag{5.46}$$

ΔU is the change in internal energy of a mole of gas as it expands from p to p_0 (at constant T). This can be measured as a function of the original high pressure, p, and is shown plotted for air in Fig. 5.10. The value ΔU is thus negative and falls linearly with pressure (at least up to 40 or 50 atm). If we differentiate Eq. 5.46 partially with respect to p (T constant) we have

$$\left(\frac{\partial \Delta U}{\partial p}\right)_T = \left(\frac{\partial U}{\partial p}\right)_T = \alpha < 0$$

where α is the constant slope of the graph in Fig. 5.10 and is the rate of change of the internal energy with pressure. Since this value is negative, the internal energy decreases with increasing pressure; that is, it decreases as the molecules are forced closer and closer together.

The results shown in Fig. 5.10 can be represented by

$$\Delta U = \alpha(p - p_0)$$

or
$$U(p, T) = U(p_0, T) + \alpha(p - p_0) \tag{5.47}$$

In the limit as $p \to 0$, the gas has become infinitely dilute, and the molecules are on the average so far apart that they no longer have any mutual attraction for one another. In this limit the internal energy no longer depends upon p (or V), as we have seen, and the gas is in the ideal state. If the internal energy

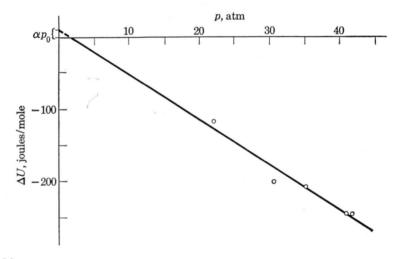

FIGURE 5.10

no longer depends on p, it must be a function of T alone, say,

$$U(p = 0, T) = U°(T)$$

where the superscript circle indicates the ideal gas state. From Eq. 5.47 we have the limit

$$\lim_{p \to 0} U(p, T) = U°(T) = U(p_0, T) - \alpha p_0$$

Insertion of this result in Eq. 5.47 gives us an *empirical energy function,*

$$U(p, T) = U°(T) + \alpha p \qquad (5.48)$$

This operation is equivalent to shifting the origin in Fig. 5.10 upward by an amount αp_0 and thus measuring U not from the state $p = p_0$ but rather from the ideal state, $p = 0$.

5.15 Heat Capacities of an Ideal Gas

We have seen that the definition of the ideal gas,

$$pV = RT$$

$$\left(\frac{\partial U}{\partial V} \right)_T = 0 \qquad (5.44)$$

leads directly to

$$U = U°(T)$$

Although these relations do not apply to any real gas, they furnish good approximations at pressures that are not too high and temperatures that are not too low and afford a direct way of deducing the ideal gas heat capacities. Of the four heat capacities discussed, C_V is the simplest, and since $C_V = (\partial U / \partial T)_V$,

$$C_V° = \frac{dU°}{dT} \qquad (5.49)$$

Since

$$L_V = \left(\frac{\partial U}{\partial V} \right)_T + p$$

$$L_V° = p \qquad (5.50)$$

and the latent heat of expansion of an ideal gas is numerically equal to the pressure.

C_p and L_p are given in terms of C_V, L_V, and derivatives involving p, V, and T only by Eqs. 5.36 and 5.37,

$$C_p = C_V + L_V \left(\frac{\partial V}{\partial T}\right)_p \tag{5.36}$$

and

$$L_p = L_V \left(\frac{\partial V}{\partial p}\right)_T \tag{5.37}$$

so that use of the equation of state gives

$$C_p^\circ = C_V^\circ + R$$

and

$$L_p^\circ = -V \tag{5.51}$$

Since C_V° is positive, we see that all the heat capacities are positive except L_p°.

It is frequently convenient to represent the ratio of C_p to C_V by a special symbol, γ. Thus for the ideal gas

$$\gamma^\circ = \frac{C_p^\circ}{C_V^\circ} = 1 + \frac{R}{C_V^\circ} \geq 1 \tag{5.52}$$

With this ratio

$$C_V^\circ = \frac{R}{\gamma^\circ - 1}$$

and

$$C_p^\circ = \frac{\gamma^\circ}{\gamma^\circ - 1} R \tag{5.53}$$

These relations are useful in reducing theoretical results to a more condensed form because γ° may be taken as a constant over considerable ranges of temperature for a good many important gases. The difference between γ and γ° may be neglected for low enough pressures.

5.16 Heat Capacities of Real Gases

The heat capacities of real gases may now be considered. For this study we return to the Onnes form of the equation of state, with the independent variables T and p, that is, Eq. 3.18,

$$pV = RT + B_1 p + B_2 p^2 + \cdots \tag{3.18}$$

The empirical energy function of Eq. 5.48 applies at low pressures and will presumably have terms in p^2, p^3, etc., at high pressures. Then we should write, in general,

$$U = U^\circ(T) + \alpha_1 p + \alpha_2 p^2 + \cdots \tag{5.54}$$

where the α's depend on the temperature.

To find C_p, for example, we need Eq. 5.26,

$$C_p = \left(\frac{\partial U}{\partial T}\right)_p + p\left(\frac{\partial V}{\partial T}\right)_p \tag{5.26}$$

From Eq. 5.54,

$$\left(\frac{\partial U}{\partial T}\right)_p = C_V^\circ + \alpha_1'p + \alpha_2'p^2 + \cdots$$

and from the equation of state, Eq. 3.18,

$$p\left(\frac{\partial V}{\partial T}\right)_p = R + B_1'p + B_2'p^2 + \cdots$$

where the primes indicate temperature derivatives.

Finally, then, since

$$C_p^\circ = C_V^\circ + R$$

we have $C_p = C_V^\circ + R + (\alpha_1' + B_1')p + (\alpha_2' + B_2')p^2 + \cdots$ (5.55)

which reduces to C_p°, as it should, as $p \to 0$.

In the same way, with

$$L_p = \left(\frac{\partial U}{\partial p}\right)_T + p\left(\frac{\partial V}{\partial p}\right)_T$$

$$L_p = -\frac{RT}{p} + \alpha_1 + (2\alpha_2 + B_2)p + \cdots \tag{5.56}$$

In this case, as $p \to 0$,

$$L_p = L_p^\circ = -V + \alpha_1$$

which is in contradiction with the result

$$L_p^\circ = -V$$

of Eq. 5.51. In fact, we must let $p \to 0$ in Eq. 5.54 before calculating $(\partial U/\partial p)_T$ rather than afterward.

5.17   Slope of the Adiabatic Curve

One of the most important curves in thermodynamics is the so-called *adiabatic* curve, along which a system moves when it is forced to change its state reversibly without any interchange of heat with its surroundings. To see the real significance of this curve, imagine the system to change by differential amounts in varying directions from a point, P (Fig. 5.11). We start with the second dQ_C equation,

$$dQ_C = C_V\,dT + L_V\,dV \tag{5.34}$$

where C_V and L_V are normally positive. Thus dQ_C will surely be positive for all changes for which dT and dV are both positive (or one positive and one zero).

All directions between PA (an isochore) and PD (an isotherm) satisfy this condition. Therefore, heat is absorbed in all directions from PA to PD.

For the opposite directions (dashed lines in the figure), dQ_C will, of course, be negative. Consequently, if we allow the direction to swing from PD to PA' (or PA to PD'), dQ_C changes sign and must therefore vanish for some intermediate direction. This defines the direction of the *adiabatic* through P (say, EE').

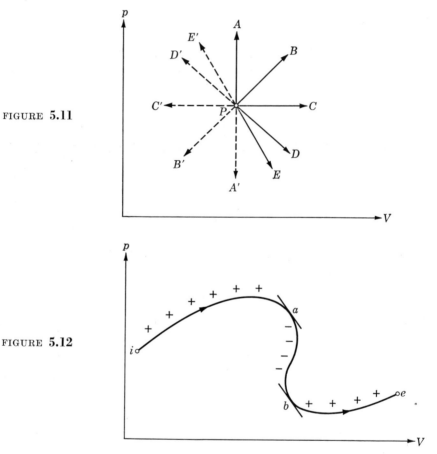

FIGURE **5.11**

FIGURE **5.12**

If we proceed from any point, P, to the *right* and *above* the adiabatic, heat is always *absorbed*, whereas in any direction to the *left* and *below*, heat is always *rejected*. The adiabatic thus separates the heat-absorbing directions from the heat-rejecting directions. With a general curve, C (Fig. 5.12), the adiabatic slopes at once enable us to divide the curve into heat-absorbing (plus signs) and heat-rejecting sections (minus signs), these being separated by points where the curve is tangent to the adiabatic.

In the particular case of closed cycles, finding these points of tangency enables the cycle to be divided into two sections, one heat-absorbing and the other heat-rejecting. The closed cycles discussed at the end of Chap. 4 are shown again in Fig. 5.13, the points of tangency being A and B. In Fig. 5.13(a), an engine cycle, heat is absorbed along the upper section and rejected along the lower. The reverse is true for Fig. 5.13(b), which represents a refrigerator. The short arrows indicate the flow of heat into and out of the system.

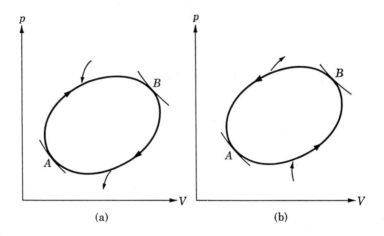

(a)   (b)

FIGURE **5.13**

To find the slope of an adiabatic, it is necessary simply to set $dQ_C = dQ_{ad} = 0$. Using the two dQ_C expressions, we obtain

$$C_p dT + L_p dp = 0$$
and
$$C_V dT + L_V dV = 0$$

Elimination of dT and use of Eq. 5.37 for the ratio of L_V to L_p gives

$$\frac{dp}{dV} = \left(\frac{C_p}{C_V}\right)\left(\frac{L_V}{L_p}\right)$$

or
$$\frac{dp}{dV} = \gamma \left(\frac{\partial p}{\partial V}\right)_T \tag{5.57}$$

But $(\partial p/\partial V)_T$ is of course the slope of the *isotherm* in this plane. The adiabatic slope in the p-V plane is therefore always *greater* by a factor of γ than the isothermal slope. (This is the reason that $E'E$ in Fig. 5.11 is drawn with a larger slope than that of $D'D$.) The result in Eq. 5.57 is quite general and holds for liquids and solids as well as for gases.

5.18   Equation of the Adiabatic for the Ideal Gas

For an ideal gas the right side of Eq. 5.57 reduces to $-\gamma^\circ p/V$, and thus

$$\frac{dp}{p} = -\gamma^\circ \frac{dV}{V} \tag{5.58}$$

is the differential equation of the ideal adiabatic. On the assumption that $\gamma°$ is constant (or for ranges of p, V, and T for which its variations may be neglected), this equation may be integrated at once to

$$\ln p = -\gamma° \ln V + \ln K$$

$$\boxed{pV^{\gamma°} = K} \tag{5.59}$$

Here K is the integration constant, to be found by direct substitution of the coordinate of a known point on the curve or of some point through which we

FIGURE **5.14**

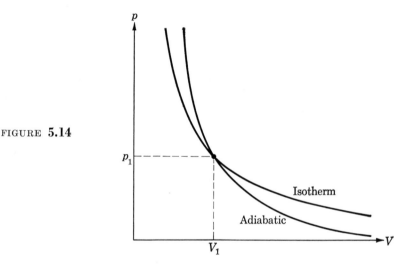

wish the curve to pass. Since K can take on a continuous range of values, Eq. 5.59 gives a family of adiabatics covering the p-V plane. The slope of these curves as given by Eq. 5.58 is single-valued, and only one adiabatic can pass through a given point. In Fig. 5.14 an adiabatic is drawn through the point p_1, V_1, together with the corresponding isotherm.

Writing γ for $\gamma°$ for simplicity, we have

$$pV^\gamma = K = p_1 V_1^\gamma$$

and therefore

$$\frac{p}{p_1} = \left(\frac{V_1}{V}\right)^\gamma \tag{5.60}$$

On taking the γth root of each side of this equation and then raising each side to the $(\gamma - 1)$th power, we obtain

$$\left(\frac{p}{p_1}\right)^{(\gamma-1)/\gamma} = \left(\frac{V_1}{V}\right)^{\gamma-1} \tag{5.61}$$

Since the gas is ideal, $pV = RT$, and $p_1 V_1 = RT_1$, or

$$\frac{TV_1}{T_1 V} = \frac{p}{p_1}$$

Eliminating p/p_1 with the help of Eq. 5.60 gives

$$\frac{T}{T_1} = \left(\frac{V_1}{V}\right)^{\gamma-1} \tag{5.62}$$

Combining this with Eq. 5.61 yields finally

$$\frac{T}{T_1} = \left(\frac{V_1}{V}\right)^{\gamma-1} = \left(\frac{p}{p_1}\right)^{(\gamma-1)/\gamma} \tag{5.63}$$

a result very useful for calculation.

In many engineering applications it is convenient to define a general type of change by means of the relation

$$pV^n = \text{constant} = K \tag{5.64}$$

where n is a parameter that may be made to assume any fixed value we like. Changes along such a curve are called *polytropic* changes, and the equation defining them is called a *polytrope*.

As n is allowed to assume in turn the values 0, 1, γ, and ∞, Eq. 5.64 reduces to an isobar, an isotherm, an adiabatic, and finally an isochore. With values near γ, for example, it is possible to approximate actual changes in engines, refrigerators, compressors, and the like in which a process is nearly but not quite adiabatic.

Problems

5.1   Construct a table corresponding to Table 5.1 for the case of a uniform filament under tension when

$$dQ_C = dU - F\,dL$$

5.2   Write out the equivalents of Eqs. 5.36 and 5.37 for this system, also.

5.3   Go through the analysis of Chap. 1 for determining the number of degrees of freedom of a system consisting of a paramagnetic material in a uniform magnetic field, $\mathcal{H}$. You may assume that $B = B(\mathcal{H}, T, p)$, where B, the magnetic induction, is related to the total magnetic moment as follows:

$$B = \mathcal{H} + \frac{4\pi M}{V}$$

5.4   Write out the equivalent forms of the four heat capacities for the surface tension system in which

$$dU = dQ_C + \mathcal{S}\,dA$$

(*Note:* In this case $\mathcal{S} = \mathcal{S}(T)$ and is independent of A.)

5.5   In a reversible electric storage cell in which the solutions are maintained in a saturated condition, all concentrations become functions of T only. Since the emf, E, of such cells depends on the concentrations, $E = E(T)$. Thus the relation

$$dU = dQ_C + E\,dz$$

although apparently similar to that for a hydrostatic system, is in reality mathematically analogous to the surface tension system of Problem 5.4. Translate a few of your results for the surface tension system to their appropriate form for the reversible saturated electric cell.

5.6   Review the discussion of Chap. 1 on independent variables, and examine the case of a bar of soft iron in a uniform magnetic field in the light of Sec. 5 of this chapter.

5.7   Evaluate the curve integral

$$\int_{0,0}^{1,1} p\,dV$$

along the following paths:
(a) straight line,
(b) parabola,
(c) elbow path $(0,0 \rightarrow 0,1 \rightarrow 1,1)$, and
(d) elbow path $(0,0 \rightarrow 1,0 \rightarrow 1,1)$;
and show that

$$\int_{0,0}^{1,1} V\,dp$$

is needed to make the result independent of the path.

5.8   Evaluate $\int X\,dx + Y\,dy$ by two different paths from $0,0$ to $2,2$, where
(a) $X = 3x^2y,\ Y = 2x^3y$;
(b) $X = x^2 + x,\ Y = y^2$; and
(c) $X = x^2 + \tfrac{1}{2}y^2,\ Y = yx^2$.

5.9   Given that

$$pV = RT + \mathcal{B}_1\frac{1}{V} + \mathcal{B}_2\frac{1}{V^2} + \cdots$$

and

$$U = U°(T) + \alpha_1 p + \alpha_2 p^2 + \cdots$$

convert the latter to a power series in powers of $1/V$,

$$U = U°(T) + \beta_1\frac{1}{V} + \beta_2\frac{1}{V^2} + \cdots$$

where $\alpha_1, \alpha_2, \ldots$ and $\beta_1, \beta_2, \ldots$ are empirical temperature functions. Show that

$$C_V = C_V° + \beta_1'\frac{1}{V} + \beta_2'\frac{1}{V^2} + \cdots$$

and

$$L_V = \frac{RT}{V} + (\mathcal{B}_1 - \beta_1)\frac{1}{V^2} + (\mathcal{B}_2 - 2\beta_2)\frac{1}{V^3} + \cdots$$

Evaluate the β's in terms of the α's by the conversion equations (Eq. 3.20).

5.10   In Sec. 9.16 it will be shown from the second law that the quantities L_p and L_V are given by Maxwell's first and second relations,

$$L_p = -T\left(\frac{\partial V}{\partial T}\right)_p$$

and

$$L_V = T\left(\frac{\partial p}{\partial T}\right)_V$$

Using the first of these, show that the α's and B's of Eq. 5.54 and 3.18 must be related by $\alpha_1 = -B_1'T$, $\alpha_2 = -\frac{1}{2}(B_2'T + B_2)$, etc., and hence that we have finally

$$C_p = C_p^\circ - B_1''Tp - \frac{1}{2}B_2''Tp^2 + \cdots$$

$$L_p = -\frac{RT}{p} - B_1'T - B_2'Tp - B_3'Tp^2 + \cdots$$

$$U = U^\circ(T) - B_1'Tp - \frac{1}{2}(B_2'T + B_2)p^2 + \cdots$$

so that the differences between the properties of real gases and those of ideal gases are expressed in terms of the virial coefficients and their derivatives.

5.11   The volume of a certain quantity of air originally at $T = 300°K$ is increased adiabatically by 25%. What is the fall in temperature?

5.12   A gram-mole of helium is expanded adiabatically from 50 to 0°C. If the initial pressure was 1 atm and the gas is taken as ideal, find
(a) the final pressure and volume,
(b) the change in U (calories), and
(c) the work gained by the gas (joules).

5.13   A gram-mole of oxygen is expanded isothermally from point A to point B and then adiabatically from point B to point C. The coordinates of these points are as follows: A. $p = 2$ atm, $T = 350°K$; B. $p = 1$ atm, $T = 350°K$; and C. $p = \frac{1}{2}$ atm, $T = T$.
Find
(a) T, the final temperature,
(b) the work gained by the gas,
(c) ΔU, and
(d) the heat gained by the gas.

5.14   In a certain polytropic change, 22.4 liters of air at 0°C and 76 cm of mercury is taken to 50 liters and 30 cm of mercury. Find
(a) the value of n,
(b) the final temperature,
(c) the heat absorbed, and
(d) the work gained by the gas.

CHAPTER SIX

Heat Capacities of Gases

6.1 Experimental Measurements of C_V, C_p, and γ

The need for accurate values of the heat capacities of gases has led to a wide variety of experimental methods for their determination.

For gases so dilute that the ideal gas approximation may be made,

$$C_p^\circ - C_V^\circ = R$$

and

$$\gamma^\circ = 1 + \frac{R}{C_V^\circ}$$

and thus a knowledge of C_V° or C_p° or γ° enables us to calculate the other two values. Unfortunately, however, gases must be used at finite pressure, and the corrections needed for calculation of the ideal gas values from the observed values of C_V and C_p are not always small. Moreover, their calculation requires information deducible only from the second law of thermodynamics and therefore must be postponed until later (Chap. 12).

The direct measurement of each of these heat capacities presents its own particular problems. Direct measurement of C_V is difficult because the heat capacity of the metal container tends to be greater than that of the gas within. This problem has been avoided in three ways. The Joly calorimeter employs gases at or near room pressure so that the walls of the container can be very thin. The method of Eucken utilizes the experimental fact that, since the heat capacities of all metals eventually fall to low values at low temperatures, it is possible to work at temperatures sufficiently low that the heat capacity of the gas actually greatly exceeds that of its container. Finally, the explosion method utilizes the heating produced by sudden explosion; the gas rises to its maximum temperature before appreciable heat flow to the heavy walls can occur.

Observations of C_p are most readily carried out by continuous-flow methods. A stream of heated gas gives up its heat to a cooler calorimeter (method of mixtures) or attains a steady state condition by flowing past heating coils (continuous-flow method). A third method involves a direct comparison with a monatomic gas, such as helium or argon, having a heat capacity shown by other methods to be independent of temperature.[1]

6.2   Joly's Steam Calorimeter for C_V

Joly measured C_V for gases by what is essentially a method of mixtures. Two identical copper spheres (Fig. 6.1) are suspended by fine wires from the pans of an equal-arm balance (not shown). One sphere contains the gas to be studied, and the other is evacuated. Live steam is allowed to flow into an inner jacketed region surrounding the spheres until the apparatus has attained the temperature of the steam, t_s. Whatever steam condenses on the metal spheres is collected in the conical pans attached below the spheres. Since the two spheres are identical in heat capacity, the difference between the masses of water collected, say, m, represents that condensed by the gas itself. If its heat capacity is C_V, then

$$m\lambda = \int_t^{t_s} C_V \, dt \tag{6.1}$$

where t is the original temperature of the gas and λ is the heat of vaporization of water. Numerous corrections are required, for details of which reference must be made to the original papers.[2]

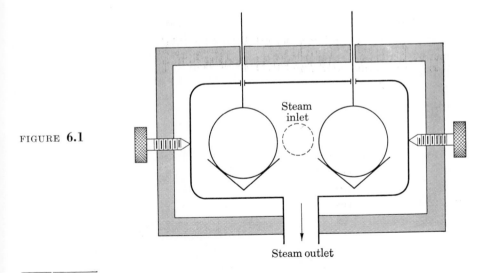

FIGURE **6.1**

Steam inlet

Steam outlet

[1] For details of this relative method, see Blackett, Henry, and Rideal, *Proc. Roy. Soc. (London)*, **A126**, 319 (1930); and Henry, *Proc. Roy. Soc. (London)*, **A126**, 675 (1930).

[2] Joly, *Proc. Roy. Soc. (London)*, **48**, 440 (1890). For a more modern version of this really very precise calorimeter, see Sutton, *Proc. Roy. Soc. (London)*, **A93**, 155 (1917). A calorimeter using the latent heat of ice in much the same way as the Joly calorimeter used that of steam was devised by Bunsen. A modern form has been described by Ginnings and Corruccini, *J. Research Natl. Bur. Standards*, **38**, 583 (1947).

6.3   Eucken's Low-Temperature Gas Calorimeter for C_V

At sufficiently low temperatures the heat capacity of a gas in a metal container becomes larger than that of the container. Eucken used a thin-walled steel flask with resistance wire wound around it. The temperature rise produced by a given expenditure of electrical energy in the wire was measured on a resistance thermometer. Here

$$\Delta Q_V = Ei\,\Delta\tau = C_V\,\Delta t$$

where Δt is the temperature rise produced by the electrical current, i, in time $\Delta\tau$.

The whole apparatus[3] was vacuum-jacketed to reduce heat interchange with the surroundings.

6.4   Explosion Method for C_V

For the study of C_V at high temperatures, a method originally due to Bunsen, Berthelot, and others has been improved by Pier,[4] whose explosion bomb is shown in Fig. 6.2. In use a measured amount of a suitable explosive mixture (such as oxygen and hydrogen), together with ν moles of the gas for which C_V is to be determined, is introduced into a steel bomb, A, contained in a large water bath, B. Suppose the initial pressure and temperature of the gaseous system are p_i and T_i, respectively. The explosion is set off by a spark, and the temperature rises rapidly to some high value, say, T_m, while the pressure rises to a maximum, p_m. This pressure is measured by the deflection of a beam of light reflected from a mirror, M, attached to a thin corrugated disk, D. The maximum deflection is recorded on a moving film, and the absolute value of p_m is found by calibration under static pressure.

FIGURE **6.2**

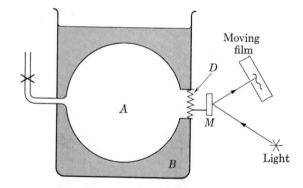

---

[3] See Eucken and Von Linde, *Z. physik. Chem.*, **B5**, 413 (1929); and Eucken and Hoffman, *Z. physik. Chem.*, **B5**, 442 (1929).

[4] Pier, *Z. physik. Chem.*, **62**, 397 (1908); **66**, 759 (1909); *Z. Elektrochem.*, **15**, 536 (1909); **16**, 897 (1910); and Wormersley, *Proc. Roy. Soc. (London)*, **A100**, 483 (1921).

As a result of the chemical reaction, the total number of moles of gas alters from ν_i, the initial number, to ν_e, the final number. If the perfect gas law is assumed, we have at the start

$$p_i V_0 = \nu_i R T_i$$

and at the point of maximum pressure and temperature

$$p_m V_0 = \nu_e R T_m$$

where V_0 is the constant volume of the bomb. Dividing one of these by the other and solving for T_m gives

$$T_m = \left(\frac{p_m}{p_i}\right)\left(\frac{\nu_i}{\nu_e}\right) T_i = \frac{P}{e} T_i \tag{6.2}$$

where $P = p_m/p_i$ and $e = \nu_e/\nu_i$.

Since the reaction takes place in a fraction of a second, the normal heat liberated, say, Q_V, is used to warm the final mixture from T_i to T_m. If this mixture contains ν moles of the original inert gas (of heat capacity νC_V), ν_1 moles of species 1 of heat capacity $(C_V)_1$, etc., then the heat capacity of the whole system after the explosion may be written

$$\nu C_V + \nu_1(C_V)_1 + \nu_2(C_V)_2 + \cdots = \nu C_V + \sum_j \nu_j(C_V)_j$$

where the summation is over the reaction products of the explosion and $(C_V)_j$ is the molar heat capacity of the jth constituent of the mixture. The final number of moles of gas, ν_e, is given by

$$\nu_e = \nu + \sum_j \nu_j$$

On the assumption that all of the heat of the reactions goes into warming the gas,

$$Q_V = \nu \int_{T_i}^{T_m} C_V \, dT + \sum_j \nu_j \int_{T_i}^{T_m} (C_V)_j \, dT \tag{6.3}$$

or

$$Q_V = \left[\nu \overline{C_V} + \sum_j \nu_j \overline{(C_V)_j} \right] (T_m - T_i) \tag{6.4}$$

where $\overline{C_V}$, $\overline{(C_V)_1}$, $\overline{(C_V)_2}$, etc., are average heat capacities over the interval $T_m - T_i$. This interval can be obtained readily from Eq. 6.2.

The inert gas referred to is, of course, the gas being studied and may be simply an excess of one of the explosive reactants (such as oxygen or hydrogen). Since only the average heat capacity of the whole gaseous system can be computed from a single experiment, it is necessary to have a range of values for

ν_i and ν_e. Then each heat capacity is expressed as a power series of the form

$$C_V = c_0 + c_1 t + c_2 t^2 + \cdots \tag{6.5}$$

where t is the Celsius temperature and the constants c_0, c_1, c_2, etc., are determined to give the best fit for the data.

Numerous corrections must be made, including those for the effects of lag in the pressure recorder, loss of heat to the walls, and incomplete chemical reaction.[5]

The explosion method is important because it makes possible the study of heat capacities at very high temperatures (up to 3000°C). It has shown that a monatomic gas, such as helium or argon, actually has a *constant* heat capacity to the highest temperatures observable.

6.5   Method of Mixtures of Holborn and Henning for C_p

In the method of Holborn and Henning, a gas preheated by passage through a spiral in an oven flows at a suitable constant pressure into a double-walled platinum tube, where it is brought to its final temperature by an electric current passing through the walls. As the gas enters the calorimeter proper, its tempera-ture is measured by a thermocouple. The calorimeter consists of three silver-foil-packed tubes connected in series and placed in a well-stirred oil bath. The hot gas loses its heat to the calorimeter and leaves at the calorimeter tempera-ture. Although the corrections are troublesome, this method has furnished valuable data on C_p up to 1400°C.[6]

6.6   Continuous-Flow Method for C_p

The continuous-flow method was first used by Swann and later by Scheel and Heuse.[7] In essence, a glass calorimeter sealed in a vacuum jacket is placed in a large constant-temperature bath (see Fig. 6.3, which is schematic only). The gas at the temperature of the bath enters the apparatus at the bottom and leaves at the top, the temperatures at these two points being measured by platinum thermometers (#1 and #2). Before reaching the heater, the gas flows up the outside wall and down the inside wall of a double-walled tube. It enters the heater at the bottom. The method has been used for temperatures as low as -180°C and up to around 350°C.

[5] Bjerrum, *Z. Elektrochem.*, **17**, 731 (1911); **18**, 101 (1912); Wohl and von Elbe, *Z. Elektro-chem.*, **35**, 644 (1920); and Wormersley, *Proc. Roy. Soc. (London)*, **A100**, 483 (1921).

[6] Holborn and Henning, *Ann. Physik*, **23**, 809 (1907) (original paper); Nernst, *Z. Elektrochem.*, **16**, 96 (1910) (NH_3); and Callendar, *Brit. Assoc. Advance. Sci. Rept.*, **1908**, 334 (corrections).

[7] Swann, *Proc. Roy. Soc. (London)*, **A82**, 147 (1909); and Scheel and Heuse, *Ann. Physik*, **37**, 79 (1912); **40**, 473 (1913); **59**, 86 (1919).

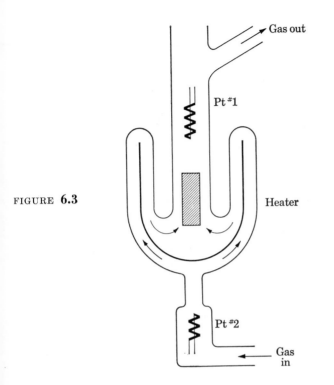

FIGURE **6.3**

Some of the standard engineering data on the properties of steam and of ammonia have been obtained with this apparatus.[8]

6.7   γ by Adiabatic Expansion

One of the simplest methods for the direct measurement of γ, the ratio of the specific heat at constant pressure to the specific heat at constant volume, is that of Clément and Desormes. A large vessel fitted with a stopcock and a manometer is used (Fig. 6.4). The steps in the process are as follows:

1. The air in the vessel is pumped up to a pressure, p_1, somewhat above atmospheric pressure. This is read on the manometer, which indicates values above and below atmospheric pressure.

2. The stopcock is opened, the pressure inside the vessel is allowed to fall to atmospheric pressure, p_0, and then the stopcock is reclosed. (This essentially adiabatic expansion cools the air.)

3. After the air has had time to come back to the atmospheric temperature, as indicated by the steadiness of the manometer, the final pressure, p_2, is read.

In Fig. 6.5 the original state of the gas at pressure p_1 is represented by point

---

[8] Knoblauch and Jacob, *Z. Ver. deut. Ing.*, **51**, 81 (1917); Knoblauch and Raisch, *Z. Ver. deut. Ing.*, **66**, 418 (1922); Haber, *Z. Elektrochem.*, **21**, 228 (1915); and Osborne, Stimson, Sligh, and Cragoe, *Refrig. Eng.*, **10**, 145 (1923).

P_1. When the stopcock is opened, the pressure falls to that of the atmosphere (zero on the manometer), point P_0. The line through P_1 and P_0 gives fairly accurately the slope of an adiabatic through P_1, provided $p_1 - p_0$ is not too large.

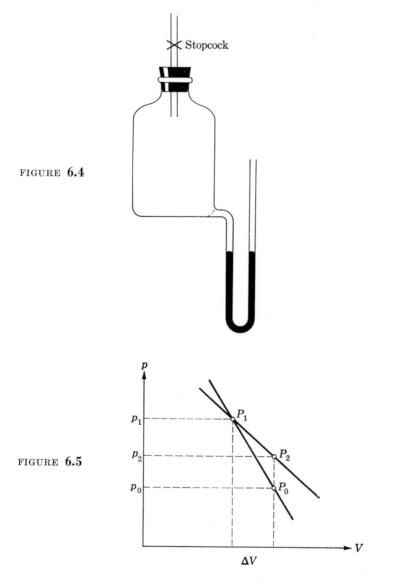

FIGURE **6.4**

FIGURE **6.5**

As the air warms to room temperature at constant volume, the pressure rises to p_2, point P_2 in the diagram. Since P_1 and P_2 are on the same isotherm, a line through these points is a good approximation to the tangent to the isotherm at P_1.

Accordingly

$$\frac{(\text{slope})_{\text{adiabatic}}}{(\text{slope})_{\text{isotherm}}} = \frac{\dfrac{-(p_1 - p_0)}{\Delta V}}{\dfrac{-(p_1 - p_2)}{\Delta V}} = \gamma$$

and the unknown value of ΔV, the volume of the escaped air, need not be measured.

The chief difficulty in this method is that oscillations of pressure occur in step 2, making it impossible to tell at what moment the stopcock should be closed once more. Lummer and Pringsheim avoided this difficulty by using a fine platinum resistance wire (or bolometer), the temperature of which could follow the rapid changes in the temperature of the gas. Partington[9] improved on their procedure by using a very large spherical vessel (35 liters) with the bolometer at its center. He used a valve with an adjustable aperture, so that with proper adjustment no oscillations took place. On expansion, the pressure sank quickly to a steady value, where it remained for a few seconds, and then rose slowly as heat was conducted in from outside. Since it was not possible to assume the ideal gas law, it was necessary to obtain a form of the adiabatic law, modified in this case for a Berthelot gas.[10]

6.8 Rüchhardt's Method for γ

An interesting method for the determination of γ for a gas was devised by Rüchhardt,[11] who modified a method developed by Assman, in which the oscillations of a mercury column enclosing a quantity of gas in a tube were used to study adiabatic changes. The apparatus required is shown in Fig. 6.6. A steel ball, which will just slide inside the vertical tube, is dropped in from the top and allowed to oscillate until friction brings it to rest at its equilibrium position. If the excursions of the ball from this position are indicated by y, then y is zero at the equilibrium position, positive above this point, and negative below it. If the cross-sectional area of the tube is A, then at $y = 0$, the pressure, p, inside the vessel is given by

$$p = p_{\text{atm}} + \frac{mg}{A}$$

g being the local acceleration of gravity, and m the mass of the ball.

Since the oscillations are sufficiently rapid for the system to remain adiabatic, we may calculate the change in pressure, Δp, and the corresponding

---

[9] Partington, *Physik. Z.*, **14**, 969 (1913); *Proc. Roy. Soc.* (*London*), **A100**, 27 (1921); and Eucken and Lude, *Z. physik. Chem.*, **B5**, 413 (1929).

[10] For details see W. Nernst, *Theoretical Chemistry*, 5th ed., English trans., Macmillan, London, 1923, p. 259. See also Problem 6.1.

[11] Rüchhardt, *Physik. Z.*, **30**, 58 (1929).

change in volume, ΔV, from the adiabatic equation, $pV^\gamma = K$. Differentiating this gives

$$V^\gamma\,dp + \gamma V^{\gamma-1}p\,dV = 0$$

or
$$dp = \frac{-\gamma p\,dV}{V}$$

For small excursions of the ball, we may write with sufficient accuracy

$$\Delta p = \frac{-\gamma p\,\Delta V}{V} \tag{6.6}$$

From Newton's second law, if F_{net} is the net force on the steel ball,

$$F_{\text{net}} = m\ddot{y} \tag{6.7}$$

where $\ddot{y}$ is the ball's acceleration. With $\Delta V = Ay$ and $F_{\text{net}} = A\,\Delta p$, substitution of Eq. 6.6 gives

$$m\ddot{y} = \frac{-\gamma pA^2 y}{V} \tag{6.8}$$

which is the equation of simple harmonic motion if we can assume that Δp and ΔV are so small that p and V are essentially constant during the oscillation.

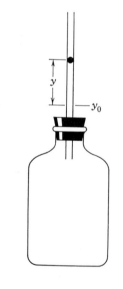

FIGURE **6.6**

On these assumptions the period τ is given by

$$\tau = 2\pi\left(\frac{mV}{\gamma pA^2}\right)^{\frac{1}{2}}$$

$$\gamma = \frac{4\pi^2 mV}{pA^2\tau^2} \tag{6.9}$$

or

6.9 Rinkel's Modified Method for γ

Rinkel[12] pointed out that a simple modification of the Rüchhardt method would yield results that were considerably more reliable. If the ball is allowed to fall from the top of the tube until it is brought to rest by the compressed gas, a distance h below its start, then it will have lost potential energy equal to mgh. This mechanical energy supplies the work done on the gas during the adiabatic compression.   Thus

$$mgh = \int_{y=0}^{y=h} F_{\text{net}} \, dy$$

where y is measured downward from the open end of the tube. On substitution from Eq. 6.8 for the net force

$$mgh = \int_0^h \frac{\gamma p A^2 y}{V} \, dy = \gamma A^2 \int_0^h \frac{p}{V} y \, dy$$

If, as before, V and p are taken as essentially constant, this reduces to

$$mgh = \frac{\gamma A^2 p h^2}{2V}$$

or

$$\gamma = \frac{2mgV}{pA^2h} \qquad\qquad \textbf{(6.10)}$$

a result that gives improved values for γ since h is larger and easier to measure than the period τ and enters Eq. 6.10 only as the first power rather than the second.[13]

6.10 Experimental Values of C_V and γ

When we examine the experimental values of C_V and γ for gases (see Table 6.1), the most striking fact is that the results tend to group themselves according to the number of atoms in the molecule. Since

$$\gamma = \frac{C_p}{C_V} = 1 + \frac{R}{C_V}$$

C_V must *increase* as γ *decreases*. We note that monatomic gases such as helium and argon have the lowest values of C_V (2.98 cal/mole-deg) and the highest values of γ (1.666, or almost exactly 5/3). With $R = 1.987$, this value of C_V is,

---

[12] Rinkel, *Physik. Z.*, **30,** 805 (1929).
[13] See Broderson, *Z. Physik*, **62,** 180 (1930); he has compared the two methods with great care.

TABLE **6.1**

Experimental Values of C_V and γ for Gases at 15°C and 1 Atm*

Number of atoms	Gas	Symbol	$(C_V)_{obs}$†	γ_{obs}	r_{eff}
1	Argon	Ar	2.98	1.666	3.00
	Helium	He	2.98	1.666	3.00
2	Air		4.94	1.4034	4.96
	Carbon monoxide	CO	4.94	1.404	4.95
	Hydrogen	H_2	4.87	1.408	4.90
	Hydrogen chloride	HCl	5.11	1.40	5.00
	Nitrogen	N_2	4.94	1.405	4.94
	Nitric oxide	NO	5.00	1.40	5.00
	Oxygen	O_2	5.04	1.396	5.05
	Chlorine	Cl_2	5.93	1.34	5.97
3	Carbon dioxide	CO_2	6.75	1.302	6.62
	Carbon disulfide	CS_2	9.77	1.235	8.51
	Hydrogen sulfide	H_2S	6.08	1.340	5.88
	Nitrous oxide	N_2O	6.81	1.300	6.66
	Sulfur dioxide	SO_2	7.49	1.285	7.02
4	Acetylene	C_2H_2	6.83	1.280	7.15
5	Methane	CH_4	6.48	1.310	6.45
6	Ethylene	C_2H_4	8.20	1.250	8.00
8	Ethane	C_2H_6	9.40	1.220	9.09

* From J. R. Partington and W. G. Shilling, *The Specific Heats of Gases*, Benn, London, 1924, p. 201.

† In calories per gram-mole-degree.

within experimental uncertainty, exactly $\frac{3}{2}R$. These results are independent of temperature to the highest observed temperatures (around 3000°C), as was pointed out earlier.

In the case of diatomic gases, C_V, although varying with temperature, tends to fall near 5 cal/mole-deg, or approximately $\frac{5}{2}R$, while γ is near 1.40 or 7/5. The notable exception is chlorine.

For triatomic gases, C_V varies even more with temperature, although the values fall near 6 cal/mole-deg, and γ lies somewhere near 4/3. In general, as the complexity of the molecule increases, the value of C_V becomes higher, and γ gets closer to its lower theoretical limit of unity.

This characteristic dependence of C_V and γ on the number of atoms in a molecule and not on their sizes, masses, or chemical nature suggests the presence of a basic simplicity for which we must now search.

Since for any ideal gas

$$U = U°(T)$$

and

$$C_V° = \frac{dU}{dT}$$

the values of C_V measure directly the rate of absorption of energy per degree rise in temperature. In the case of the monatomic molecule, in the absence of electronic excitation, of course, this energy presumably goes solely into increasing the kinetic energy of translation of the molecule. The sudden rise in C_V as we pass to the diatomic molecule indicates that this more complicated molecule is absorbing energy more rapidly than the monatomic one. This means that the diatomic molecule, in addition to moving faster as it is heated, also increases its internal energy in some other way. The only internal motions of a purely mechanical nature that the diatomic molecule can have are a vibration of the two atoms along the line of centers and a rotation of the structure about its own center of mass. As the structure becomes more complicated, the numbers of different kinds of vibration possible become greater, and therefore, on this basis, C_V should increase even more as we pass to polyatomic molecules. Thus a detailed study of C_V and γ and their variation with structure and temperature should furnish direct evidence of the way in which molecules behave on heating.

For the purposes of such a study, we must naturally adopt the microscopic view and examine the kinetic theory of the ideal gas as well as some of the more general results of classical Newtonian mechanics as applied to molecular systems. The following four sections will give a brief account of behavior to be treated in detail in the chapters on statistical mechanics.

6.11   Kinetic Theory of the Ideal Gas

In Chap. 15 it will be shown that the kinetic theory of an ideal gas leads to the relation

$$pV = \frac{2}{3} N_0 \frac{m\overline{v^2}}{2} \tag{6.11}$$

where N_0 is Avogadro's number, m is the mass of a molecule, and $\overline{v^2}$ is the mean squared velocity of all the molecules present. Here

$$\overline{v^2} = \overline{\dot{x}^2} + \overline{\dot{y}^2} + \overline{\dot{z}^2}$$

where $\overline{\dot{x}^2}$, $\overline{\dot{y}^2}$, and $\overline{\dot{z}^2}$ are the mean squared values of the velocity components along the x, y, and z axes. Since there are no preferred directions,

$$\overline{\dot{x}^2} = \overline{\dot{y}^2} = \overline{\dot{z}^2}$$

and the average kinetic energies associated with the components of velocity are alike. Thus

$$\frac{1}{2} m\overline{\dot{x}^2} = \frac{1}{2} m\overline{\dot{y}^2} = \frac{1}{2} m\overline{\dot{z}^2} = \frac{1}{2} \frac{m\overline{v^2}}{3}$$

From Eq. 6.11

$$\frac{1}{2}\, m\overline{v^2} = \frac{3}{2}\frac{pV}{N_0} \tag{6.12}$$

and from the perfect gas law

$$\frac{3}{2}\frac{pV}{N_0} = \frac{3}{2}\frac{RT}{N_0} = \frac{3}{2}kT \tag{6.13}$$

and thus $\tfrac{1}{2}m\overline{\dot{x}^2} + \tfrac{1}{2}m\overline{\dot{y}^2} + \tfrac{1}{2}m\overline{\dot{z}^2} = \tfrac{1}{2}m\overline{v^2} = \tfrac{3}{2}kT$ (6.14)

where k is Boltzmann's constant, or R/N_0, the gas constant per molecule. This result means that the average kinetic energy of a molecule is fixed at $\tfrac{3}{2}kT$. In terms of a single component of the velocity,

$$\tfrac{1}{2}m\overline{\dot{x}^2} = \tfrac{1}{2}m\overline{\dot{y}^2} = \tfrac{1}{2}m\overline{\dot{z}^2} = \tfrac{1}{2}kT \tag{6.15}$$

This important equation states that on the average the kinetic energy associated with a single degree of translatory freedom is always $kT/2$ and independent of the mass or nature of the molecule.

Expressed in terms of a gram-mole of gas, the total kinetic energy of translation is

$$KE^{\mathrm{trn}} = 3N_0\frac{kT}{2} = \frac{3}{2}RT \tag{6.16}$$

For an ideal monatomic gas *all* of the internal energy is in translational form. Hence Eq. 6.16 represents the internal energy, U, and with

$$U = \tfrac{3}{2}RT = U^\circ(T) \tag{6.17}$$

$$C_V^\circ = \frac{dU^\circ}{dT} = \frac{3}{2}R = 2.980 \text{ cal/mole-deg} \tag{6.18}$$

This figure agrees remarkably well with observations on the monatomic gases, for which the observed values are precisely this up to the limit of measurements.

Further

$$C_p^\circ = C_V^\circ + R = \tfrac{5}{2}R$$

and

$$\gamma^\circ = \frac{C_p^\circ}{C_V^\circ} = \frac{5}{3} = 1.666$$

again in close agreement with observations. It appears, therefore, that the kinetic theory of monatomic gases gives a good account of the actually observed values of C_V and γ as well as of their independence of temperature.

6.12   Equipartition of Energy

The result in Eq. 6.15 is a special case of a very general theorem in classical kinetic theory, known as the *equipartition of energy* theorem. It was first established on a broad basis by Maxwell and extended by Boltzmann. The theorem predicts a very simple fact about the average values of the energies associated with the independent components of a molecule's motion. Given an insulated system made up of identical particles in complete equilibrium, let the total energy, ϵ, of a single particle be represented as the sum of a set of r squared terms of the form

$$\epsilon = \frac{1}{2}\lambda_1\xi_1{}^2 + \frac{1}{2}\lambda_2\xi_2{}^2 + \cdots = \sum_{j=1}^{r}\frac{1}{2}\lambda_j\xi_j{}^2 \tag{6.19}$$

The λ's are molecular parameters (usually constants) such as mass and moments of inertia, and the ξ's are the corresponding molecular coordinates. The ξ's may be velocity coordinates, such as $\dot{x}$, $\dot{y}$, and $\dot{z}$, components of angular velocities, etc. The general theorem, to be proved in Chap. 16, states that in the state of equilibrium at temperature T, the internal energy of a system of N particles is

$$U = r\frac{NkT}{2} \tag{6.20}$$

so that the average energy per particle, $\bar{\epsilon}$, becomes

$$\bar{\epsilon} = \frac{U}{N} = r\frac{kT}{2} \tag{6.21}$$

This means that $\bar{\epsilon}/r$, the *average energy per particle per squared term* in Eq. 6.19, is exactly $kT/2$.

The molar heat capacity, C_V°, then becomes

$$C_V^\circ = \frac{dU^\circ}{dT} = r\frac{R}{2} \tag{6.22}$$

and is therefore some integer times $R/2$. Since $R = 1.987$ and is so very nearly 2, C_V° should be nearly equal to r for a particular type of molecule. For monatomic gases, since $U^\circ = \frac{3}{2}RT$ and $C_V^\circ = 3R/2 = 2.98$, $r = 3$. For diatomic gases, except chlorine, C_V° is near 5, which suggests that $r = 5$. For the other gases the values are all higher. If we introduce an experimental *effective* value of r, say, r_{eff}, defined by

$$(C_V)_{\text{obs}} = r_{\text{eff}}\frac{R}{2} \tag{6.23}$$

then

$$r_{\text{eff}} = \frac{2(C_V)_{\text{obs}}}{R} = \frac{2}{\gamma_{\text{obs}} - 1} \tag{6.24}$$

and r_{eff} becomes an empirical measure of the effective number of energy terms in Eq. 6.19.

The values of r_{eff} as calculated from the observed values of γ are given in the last column of Table 6.1. Although nonintegral for most of the gases, they are exactly 3 for the monatomic gases and very nearly 5 for the diatomic gases. The values for the triatomic gases are in the 6 to 7 range and tend toward even larger values for the molecules with more atoms. These regularities suggest a basic underlying pattern, which can best be revealed by examining the question of the degrees of freedom of various molecular types.

6.13   Degrees of Freedom of Molecules

The expression *degrees of freedom* occurs in a variety of situations. It has been used here to designate the number of macroscopic variables, n, necessary to fix the thermodynamic state of a system. It is employed in mechanics for the number of geometric quantities required to determine the configuration of a mechanical object or system. Thus a mass point has three degrees of freedom, a line segment five, a solid body six, etc.

We must now examine a gas from the microscopic standpoint and determine the number of degrees of freedom (designated by f) to be expected for its individual molecules, the simplest mechanical models being used. The monatomic molecule, if regarded as a structureless mass point, has $f = 3$. For the diatomic case the value of f depends on whether the molecule is rigid or not. If it is regarded as two mass points at a constant distance, r_0, apart (the rigid dumbbell model), it is mechanically similar to a line segment, and $f = 5$. The necessary variables may be chosen as the three Cartesian coordinates (x, y, and z) needed to fix the center of mass of the molecule with two angles to determine the orientation of the interatomic axis. With motion each of these coordinates has a time derivative, giving five velocities and five energy terms in Eq. 6.19. Thus $r = f = 5$.

For a rigid molecule with more than two atoms (provided they are not exactly in line), f has the same value as for the general rigid body, that is, $f = 6$. Since each of these produces a term in Eq. 6.19, $r = f = 6$. In other words, for all rigid molecules r is exactly equal to the number of degrees of freedom, f, and

$$C_V = \frac{dU}{dT} = r\frac{R}{2} = f\frac{R}{2}$$

6.14   Molecular Vibration

As soon as a molecule is regarded as nonrigid, the situation becomes more complicated in that vibration becomes possible.   The atoms oscillate back and forth about their equilibrium positions and introduce new energy terms, potential as well as kinetic, so that r is always greater than f.

In the diatomic case the only vibratory motion possible is a simple to and fro oscillation of the two nuclei along the line of centers. Since the center of mass must be unaffected by such a purely internal motion, the two masses, m_1 and m_2, move in phase, so that the nuclear separation, r, varies around its equilibrium value, r_0 (Fig. 6.7). If the oscillations are of small amplitude, they may be taken as simple harmonic movements and described in terms of a single geometric variable, ξ, where

$$\xi = r - r_0$$

and $$\dot{\xi} = \dot{r}$$

It is shown in Sec. 16.3 that the energy of vibration can then be written

$$\epsilon^{\text{vib}} = \tfrac{1}{2}m'\dot{\xi}^2 + \tfrac{1}{2}K\xi^2 \qquad (6.25)$$

where $m'\,[= m_1m_2/(m_1 + m_2)]$ is the *reduced* mass of the molecule and K is the harmonic force constant in the relation $F = -K\xi$. The frequency, ν, is given by

$$\nu = 2\pi \left(\frac{K}{m'}\right)^{\frac{1}{2}}$$

Thus the vibration adds two new energy terms, a kinetic term corresponding to a fictitious mass, m', moving with speed $\dot{\xi}$ and a potential term due to the spring constant, K, and involving ξ. Consequently, r is increased by 2, and $r = 7$ for the rotating, vibrating diatomic molecule.

In general, with more than two atoms in the molecule, more than one characteristic type of vibration is possible. The vibrations can be of a very complicated nature, and their detailed analysis is beyond the present scope.[14] If the oscillations are regarded as small, however, a general analysis shows that all possible vibratory motions can be described in terms of certain characteristic or *normal modes of vibration*. In a normal mode the atoms vibrate in phase at some characteristic frequency for the mode. For a triangular molecule of the type XY_2 (such as water, H_2O) there are three normal modes and three characteristic frequencies, ν_1, ν_2, and ν_3. These are illustrated in Fig. 6.8(a) for the water molecule. The arrows represent displacements and are not drawn to scale. In each mode the nuclei move with such velocities as to produce zero linear and zero angular momentum for the whole molecule. A special situation arises when the atoms are in a line, as in carbon dioxide, CO_2. Then the modes are those shown in Fig. 6.8(b). In mode 1 the carbon atom is stationary, and in mode 3 the two oxygen atoms retain a fixed separation and move in opposi-

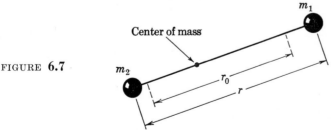

FIGURE **6.7**

---

[14] See, for example, E. B. Wilson, J. C. Decius, and P. C. Cross, *Molecular Vibrations*, McGraw-Hill, New York, 1955; and Dennison, *Revs. Modern Phys.*, **3**, 280 (1931).

tion to the carbon atom. Mode 2 now becomes a double one, since the molecule can vibrate in the plane of the paper or at right angles to it. These two modes have the same frequency and are said to be *degenerate*. Thus the linear triatomic molecule has four rather than three vibrational modes.

Generally a normal mode has a single displacement coordinate, say, ξ, and a corresponding velocity, $\dot{\xi}$, and the total energy of the mode contains two terms similar to those for the diatomic vibrator (Eq. 6.25). Thus

$$\epsilon^{\text{vib}} = \sum_{i=1}^{f^{\text{vib}}} \frac{1}{2} \lambda_i \dot{\xi}_i{}^2 + \frac{1}{2} K_i \xi_i{}^2 \tag{6.26}$$

where λ_i and K_i are mass and force parameters for the ith mode and the summation takes place over all the normal modes, equal in number to, say, f^{vib}, the number of degrees of vibratory freedom. We may write

$$f = f^{\text{trn}} + f^{\text{rot}} + f^{\text{vib}}$$

Then
$$r = 3 + \begin{bmatrix} 0 \\ 2 \\ 3 \end{bmatrix} + 2 \begin{bmatrix} 0 \\ 1 \\ f^{\text{vib}} \end{bmatrix} \tag{6.27}$$

where the numbers in the brackets refer to monatomic, diatomic, and polyatomic (nonlinear) molecules, respectively.

A polyatomic molecule made up of n_a atoms has a total number of degrees of freedom given as

$$f = 3n_a$$

and is thus the same for a given number of atoms, n_a, whether they are free or

FIGURE **6.8**

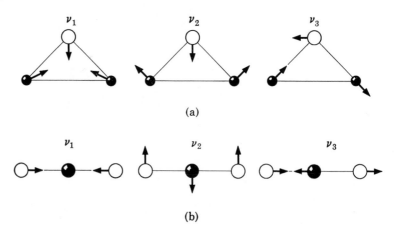

(a)

(b)

bound into an elastic structure. For the nonlinear case $(n_a > 2)$,

$$f = 3 + 3 + f^{\text{vib}}$$

and thus

$$f^{\text{vib}} = (3n_a - 6) = 3(n_a - 2) \tag{6.28}$$

A molecule with n_a atoms therefore has $3n_a - 6$ normal modes of vibration, each with its own energy terms. Consequently,

$$r = 3 + \begin{bmatrix} 0 \\ 2 \\ 3 \end{bmatrix} + \begin{bmatrix} 0 \\ 2 \\ 6(n_a - 2) \end{bmatrix} \tag{6.29}$$

with the same conventions as in Eq. 6.27. The number of energy terms accordingly increases rapidly with an increase in the number of atoms. For the general nonlinear molecule

$$U = r\frac{R}{2}T = 6(n_a - 1)\frac{R}{2}T \qquad n_a > 2 \tag{6.30}$$

$$C_V = 3(n_a - 1)R \qquad n_a > 2 \tag{6.31}$$

and

$$\gamma = 1 + \frac{1}{3(n_a - 1)} \qquad n_a > 2 \tag{6.32}$$

A few predictions from these equations are given in Table 6.2, which includes two types of linear molecules, diatomic linear (such as carbon dioxide) and tetratomic (such as acetylene, HCCH). In the linear case with only *two* active degrees of rotary freedom, Eqs. 6.28 and 6.29 must be altered to read

$$f^{\text{vib}} = (3n_a - 5)$$

and

$$r = (6n_a - 5) \tag{6.33}$$

As a result carbon dioxide has four normal modes and $r = 13$, whereas acetylene has seven normal modes and $r = 19$.

TABLE **6.2**

Predictions from Newtonian Mechanics

Type of molecule	n_a	f	f^{vib}	r	C_V	γ
Monatomic	1	1	0	3	2.98	1.666
Diatomic (rigid)	2	5	0	5	4.95	1.400
Diatomic	2	6	1	7	6.98	1.284
Triatomic	3	9	3	12	11.92	1.167
Triatomic (linear)	3	9	4	13	12.90	1.154
Tetratomic	4	12	6	18	17.87	1.111
Tetratomic (linear)	4	12	7	19	18.85	1.105
Pentatomic	5	15	9	24	26.7	1.074
Polyatomic (nonlinear)	n_a	$3n_a$	$3(n_a - 2)$	$6(n_a - 1)$	$3(n_a - 1)R$	$1 + 1/(3n_a - 1)$

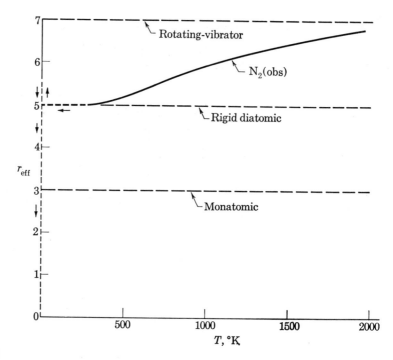

FIGURE **6.9**

A glance at Table 6.2 shows that although C_V does ordinarily increase with the number of atoms in the molecule, it never reaches very large values, nor does r_{eff} often turn out to be integral or very large. The situation is even more unsatisfactory when we consider that an atom has a finite extension in space and should therefore rotate as a solid body and have $r = 6$ whether or not internal vibrations take place. Similarly the diatomic molecule should rotate about the figure axis and have $r = 8$, at least.

Historically the situation worsened when it was found that r_{eff}, although integral for some molecules at room temperature, was sensitive to temperature. Fig. 6.9 gives a graph of $r_{eff} = 2C_V/R$ for nitrogen as a function of temperature. The solid curve shows the observed behavior to be a slow rise from $r_{eff} = 5$ at room temperatures to a value somewhat below the classical $r_{eff} = 7$ (for the rotating vibrator) at the right end of the curve. The dashed portion is drawn from quantum theory and indicates a continuance of $r_{eff} = 5$ down to within a few degrees of 0°K. Then there is a rapid rise followed by an more rapid fall to $r_{eff} = 3$ and finally an even more precipitous drop to $r_{eff} = 0$ in the near neighborhood of 0°K.

We can only interpret this curve as indicating a molecule that is rigid and motionless at very low temperatures but which, as the temperature rises, acquires translation and more and more rotation until it attains the value $r = 5$ for the rigid dumbbell, only to increase slowly beyond that to the classical limit $r = 7$

for the rotating, vibrating diatomic molecule. However, according to the equi-partition theorem, the corresponding value of $C_V = 7R/2$ should apply at all temperatures, high or low. This example illustrates the stark contradiction between experiment and the predictions of the kinetic theory and gives an idea of what Kelvin described as the "black cloud" lying over the subject.

A proper accounting for the observed behavior must not only include the exact shapes of the C_V versus temperature curves. It must also explain why diatomic molecules apparently never rotate about the nuclear axis and why monatomic molecules do not rotate at all.

The inconsistencies in the kinetic theory are particularly disturbing from the strictly mechanical view. An atom should be capable of internal vibrations. Protons and electrons should also have rotation and internal vibration. And presumably any as yet undiscovered internal structure should add even more degrees of freedom. The situation gets rapidly out of hand, and a thorough-going interpretation has a whole range of negative as well as positive facts to account for.

This thoroughgoing analysis has been furnished by the quantum theory, and its clear-cut and decisive agreement with all observations to date represents one of the most spectacular triumphs of twentieth century physics. A brief qualita-tive account of the quantum theory approach is given in the next section, more detailed consideration being reserved for Chaps. 17 and 18.

6.15 Quantization of Energy

The results of classical mechanics as embodied in the equipartition theorem depend upon the basic and intuitively obvious assumption that the energy of atoms and molecules, like that of large-scale bodies, can take on a continuous range of values, from zero to very high ones. According to quantum theory, most types of energy, even translation, are restricted to a discrete sequence of values; that is, they are *quantized*. Such a sequence of permitted energies, ϵ_0, ϵ_1, ϵ_2, etc., is shown in Fig. 6.10. For simplicity the sequence has been drawn with a constant energy separation, although this is not necessary to the argument.

Now imagine many such particles in equilibrium with, say, a monatomic gas, such as helium, at some temperature, T. The average energy of a helium atom is $\frac{3}{2}kT$. As long as $\frac{3}{2}kT \ll \epsilon_1 - \epsilon_0$ (or $kT \ll \epsilon_1 - \epsilon_0$, for that matter) most of the particles will be in the lowest state of energy, ϵ_0. A small rise in temperature will not be able to raise an appreciable number even to the first excited level, ϵ_1. Thus that part of the internal energy associated with the energy levels of Fig. 6.10 will be *independent* of temperature, and the cor-responding contribution to C_V will be zero. As the temperature rises until kT is of the order of $\epsilon_1 - \epsilon_0 = \Delta\epsilon$, or larger, more and more particles will be raised to higher energy levels, and a contribution to C_V will be made. Finally, at tempera-tures so high that $kT \gg \Delta\epsilon$, the discreteness of the energy states will become unimportant, and the energy spectrum may be thought of as continuous. This

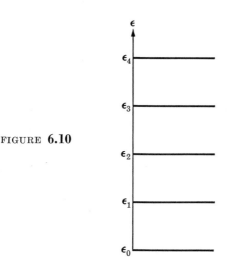

FIGURE 6.10

is the region of validity of classical kinetic theory, where equipartition of energy actually exists for the types of motion in question.

As we shall see in Chaps. 17 and 18, translatory, rotational, and vibratory energies are each quantized, and therefore each is expected to obey the equipartition theorem only for appropriately high temperatures. At *low* enough temperatures, on the other hand, each type of motion becomes frozen, and the system from there down to 0°K behaves like a system made up of simpler molecules.

For purposes of argument, suppose that the separation between the lowest and the first permitted excited state for the three cases of interest here are, respectively, $\Delta\epsilon^{trn}$, $\Delta\epsilon^{rot}$, and $\Delta\epsilon^{vib}$ (whether the possible states are equidistant or not is immaterial). These separations are generally of quite different size.

For translation, due to the wave properties of all particles, the wave length, λ, of a particle of momentum mv is

$$\lambda = \frac{h}{mv}$$

where h is Planck's constant. No speeds are possible except those that provide standing waves with an integral number of half waves in each dimension of the box or container. With a cubic vessel of volume V, we have (see Sec. 18.4)

$$\Delta\epsilon^{trn} = \frac{h^2}{8mV^{2/3}}$$

If we take the ratio (see Eq. 18.21)

$$\frac{\Delta\epsilon^{trn}}{kT} = \frac{h^2}{8mV^{2/3}k}\frac{1}{T} = \frac{\Theta^{trn}}{T}$$

where k is Boltzmann's constant, so that

$$\Theta^{\text{trn}} = \frac{h^2}{8mV^{2/3}k}$$

then Θ^{trn} is a constant of the dimensions of temperature, the ratio of which to T is most significant. Calling Θ^{trn} the *characteristic temperature for translation*, we find that only when

$$T \ll \Theta^{\text{trn}}$$

does the freezing of translation take place. For ordinary-sized vessels and the lightest of molecules,

$$\Theta^{\text{trn}} = 10^{-15} \text{ deg}$$

As a result we can scarcely hope to observe this effect at all and may with confidence treat translation as a classical phenomenon at all attainable temperatures.

In the case of rotation,

$$\Delta\epsilon^{\text{rot}} = \frac{h^2}{8\pi^2 I}$$

where I is the moment of inertia for the mode of rotation in question. Defining a *characteristic temperature for rotation*, Θ^{rot}, as before, we have

$$\frac{\Delta\epsilon^{\text{rot}}}{kT} = \frac{h^2}{8\pi^2 kI}\frac{1}{T} = \frac{\Theta^{\text{rot}}}{T}$$

or

$$\Theta^{\text{rot}} = \frac{h^2}{8\pi^2 kI}$$

In other words, Θ^{rot} is inversely proportional to the moment of inertia. If a particular moment of inertia is large enough, Θ^{rot} may be low. For ordinary diatomic molecules, except hydrogen, H_2, and hydride molecules, Θ^{rot} is of the order of a few degrees. Thus for nitrogen, N_2, $\Theta^{\text{rot}} = 3K°$, and this low value is responsible for the very rapid rise of the curve in Fig. 6.9 to the value of $r = 5$. Even in the case of hydrogen, where $\Theta^{\text{rot}} = 99K°$, the full classically expected value of rotation is essentially reached at room temperatures.

The vibration of a diatomic molecule was actually the first motion to be treated from the quantum standpoint. It was Einstein who suggested the application of Planck's linear oscillator theory to this problem. He assumed the vibrational motion of the molecule to be quantized, with energy levels of constant separation, $h\nu$, as in Fig. 6.10. Thus the vibratory contributions to internal energy and to the heat capacity become functions of a ratio that we shall call u, where

$$u = \frac{h\nu}{kT} = \frac{\Theta^{\text{vib}}}{T}$$

and $\Theta^{\text{vib}} = h\nu/k$ becomes the *characteristic temperature for vibration*. As we shall see in Sec. 17.12, the resultant expression for the vibratory heat capacity at constant volume, say, C_V^{vib}, then becomes

$$C_V^{\text{vib}} = R \frac{u^2 e^u}{(e^u - 1)^2} = RE(u)$$

where

$$E(u) = \frac{u^2 e^u}{(e^u - 1)^2} \tag{6.34}$$

is the so-called Einstein function. As T varies from $0°K$ to ∞ (and hence u from ∞ to 0), $E(u)$ varies in a smooth S-shaped curve from 0 to 1 (see, for example, Fig. 17.13). For temperatures at which $T \ll \Theta^{\text{vib}}$, u is large, and $E(u) = 0$. As the temperature rises, more and more molecules acquire one or more units of vibratory energy, $h\nu$, and C_V^{vib} increases, only to reach the classical limit of R as $T \to \infty$. For hydrogen $\Theta^{\text{vib}} = 6300°K$, u remains large for all ordinary temperatures, and little vibration occurs. For chlorine, Cl_2, on the other hand, $\Theta^{\text{vib}} = 814°K$, and at room temperatures $u = 814/300 = 2.7$, and $E(2.7)$ turns out to be about 0.563, already well toward the limit of 1. This behavior explains why chlorine has the highest value of C_V and r_{eff} in the diatomic group (see Table 6.1).

Similar considerations apply to the modes of vibration of a polyatomic molecule. Those with the lowest values of Θ^{vib} are excited first, and the full maximum contribution to C_V may be reached by some modes before others are significantly excited. Most polyatomic molecules undergo thermal decomposition before the classical limit of $f^{\text{vib}}R$ has been reached for all modes.

Let us now return to the question of the absence of rotation of atoms (or of linear molecules about the nuclear axis). In a molecule like hydrogen, the two atoms have a separation of roughly 10^{-8} cm. The moment of inertia, I_0, of the hydrogen molecule is therefore

$$I_0 \approx m(5 \times 10^{-17}) \text{ cgs units}$$

In a single hydrogen atom, the electron makes the major contribution, and for the first Bohr orbit we have

$$I_0 \approx \frac{m}{2000} \times (0.5 \times 10^{-8})^2 \approx m \times 10^{-20} \text{ cgs units}$$

which differs in the order of 10^{-4} from the first figure. Consequently, the first rotational level for atomic hydrogen should be 10^4 times as high as that for molecular hydrogen, and atomic rotation can hardly be expected at earthly temperatures. Similar arguments apply to the absence of rotation about the nuclear axis in a linear molecule, as well as to the nonexistence of changes in the internal energies of protons, electrons, etc., and of any other finer structures that remain to be discovered. The characteristic temperatures are so high as to eliminate any necessity for their being taken into account in the present context.

6.16 Empirical Formula for Variation of C_p with T

The theoretical quantum expressions for the contributions of rotation and vibration to C_V are rather cumbersome for ordinary thermodynamic calculations. For practical purposes, therefore, it is desirable to have a more convenient method of representing the temperature variation of C_p and C_V.

Gilbert and Lewis have shown that the theoretical values for C_p for a number of important gases can be represented within 1 % by a series of the form

$$C_p = d_0 + d_1 T + d_2 T^2 + \cdots \tag{6.35}$$

where the coefficients d_0, d_1, d_2, etc., are calculated from the theoretical quantum expression, the empirical constants obtained from spectroscopy being used. The resulting heat capacities agree with direct experimental observations (when they exist) and, being calculated from highly precise spectroscopic data, are presumably more reliable than the results of the less precise thermal measurements.

The results for a number of common gases are collected in Table 6.3, where the values of the constants vary considerably with the exact range employed

TABLE **6.3**

Heat Capacities of Gases at 1 Atm*

Gas	d_0	$d_1 \times 10^3$	$d_2 \times 10^7$	$d_3 \times 10^9$	Deviation, % Max	Deviation, % Av
H_2	6.947	−0.200	4.808		0.49	0.19
O_2	6.0954	3.2533	−10.171		.57	.23
N_2	6.4492	1.4125	−0.807		1.35	.54
CO	6.3424	1.836	−2.801		1.38	.47
HCl	6.7319	0.4325	3.697		.98	.48
HBr	6.7776	0.9550	1.581		1.23	.54
CO_2	6.214	10.396	−35.45		1.41	.77
	5.152	15.224	−96.81	2.313	.30	.14
N_2O	6.529	10.515	−35.71		1.26	.68
SO_2†	6.147	13.844	−91.03	2.057	.43	.23
H_2O	7.256	2.298	2.83		.74	.45
NH_3‡	6.189	7.887	−7.28		.65	.23
CH_4	3.381	18.044	−43.00		1.80	.52
	4.171	14.450	2.67	−1.722	1.03	.41

* In calories per mole-degree.
† Valid from 300 to 1800°K.
‡ Valid from 290 to 1000°K.

for their determination.[15] This range is around 300 to 1500°K, save for the two exceptions noted. Expression of the form of Eq. 6.35 may not be used safely for extrapolation outside this range (particularly at the lower end). When an alternate formula with a T^3 term is given, it simply provides for a more accurate representation of the quantum theory values. The last two columns of the table give the *maximum* and the *mean* deviations between the calculated values and the correct values.

Since the results of Table 6.3 are given for $p = 1$ atm, values of C_V adequate for many purposes may be obtained by simply subtracting R. (For pressure corrections for C_p see Eq. 12.41.)

Problems

6.1   Calculate the difference to be expected between the speeds of sound in pure nitrogen at 0°C and $p = 1$ atm when the gas is treated as ideal and when Berthelot's equation of state is used. See J. K. Roberts and A. R. Miller, *Heat and Thermodynamics*, Blackie, London, 1952, p. 184.

6.2   Calculate the velocity of sound in carbon monoxide at $T = 2000$°K. (Assume the ideal state.)

6.3   Show that when measuring γ by the method of Clément and Desormes, with large pressure changes, we must use

$$\gamma = \frac{\ln p_1 - \ln p_0}{\ln p_1 - \ln p_2}$$

where p_1, p_2, and p_0 are the initial, final, and atmospheric pressure readings, respectively.

6.4   With the apparatus of Rüchhardt (Fig. 6.6), two determinations of γ are made, one with the vessel filled with air and the other with the vessel filled with carbon dioxide. Find the ratio of the periods τ_{air} and τ_{CO_2}.

6.5   In a Rüchhardt apparatus the steel ball has a ½ in radius, and the volume of the main vessel is 15 liters. What value of h do you expect for air?

6.6   What is the heat capacity, C_V, to be expected for carbon dioxide if we assume it to be a strictly linear molecule with its four modes of vibration fully excited?

6.7   Suppose that the heat capacity of oxygen is to be studied by the explosion method and that the volume of the pressure vessel (A, Fig. 6.2) is 1 liter. The vessel is filled to a pressure of 10 atm with a mixture of oxygen and hydrogen in the ratio of 9 moles of oxygen to 1 of hydrogen. Assuming the heat capacities of the two gases to be constant, make an estimate of the maximum temperatures and pressures to be expected if the initial temperature is taken as 300°K. How would you obtain a better estimate of the maximum temperature?

6.8   Use the data of Table 6.3 to obtain an average value of C_p for oxygen over the range 300 to 1000°K.

---

[15] Spencer and Justice, *J. Am. Chem. Soc.*, **56**, 2311 (1934); Spencer and Flannagan, *J. Am. Chem. Soc.*, **64**, 2511 (1942); Spencer, *J. Am. Chem. Soc.*, **67**, 1859 (1945); and Bryant, *Ind. Eng. Chem.*, **25**, 820 (1933). See also Bernstein, *J. Chem. Phys.*, **24**, 911 (1956), where it is shown that a series in $1/T$ may in many cases represent the data with a smaller average deviation.

Solids, Liquids, and Change of Phase

7.1 Measurement of the Heat Capacities of Solids

Because of the theoretical interest in the internal energies of solids, a great deal of effort has been devoted to the measurement of their heat capacities. Since all solids expand with temperature, direct observation of C_V is not possible. All measurements, therefore, involve C_p, C_V being calculated by the general relation given in Eq. 7.12 and derived in Chap. 9 from the second law (see Problem 7.1).

Since electrical methods are employed almost exclusively, we begin with the version of the first law suitable for systems with electrical dissipation, Eq. (5.21):

$$dU = dQ_C - p\,dV + E\,|dz| \qquad (5.21)$$

Solving this relation for dQ_C and expressing dU and dV in terms of the independent variables T and p gives

$$dQ_C = \left[\left(\frac{\partial U}{\partial T}\right)_p + p\left(\frac{\partial V}{\partial T}\right)_p\right]dT + \left[\left(\frac{\partial U}{\partial p}\right)_T + p\left(\frac{\partial V}{\partial p}\right)_T\right]dp - E\,|dz|$$

or
$$dQ_C = C_p\,dT + L_p\,dp - E\,|dz| \qquad (7.1)$$

In this case U and V are functions of T and p only, despite the electrical heating, provided that the heating is slow enough for substantial equilibrium to be maintained at all times.

For isobaric processes

$$C_p\,dT = dQ_p + E\,|dz| \qquad (7.2)$$

or, for small finite changes,

$$C_p\,\Delta T = \Delta Q_p + \frac{Ei}{J}\Delta\tau \qquad (7.3)$$

where, with Ei in joules, the last term is expressed in heat units and $\Delta\tau$ is the (always positive) time the electrical power is on. Since there is no heat flow except the unavoidable flow through the insulation of the calorimeter, ΔQ_p is usually small. For calorimeters using the cumulative method, the calorimeter is at or above the temperature of the outer liquid bath, and ΔQ_p is negative. Finally

$$C_p = \frac{Ei\,\Delta\tau}{J\,\Delta T} - \frac{|\Delta Q_p|}{\Delta T} \tag{7.4}$$

where the last term is a small heat loss correction.

Since so much theoretical interest centers in the low-temperature behavior of specific heats and heat capacities, we shall consider methods chiefly adapted to low-temperature work.

7.2   The Nernst-Lindemann Vacuum Calorimeter

In a method devised by Gaede but developed by Nernst and Lindemann,[1] the heat loss is reduced to a very small value by suspension of the calorimeter proper in an evacuable glass jacket [Fig. 7.1(a)]. The glass bulb is surrounded by a liquid at the desired temperature, and the space between the calorimeter and the bulb is filled with hydrogen or helium gas, which acts as a heat inter-changer. When equilibrium has been reached, this space is thoroughly exhausted, a certain quantity of electrical energy is dissipated in the insulated calorimeter, the new temperature is measured, etc.

When a metal is to be studied, a cylindrical block of the metal acts as its own calorimeter [Fig. 7.1(b)]. A hole is bored most of the length of the cylinder, and a cylindrical plug of the same metal carrying an insulated coil of pure platinum wire is inserted in the hole. All intervening cavities are filled with paraffin. The coil of platinum is used both as a heater and as a resistance thermometer.

For poor conductors the calorimeter takes the form shown in Fig. 7.1(c). A silver cylinder with heating coils in its outer surface is filled with the solid in powder form, and a silver cap is soldered in place. Silver foil covers the heating coils to reduce radiation while the hydrogen or helium is run through a tube in the cap, which is later sealed off. The calorimeter is then ready to be hung in its vacuum-tight glass jacket.

For a vacuum calorimeter the heat loss, $|\Delta Q_p|$, although small, is not negligible. Solving Eq. 7.3 for ΔT (or more precisely ΔT_{obs}), the actually observed rise due to the heating, gives

$$\Delta T = \Delta T_{obs} = \frac{Ei\,\Delta\tau}{JC_p} - \frac{|\Delta Q_p|}{C_p} \tag{7.5}$$

or

$$\Delta T_{obs} = \Delta T_1 - \Delta T_2$$

where ΔT_1 is the rise that would have occurred with *no heat* loss and ΔT_2 is the

---

[1] Gaede, *Physik. Z.*, **4**, 105 (1902); Nernst and Lindemann, *Ann. Physik*, **36**, 395 (1911); and W. H. Nernst, *New Heat Theorem*, 2nd ed., English trans., Dutton, New York, 1926, pp. 24–53.

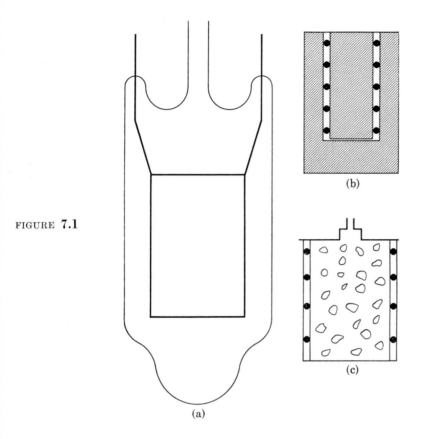

FIGURE **7.1**

(a)

(b)

(c)

temperature drop in the system due to heat leakage. Thus ΔT_1, the quantity we wish to know, is

$$\Delta T_1 = \Delta T_{\text{obs}} + \Delta T_2 \tag{7.6}$$

where ΔT_2 is a small correction to be determined.

In practice, the ΔT_{obs} of Eq. 7.6 is not in fact directly observable, since the temperature does not attain its maximum value at the instant the power is shut off. The situation can best be studied from Fig. 7.2, where the temperature of the calorimeter, originally at the bath temperature, T_i, is plotted versus the time. The heater is turned on at τ_1 and off at τ_2, whereas the temperature rises rapidly to a maximum a little later than τ_2, eventually to fall off linearly according to Newton's law of cooling (*b* to *a* in the figure).

It is assumed that the linear rate of cooling is effective from τ_2 onward, and the linear cooling curve is accordingly projected back to intersect a vertical through τ_2 at the point *c*. Then the ΔT_{obs} of Eq. 7.6 is taken as

$$\Delta T_{\text{obs}} = T_c - T_i$$

Since during the heating interval, $\Delta \tau = \tau_2 - \tau_1$, the system cools at a rate that varies from zero at τ_1 to the maximum rate at τ_2, it is assumed that the effective

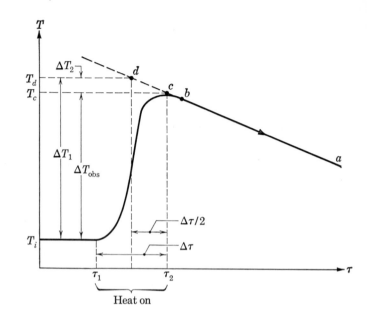

FIGURE **7.2**

rate is exactly one half of the final rate. One half of the final rate for $\Delta\tau$ is equivalent to the final rate for $\Delta\tau/2$. Therefore, projecting the line *abc* to an intersection, *d*, with a vertical at the *mid-point* of the heating interval gives the corrected theoretical maximum temperature, T_d. Thus

$$\Delta T_2 = T_d - T_c$$

and hence $$\Delta T_1 = T_d - T_i = \Delta T_{\text{obs}} + \Delta T_2$$

Here ΔT_1 is the rise to be expected with no heat loss, that is, with $\Delta Q_p = 0$; consequently,

$$C_p = \frac{Ei\,\Delta\tau}{J\,\Delta T_1} \qquad (7.7)$$

7.3   The Adiabatic Vacuum Calorimeter

Although the cooling corrections of Sec. 7.2 are normally small, their determinations are troublesome, and it is naturally desirable to eliminate them altogether. With this purpose in view, the *adiabatic vacuum* calorimeter was devised by Richards and developed by Simon and Lange.[2] In the form used by the latter investigators, it consists of a thin-walled copper calorimeter (Fig. 7.3) provided with heating coils and a lead resistance thermometer, the leads to which come out through vacuum-tight lead-glass seals. This calorimeter is surrounded by a brass cylindrical shield having its own heating coils. The current is regulated so that a thermocouple with one element in the calorimeter

---

[2] Simon and Lange, *Z. physik. Chem.*, **110**, 343 (1924).

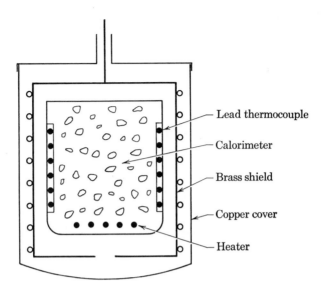

FIGURE **7.3**

Lead thermocouple

Calorimeter

Brass shield

Copper cover

Heater

and the other in the shield always reads zero. The calorimeter and shield are surrounded by an evacuable copper vessel, which can be immersed in a bath very much as in the Nernst-Lindemann calorimeter.

Since the calorimeter is strictly adiabatic, Eq. 7.3 can be used, with $dQ_p = 0$, so that

$$C_p = \frac{Ei\,d\tau}{J\,dT} \tag{7.8}$$

The values of E, the potential drop, and i, the current, are adjusted to suitable values and thereafter kept constant. Then T is observed as a function of time, and a heating curve of T versus τ is plotted. The slope of this curve, obtained graphically, is $dT/d\tau$. The product of its reciprocal with Ei/J gives C_p.

This procedure with the adiabatic calorimeter constitutes a *constant-power input* method.

7.4   Equilibrium Method

The static or equilibrium method is a variation of the preceding method. In this case the objective is not to retain an adiabatic balance between the calorimeter and its surroundings but rather to preserve *constancy* of the temperature of the surroundings. The heater is turned on at some value of the power Ei, and the calorimeter is allowed to attain a constant equilibrium temperature, where the power input exactly balances the rate of heat loss, dQ_p/dT, to the surroundings. Thus Eq. 7.3 gives

$$C_p\frac{dT}{d\tau} = 0 = \frac{dQ_p}{d\tau} + \frac{Ei}{J}$$

or

$$\frac{dQ_p}{d\tau} = -\frac{Ei}{J} \tag{7.9}$$

FIGURE **7.4**

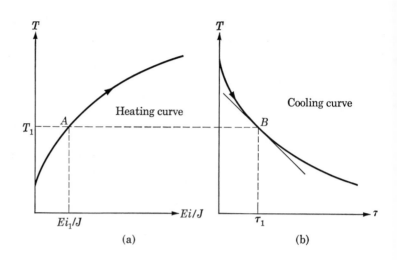

(a)   (b)

The power is then increased, a new equilibrium temperature reached, etc. Finally, when as high a temperature has been attained as is desired, the power is turned off. As the calorimeter cools, data are taken for a cooling curve.

In Fig. 7.4 two curves are plotted. The first, Fig. 7.4(a), represents the heating curve, T versus "power in," Ei/J, and the other, Fig. 7.4(b), is the cooling curve, T versus τ. For all points of the cooling curve, $Ei = 0$, and thus

$$\frac{dQ_p}{d\tau} = C_p \frac{dT}{d\tau} \tag{7.10}$$

where $dT/d\tau$ is the slope of the cooling curve (a negative quantity) and $dQ_p/d\tau$ is the rate of heat loss for the temperature concerned. Since the latter value depends only on T itself, provided the surroundings have not altered, it may be read off the power input axis of the first curve. Thus for any temperature, say, T_1 in the figure, we obtain the slope $dT/d\tau$ at B on the cooling curve and read off the corresponding power, Ei_1/J, directly under A on the other curve. Equating the right term of Eq. 7.9 with the right term of Eq. 7.10 gives

$$C_p \frac{dT_1}{d\tau} = -\frac{Ei_1}{J}$$

or

$$C_p = \frac{Ei_1}{J} \left| \frac{d\tau}{dT_1} \right| \tag{7.11}$$

where $|d\tau/dT_1|$ is the magnitude of the reciprocal of the rate of cooling at τ_1. This result is of the same form as Eq. 7.8 although of quite different origin.

This method assumes, as does the adiabatic one, that the calorimeter and its contents are sufficiently conducting (or rendered so by the addition of a suitable gas) for the whole system at any instant to be isothermal.

7.5   The Law of Dulong and Petit

It was discovered as early as 1819 by Dulong and Petit that the specific heats of the solid elements showed a regular decrease with increasing atomic weight. In fact, the product of the atomic weight, A, and c_p is approximately a constant. Since this constant is about 6.2 cal/g-atom-deg, the law of Dulong and Petit may be written as

$$A c_p = 6.2 \text{ cal/g-atom-deg}$$

Column 3 of Table 7.1 gives a number of experimental values for the atomic heats $C_p = A c_p$. It is apparent that the law of Dulong and Petit expresses the behavior of metals more nearly than that of nonmetals. The very low values for boron, graphite, and diamond are particularly striking.

Since the atomic heat at constant volume, C_V, is more significant theoretically than C_p, its calculation from the observed values of C_p is desirable. The difference $C_p - C_V$ is small for solids and liquids, but its determination requires use of the second law. The needed result may be obtained from Maxwell's second relation (as indicated in Problem 7.1), which will be proved in

TABLE **7.1**

*Atomic Heats of Elements**

Element	A, at wt	C_p	$C_p - C_V$	C_V
Lithium	6.94	5.52	0.08	5.44
Sodium	23.0	7.06	0.52	6.54
Aluminum	27.1	5.83	0.47	5.36
Iron	55.84	6.14	0.11	6.03
Copper	63.57	5.97	0.22	5.75
Silver	107.8	6.03	0.26	5.77
Platinum	195.2	6.21	0.08	6.09
Gold	197.2	6.10	0.24	5.86
Lead	207.2	6.43	0.40	6.03
Bismuth	209.0	6.22	0.09	6.13
Av		6.14($\pm$.4)		5.87($\pm$.4)
Boron	11.0	2.86		
Graphite	12.0	2.60	0.03	2.57
Diamond	12.0	1.36		
Silicon	28.3	5.02	0.16	4.86
Sulfur	32.07	5.78	0.51	5.27
Phosphorus	33.04	6.37	0.11	6.26
Iodine	126.9	6.80		

* In cal/g-mole-deg between 15 and 100°C. See A. Eucken, *Handbuch der Experimental Physik*, Akad. Verlag., Leipzig, 1929, Vol. VIII, Teil I, pp. 183–200.

TABLE **7.2**

Molecular Heats of Metallic Oxides

Compound	c_p, cal/g-deg	M, mol wt	C_p, cal/mole-deg
Fe_2O_3	0.1700	159.0	27.2
Cr_2O_3	0.1796	152.0	27.4
As_2O_3	0.1277	197.8	25.3
Sb_2O_3	0.0901	287.8	25.9
Bi_2O_3	0.0605	464.8	28.1

Sec. 9.16. This needed result is

$$C_p - C_V = \frac{V\beta_p{}^2 T}{\kappa_T} = \frac{A}{\rho}\frac{\beta_p{}^2 T}{\kappa_T} \tag{7.12}$$

where A/ρ has been substituted for the atomic volume, V. Calculated values of $C_p - C_V$ are given in column 4 of Table 7.1, and of C_V in the last column. The average values for C_V are only about 0.27 cal/g-mole-deg below those for C_p, although for the ideal gas the needed correction is much larger, being in fact equal to R (that is, 1.987 cal/mole-deg).

Similar regularities for compounds were first pointed out by Neumann in 1831. The product of the molecular weight, M, of a compound by its specific heat is approximately a constant for compounds of similar composition; that is,

$$Mc_p \approx \text{constant}$$

This is illustrated for a group of metallic oxides of the type X_2Y_3 in Table 7.2, where the molecular heat capacity, $(C_p)_{\text{mol}}$, given in the last column, has an average value of 26.8($\pm$.8) cal/g-mole-deg. This value, as we might expect, is much larger than an atomic heat capacity. Dividing the molecular heats by 5, the number of atoms in each molecule, gives the average atomic heat for the compound, $\overline{(C_p)}_{\text{at}}$. This is 5.75($\pm$.16), a result only slightly smaller than the Dulong and Petit value for elementary metals.

7.6   Temperature Variation of C_V

The true significance of the law of Dulong and Petit as well as the reason for its failures is made clear by a study of the temperature variation of C_V. Most solids have heat capacities that rise from low temperatures in an S-shaped curve, leveling off at high temperatures to a constant or nearly constant value. A rather large group of solids, including both elements and compounds, is characterized by a common lower limit of zero and a common upper limit of

5.96 cal/mole-deg; that is,

$$\lim_{T \to 0} C_V = 0$$

and

$$\lim_{T \to \infty} C_V = 5.96 = 3R$$

This behavior is illustrated in Fig. 7.5 for lead, cadmium, aluminum, and diamond, which are of the class of substances often called "thermally simple," and it is the basis of both the regularities expressed by the law of Dulong and Petit and the exceptions to it. The low values observed for diamond and a number of other elements result from the fact that room temperatures are too low for the asymptotic limit to be reached. In general, soft materials like lead reach the theoretical limit at the lowest temperatures, and the rate of approach becomes slower as hardness increases. Thus diamond, the hardest material in the class, has the lowest observed value of C_V at room temperatures and approaches the theoretical limit only at the highest temperatures.

The lowering of C_V with temperature to zero values at 0°K seems to be a general characteristic of all solids. Despite local anomalies, C_V can be made as small as desired by lowering the temperature.

As T is raised from 0°K, we may write

$$C_V = aT + bT^n$$

where the range of validity and the values of the constants a and b and the power n vary from substance to substance. For a large class of nonmetals,

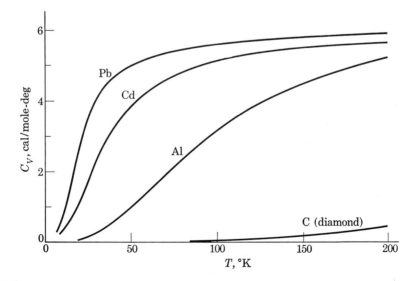

FIGURE **7.5**

$a = 0$, and $n = 3$, so that

$$C_V = bT^3$$

a result known as Debye's *cube law*. For a great many metals, n is also 3, but the small linear term, aT, is needed to take account of the contribution of free electrons. (See Sec. 19.18.)

For the thermally simple compounds, the curves of Fig. 7.5 are all of the same mathematical form and may be made to coincide by a suitable change of scale on the T axis. Thus there exists for each of these substances a characteristic constant having the dimensions of temperature, analogous to the characteristic temperature for vibration discussed in Sec. 6.17. Indicating this constant by Θ (written Θ_m in Sec. 19.18), we have

$$\frac{\Theta}{T} = \frac{h\nu}{kT}$$

where ν is a characteristic frequency for the solid and h is Planck's constant. With C_V plotted versus this ratio (or its reciprocal, T/Θ), all the curves coincide. This behavior indicates that C_V is a common function of Θ/T, and we write

$$C_V = F\left(\frac{\Theta}{T}\right)$$

where

$$\lim_{T\to 0} F\left(\frac{\Theta}{T}\right) = 0$$

and

$$\lim_{T\to\infty} F\left(\frac{\Theta}{T}\right) = 3R$$

Dividing $F(\Theta/T)$ by $3R$, we have finally

$$C_V = 3RD\left(\frac{\Theta}{T}\right) \tag{7.13}$$

where $D(\Theta/T)$ is the so-called *Debye function*, a dimensionless function varying between 0 and 1 as T/Θ varies from 0 to ∞. This function, arrived at theoretically by Debye, is expressed as an integral, and tables of it are given in many handbooks. The origin of the Debye function will be discussed qualitatively in the next section and in more detail in Chap. 19 (Secs. 19.11 to 19.13).

The Debye temperature, Θ, is an important quantity and may be determined in a number of ways. In Table 7.3 values of Θ determined by fitting the observed heat capacities to a Debye function are given together with the temperature ranges employed. This table includes most of the members of the thermally simple class. The substances are arranged in the order of increasing Θ, from lead with the lowest value of 88° to diamond with the highest value, 1860°.

TABLE **7.3**

*Debye Temperatures for Simple Solids**

Substance	Range, °K	θ	Substance	Range, °K	θ
Lead	14–573	88	Silvium (KCl)	23–550	230
Thallium	23–301	96	Zinc	33–673	235
Mercury	31–232	97	Rock salt (NaCl)	25–664	281
Iodine	22–298	106	Copper	14–773	315
Cadmium	50–380	168	Aluminum	19–773	398
Sodium	50–240	172	Iron	32–95	453
Potassium bromide	79–417	177	Fluorspar (CaF$_2$)	17–328	474
Silver	35–873	215	Pyrites (FeS$_2$)	22–57	645
Calcium	22–62	226	Diamond	30–1169	1860

* See Schrödinger, *Physik. Z.*, **20**, 452 (1919), from which the data is taken.

Typical results for four metals with θ values varying from 168 to 315 are plotted in Fig. 7.6, where the solid curve marked Debye represents the Debye expression,

$$3RD\left(\frac{\theta}{T}\right) = 3RD(u)$$

plotted versus $T/\theta = 1/u$, u being a dimensionless parameter.

It is clear that the change of scale from T to T/θ brings all the data to substantially the same curve. The other curve in the figure represents the Einstein formula to be discussed in Sec. 7.7.

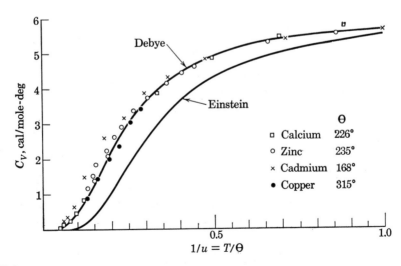

FIGURE **7.6**

A good many other substances that crystallize in systems more complicated than the cubic obey Dulong and Petit's law at room temperatures, only to have C_V fall off in some other fashion as T is lowered. With others neither the law of Dulong and Petit nor that of Debye is obeyed. In these cases the C_V curves do not rise in accordance with a constant Θ, nor do they level off at higher temperatures. They continue rising with increasing temperatures. In fact, many of the "simple" substances of Table 7.3 exhibit a definite rise in C_V above the temperature ranges indicated in the table. The Debye result is none the less a very important one in the subject of heat capacities of soilds.

7.7   Theoretical Interpretation of C_V for Solids

Einstein was first to offer a theoretical explanation of the behavior of C_V for solids.[3] He pointed out that if each particle in a crystal were thought of as bound to its theoretical lattice point by a linear restoring force, then its motion would correspond to a three-dimensional analog of the one-dimensional vibration in the diatomic gas molecule discussed in Sec. 6.17. If the frequency of the vibration is taken as ν, the energy of a single vibration along the x, y, or z axis can change in units of $h\nu$ only.

If the three vibrations are assumed to be independent, the internal energy, and hence C_V, is expected to rise with temperature as it does for a diatomic molecule, but with absolute values three times as large. If we multiply the Einstein function of Sec. 6.17 by $3R$ to take care of the three independent vibrations,

$$C_V = 3RE\left(\frac{\Theta}{T}\right) = 3RE(u) \tag{7.14}$$

where $\Theta/T = h\nu/kT = 1/u$ as before and $E(u)$ is the Einstein function for the linear vibrator, given in Eq. 6.34 as

$$E(u) = \frac{u^2 e^u}{(e^u - 1)^2}$$

Thus the characteristic temperature, Θ, is given by $h\nu/k$ and varies directly with ν. Although the Einstein formula has the proper limits for $T = 0$ and T large, it falls much too rapidly as T is lowered and departs more and more from the experimental observations as $0°K$ is approached. See Fig. 7.6, where the second solid curve is the Einstein formula, $3RE(u)$.

It was, of course, hardly to be expected that all the individual vibrators in a solid could be treated as having exactly the same frequency, as though the crystal were made up of $3N$ identical monochromatic oscillators (where N represents the number of atoms present), isolated and having no influence on one another. In 1912 Debye[4] took up the problem of C_V for solids and assigned

---

[3] Einstein, *Ann. Physik*, **22**, 180, 800 (1907); **34**, 170, 590 (1911).
[4] Debye, *Ann. Physik*, **39**, 789 (1912).

not a single frequency to each of the $3N$ linear oscillators but rather a continuous spectrum of frequencies. He took the $3N$ possible frequencies to be those given by the lowest $3N$ stable modes of vibration of the soild, considered as a continuous elastic medium. The thermal motions of the particles about their lattice points were thus regarded as due to the superposition of all of the standing elastic wave patterns possible for the solid sample. Actually the frequencies of these elastic standing waves form a discrete spectrum extending from a lowest frequency to a maximum frequency.

Of course, it is rather artificial to treat a body consisting of discrete particles as an elastic continuum when the wave lengths of the elastic waves are comparable with the lattice spacing. But since only $3N$ frequencies were needed— one for each of the equivalent linear oscillators—the possibility of trouble was minimized by the use of only the first $3N$ frequencies, counting from the lowest.

The distribution of frequencies obtained by Debye is shown in Fig. 7.7, where dN_ν is the number of vibrations lying in a range between ν and $\nu + d\nu$. The spectrum is broken off at a maximum frequency, ν_{max}, the spectrum below this being treated, for analytic simplicity, as a continuous one spreading from $\nu = 0$ to $\nu = \nu_{max}$. Here ν_{max} corresponds closely to the single monochromatic frequency used by Einstein.

The statistical analysis leading from this initial picture to the final Debye function will be postponed until Chap. 19 (see Secs. 19.10 to 19.14). Since, as we shall see, the Debye function can be represented only by an integral and thus requires numerical evaluation, its discussion will also be postponed, its general shape being given clearly enough for present empirical purposes by the graph of Fig. 7.6.

It should be re-emphasized that there are many bodies that do not follow the simple Debye curve. When noncubic crystals are involved, the elastic constants are different in different directions, and a combination of two or three Debye functions, each with its own Θ, is often needed. When the lattice points of a crystal are occupied by radicals or groups of atoms, then additional terms of the Einstein type are required, one for each characteristic internal vibration of the group. Thus in many complicated cases there is no indication of approach

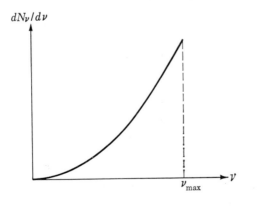

FIGURE **7.7**

to an asymptote, and the C_V curve continues its smooth rise with temperature to the melting point of the solid. In this connection see the curves for ice, solid benzene, and solid carbon monoxide, Fig. 7.8.

7.8 Heat Capacities of Liquids

It is difficult to make generalizations about the heat capacities of the liquid phase, intermediate between the theoretically simpler solid and gaseous phases.

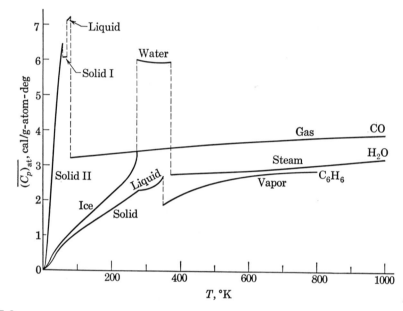

FIGURE **7.8**

For monatomic elements (argon, mercury, potassium, tin, lead, etc.), there is little change in C_V on solidification. The same behavior is typical of many organic substances. For diatomic molecules and a host of more complicated substances, C_V for the liquid is considerably larger than that for either the solid or the gaseous phase. Table 7.4 gives values of C_p, C_V, and γ for a few liquids. The values of γ are seen to be usually much larger than the upper limits possible for gases.

Fig. 7.8 illustrates the over-all behavior of heat capacity with change in temperature and phase. It shows the average atomic heat, $\overline{(C_p)_\text{at}}$, for three substances: *carbon monoxide*, a typical diatomic substance; *water*, which is notoriously anomalous; and *benzene*, a typical aromatic organic compound. The differences in behavior are striking, although in each case a large drop in $\overline{(C_p)_\text{at}}$ occurs on vaporization of the liquid.

TABLE **7.4**

Heat Capacities for Liquids

Liquid	T, °K	C_p	C_V	γ
Hydrogen	20.4	4.53	2.78	1.629
Argon	89.3	10.52	5.50	1.912
	140.4	15.41	4.65	3.32
Carbon dioxide	223.2	19.00	10.30	1.844
	293.2	33.10	12.70	2.606
Ether	110.0	18.5	11.2	1.60
	270.0	25.0	11.8	2.12

7.9   Change of Phase

When a solid melts or a liquid vaporizes, there is heat absorption with no change in temperature. This heat absorption is the latent heat of change of phase and can readily be expressed in terms of related quantities by the first law.

Suppose we begin with a system of m'' grams of liquid in equilibrium with m' grams of vapor and allow exactly 1 g of liquid to vaporize. Then m'' changes to $m'' - 1$, and m' to $m' + 1$, and the heat absorbed is by definition the latent heat of vaporization, λ. Integrating the first law gives

$$\lambda = \int_i^e dQ_p = \int_i^e dU + p \int_i^e dV \tag{7.15}$$

or

$$\lambda = U_e - U_i + p(V_e - V_i) \tag{7.16}$$

To simplify these relations, we now write down the initial and final conditions in terms of the masses of the respective phases and the specific internal energies and volumes.

Initial state	*Final state*
$m_i = m'' + m'$	$m_i = m_e = (m'' - 1) + (m' + 1)$
$V_i = m''v'' + m'v'$	$V_e = (m'' - 1)v'' + (m' + 1)v'$
$U_i = m''u'' + m'u'$	$U_e = (m'' - 1)u'' + (m' + 1)u'$

Substitution of these results reduces Eq. 7.16 to

$$\lambda = u' - u'' + p(v' - v'') \tag{7.17}$$

The latent heat absorbed in vaporization is thus used in two ways. Part of it represents the difference between the internal energy of the vapor and that of the liquid, and the rest goes into external work. Since the change is from phase 2 to phase 1, we indicate this latent heat by λ_{21} to differentiate it from other latent heats. Then

$$\lambda_{21} = \Delta_{21}u + p\,\Delta_{21}v \tag{7.18}$$

or, generally, for a change from phase i to phase j,

$$\lambda_{ij} = \Delta_{ij}u + p\,\Delta_{ij}v \qquad (7.19)$$

Since a given substance may have several solid phases but only a *single* liquid and a *single* gaseous phase, it is convenient to begin numbering the phases from the one stable at the highest temperature. For example, with carbon monoxide we should write v', v'', v''', and v'''' for the specific volumes of the series vapor, liquid, solid I, and solid II, respectively. Since usually $v''' < v'' < v'$, the correction term, $p\,\Delta_{ij}v$, of Eq. 7.19 is positive but of small significance numerically except for sublimation or vaporization. When only two phases are under discussion, only single and double primes need be used, the single prime referring to the phase stable at the higher temperatures, whatever it may be.

7.10   Enthalpy

At this point it is convenient to return to the total heat or enthalpy function defined in Sec. 4.3 by means of the constant-pressure integral,

$$h = \int_0^t c_p\,dt \qquad (4.7)$$

Replacing t by T and differentiating both sides by T at constant pressure gives

$$\left(\frac{\partial h}{\partial T}\right)_p = c_p$$

But by Eq. 5.26, which we write here for unit mass,

$$\left(\frac{\partial h}{\partial T}\right)_p = \left(\frac{\partial u}{\partial T}\right)_p + p\left(\frac{\partial v}{\partial T}\right)_p = \left[\frac{\partial(u+pv)}{\partial T}\right]_p \qquad (7.20)$$

and, consequently, h is given by

$$\boxed{h = u + pv}$$

or

$$\boxed{H = U + pV} \qquad (7.21)$$

Since U and pV are fixed by the state of the system, enthalpy becomes a thermodynamic function along with U itself.

Combining the first law,

$$dq_C = du + p\,dv$$

with the differential of Eq. 7.21,

$$dh = du + p\,dv + v\,dp$$

gives

$$dh = dq_C + v\,dp$$

Thus for an isobaric process

$$dh_p = dq_p \tag{7.22}$$

and enthalpy is such a function that its change at constant pressure is always the *heat absorbed for the process.*

Integrating Eq. 7.22 gives

$$q_p = \int_i^e dq_p = \int_i^e dh = (h_e - h_i)_p$$

or

$$q_p = (h_e - h_i)_p = \Delta h_p \tag{7.23}$$

The change in h is entirely independent of the details of the process whereby the system passes from i to e. Thus in Fig. 7.9 Δh is the same for all of the three paths connecting i and e and is evaluated for the simplest path that we can discover. The heat absorbed by the system, however, equals Δh only for the isobaric path.

From the first law,

$$dq_C = du + p\,dv$$

for any change at constant *volume*

$$dq_v = du_v \tag{7.24}$$

and the heat absorbed in an isochoric process is measured by the change in internal energy. Thus internal energy plays the same role in isochoric processes that enthalpy plays in isobaric processes. Since, however, the applications of thermodynamics involve isobaric processes more often than isochoric ones,

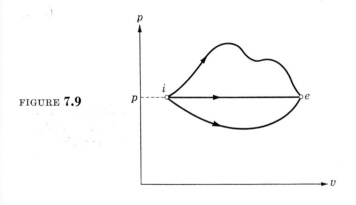

FIGURE **7.9**

enthalpy is more useful than internal energy. Chemical reactions of all sorts take place in the laboratory under constant atmospheric pressure. When cold water is pumped into a steam engine boiler and eventually vaporized, the passage from cold boiler water to steam takes place at the constant boiler pressure. When the exhaust steam is condensed to liquid in the condenser, the process is again isobaric but at the lower condenser pressure. In all these cases the heat gained (or lost) by the system is given by the corresponding change in enthalpy.

The changes in enthalpies for the changes of phase discussed in Sec. 7.9 may be written down at once, the other cases being reserved for later discussion. Returning to Eq. 7.19 for a phase change at pressure p, we have

$$\lambda_{ij} = \Delta_{ij} u + p \, \Delta_{ij} v \qquad (7.19)$$

or

$$\lambda_{ij} = \Delta_{ij}(u + pv) = \Delta_{ij} h = h_j - h_i \qquad (7.25)$$

In other words, when any pure substance undergoes a change at pressure p from the phase i to the phase j, the latent heat is simply the difference between the specific enthalpies for the two phases.

With a condensed phase (that is, a solid or a liquid), the term pv is very small compared to u. Consequently, $h \approx u$, and for changes between condensed phases

$$\lambda_{ij} = h_j - h_i \approx u_j - u_i$$

When one phase is gaseous, this equation does not apply. If we take a gram-mole of the substance and treat the vapor as an ideal gas,

$$H' = U' + pV' = U' + RT$$

and for the liquid

$$H'' = U'' + pV'' \approx U''$$

so that the latent heat of vaporization becomes

$$\Lambda_{21} = H' - H'' \approx U' - U'' + RT \qquad (7.26)$$

A similar relation holds, of course, for sublimation.

7.11 Enthalpy and Internal Energy

The evaluation of internal energy and enthalpy functions requires the integration of the appropriate differential expressions for dU and dH along suitable paths from some standard state to the state in question. For dU, combining the first law,

$$dU = dQ_C - p \, dV$$

and the second dQ_C expression,

$$dQ_C = C_V dT + L_V dV \qquad (5.34)$$

gives

$$\boxed{dU = C_V dT + (L_V - p) dV} \qquad (7.27)$$

General integration of this equation requires a knowledge not only of C_V but also of L_V. We saw in Chap. 5 that for the ideal gas

$$C_V^\circ = C_V^\circ(T)$$

and

$$L_V^\circ = p$$

so that the last term of Eq. 7.27 drops out and

$$dU^\circ = C_V^\circ(T) dT \qquad (7.28)$$

This is integrable as soon as C_V° is known as a function of T.
Likewise, for dH, since

$$dH = dU + d(pV)$$

$$dH = dQ_C + V dp$$

and, from the first dQ_C expression, Eq. 5.29,

$$dH = C_p dT + (L_p + V) dp \qquad (7.29)$$

Again, for the ideal gas, as we saw in Chap. 5,

$$C_p^\circ = C_V^\circ(T) + R$$

and

$$L_p^\circ = -V$$

so that

$$dH^\circ = C_p^\circ(T) dT = [C_V^\circ(T) + R] dT \qquad (7.30)$$

Integration of both Eqs. 7.28 and 7.30 is possible as soon as the function of $C_V^\circ(T)$ is known. Integration between $0°K$ and T gives

$$U^\circ - U_0^\circ = \int_0^T C_V^\circ(T) dT \qquad (7.31)$$

and

$$H^\circ - H_0^\circ = \int_0^T C_V^\circ(T) dT + RT = U^\circ - U_0^\circ + RT \qquad (7.32)$$

Since $H = U + pV$,

$$H_0^\circ = U_0^\circ + pV^\circ = U_0^\circ$$

where U_0°, an arbitrary integration constant, is the value of the internal energy of the ideal gas at $0°K$. At this temperature (to remain ideal) the gas must have infinite dispersion. As a result, the molecules can exert no forces on one another.

It is convenient, therefore, to take their mutual potential energy as zero. Since from the kinetic theory they possess no kinetic energy either, we set $U_0^\circ = 0$ and take this state as the arbitrary zero from which *internal* energy and *enthalpy* are measured. Thus finally

$$U^\circ = \int_0^T C_V^\circ(T)\,dT \tag{7.33}$$

and

$$H^\circ = \int_0^T C_V^\circ(T)\,dT + RT \tag{7.34}$$

In the particular case of monatomic gases,

$$C_V^\circ = \tfrac{3}{2}R$$

and therefore these integrals become simply

$$U^\circ = \tfrac{3}{2}RT$$

and

$$H^\circ = \tfrac{5}{2}RT \tag{7.35}$$

For nonideal gases and condensed phases, the second law is necessary to provide expressions for L_V and L_p. These expressions, as we shall see in Chap. 9, indicate that both L_V and L_p are quite small for condensed phases and depart only slightly from p and $-V$, respectively, for real gases at not too high pressures or too low temperatures.

7.12   Heat of Sublimation of a Monatomic Solid

The preceding considerations lead to a very useful relation first obtained by Kirchhoff. If we restrict ourselves to a solid with strictly monatomic vapor, the results given in Eq. 7.35 hold, provided that the pressures are low enough for the vapor to behave as an ideal gas. As the temperature is lowered, the vapor pressure of all solids is found to fall rapidly toward a zero value at 0°K. See Fig. 7.10, which shows a portion of the vapor pressure curve separating the regions of existence of solid and vapor. At any point on this curve, the solid and vapor are in equilibrium, and, in particular, the molar heat of sublimation, Λ_{31}, is given by

$$\Lambda_{31} = H' - H''' \tag{7.36}$$

the single and triple primes referring to the vapor and solid states as before. Applying this relation at the origin (point a, Fig. 7.10) and calling the heat of sublimation at that point Λ_0, we have

$$\Lambda_0 = H'_a - H'''_a = H'_0 - H'''_0 = -H'''_a \tag{7.37}$$

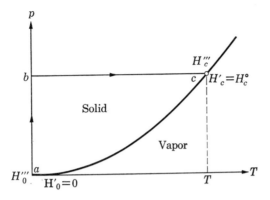

FIGURE **7.10**

(since $H'_0 = 0$). According to this equation, since $\Lambda_0 > 0$, H'''_a must be *negative*. This result is understandable in terms of the arbitrary assignment of $H'_0 = 0$. For if the vapor has zero energy at $0°$K, energy is evolved on condensation, and enthalpy must decrease still further.

At any variable point, say, c, on the general vapor pressure curve, the heat of sublimation may be written

$$\Lambda_{31} = H'_c - H'''_c = H°_c - H'''_c = \tfrac{5}{2}RT - H'''_c \qquad (7.38)$$

Obtaining H'''_c requires integration of the general expression for dH, Eq. 7.29 for the solid. Carrying this out along the path abc leads to

$$H'''_c - H'''_a = \int_a^c dH''' = \underset{\text{(constant } T)}{\int_a^b dH'''} + \underset{\text{(constant } p)}{\int_b^c dH'''}$$

Along the section a to b, T is constant, and the second term of Eq. 7.29 drops out, whereas between b and c, the pressure is constant, and the last term vanishes. Thus

$$H'''_c - H'''_a = H'''_c + \Lambda_0 = \underset{(T = 0°\text{K})}{\int_0^p (L_p + V)\,dp} + \underset{(p = \text{constant})}{\int_0^T C_p'''\,dT}$$

If $L_p + V$ is taken out of the integral as an average, the first integral becomes simply $(\overline{L_p + V})p$. Here the value of $\overline{L_p + V}$ at $0°$K is small,[5] and p is usually very small. Thus the product may be safely neglected, and

$$H'''_c = -\Lambda_0 + \int_0^T C_p'''\,dT$$

---

[5] We shall see in Sec. 14.15 that L_p itself vanishes here, that is, for a solid.

Insertion of this result in Eq. 7.38 gives

$$\Lambda_{31} = \Lambda_0 + \tfrac{5}{2}RT - \int_0^T C_p''' dT \qquad (7.39)$$

or

$$\Lambda_{31} = \Lambda_0 + \int_0^T (C_p^{\circ} - C_p''') dT \qquad (7.40)$$

If C_p''' can be expressed as a temperature function and Λ_{31} can be measured (or calculated from other data), we are in a position to find Λ_0, the theoretically important heat of sublimation at 0°K. Use of this valuable result will be made in Sec. 12.13 to obtain another of Kirchhoff's formulas—the Kirchhoff vapor pressure formula for solids. This formula will make possible the calculation of the vapor pressure curve of Fig. 7.10 from purely thermal data.

7.13   Enthalpy and Internal Energy for Simple Substances

One method for determining Λ_0 requires that latent heats be measured at some high pressures where calorimetry is feasible. Fig. 7.11 shows a portion of the phase diagram for a normal substance with a single solid phase. We carry out the same calculations as those connected with Fig. 7.10; that is, we determine H', the enthalpy of the saturated vapor at a point c on the liquid-vapor curve, by two methods. In the first, assuming the ideal gas law, we use Eq. 7.35 to obtain

$$H'_c = H_c^{\circ} = \tfrac{5}{2}RT_{21} = \int_0^{T_{21}} C_p' dT \qquad (7.41)$$

T_{21} being the boiling point at the pressure of point c and C_p' the heat capacity

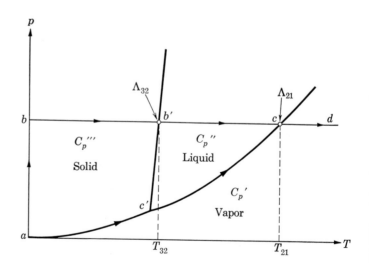

FIGURE **7.11**

of the vapor. In the second method, we integrate dH along the path $abb'c$, starting with the vapor phase at $0°K$. If C_p''' and C_p'' are the heat capacities of the solid and liquid, respectively, Λ_{32} is the heat of fusion, and Λ_{21} is the heat of vaporization, we write

$$H_c° - H_0° = H_c° = \int_a^c dH$$

or $\qquad H_c° = -\Lambda_0 + \int_a^b dU''' + \int_b^{b'} C_p''' dT + \Lambda_{32} + \int_{b'}^c C_p'' dT + \Lambda_{21}$

Since U''' varies only slightly with pressure, the first integral is neglected, and

$$H_c° = -\Lambda_0 + \int_0^{T_{32}} C_p''' dT + \Lambda_{32} + \int_{T_{32}}^{T_{21}} C_p'' dT + \Lambda_{21} \qquad (7.42)$$

Equating Eqs. 7.41 and 7.42 gives finally

$$\Lambda_0 = \int_0^{T_{32}} C_p''' dT + \Lambda_{32} + \int_{T_{32}}^{T_{21}} C_p'' \, dT + \Lambda_{21} - \int_0^{T_{21}} C_p' dT \qquad (7.43)$$

Λ_0 is thus given in terms of data that can, in principle, be obtained for most substances.

Since the latent heats and heat capacities are insensitive to small pressure changes and the slope of the melting curve is large, the same data can be employed to evaluate the actual change in H along the equilibrium curve $(ac'c)$ and out to any point d in the vapor region. The general result of such calculations for a normal substance is given in Fig. 7.12, where the pressure of the line $bb'c$ of Fig. 7.11 is taken as atmospheric. The curves for $H°$ and $U°$ are given by $\frac{5}{2}RT$ and $\frac{3}{2}RT$, respectively. These curves are dashed between $0°K$ and T_{21}, the normal boiling point, since the vapor cannot exist at 1 atm in this region. The general enthalpy curve then begins at a point $-\Lambda_0$ below the energy origin and rises in four sections due to warming of the solid, melting of the

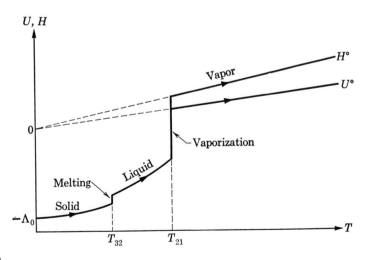

FIGURE **7.12**

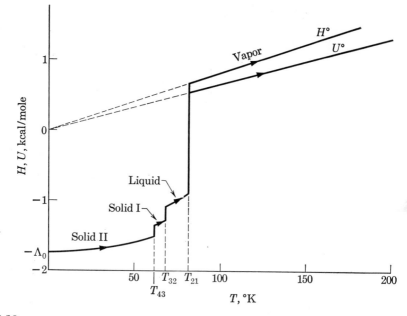

FIGURE **7.13**

solid, further warming of the liquid, and finally vaporizing of the liquid to meet the vapor curve at c. The internal energy curves for the condensed phases are too close to the enthalpy curves to be included.

Similar calculations can be carried out for more complicated substances with more than one solid modification. Fig. 7.13 shows the results of such a calculation for the diatomic molecule carbon monoxide, for which two solid modifications exist. For this curve the transition data of Clayton and Giauque,[6] as given in Table 7.5, were used. The vapor was treated as ideal, and it was assumed for simplicity that at the temperatures involved no appreciable vibration was excited.

TABLE **7.5**

**Phase Transition Data
for Carbon Monoxide at 1 Atm**

Transition	T_{ij}, °K	λ_{ij}, cal/mole
$4 \to 3$	61.55	151.3
$3 \to 2$	68.09	199.7
$2 \to 1$	81.61	1443.6

[6] Clayton and Giauque, *J. Am. Chem. Soc.*, **54**, 2610 (1932); **55**, 5071 (1935); and Clusius, *Z. physik. Chem.*, **B3**, 41 (1929).

7.14   Heat of Reaction and Enthalpy Tables

As we have seen, the net change in enthalpy, ΔH, for any process is independent of the details. Thus, if the pressure is constant throughout,

$$\Delta H_p = Q_p = \text{net heat absorbed}$$

whether we are dealing with a simple physical change, a phase change, a solution of a substance in a liquid, a chemical reaction, or any combination of these. This fact forms the general basis of thermochemical calculations.

Suppose that we start with a given set of substances and arrive at a final set of products by alternate paths. The over-all net heat absorption is independent of the different chemical and physical reactions used as intermediate steps and is the same for both paths. This situation can be readily understood from the following scheme:

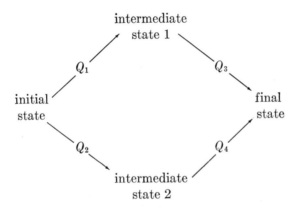

where, for simplicity, only one intermediate state is indicated for each path and Q_1, Q_2, Q_3, and Q_4 are the heats of the various reactions involved in the alternate paths (here reckoned as positive when heat is absorbed). In this case

$$\Delta H_p = Q_1 + Q_3 = Q_2 + Q_4$$

If one of the reactions in the scheme cannot be carried out in the laboratory, its heat of reaction can always be calculated as soon as the other three are known.

As an example, consider the reaction whereby carbon in the form of graphite is converted into diamond:

$$C(\text{graphite}) \rightarrow C(\text{diamond})$$

Although this process can be carried out to a modest extent in the laboratory, it is quite unsuited for direct calorimetric measurement. Suppose, however, that we set up the following scheme:

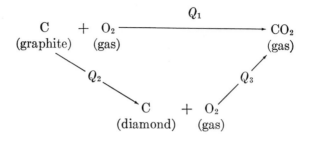

where the upper branch involves the direct combustion of the graphite to carbon dioxide, CO_2 (in the gaseous state and at some definite temperature), and the lower branch involves first the conversion of the graphite to diamond and then its combustion to CO_2 and arrival at the same temperature as before. Direct observation, starting with the β form of graphite and with the initial, intermediate, and final states all at 18°C and 1 atm gives

$$Q_1 = \Delta H_p = -94.23 \text{ kcal}$$
and
$$Q_3 = -94.45 \text{ kcal}$$
so that
$$Q_2 = +0.23 \text{ kcal}$$

Thus $H_{\text{diamond}} - H_{\text{graphite}} = 0.23$ kcal under the assumed conditions. Since for solids U and H are nearly equal, diamond is therefore the more energetic form of carbon.

Again, consider the heat of formation of gaseous methane, CH_4, out of its elements, carbon and hydrogen. The following scheme may be used:

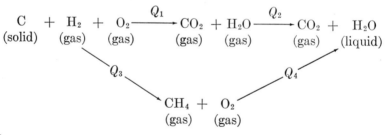

In this case
$Q_1 =$ heat of combustion of solid C and gaseous $H_2 = -210.05$ kcal
$Q_2 =$ latent heat of condensation of water vapor (18°C) $= -21.12$ kcal
$Q_4 =$ heat of combustion of $CH_4 = -213.01$ kcal
Hence $Q_3 =$ heat of formation of methane $= -18.16$ kcal

Heat is therefore evolved when methane is formed from its constituents.

The desirability of constructing standard tables for as many elements and compounds as possible, both to serve as an indication of the relative stabilities of the compounds and to permit the heats of various reactions and processes to be predicted as needed, is obvious. Data are usually lacking for calculation of the enthalpy of each element from the zero adopted for carbon monoxide in the last section. Since, however, only differences in enthalpy are used, any convenient fixed point may be taken as an energy reference level. It is, accordingly, customary to assign zero values to the enthalpy of *each element* in the stable phase in which it exists at 1 atm and a convenient temperature, such as 18°C.

As examples, consider the three elements carbon, hydrogen, and oxygen. Carbon in the form of diamond is taken as the zero reference state, owing to the definite and reproducible nature of this modification. The two gaseous elements are taken as the naturally occurring gases in their normal spectroscopic ground states (and with the natural mixture of isotopes and a stable equilibrium distribution of odd and even rotational states) at 18°C and 1 atm. Enthalpy values can be included for sublimed carbon (vapor), atomic oxygen, and atomic hydrogen in their various spectroscopic states, for the ions C^+, O^+, H^+, etc., and for various compounds in solid, liquid, and gaseous states as well as in dilute aqueous solutions. Data are then available for the direct evaluation of ΔH_p for a host of isobaric processes. Some of these data[7] are reproduced graphically in Fig. 7.14, where the enthalpy values (in kilocalories) are plotted vertically above and below the normal states of the elements taken as zero. Since the excited spectroscopic and ionic states occur at such high values, only that of CO excited to its first molecular level (a triplet Π state) has been shown. The three vertical arrows represent, in descending order, (1) the heat of combustion of carbon in the form of diamond to form a mole of CO ($\Delta H = -26.84$ kcal), (2) the molar heat of condensation of water vapor ($\Delta H = -10.6$ kcal), and (3) the molar heat of solution of gaseous CO_2 to form a dilute aqueous solution ($\Delta H = -3.84$ kcal).

The data refer to the gram-molecules or gram-atoms indicated on the right, and the proper integral multipliers must be used from the chemical equations of the reactions being considered. Thus $H(^2S)$ refers to a gram-atom of hydrogen in the ^2S state, and so, to find Q_p for the formation of molecular hydrogen from atomic hydrogen,

$$H + H \rightarrow H_2$$

we have

$$Q_p = \Delta H = -2 \times 51.90 = -103.80 \text{ kcal}$$

For purposes of comparison, the ΔH changes for the atomic and nuclear processes of splitting the atomic elements into protons, neutrons, and electrons are interesting. Indicating these particles by the symbols p^+, e^-, and n°, we have

Reaction	ΔH, kcal
$_1H^1 \rightarrow p^+ + e^-$	3.65×10^2
$_6C^{12} \rightarrow 6p^+ + 6n^\circ + 12e^-$	2.1×10^9
$_8O^{16} \rightarrow 8p^+ + 8n^\circ + 16e^-$	2.96×10^{10}

[7] F. R. Bichowsky and F. D. Rossini, *Thermochemistry of Chemical Substances*, Reinhold, New York, 1936.

FIGURE **7.14**

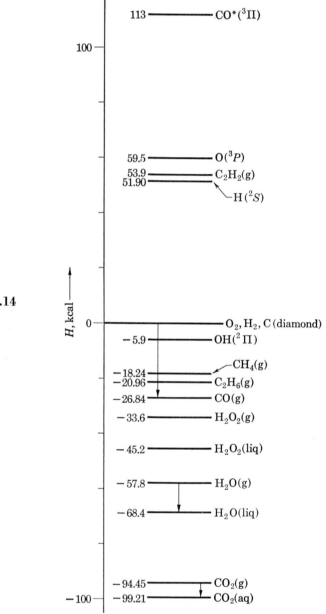

Except for the first reaction, which represents a simple ionization, these energies are of a quite different order of magnitude from those in Fig. 7.14.

7.15 Kirchhoff's Heat Capacity Formulas

Consider a portion of a two-phase equilibrium curve, say, for liquid and vapor (Fig. 7.15), with a mole each of liquid and vapor at equilibrium on the curve at temperature T. Let each be warmed to $T + dT$ along the curve. If the original values of enthalpy were H'' and H', they change to $H'' + dH''$ and $H' + dH'$. To pass from the liquid to the vapor isobarically at T requires the absorption of the heat of vaporization, Λ_{21}, and at $T + dT$, the absorption of $\Lambda_{21} + d\Lambda_{21}$, where

$$H' - H'' = \Lambda_{21}$$

and

$$H' + dH' - (H'' - dH'') = \Lambda_{21} + d\Lambda_{21}$$

so that

$$d\Lambda_{21} = dH' - dH''$$

Combining this with the general relation for dH, Eq. 7.29, gives

$$d\Lambda_{21} = (C_p' - C_p'')\, dT + [(L_p' - V') - (L_p'' - V'')]\, dp$$

Just as before, the coefficient of dp is neglected, and the useful approximate result follows:

$$\boxed{\frac{d\Lambda_{21}}{dT} \approx C_p' - C_p'' = \Delta C_p} \qquad (7.44)$$

This is one of Kirchhoff's heat capacity formulas. It shows that the rate of change of Λ_{21} with temperature is given by the excess of the heat capacity of the vapor over that of the liquid phase. Since this excess is usually negative, Λ_{21} must normally fall with rising temperature. Similar relations apply for the latent heats of fusion and sublimation.

FIGURE **7.15**

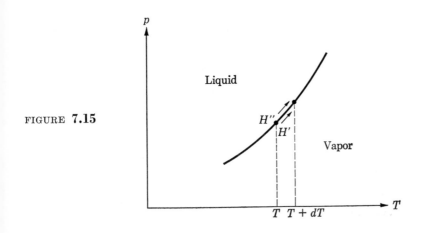

In the case of isobaric chemical reactions, also, a similar relation can be written down. Take a chemical reaction in which, say, ν_1 moles of A_1 react with ν_2 moles of A_2 to produce ν_3 moles of A_3 and ν_4 moles of A_4; that is,

$$\nu_1 A_1 + \nu_2 A_2 \rightarrow \nu_3 A_3 + \nu_4 A_4$$

This we write

$$\sum_{i=1}^{4} \nu_i A_i = 0 \tag{7.45}$$

where in the summation the ν's for the *products* are taken as *positive* and those for the *reactants* as *negative*. If H_1, H_2, H_3, and H_4 are the respective molar enthalpies of these substances all at the same temperature and pressure, the heat of reaction, Q_p, is given by

$$Q_p = \Delta H_p = \sum_{i=1}^{4} \nu_i H_i \tag{7.46}$$

Considering the change in Eq. 7.46 at some higher temperature, $T + dT$, we can then write to the same approximation as in Eq. 7.44,

$$\frac{d(\Delta H_p)}{dT} = \frac{dQ_p}{dT} \approx \sum_{i} \nu_i C_p{}^i \tag{7.47}$$

where $\sum_{i} \nu_i C_p{}^i$ is the net excess of the heat capacity of the products over that of the reactants and measures approximately the rate of temperature rise of the isobaric heat of reaction.

7.16   The First Law with Mass Flow

The usefulness of enthalpy as a thermodynamic function is further emphasized if we apply the conservation of energy principle to systems for which large-scale kinetic and gravitational potential energies are important. In order to apply this principle most simply, we envisage a system in a steady state. This system may be of the most general sort and may be thought of as contained in an enclosure (Fig. 7.16), with the working substance pumped in by a piston at the lower left and out by a piston at the upper right. Since a steady state exists, the conditions of the working substance at the inlet and outlet are constant in time and are indicated as follows:

	Inlet	*Outlet*
Pressure	p_1	p_2
Temperature	T_1	T_2
Specific volume	v_1	v_2
Specific internal energy	u_1	u_1
Speed of flow	$\mathcal{V}_1$	$\mathcal{V}_2$
Vertical elevation	z_1	z_2

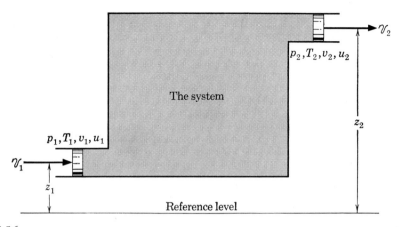

FIGURE **7.16**

If the time rate of flow of mass into the system (which, of course, equals the rate of outflow) is designated by $\dot{m}$, it is convenient to express the rates of heat and work flow into and out of the system as proportional to this mass flow rate. Thus we write

$$\dot{m} = \text{mass flow rate through the system}$$
$$\dot{m}q = \text{heat flow rate}$$
$$\dot{m}w = \text{work flow rate}$$

Subscripts 1 and 2 will be used as before to represent flow *into* or *out of* the system.

For a steady state there must be equality between the rate of inflow and the rate of outflow; that is,

$$\text{(rate of energy inflow)} - \text{(rate of energy outflow)} = 0 \qquad \textbf{(7.48)}$$

Each of these rates includes the following five terms due specifically to the factors indicated.

$\dot{m}u$	direct transport of internal energy
$\dfrac{\dot{m}\mathcal{V}}{2}$	direct transport of large-scale kinetic energy
$\dot{m}gz$	direct transport of large-scale potential energy
$\dot{m}q$	flow of heat across the system boundaries
$\dot{m}pv$	work done on the system by the piston (either inflow or outflow)

Here $\mathcal{V}$ is a large-scale speed of flow, g is the local value of the acceleration of gravity, and pv represents the hydrostatic work due to a unit mass transfer.

Moreover, the system as a whole may perform useful external work (in addition to that due to the outflow piston) at a rate, $\dot{m}w_{ext}$, where w_{ext} is the useful external work per unit mass flow rate. No indication of the mechanisms whereby this work is performed is given in the figure.

Insertion of these terms in Eq. 7.48, with the appropriate subscripts to indicate inflow and outflow quantities, gives

$$\left(u_1 + \frac{\mathcal{V}_1{}^2}{2} + gz_1 + q_1 + p_1v_1 \right) - \left(u_2 + \frac{\mathcal{V}_2{}^2}{2} + gz_2 + q_2 + p_2v_2 + w_{ext} \right) = 0$$

or, on regrouping and use of the definition of enthalpy,

$$(h_1 - h_2) + (q_1 - q_2) = \frac{(\mathcal{V}_2{}^2 - \mathcal{V}_1{}^2)}{2} + (z_2 - z_1)g + w_{ext} \qquad \textbf{(7.49)}$$

This is the first law with steady mass flow. It shows that the drop in specific enthalpy plus the net heat added per unit mass flow must always equal the gain in kinetic and potential energies of the effluent plus the useful external work performed. It can, of course, furnish no clue as to just how great a drop in enthalpy we can expect in a given device and hence of the upper limit of conversion of thermal into mechanical energy. For this information we must wait for the next chapter and the second law.

Since Eq. 7.49 is essentially an integral statement, there are no quasistatic or reversible restrictions. It can therefore be used directly in a whole range of thermomechanical, hydrodynamical, and heat engineering applications. A few special cases deserve mention.

The Constant-Flow Calorimeter. With the constant-flow calorimeter all the terms on the right of Eq. 7.49 vanish, and for constant pressure $q_1 - q_2 = q_p > 0$. Thus Eq. 7.49 reduces to

$$h_2 = h_1 + q_p \qquad \textbf{(7.50)}$$

That is, the heat added simply increases the enthalpy, h_1, to h_2 as the fluid flows through the calorimeter.

The Porous Plug and the Throttle Valve. A throttle valve is any device in a pipe or tube that serves to reduce the pressure of a gas flowing through the pipe. Since it is not designed to perform external work and may be thought of as horizontal and well insulated, Eq. 7.49 reduces to

$$h_1 - h_2 = \frac{\mathcal{V}_2{}^2 - \mathcal{V}_1{}^2}{2}$$

If we introduce a great deal of friction so as to reduce kinetic energies to negligible amounts, both $\mathscr{V}_1$ and $\mathscr{V}_2$ may be neglected, and therefore

$$h_1 - h_2 = 0 \tag{7.51}$$

This is essentially the procedure that Joule and Kelvin followed in their porous plug experiment described in Sec. 5.14 and illustrated in Fig. 5.8. Here gas at a high pressure, p ($p = p_1$), streams through the plug to a low pressure, p_0 ($p_0 = p_2$), and the flow, although quite irreversible, takes place with no net change in enthalpy.

With an ordinary pressure valve $\mathscr{V}_1$ is usually negligible, and $\mathscr{V}_2$ is small. In this case

$$h_1 = h_2 + \frac{\mathscr{V}_2{}^2}{2} \tag{7.52}$$

and there is a slight drop in enthalpy, a large drop in pressure, and the production of some kinetic energy. Such devices are usually called *throttling* valves. The porous plug is therefore an *ideal* throttling valve; it reduces pressure without any significant production of kinetic energy.

The Ideal Nozzle. An ideal nozzle (see Fig. 7.17) is at the opposite extreme from the perfect throttle. In its design every effort is made to prevent friction, reduce turbulence, etc., and increase $\mathscr{V}_2$ as much as possible. Since $\mathscr{V}_1$ is taken as the velocity in the pressure tank or boiler, it is usually negligible, as before, and the result again reduces to Eq. 7.52, which we now write as

$$h_1 - h_2 = \frac{\mathscr{V}_2{}^2}{2} \tag{7.53}$$

where $h_1 - h_2$ is *large*. A high-speed jet is therefore produced by a large drop in enthalpy.

The Steam Turbine. In the simple impulse turbine the drop in enthalpy in a well-designed nozzle produces a high-speed jet of steam, which in turn drives turbine blades. The object of good design is to convert as much as

FIGURE **7.17**

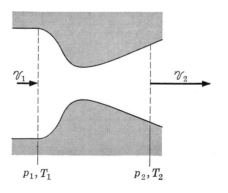

p_1, T_1 p_2, T_2

possible of the kinetic energy of the steam into blade rotation and therefore to reduce $\mathscr{V}_2$ to a minimum. Thus for the over-all turbine, with $\mathscr{V}_1$ again neglected, Eq. 7.49 reduces to

$$h_1 - h_2 = w_{\text{ext}} + \frac{\mathscr{V}_2{}^2}{2} \qquad (7.54)$$

Here, as was remarked before, the energy principle is simply a statement of energy balance and does not enable us to predict the size of h_2 or to say to how low a value it may be reduced by proper design. Such problems require the extra information given by the second law.

Problems

7.1 Using Maxwell's second relation given in Problem 5.10 (and to be proved in Sec. 9.16),

$$L_V = T\left(\frac{\partial p}{\partial T}\right)_V$$

show that the general relation obtained in Chap. 5,

$$C_p = C_V + L_V \left(\frac{\partial V}{\partial T}\right)_p$$

takes the form

$$C_p = C_V + \frac{V\beta_p{}^2 T}{\kappa_T} \qquad (7.12)$$

where β_p and κ_T are the coefficients of volume expansion and compressibility, respectively.

7.2 Calculate the difference between h''_{sat} and u''_{sat} for water at 100°C and 1 atm.

7.3 A gram of water is compressed isothermally from the triple point ($t \approx 0$°C and $p \approx 0$) to $p = 150$ lbs/in². Using Eq. 7.29 and Maxwell's first relation,

$$L_p = -T\left(\frac{\partial V}{\partial T}\right)_p$$

find the approximate change in h for 1 lb of water.

7.4 A gram-mole of ethyl alcohol is allowed to boil off at 78.1°C and 1 atm. If $\lambda = 205$ cal/g is the observed heat of evaporation, what heat would you expect to be absorbed for evaporation into a perfect vacuum?

7.5 When a gram-atom of zinc dissolves in dilute hydrochloric acid, HCl, at 20°C and 1 atm, 1 mole of H_2 gas is evolved, together with 36.1 kcal of heat. Find ΔU_p for this reaction.

7.6 The values of $C_p{}'$ and $C_p{}''$ for pure water are, respectively, 8.154 and 18.153 cal/g-mole-deg at 100°C. Using Kirchhoff's formula, Eq. 7.44, calculate the values of λ_{21} at 99 and 101°C, and compare with the data given in steam tables. Take λ_{21} at 100°C as 538.7 cal/g.

7.7 From Fig. 7.14 find the heats of combustion of methane (CH_4) and acetylene (C_2H_2) gases to form liquid water and CO_2.

7.8 What heat evolution would you expect from the formation of a mole of liquid water from atomic hydrogen and oxygen?

7.9 Apply the general first law with mass flow as given in Eq. 7.49 to
   (a) the Bernoulli flow of a liquid through a horizontal tube with a constriction at its middle, and
   (b) the Rossini-Frandsen apparatus, Fig. 5.9, used in the study of the internal energy of real gases.

7.10 Apply Kirchhoff's heat capacity formula, Eq. 7.47, to the constant-pressure reaction

$$H_2 \;+\; \tfrac{1}{2}O_2 \rightarrow \quad H_2O$$
$$\text{(gas)} \quad \text{(gas)} \quad \text{(liquid)}$$

Using a temperature of, say, 500°K, determine whether the heat of the reaction increases or decreases with temperature. Find the rate.

7.11 Show that at the triple point
$$\lambda_{31} = \lambda_{32} + \lambda_{21}$$

CHAPTER EIGHT

Heat Engines
and the Second Law

8.1 Heat Engines

A heat engine is any device that is able to absorb heat, convert more or less of it into useful external work, and repeat this performance indefinitely. Many systems that can absorb heat and perform external work are not heat engines. A compressed gas may expand and do work at the expense of its internal energy, a liquid may evaporate and push back a piston, a firecracker may explode and push back the atmosphere, etc. But such systems cannot repeat this process over and over and are therefore not heat engines as defined.

Suppose that we have a cylinder of compressed gas at room temperature. If it is provided with a tight-fitting piston, we might insulate the system and allow it to expand slowly along an adiabatic from 1 to 2 (Fig. 8.1) and thus cool itself from room temperature, T_1, to a lower temperature, T_2. We might next add heat to the cylinder or allow heat to flow into the gas from the atmosphere until the temperature rises to the original one ($2 \rightarrow 3$). Here a temperature rise occurs at constant volume, and no work is involved. To make these two processes capable of repetition, we must return the system to its starting point, 1. We cannot do this without doing work on the gas. Once the gas has been compressed back to point 1, we have achieved a closed cycle that can be repeated as often as desired. But it is clear that we do more work on the system in returning it from 3 to 1 than it furnishes us in expanding from 1 to 2. In other words, the counterclockwise cycle actually *requires* work for its execution.

If, however, we compress the gas isothermally at the lower temperature, T_2, from 2 to, say, 4 and thereafter allow it to warm isochorically to 1, the objection is removed, and a work-producing cycle is achieved. This cycle, 1241, differs fundamentally from 1231 in another way. It requires us to have a body at or below the lower temperature, T_2, to receive the heat, Q_T, rejected on isothermal compression. Had the cylinder simply been insulated on the compression, the gas would have returned along $2 \rightarrow 1$, giving us a collapsed or

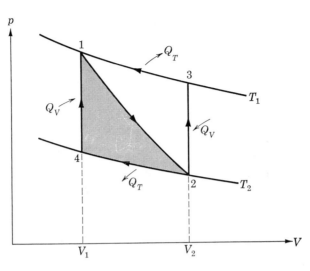

FIGURE **8.1**

no-work cycle. Thus a reservoir below room temperatures is essential for the operation of such a working cycle.

Examination of all heat engines shows the reservoir requirement to be a common property. For work to be produced out of heat continuously, that is, in a cyclic process that can be repeated at will, there must be at least *two* heat reservoirs at *different* temperatures. Reservoirs from which heat is taken are called heat *sources*, whereas those to which heat is rejected are called heat *sinks*. In an actual engine, of course, there may be a succession or continuous array of heat sources and sinks, but in no case can the engine operate without at least two, one of each type.

We notice further that a refrigerating cycle, which the original triangular cycle (1231) actually represents, can always begin to operate with only one reservoir, the sink into which the heat is rejected (here the atmosphere at T_1). Then the heat absorbed along $2 \rightarrow 3$ can produce local cooling below T_1 in some small subregion of the larger surrounding system.

The impossibility of producing useful work without sources and sinks at finite temperature differences and the impossibility of producing local refrigeration without external sources of work may be taken as equivalent bases of the second law of thermodynamics. Obviously these considerations involve information quite different from that supplied by the first law. We shall return to them later in the chapter, after examining the efficiency of a few heat engines by use of the first law alone.

8.2 Thermal Efficiency

We saw in Sec. 4.13 that by the first law the net external work performed during a reversible cycle was always exactly equal to the net heat absorbed by the system. Indicating the numerical value of this work by W, we have

$$W = -\oint dW_C = \oint dQ_C = \text{net heat absorbed by the system}$$

the heat integral representing the excess of heat taken in over heat rejected.
If we set

$$Q_1 = \text{heat absorbed (from one or more sources)}$$

and $\qquad Q_2 = \text{heat rejected (to one or more sinks)}$

where Q_1 and Q_2 are both taken as positive, then we have

$$W = Q_1 - Q_2$$

The thermal efficiency, η, is then defined as

$$\eta = \text{thermal efficiency} = \frac{\text{net output of useful work}}{\text{heat input}}$$

where, of course, the same energy units are understood throughout. Thus

$$\eta = \frac{W}{Q_1} = \frac{Q_1 - Q_2}{Q_1} = 1 - \frac{Q_2}{Q_1} \tag{8.1}$$

As long as *any* heat whatsoever is rejected, Q_2/Q_1 is finite, and $\eta < 1$. Consequently, we must always expect efficiencies less than 100%, since no cycle has ever been realized that does not involve some heat rejection to at least one sink.

Returning to the cycle 1241 of Fig. 8.1, let us calculate η. This we may do readily if we take the gas to be, say, air, treat it as an ideal gas, and assume that its heat capacity, C_V, is constant along the path $4 \rightarrow 1$. We may calculate W by integrating $p \, dV$ around the cycle and obtain η by dividing the result by Q_1. We may also obtain η directly from Q_1 and Q_2. Using the latter course, we proceed to find Q_1 and Q_2.

$$Q_1 = Q_V = \int_{T_4}^{T_1} C_V \, dT = C_V(T_1 - T_2)$$

since $T_4 = T_2$.

Likewise, for the isothermal path $2 \rightarrow 4$,

$$Q_2 = Q_T = \int_2^4 dU + \int_2^4 p \, dV = \int_2^4 p \, dV$$

since dU vanishes along an isotherm. From the ideal gas law

$$Q_T = RT_2 \ln \frac{V_4}{V_2}$$

and therefore numerically

$$Q_2 = RT_2 \ln \frac{V_2}{V_4} = RT_2 \ln \frac{V_2}{V_1}$$

Since path $1 \rightarrow 2$ is an adiabatic,

$$\frac{T_1}{T_2} = \left(\frac{V_2}{V_1}\right)^{\gamma-1}$$

or

$$\frac{V_2}{V_1} = \left(\frac{T_1}{T_2}\right)^{1/(\gamma-1)}$$

and consequently

$$\ln \frac{V_2}{V_1} = \frac{1}{\gamma - 1} \ln \frac{T_1}{T_2}$$

Thus

$$\eta = 1 - \frac{RT_2 \ln T_1/T_2}{C_V(\gamma - 1)(T_1 - T_2)} \tag{8.2}$$

But since

$$C_p = C_V + R$$

and

$$\gamma - 1 = \frac{R}{C_V}$$

finally

$$\eta = 1 - \frac{T_2 \ln \dfrac{T_1}{T_2}}{T_1 - T_2} \tag{8.3}$$

If, for example, we take $T_1 = 350°C$ and $T_2 = 300°C$,

$$\eta = 1 - \frac{300}{50} \ln \frac{350}{300} = 1 - \frac{46.2}{50.0} = 0.075$$

or the efficiency is only 7.5%. The rejected heat is 92.5% of Q_1, and the only way we can reduce this proportion is to make T_1 as high and T_2 as low as possible (this procedure increases $T_1 - T_2$ more rapidly than it does the logarithmic term).

Although no practical engine has a cycle made up of three parts only, requirements similar to those just discussed apply for all engines. Since the lowest temperature cannot be reduced economically below that of the surroundings, we can only raise T_1. This high temperature can be produced in a furnace outside the engine or by an explosion inside the engine itself. The first method, of course, is represented by the steam engine, and the second by the internal combustion engine, in which gasoline is exploded or heavy oil burned inside the working cylinder.

8.3 Idealized Engine Cycles

In order to give anything like a general account of engines, we must make a number of approximations and simplifications. Otherwise, the theory would be burdened with a plethora of specific details of particular types of heat engines. We are thus forced to invent idealized cycles that represent simplified approximations to what goes on in actual engines but that provide universal theoretical upper limits to the work output and efficiency of these engines. The approximations may be summarized as follows:

Reversible Cycles.   These cycles are quasistatic and can be plotted in any plane we choose, say, the p-V plane. All friction, both that internal in the working substance and that between moving surfaces, is neglected. Such engines, of course, have to operate infinitely slowly, receive their heat reversibly, reject all heat reversibly, etc. Since real engines must operate at high speeds, they are subject to turbulences, pressure drops due to friction in pipes, valves, etc., dynamic effects due to accelerations and decelerations, heat flows through finite gradients—literally a host of irreversible effects.

Single Pure Substance as Working Substance.   In the steam engine, we actually do have a single substance, water, throughout the cycle. It does, of course, exist as liquid water, as steam, and as a mixture of these in various parts of the cycle. In the internal combustion engine, on the other hand, the working substance includes, in turn, pure air, the mixture to be burned or exploded, and the combustion products and residues mixed with air. Since the mole fraction of air is predominant at all times, the idealized cycle is carried out with pure air and becomes the "air standard cycle."

Ideal Gas.   Since the properties of ideal gases are so simple, this approximation is almost universal. It is further assumed that over the ranges of temperature involved both C_p and C_V are independent of temperature. Thus γ is a constant, and all adiabatics can be represented by

$$pV^\gamma = K$$

or
$$TV^{\gamma-1} = K'$$

where the constants may readily be evaluated by substitution of known values of the coordinates of points on the curves.

Infinite Reservoirs.   If we assume that all heat sources and sinks are infinite in extent and that therefore no finite heat additions or losses alter the reservoir temperatures, we may conclude that all heat interchanges take place reversibly at well-defined temperatures.

When the system in Fig. 8.1 is warmed through a finite interval along the path $4 \rightarrow 1$, we assume an array of reservoirs differing infinitesimally in temperature from one to the next and forming a continuous sequence from T_2 to T_1. The reception of heat from each of these in turn as the system warms from T_2 to T_1 ensures that the whole process will take place reversibly. Such reversible heat additions will be used to represent the temperature rise produced in all internal combustions, as well as the temperature fall that occurs when an exhaust is opened and the exhaust gas is cooled by sudden expansion.

A great many cycles with four effective parts or steps have been proposed, the parts being taken from sets of adiabatics, isobars, isochores, and isotherms. Five such cycles are sketched in Fig. 8.2 in the p-V plane so that isobars are horizontal and isochores are vertical. Of these five, only the Carnot cycle employs isotherms. The Otto cycle results when the two isobars of the Joule

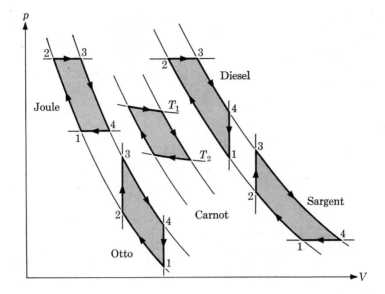

FIGURE **8.2**

cycle are changed to isochores. The Diesel and Sargent cycles differ only in the
order of execution of the isochores and isobars.

8.4 The Gasoline Engine

The Otto cycle executed with pure air is the idealization of the gasoline engine
cycle. Fig. 8.3 shows the detailed cycle, which proceeds in the order 0123410
and thus consists of six parts. Of these six parts, only four involve any motion

FIGURE **8.3**

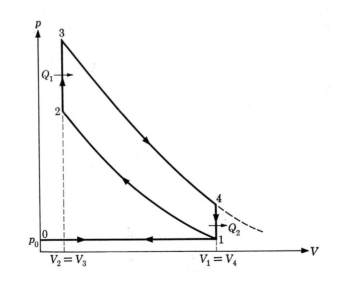

of the piston, and these are called *strokes*. The six parts of the cycle follow, in order:

$0 \to 1$ *Input stroke*. The gasoline-air mixture is slowly drawn in from the outside at a constant pressure taken as exactly equal to the external atmospheric pressure, p_0.

$1 \to 2$ *Compression stroke*. The piston, with the intake valve closed, compresses the gas adiabatically from V_1 to V_2. The temperature rises accordingly from T_1 to T_2.

$2 \to 3$ *Explosion*. The spark at 2 explodes the mixture, and the temperature rises rapidly to a high value. This change takes place so rapidly that the piston is unable to move significantly during the process, which is therefore idealized as strictly isochoric. In this idealization the actual rise in temperature from T_2 to T_3 is brought about by the reversible addition of heat, Q_1, from a suitable set of external reservoirs.

$3 \to 4$ *Power stroke*. The hot mixture expands, driving the piston back until the volume has reached $V_4 (= V_1)$ once more. This change is treated as a strictly adiabatic expansion, with no heat lost to or gained from the walls by the expanding gas (now pure air).

$4 \to 1$ *Valve exhaust*. At 4 the exhaust port opens, and the combustion products are allowed to expand to the external pressure, p_0. This sudden expansion is taken as isochoric, the actual adiabatic temperature fall being replaced by an equivalent reversible heat loss, Q_2, to another set of external reservoirs.

$1 \to 0$ *Exhaust stroke*. The piston now forces most of the remaining exhaust gases out of the cylinder. In the ideal cycle the slow reversible exhaust stroke occurs at the same pressure as the intake stroke, and the two strokes cancel, leaving the net work the area of the cycle.

The precise details of each step in the cycle of an actual engine are so complicated as to defy analysis and, of course, change with speed, settings of valves, richness of the mixture, etc., precluding any general account of the cycle. By the preceding rather drastic simplifications, however, the dynamic problem is reduced to a thermostatic one, which is readily solvable.

8.5   The Air Standard Otto Cycle

The closed cycle, 12341, of Fig. 8.3 executed reversibly with a constant mass of pure air as the sole working substance was proposed by Otto as the theoretical prototype of the gasoline engine cycle. When the air is further treated as a simple diatomic ideal gas of constant heat capacity, we have the *air standard Otto cycle*.

Let us determine the thermal efficiency of this cycle. Since the mass of air is constant, we may for simplicity take it as 1 mole. Then the temperature rise T_2 to T_3 is brought about by the reversible addition of heat, Q_1, where

$$Q_1 = \int_{T_2}^{T_3} C_V \, dT = C_V(T_3 - T_2)$$

Similarly, the absolute amount of heat rejected, Q_2, during the valve exhaust is given as that necessary to warm the air at constant volume from T_1 to T_4. Thus

$$Q_2 = \int_{T_1}^{T_4} C_V \, dT = C_V(T_4 - T_1)$$

and the thermal efficiency becomes

$$\eta = 1 - \frac{Q_2}{Q_1} = 1 - \frac{(T_4 - T_1)}{(T_3 - T_2)} \tag{8.4}$$

For adiabatics such as $3 \to 4$ and $1 \to 2$, $TV^{\gamma-1} = K'$, and therefore

$$T_4 V_4{}^{\gamma-1} = T_3 V_3{}^{\gamma-1}$$

and

$$T_1 V_1{}^{\gamma-1} = T_2 V_2{}^{\gamma-1}$$

Subtracting gives

$$(T_4 - T_1)V_1{}^{\gamma-1} = (T_3 - T_2)V_2{}^{\gamma-1}$$

since $V_1 = V_4$ and $V_2 = V_3$. Thus finally

$$\frac{(T_4 - T_1)}{(T_3 - T_2)} = \left(\frac{V_2}{V_1}\right)^{\gamma-1} = \frac{1}{r^{\gamma-1}} \tag{8.5}$$

where $r = V_1/V_2$ is the so-called *compression* ratio (which could equally well be called the expansion ratio). Use of Eq. 8.5 reduces Eq. 8.4 at once to

$$\eta = 1 - \frac{1}{r^{\gamma-1}} \tag{8.6}$$

Obviously the larger the compression ratio, the greater the efficiency. If r is made too great in practice, however, the mixture is heated to the ignition point before 2 is reached, and preignition occurs. This is destructive of engine bearings and wasteful of power and is accordingly to be avoided. Taking 5 as a working value of r and $\gamma = 1.4$ for pure air,

$$\eta = 1 - \frac{1}{5^{0.4}} = 1 - 0.52 = 0.48$$

This efficiency of 48 % is, of course, a theoretical upper limit, and no real engine will be expected to attain it. With $r = 5$ the actual brake efficiency will probably be nearer 20 to 30 %.

8.6 The Air Standard Diesel Cycle

The idealized Diesel cycle is shown on a large scale in Fig. 8.4. As in the Otto cycle, the intake and exhaust strokes, $0 \to 1$ and $1 \to 0$, cancel, leaving only the closed four-part cycle. In this engine pure air is drawn in during the intake, $0 \to 1$, and compressed adiabatically to a temperature, T_2, at 2 such that when the fuel is sprayed in it ignites, producing expansion from 2 to 3 (here idealized as isobaric). At 3 the combustion is finished, and the mixture expands to 4, an expansion regarded as truly adiabatic. At 4 the exhaust port

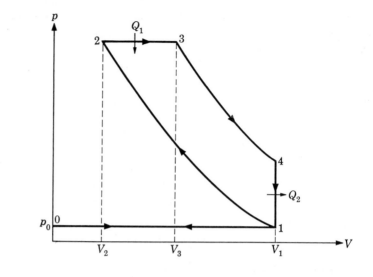

FIGURE **8.4**

opens, with a resultant drop in temperature to T_1 at 1, and finally the exhaust stroke clears the cylinder of most of the products of combustion. The idealized reversible cycle with pure air treated as an ideal gas with constant heat capacities constitutes the *air standard Diesel cycle.*

Since heat is added at constant pressure from $2 \rightarrow 3$, we write

$$Q_1 = \int_{T_2}^{T_3} C_p \, dT = C_p(T_3 - T_2)$$

As in the Otto cycle,

$$Q_2 = \int_{T_1}^{T_4} C_V \, dT = C_V(T_4 - T_1)$$

Thus

$$\eta = 1 - \frac{(T_4 - T_1)}{\gamma(T_3 - T_2)} \tag{8.7}$$

To translate Eq. 8.7 into an expression involving only volume ratios, we express all the other temperatures in terms of the lowest, T_1. Starting with the compression ratio,

$$r = \frac{V_1}{V_2}$$

we write for the lower adiabatic

$$T_2 V_2^{\gamma-1} = T_1 V_1^{\gamma-1}$$

or
$$T_2 = r^{\gamma-1} T_1 \tag{8.8}$$

Since 2 and 3 are at the same pressure,

$$\frac{T_3}{T_2} = \frac{V_3}{V_2} = r_{\text{cut}} \tag{8.9}$$

Here r_{cut} is a new ratio, the so-called *cutoff* ratio, defined as V_3/V_2. Then, by Eqs. 8.8 and 8.9,

$$T_3 = r_{cut}r^{\gamma-1}T_1 \tag{8.10}$$

Finally, for the upper adiabatic,

$$T_4V_4{}^{\gamma-1} = T_3V_3{}^{\gamma-1}$$

or, from Eq. 8.10 and the definitions of r and r_{cut},

$$T_4 = r_{cut}^{\gamma}T_1 \tag{8.11}$$

Insertion of the expressions for T_2, T_3, and T_4 in Eq. 8.7 gives

$$\eta = 1 - \frac{1}{r^{\gamma-1}}\left[\frac{(r_{cut}^{\gamma} - 1)}{\gamma(r_{cut} - 1)}\right] \tag{8.12}$$

This result is the expression for the efficiency of the Otto cycle, Eq. 8.6, except for the factor in brackets. In practice, r_{cut} is so much larger than unity that this factor always exceeds unity, despite the γ in the denominator. Thus Diesel cycles are less efficient than Otto cycles with the same compression ratio. However, much higher compression ratios are possible in the Diesel cycle. Preignition cannot occur, the adiabatic heating on compression being depended on to produce the necessary ignition temperature. Consequently, actual Diesel cycles tend to be more efficient than Otto cycles.

As an exmple, let $r = 14$ and $r_{cut} = 5$.

Then
$$\eta = 1 - \frac{1}{14^{0.4}}\left[\frac{5^{1.4} - 1}{1.4(5 - 1)}\right] = 0.495$$

As noted before, the efficiency of the actual engine is much below this theoretical upper limit (49.5%) but may well be 30 to 35%.

8.7   Carnot's Principle

Although an expression for η has been obtained for each of the cycles discussed, no general criteria have been provided that indicate why one cycle utilizes its heat more efficiently than another.

Sadi Carnot in his famous treatise on "The Motive Power of Heat" (1824) was the first to state the essential requirements for highest efficiency. Recognizing reversible cycles as better than nonreversible cycles, he was able to show that establishment of a general criterion of engine efficiency demanded the use of the minimum number of heat reservoirs, namely, two. Accordingly, heat can be absorbed only along the *higher* isotherm, and none may be rejected except along the *lower* isotherm. Thus the Carnot cycle consists of *two isotherms* connected by *two adiabatics* to form a closed four-part reversible cycle. With this cycle in mind, Carnot stated his famous principle: "Given an engine that is *reversible* and that operates between *two* fixed temperatures. Then no other engine operating between these same temperatures *can exceed* this engine in efficiency."

We shall take Carnot's principle as our first statement of the second law and designate it as form IIA. The proof of this principle follows from the empirical observation that all heat engines, whatever their nature, always withdraw heat from a hot reservoir and reject unusable heat to a cold reservoir. Thus the former tends to cool, and the latter to warm, and no case has ever been observed in which the reverse effect occurred, that is, the heating of the *hot* reservoir and the cooling of the *cold* one.

With Carnot's principle in mind, we arrange two heat engines to operate between two common reservoirs as in Fig. 8.5. Let one engine be a reversible engine, R, and let the other be any engine, A, that we wish to compare with it. Let the two efficiencies be indicated by η_R and η_A, respectively.

If the reversible engine absorbs Q_1 at T_1 and rejects Q_2 at T_2,

$$\eta_R = \frac{Q_1 - Q_2}{Q_1} = \frac{W}{Q_1}$$

where W is the work delivered per cycle. Now suppose that the other engine is of such a size that it absorbs Q_1', rejects Q_2', and delivers exactly the same amount of work per cycle as the reversible engine. (This provision is not essential to the argument but merely makes it simpler.) Then

$$\eta_A = \frac{Q_1' - Q_2'}{Q_1'} = \frac{W}{Q_1'}$$

We wish to show that

$$\eta_A \not> \eta_R$$

This we do by assuming that the contrary is true and proving that the assumption leads to a contradiction with experience. We assume that in fact

$$\eta_A > \eta_R$$

Now we arrange for the reversible engine to run backward, driven by the

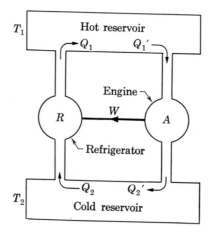

FIGURE **8.5**

work, W, delivered by the other engine running forward. Since the reversible engine *is* reversible, the magnitudes of Q_1 and Q_2 do not alter, but Q_2 is now withdrawn from the cooler reservoir, and Q_1 rejected to the hotter reservoir.

Since by assumption $\eta_A > \eta_R$,

$$\frac{W}{Q_1'} > \frac{W}{Q_1}$$

or

$$Q_1 > Q'_1$$

which means that $Q_1 - Q_1'$ units of heat are gained by the hot reservoir per cycle of this combination. We thus have a thermal device that, without aid from outside, causes the hot reservoir to gain heat at the expense of the cold reservoir. Since such a process is contrary to experience, we conclude that our original assumption is impossible and that in fact

$$\eta_A \leq \eta_R$$

Therefore, no heat engine can *exceed* in efficiency the reversible heat engine operating between two given reservoirs.

Of course, if the upper sign of the inequality holds, $\eta_A < \eta_R$. Then $Q_1 < Q_1'$, and in each cycle the hot reservoir loses net heat of an amount equal to $Q_1' - Q_1$ to the cold reservoir. There is no law of nature to prevent heat from running from a high temperature to a low temperature. In fact, this transfer would be brought about normally by conduction and radiation, without our engine-refrigerator system's being necessary at all.

Only in the event that $Q_1' = Q_1$ does the net heat extracted from the hot reservoir (and that rejected to the cold reservoir) vanish. In this case T_1 and T_2 remain constant, a condition that again is, in principle, possible and equivalent to having the two reservoirs insulated from one another. Since engine A has precisely the same operating efficiency as the reversible engine, it must have no avoidable heat losses and must be in all respects equivalent to the reversible engine. Thus it too must be reversible.

Any engine that executes a Carnot cycle reversibly is called a *Carnot* engine. Expressing the second law in form A, then, is equivalent to stating that for a given pair of reservoirs all Carnot engines have the same efficiency, an efficiency exceeded by no other engine, whatever its nature.

8.8   Carnot's Theorem

Since no account was taken in the preceding section of the detailed nature of the Carnot engine, we may assume that it is immaterial to the argument. To have the same efficiency, two engines need only to be reversible and to utilize the same temperatures, T_1 and T_2. We conclude therefore that the efficiency must be some universal function of T_1 and T_2; that is,

$$\eta_R = \eta_R(T_1, T_2) \tag{8.13}$$

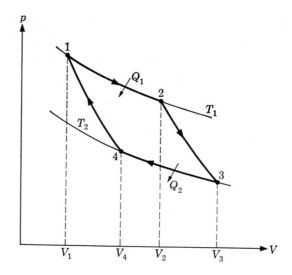

FIGURE **8.6**

where $\eta_R(T_1, T_2)$ is the so-called Carnot function. If this function can be evaluated for a Carnot engine with some particular working substance, the result must hold for all Carnot engines. The working substance with the simplest properties is, of course, the ideal gas, and the calculations take the simplest form for it.

Imagine a reversible engine using an ideal gas and operating in a Carnot cycle. Since the amount of gas is immaterial, let it be taken as a gram-mole. According to Fig. 8.6, the desired cycle is 12341, in which the steps are as follows:

$1 \rightarrow 2$ Isothermal absorption of heat Q_1 at T_1.
$2 \rightarrow 3$ Adiabatic expansion from 2 to 3, cooling the gas from T_1 to T_2.
$3 \rightarrow 4$ Isothermal rejection of heat Q_2 at T_2.
$4 \rightarrow 1$ Adiabatic compression from 4 to 1, heating the gas from T_2 back to T_1.

Since $W = Q_1 - Q_2$, the efficiency becomes

$$\eta_R = 1 - \frac{Q_2}{Q_1}$$

Just as in the discussion in Sec. 8.2, the heat absorption, Q_T, for an isothermal change from V_i to V_e in an ideal gas is always

$$Q_T = \int_i^e dQ_T = \int_i^e dU + \int_i^e p\, dV = RT \ln \frac{V_e}{V_i}$$

Therefore,

$$Q_1 = RT_1 \ln \frac{V_2}{V_1}$$

and

$$Q_2 = RT_2 \ln \frac{V_3}{V_4}$$

since Q_2 is simply the magnitude of the rejected heat.

Thus
$$\eta_R = 1 - \frac{T_2 \ln \dfrac{V_3}{V_4}}{T_1 \ln \dfrac{V_2}{V_1}} \tag{8.14}$$

Of course, 1 and 4 are on the same adiabatic, as are 2 and 3. Using the adiabatic law as before, we have

$$T_1 V_1{}^{\gamma-1} = T_2 V_4{}^{\gamma-1}$$

and
$$T_1 V_2{}^{\gamma-1} = T_2 V_3{}^{\gamma-1}$$

On division the temperatures cancel, and

$$\frac{V_2}{V_1} = \frac{V_3}{V_4}$$

Consequently, the logarithmetic terms in Eq. 8.14 cancel, leaving

$$\eta_R = 1 - \frac{T_2}{T_1} = \frac{T_1 - T_2}{T_1} \tag{8.15}$$

Carnot's function has been evaluated, and the result may be taken as another form of the second law. We shall refer to this as form IIB.

It is at once clear why no engine can ever have a thermal efficiency of 100%. Such an efficiency would require a cold reservoir at 0°K. Since this possibility is impractical, we can only raise the efficiency by making T_2 as low and T_1 as high as possible. It is also apparent why calorie for calorie the Otto and Diesel cycles utilize the heat they take in less efficiently than if all the heat were absorbed at the *highest* temperature and all waste heat were eliminated at the *lowest* temperature in the cycle. Furthermore, if we did have two fixed reservoirs at, say, T_1 and T_2, for the Otto and Diesel cycles, neither cycle would be reversible. Each would involve direct flow of heat through finite temperature differences, a situation that is essentially irreversible. Thus the Carnot engine emerges as the *only* one that can operate *reversibly between two single reservoirs*. It is in this sense unique. (See Problem 8.9.)

8.9   Clausius' Statement of the Second Law

Clausius, in his statement of the second law, chose to emphasize the essential difference between the natural (and, in fact, well-nigh unavoidable) tendency of heat to flow from a hot body to a cold body and the unnatural aspects of passage in the opposite direction. His statement, which we shall designate form IIC, reads: "It is natural for heat to flow from high temperatures to low temperatures, but no *self-acting* and *cyclic* device exists that can cause heat to pass from a cold body to a hot body."

This may be paraphrased to say that although heat naturally flows down-hill (that is, down a temperature gradient), it will not of itself flow uphill (that is, up a temperature gradient). Both of the limitations that appear in italics are essential. If we omitted the *self-acting* restriction, an ordinary household refrigerator would be an obvious exception to the law, since it does cause heat to pass from the cold interior to the hotter outside. The *cyclic* restriction is necessary because numerous devices could be arranged to cause the transfer of a small finite amount of heat from any one body to another initially hotter body. However, they could not repeat the performance over and over again without being cyclic and requiring outside assistance.

The proof of Clausius' statement follows from the arrangement (Fig. 8.5) used to establish Carnot's principle. If the system consisting of engine A and the reversed Carnot engine is insulated from the outside world, when $\eta_A < \eta_R$, heat is transferred from the hotter reservoir to the colder reservoir, which is natural. This transfer can be reduced to zero only by making engine A reversible. To *reverse* the direction of net heat flow so that it would proceed from the cold reservoir to the hot reservoir would require efficiencies greater than Carnot efficiencies. Hence Clausius' result holds.

8.10   The Second Law According to Kelvin and Planck

Lord Kelvin formulated another statement, as follows: "It is impossible to construct any cyclic device that can extract useful work from an isothermal system."

This result, form IID of the second law, follows from form IIB of Carnot,

FIGURE **8.7**

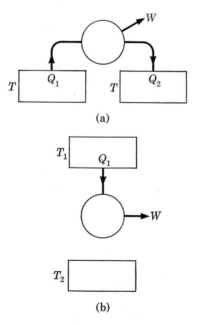

(a)

(b)

since the efficiency of a Carnot engine depends directly on the value of the temperature difference, ΔT, between its heat source and its sink. If $\Delta T = 0$, then the efficiency vanishes. See Fig. 8.7(a).

A variation of Kelvin's statement was favored by Planck: "It is impossible to construct a cyclic device that can extract heat from a reservoir and produce no other thermal effects whatever." This represents form IIE of the second law.

As Fig. 8.7(b) indicates, a device that absorbs heat, Q_1, at T_1 and rejects none to a reservoir at a lower temperature must convert it all into work by the first law. By form IID of the second law such a device, which would be able to operate in an isothermal system since it would require only a single reservoir, is not possible. Thus form IID implies form IIE; that is to say, form IID is a sufficient condition for the truth of form IIE.

8.11   Criteria for Equivalence

In general, to establish the equivalence of two principles or propositions, we must prove two things. We must show that the truth of the first principle is both (1) a *sufficient* condition and (2) a *necessary* condition for the truth of the second. Then the two principles or theorems are equivalent, and an argument may be made to depend on either at will.

As an example, consider the equivalence of Lord Kelvin's (IID) and Planck's (IIE) statements of the second law. The first part of Sec. 8.10 establishes that IID is *sufficient* to guarantee the truth of IIE, since IIE follows from IID.

To establish the second condition, that IID is *necessary* for the truth of IIE, we proceed as follows. We show that if IID is *false*, then IIE is also false; that is, the truth of IID is required to make IIE true. If we assume IID to be false, we have a device, Fig. 8.7(a), which, although operating in an isothermal system (that is, without a cold reservoir), delivers work. Such a device contradicts IIE. Thus the falseness of IID implies the falseness of IIE, and the equivalence is established.

The corresponding proof for the two statements IIC and IID brings up these interesting points:

1. IIC is *sufficient* to establish the truth of IID. This condition was demonstrated in the discussion of IIC in Sec. 8.9, since the truth of IIC implies the truth of IIA, which in turn leads to IIB and thence to IID.

2. IIC is *necessary* for the truth of IID. To show that this condition applies, we assume that IIC is false. If IIC is false, we can have a refrigerator that operates without external work input. Such a refrigerator is illustrated at the left in Fig. 8.8(a), drawing heat, Q_2, from the cold reservoir and pumping it into the hot reservoir without requiring any work for its operation. At the right of the refrigerator, drawing heat from the hot reservoir, is a heat engine, which delivers work, W, to the outside world and which is of such size as to deliver heat of the amount Q_2 to the cold reservoir.

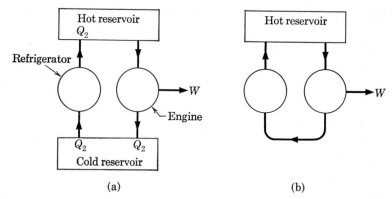

FIGURE **8.8**

Since Q_2 is just the heat absorbed by the refrigerator, we may eliminate the cold reservoir altogether and connect the engine exhaust directly to the refrigerator intake [Fig. 8.8(b)]. This procedure gives us a device that operates from a single reservoir and delivers work to the outside world. Such a device, of course, contradicts IID. Thus the falseness of IIC implies the falseness of IID, and the equivalence is established.

8.12   The Carnot Refrigerator

In a Carnot refrigerator, indicated schematically in Fig. 8.9, we have

Q_2 = heat absorbed from a cold reservoir at T_2
Q_1 = heat rejected to a hot reservoir at T_1
W = net work required from the outside (a positive number)

Since the process is cyclic, the first law becomes

$$Q_2 - Q_1 = -W$$
or
$$Q_1 = Q_2 + W$$

which means simply that the heat rejected to the hot reservoir is the sum of

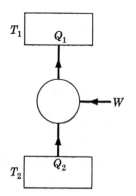

FIGURE **8.9**

the heat abstracted from the cold reservoir and the work used to run the device.

In measuring the performance of a refrigerator, it is convenient to use the so-called coefficient of performance, K_{ref}, where

$$K_{ref} = \begin{pmatrix} \text{coefficient of} \\ \text{performance as} \\ \text{a refrigerator} \end{pmatrix} = \frac{Q_2}{W} \qquad (8.16)$$

or the heat removed from the body being cooled per unit of work input. For any refrigerator

$$K_{ref} = \frac{Q_2}{Q_1 - Q_2}$$

From form IIB of the second law, for a Carnot engine, we can always write

$$\frac{Q_1 - Q_2}{Q_1} = \frac{T_1 - T_2}{T_1}$$

or

$$\frac{Q_2}{Q_1 - Q_2} = \frac{T_2}{T_1 - T_2}$$

Thus for a Carnot refrigerator

$$(K_{ref})_{Carnot} = \frac{T_2}{T_1 - T_2} = \frac{T_2}{\Delta T} \qquad (8.17)$$

The coefficient of performance increases as T_2 is made *high* and as the temperature interval through which the heat must be raised is made *small*.

In so-called heat pump applications, we are interested not so much in Q_2 as in Q_1, the total amount of heat that we succeed in "pumping" into the hot reservoir. In this connection, a heat pump coefficient, K_{hp}, is defined, where

$$K_{hp} = \begin{pmatrix} \text{coefficient} \\ \text{of performance} \\ \text{as a heat pump} \end{pmatrix} = \frac{Q_1}{W}$$

For a reversed Carnot cycle this becomes

$$(K_{hp})_{Carnot} = \frac{T_1}{T_1 - T_2} = \frac{T_1}{\Delta T} = (K_{ref})_{Carnot} + 1 \qquad (8.18)$$

This coefficient increases as the upper temperature, T_1, is raised and the interval, ΔT, through which the heat must be elevated is reduced. The use of these results will be illustrated in the next section.

8.13   Kelvin's Thermodynamic Heating

Kelvin[1] was the first to point out the thermodynamic wastefulness of burning fuel for direct heating of a house. It is much more economical to use the

---

[1] Thomson, *Proc. Roy. Phil. Soc. (Glasgow)*, **3**, 269 (1852); and J. Larmor, ed., *Mathematical and Physical Papers of Lord Kelvin*, Cambridge Univ. Press, Cambridge, 1911, Vol. 5, pp. 124–33.

high-temperature heat produced by combustion in a heat engine and then to use the work so developed to pump heat from outdoors up to the temperature desired in the house. In Fig. 8.10 a boiler furnishes heat, Q_1, at a high temperature, T_1. This heat is absorbed by a heat engine, which extracts work, W, and rejects the waste heat, Q_2, into the house at T_2. The work, W, is in turn used to operate a mechanical refrigerator or heat pump, which extracts Q_3 from the outdoors at temperature T_3 and rejects Q_2' (where $Q_2' = W + Q_3$) into the house.

As a result of this cycle of operations, a total quantity of heat equal to $Q_2 + Q_2'$ is liberated in the house, as against Q_1, which would be provided directly by the ordinary combustion of the fuel. Thus the ratio

$$\frac{Q_2 + Q_2'}{Q_1}$$

represents the heat multiplication factor of this method. To calculate it, we need only express Q_2 and Q_2' in terms of Q_1.

To find Q_2, we merely rewrite Carnot's theorem,

$$\frac{W}{Q_1} = \frac{Q_1 - Q_2}{Q_1} = \frac{T_1 - T_2}{T_1}$$

as

$$1 - \frac{Q_2}{Q_1} = 1 - \frac{T_2}{T_1}$$

or

$$Q_2 = Q_1 \left(\frac{T_2}{T_1}\right) \tag{8.19}$$

The work, W, delivered by the Carnot engine is defined by

$$W = Q_1 \frac{\Delta T}{T_1} \tag{8.20}$$

where $\Delta T = T_1 - T_2$, the temperature drop between the boiler and the house.

To find Q_2', we need the coefficient of performance of a refrigerator used as a heat pump, K_{hp}. From the definition of K_{hp} in Eq. 8.18, we obtain

$$K_{hp} = \frac{Q_2'}{W} = \frac{T_2}{\Delta T'} \tag{8.21}$$

where $\Delta T' = T_2 - T_3$, the difference between the temperature of the room and that of the outdoors.

Eliminating W from Eqs. 8.20 and 8.21 to obtain Q_2' and using the value of Q_2 from Eq. 8.19 gives for the ratio we seek

$$\left(\begin{array}{c} \text{heat} \\ \text{multiplication} \\ \text{factor} \end{array}\right) = \frac{T_2}{T_1}\left(1 + \frac{\Delta T}{\Delta T'}\right) \tag{8.22}$$

In this expression the ratio T_2/T_1, of the room temperature to the boiler temperature, is less than unity, but the ratio of the two temperature intervals,

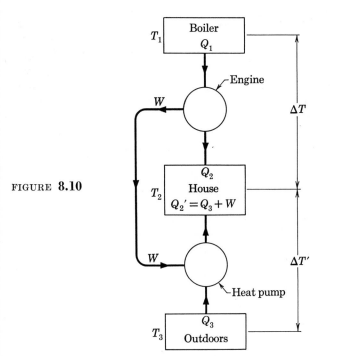

FIGURE **8.10**

$\Delta T / \Delta T'$, can be so much larger than unity that a large theoretical multiplication factor results.

As an example, let us take the following hypothetical values:

$$
\begin{aligned}
T_1 &= 273 + 200 = 473°\text{K} \\
T_2 &= 273 + 20 = 293°\text{K} \\
T_3 &= 273°\text{K} \\
\Delta T &= 180°\text{K} \\
\Delta T' &= 20°\text{K}
\end{aligned}
$$

The result is

$$
\begin{pmatrix} \text{heat} \\ \text{multiplication} \\ \text{factor} \end{pmatrix} = \frac{293}{473}\left(1 + \frac{180}{20}\right) = 6.2
$$

which means that every ton of coal burned would deliver the heat equivalent of over 6 tons. Of course, in an actual case the efficiencies would be less than Carnot efficiencies, but even with a reduction of 50%, the possible savings would be noteworthy.[2]

---

[2] For details of actual installations, as well as a bibliography of the extensive literature, see the publications of Penrod and his colleagues, notably, Penrod, *Kentucky Univ. Eng. Exp. Sta. Bull.*, No. 4 (1947); *Trans. Kentucky Acad. Sci.*, **13**, 1 (1949).

8.14   Various Carnot Cycles

We have seen that the Carnot cycle is essentially a cycle involving two isotherms and two adiabatics. Any system, whether a simple gas, a liquid, a
chemical system, or a magnetic or electrical system, can, in principle, be
taken through such a cycle. When the cycle is executed reversibly, the efficiency is at once the same for all systems and given by the Carnot function,
$\eta_R = (T_1 - T_2)/T_1$. The particular shape of the Carnot cycle is, of course,
determined by the system or material chosen as the working substance and the
variables used. For the ideal gas the Carnot cycle is drawn from the known
equation of state and the equation of the adiabatic. For a nonideal gas the
isotherms and adiabatics assume a somewhat different form, depending
on the gas and its departures from idealness, but resemble qualitatively the
curves for the ideal gas. Let us now examine a few other interesting special
cases.

Two-Phase System.   For a two-phase system such as steam and water,
the Carnot cycle has a shape quite different from that for a gaseous system.
In Fig. 8.11 the dashed curve is the saturation curve separating the liquid
and vapor from the two-phase region. The Carnot cycle is then the cycle
12341, with the following parts:

$1 \rightarrow 2$ Isothermal (and hence isobaric) evaporation of saturated water
at 1 to saturated steam at 2, with absorption of heat Q_1.

$2 \rightarrow 3$ Adiabatic expansion of saturated steam, during which some condensation occurs to produce a mixture of steam and a small amount of water
at 3.

$3 \rightarrow 4$ Isothermal condensation of most of the remaining steam to a
mixture, chiefly water, at 4, with rejection of heat Q_2.

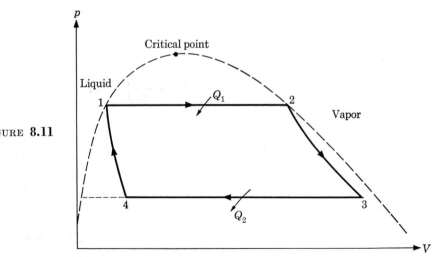

FIGURE **8.11**

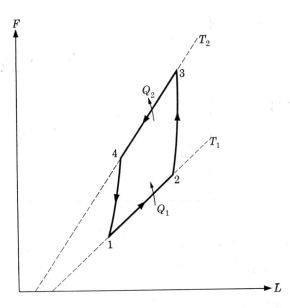

FIGURE **8.12**

$4 \to 1$ Adiabatic compression of the mixture to the saturated liquid state at 1, the starting point of the cycle. The compression and the condensation warm the system to the original temperature.

Stretched Elastic Wire.   Consider a thin wire of length L under tension F. As long as the elastic limit is not exceeded and T is constant, the force and the length rise proportionally. Hence the isotherms are straight lines, the one with the higher temperature lying to the right (Fig. 8.12). The cycle consists of these parts:

$1 \to 2$ Isothermal stretching of the wire at T_1 (when Q_1 is absorbed).

$2 \to 3$ Adiabatic stretching of the wire, which cools it from T_1 to T_2.

$3 \to 4$ Isothermal contraction of the wire at T_2 when it rejects Q_2 to the cold reservoir.

$4 \to 1$ Adiabatic contraction of the wire, which allows it to warm back to T_1 once more.

Note that in this plane the cycle is counterclockwise. Its direction results from the fact that

$$dW_C = +F\,dL$$

and hence that external work is done only when dL is negative and the wire contracts, that is, from $3 \to 4$ and $4 \to 1$. (See Problems 8.8 and 13.15.)

Surface Film.   Consider a stretched surface film for which

$$dW_C = +\mathcal{S}\,dA$$

Here $\mathcal{S}$ is a function of T only and decreases as T rises (eventually to vanish at the critical point). Then we have the situation represented in Fig. 8.13,

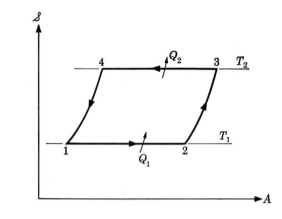

FIGURE **8.13**

where the numbering is the same as for the other Carnot cycles. Here again heat is absorbed along $1 \rightarrow 2$ and rejected along $3 \rightarrow 4$.

8.15   The Kelvin Temperature Scale

Since the efficiency of a Carnot engine is

$$\eta_R = 1 - \frac{Q_2}{Q_1} = 1 - \frac{T_2}{T_1}$$

we cannot have $\eta_R = 1$ unless the heat sink is at $0°K$. Under this condition $Q_2 = 0$, and $W = Q_1$; that is, all the heat absorbed is converted into work. If we could have a temperature below $0°K$, we should have $T_2 < 0$ and $\eta_R > 1$, which would mean that

$$W > Q_1$$

Since this relation contradicts the first law, we conclude that $T_2 \not< 0$ and that no temperature below $0°K$ exists. The absolute zero thus represents an *absolute zero of energy* (that is, extractable energy) as well as an absolute zero of temperature.

   With this result in mind, Kelvin set up a thermodynamic scale of temperature based on universal properties of energy. Since any system can be taken through a Carnot cycle, the new scale is independent of the properties of any particular body or system, in contrast to the absolute gas scale of temperature employed so far. Kelvin proposed a series of reversible Carnot engines working between any temperature, T, on the absolute gas scale and the absolute zero. The first engine takes in heat, Q, at T, delivers work, w, and rejects $Q - w$ to the second engine. This in turn delivers w units of work and rejects $Q - 2w$ to the third engine, etc., until finally the last engine, with its exhaust at $0°K$, converts all the heat that it receives into work.

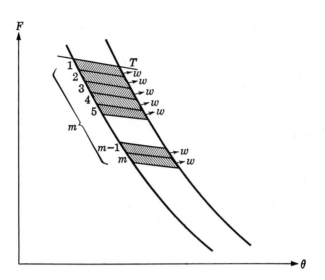

FIGURE **8.14**

Consider two adiabatics on the F-θ plane (Fig. 8.14), where F is a generalized force and θ is the conjugate geometric variable. Across them draw isotherms so spaced that the areas of the small cycles are alike and equal to w. Then let these isotherms determine the *degree marks on the new scale*. This new scale is fixed by three factors, as follows: (1) the temperature of the highest isotherm; (2) the temperature at which the heat energy, Q, is entirely converted into work; and (3) the number of engines used, say, n.

Since the first engine takes in the Q units of heat at T and we have n engines, $Q = nw$. Therefore, if the first engine receives $Q = nw$ units, the second engine receives $Q - w = w(n - 1)$ units, the third engine receives $Q - 2w = w(n - 2)$ units, etc. Finally the $(n - 1)$th engine gives the nth engine $Q - (n - 1)w$ heat units. Since this is the bottom engine in the series, with its exhaust at $0°K$, it rejects nothing. Let the isotherms be numbered from the bottom up, beginning with that at $0°K$, which we call the zeroth. Then the top isotherm is number τ, say, where τ is numerically equal to n and is taken as the temperature of the top isotherm on the new scale.

Now arrange the top m engines to work together as a single Carnot unit, taking in Q heat units at τ and rejecting $Q - mw$ units at $\tau - m$. The efficiency of this Carnot unit must be, by definition,

$$\eta_R = \frac{Q - (Q - mw)}{Q} = \frac{m}{n} = \frac{m}{\tau}$$

or

$$\eta_R = \frac{\Delta\tau}{\tau}$$

since $n = \tau$ and $m = \tau - (\tau - m) = \Delta\tau$, the difference in temperature between the top and bottom isotherms of the unit.

Then we have

$$\eta_R = \frac{\Delta\tau}{\tau} = \frac{\Delta T}{T}$$

Hence, in general,

$$\frac{\tau_1 - \tau_2}{\tau_1} = \frac{T_1 - T_2}{T_1}$$

or simply

$$\frac{\tau_1}{\tau_2} = \frac{T_1}{T_2} \tag{8.23}$$

where τ_1 and τ_2 are the temperatures on the new scale corresponding to the values T_1 and T_2 on the absolute gas scale.

From Eq. 8.23 we can write

$$\frac{\tau_1}{T_1} = \frac{\tau_2}{T_2} = \text{constant} = K$$

Since T_1 and T_2 are *any two* temperatures and the ratio is the same whatever they are, we conclude that

$$\tau = KT$$

That is, the two scales are proportional (and, of course, have a common zero). Since there is no particular advantage in having $K \neq 1$, we set $K = 1$ and have

$$\boxed{\tau = T}$$

Thus the ideal gas scale as previously defined becomes identical with the new scale, and the symbol τ is no longer needed. This conclusion does not mean that this long argument has accomplished nothing. It shows that the original scale, defined in terms of the extrapolated properties of gases, is in fact much more general. The scale is now based on the universal properties of energy rather than on the specific properties of a particular class of substances. Because of the general thermodynamic basis of the argument, the gas scale is renamed the *absolute thermodynamic* or *Kelvin scale* (with readings indicated by °K, as before).

To avoid introducing a new symbol for temperatures on this new scale, we originally designated temperatures on the extrapolated gas scale by the symbol T. We shall continue to use this symbol, with, however, the knowledge that the temperatures so designated are on a scale of much broader significance than we could have imagined earlier.

It is instructive to return to Carnot's theorem (IIB), which we have written several times as

$$\frac{T_2}{T_1} = \frac{Q_2}{Q_1}$$

or

$$\frac{T_2}{Q_2} = \frac{T_1}{Q_1}$$

Since T_1 and T_2 are any independent temperatures, each ratio must be a constant, say, α. Then

$$T = \alpha Q \qquad\qquad (8.24)$$

where the heat, Q, taken in by a Carnot engine (with fixed adiabatics) is regarded as the thermometric "property."

For the ice and steam points,

$$T_i = \alpha Q_i$$

and

$$T_s = \alpha Q_s$$

and therefore

$$T_s - T_i = \alpha(Q_s - Q_i)$$

or

$$\alpha = \frac{T_s - T_i}{Q_s - Q_i} = \frac{100}{Q_s - Q_i} = \frac{100}{Q_{100} - Q_0}$$

This value of α in Eq. 8.24 gives

$$T = 100 \frac{Q}{Q_{100} - Q_0} \qquad\qquad (8.25)$$

which becomes the general energetic definition of temperature on the Kelvin scale. It corresponds to the general result for any thermometric property, X, which vanishes at $0°K$, that is,

$$T = 100 \frac{X}{X_{100} - X_0}$$

or to the original definition of the ideal gas scale in Chap. 2 as

$$T = 100 \frac{\lim_{p \to 0} (pV)_t}{\lim (pV)_{100} - \lim (pV)_0} \qquad\qquad (2.30)$$

Problems

8.1   Go over the gasoline engine cycle step by step, indicating the simplifications and idealizations made in the air standard Otto cycle.

8.2 The approach employed in the Otto and Diesel cycles shows that the efficiency of a reversible Sargent cycle is

$$\eta = 1 - \gamma \frac{(T_4 - T_1)}{(T_3 - T_2)}$$

with the notation used in Fig. 8.2. Prove this.

8.3 Carry out the same calculations as in Problem 8.2 for the Joule cycle to show that for it

$$\eta = 1 - \left(\frac{p_1}{p_2}\right)^{(\gamma-1)/\gamma}.$$

8.4 Discuss in the same way a rectangular cycle in the p-V plane (Fig. 8.15), and show that for it

$$\eta = \frac{\gamma - 1}{\dfrac{\gamma p_2}{p_2 - p_1} + \dfrac{V_1}{V_4 - V_1}}$$

FIGURE **8.15**

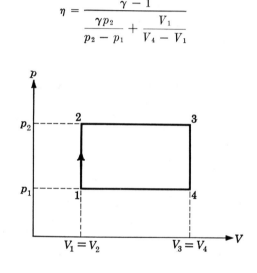

8.5 Referring to Fig. 8.6, show by direct integration of $p\,dV$ around the Carnot cycle that the total external work performed is

$$W = R(T_1 - T_2) \ln \frac{V_2}{V_1}$$

and hence that the efficiency is that given in Eq. 8.15.

8.6 Calculate the slope of the adiabatic curve for an ideal gas in the T-V, p-V, and T-p planes.

8.7 Show that forms IIA and IID of the second law are equivalent statements by proving that IIA is both sufficient and necessary for the truth of IID.

8.8 Give physical arguments that justify the drawing of the upper temperature (T_1) isotherm of Fig. 8.12 *below* the isotherm for the lower temperature, T_2. Why would you expect the adiabatics to be concave toward the left as drawn?

8.9 The superior efficiency of the Carnot cycle is due to its absorbing all heat at the highest temperature and rejecting all waste heat at the lowest temperature. The triangular work cycle of Fig. 8.1 may be regarded as part of a Carnot cycle with the upper and lower isotherms at T_1 and T_2, respectively (see Fig. 8.16). If the triangular cycle is divided into differential Carnot cycles, the heat, dQ_V, absorbed at a, for example, would be clearly more efficiently utilized if absorbed at b on the isotherm for T_1. All but an infinitesimal amount of the heat absorbed along $4 \rightarrow 1$ in the diagram is taken in below T_1 and thus less effectively utilized than in the Carnot cycle. Discuss the four cycles (Joule, Otto, Diesel, and Sargent) shown in Fig. 8.2 from this standpoint.

FIGURE **8.16**

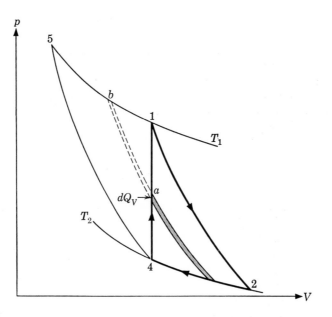

CHAPTER NINE

Entropy and the Second Law

9.1 Entropy and Necessary Waste

We have seen that in the production of work out of heat even in the best possible engine, the Carnot engine, there is a necessary and unavoidable wastage of heat. With Q_1 taken in at T_1, the minimum heat, Q_2, which must be rejected at T_2 as *useless for mechanical purposes* is given by

$$Q_2 = \left(\frac{Q_1}{T_1}\right) T_2 \tag{9.1}$$

The smaller the ratio Q_1/T_1 and the lower T_2, the less the mechanically useless heat. Clausius regarded the ratio Q_1/T_1 as an essential property of the heat reversibly absorbed from a reservoir. He called this property the *entropy of the heat taken in.*

Heat absorbed reversibly from a high-temperature source has low entropy and will always have less waste than high-entropy heat. Thus low-entropy heat is more valuable mechanically than high-entropy heat. In fact, the *entropy* of the heat is more important than the *amount* of the heat. As an example, consider a sink at $T = 300°$K. Let it absorb 1000 cal at $1000°$K. Its entropy is 1 cal/deg, and the necessary waste is 1 cal/deg $\times$ $300°$ = 300 cal. Any other amount of heat taken in at this same entropy and with the common sink at $300°$K involves precisely this wastage, as, for example, 500 cal at $500°$K or 300 cal at $300°$K. In the latter case, of course, all the heat is waste heat.

Naturally, with irreversible cycles the actual heat loss will exceed the minimum. Therefore, we define the entropy of a given quantity of heat as that property of the heat which fixes the *minimum unavailable* or the *maximum available* when cyclic devices are used to produce mechanical work.

If W is the external work produced, then, with the usual notation,

$$W = Q_1 - Q_2 \geq Q_1 - \left(\begin{array}{c}\text{entropy of the}\\ \text{heat taken in}\end{array}\right) T_2$$

where the equality holds only for the Carnot engine. Even then $W < Q_1$ unless the entropy or T_2 vanishes, and neither of these possibilities is of practical importance.

Since no heat is absorbed along adiabatics, the entropy of heat taken in just cancels that of the heat rejected for the Carnot cycle as a whole; that is,

$$\frac{Q_1}{T_1} - \frac{Q_2}{T_2} = 0$$

With this rather special approach to the subject of entropy, we must now inquire whether the system can be said to gain entropy when it takes in heat. Such an interpretation is possible only if we can show that entropy exists as a *property* of the system fixed by its *state alone*. Showing this requires proof of the famous "sum theorem" of Clausius.

9.2   The Clausius Sum for a Closed Cycle

Clausius, recognizing the importance of the ratio Q/T for isothermal processes, extended the concept to the general heat absorption process. Consider a system that undergoes a cyclic process. This cycle need not be reversible; the only requirement is that the system, after some sequence of changes, end in its initial state (which must be an equilibrium one). Let the system absorb heats $Q_1, Q_2, \ldots, Q_i, \ldots, Q_k$ from a set of auxiliary reservoirs at temperatures $T_1, T_2, \ldots, T_i, \ldots, T_k$ and reject heats $Q_{k+1}, \ldots, Q_j, \ldots, Q_n$ to reservoirs $T_{k+1}, \ldots, T_j, \ldots, T_n$. For heat absorption the auxiliary reservoirs must be at least as hot as (and for rejection at least as cold as) that part of the system involved in the heat interchange. Otherwise, we make no restrictions.

For such a cyclic process Clausius proved his sum theorem, which may be stated as follows: "For any closed cycle that a system may undergo

$$\sum_{i=1}^{k} \frac{Q_i}{T_i} - \sum_{j=k+1}^{n} \frac{Q_j}{T_j} = \sum_{i=1}^{n} \frac{Q_i}{T_i} \leq 0$$

where the *equality* holds for reversible cycles only and the *inequality* for all others."

To prove this theorem, we introduce another reservoir, say, the *main* reservoir (Fig. 9.1), which is the ultimate source or sink of all heat quantities involved. Its temperature is T_0, higher than that of any of the n auxiliary reservoirs. To effect the transfer of heat between the main reservoir and the n auxiliary reservoirs, n Carnot engines are utilized.

Of these the numbers $1, 2, \ldots, i, \ldots, k$ operate in the forward direction. Only the ith of these engines is shown, as a circle, in Fig. 9.1. It absorbs Q_{0i} from the main reservoir and delivers Q_i to the ith auxiliary reservoir

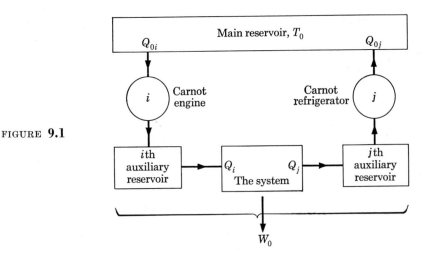

FIGURE **9.1**

(shown as a square in the figure), which in turn delivers this heat to the system. For this cycle, by Carnot's theorem,

$$Q_{0i} = \left(\frac{Q_i}{T_i}\right) T_0 \qquad (9.2)$$

The remaining engines, $k + 1$, $k + 2$, . . . , j, . . . n, operate in a similar way in the reverse direction as refrigerators. The jth absorbs heat Q_j from the jth auxiliary reservoir (which took it in turn from the system) and delivers Q_{0j} to the main reservoir. Thus we have

$$Q_{0j} = \left(\frac{Q_j}{T_j}\right) T_0 \qquad (9.3)$$

Now imagine a complex cycle in which each engine, each refrigerator, and the system go through one cycle. Suppose that the net result of this complex cycle is the delivery of a net quantity of work, W_0, to the outside world. Since all the working substances, including the system, have executed cycles, they are all left exactly as at the start. The work, therefore, can only have come as a net heat extraction, say, Q_0, from the main reservoir. By the first law this must be equal to W_0, or

$$W_0 = Q_0 = \sum_1^k Q_{0i} - \sum_{k+1}^n Q_{0j} \qquad (9.4)$$

Inserting Eqs. 9.2 and 9.3 in this result gives

$$W_0 = T_0 \left(\sum_1^k \frac{Q_i}{T_i} - \sum_{k+1}^n \frac{Q_j}{T_j} \right) = T_0 \sum_1^n \frac{Q_i}{T_i} \qquad (9.5)$$

where the last summation is indicated with a single summation variable and due account must be taken of signs. By the second law (form IID) it is impossible to construct a cyclic device (however complex) that will absorb heat from a single source (the main reservoir) and produce useful work. Thus W_0 cannot be greater than zero, although, of course, it might be zero or even negative (that is, net work might be required to carry out the complex cycle). Consequently,

$$W_0 = Q_0 \leq 0$$

and since $T_0 > 0$ by hypothesis,

$$\sum_1^n \frac{Q_i}{T_i} \leq 0 \qquad (9.6)$$

This is the Clausius sum involved in the theorem. Under no conditions can this sum be positive.

Consider now the special case of a *reversible* cycle. In this case we may, without altering any magnitudes, carry out the complex cycle in the opposite sense. The result would be to change only the sign of each Q_i in the sum of Eq. 9.6. By the same argument as before, therefore, we should have

$$\sum_1^n -\frac{Q_i}{T_i} \leq 0$$

or simply

$$\sum_1^n \frac{Q_i}{T_i} \geq 0 \qquad (9.7)$$

Of course, Eqs. 9.6 and 9.7 can be true together only if the equality sign holds. Thus for any reversible cycle the Clausius sum must become

$$\sum_1^n \frac{Q_i}{T_i} = 0 \qquad (9.8)$$

The inequality of the theorem applies to all other (that is, nonreversible) cycles. This theorem may be taken as a new statement, form IIF, of the second law.

We note that the Clausius sum for a Carnot cycle reduces to two canceling terms since there is no heat transfer along adiabatics (see Sec. 9.1).

9.3   The Clausius Sum as an Integral

Thus far a general cycle for a system has been treated as though it could be carried out with a finite number, n, of auxiliary reservoirs. When, however, the system absorbs heat over a continuous range of temperatures, we must imagine an infinite number of reservoirs spread over this temperature range.

The finite quantity Q_i must then be replaced by a differential interchange, say, dQ. The differential interchange with the main reservoir, say, dQ_0, is given by

$$dQ_0 = \left(\frac{dQ}{T}\right) T_0$$

The Carnot engine's dQ is supplied to the auxiliary reservoir at T, which rejects the same amount of heat to the system, etc., as before. The argument is similar for the Carnot refrigerator, and the general Clausius sum is replaced by an integral. Thus we write

$$\int \frac{dQ}{T} \leq 0 \tag{9.9}$$

where the integral is taken from some initial temperature over a closed range of auxiliary reservoir temperatures back to the initial temperature. For a reversible cycle the temperature T is essentially that of the system itself. Since the system is being taken through a reversible cycle, the *path* of the system is some continuous curve, C, and we write

$$dQ = dQ_C$$

as we have done hitherto for all quasistatic processes. Therefore, Eq. 9.9 becomes

$$\oint \frac{dQ_C}{T} = 0 \qquad\qquad \text{reversible} \tag{9.10}$$

where everything refers to the *system* and the cycle that it undergoes.

The inequality of Eq. 9.9 applies to an irreversible cycle, and although dQ is heat given to the system (ultimately), the system does not change quasistatically. It may have no system temperature and it has no curve of change. T refers entirely to *reservoir* temperatures, and dQ is written as dQ_r and T as T_r to emphasize this relationship. Thus

$$\oint \frac{dQ_r}{T_r} < 0 \qquad\qquad \text{irreversible} \tag{9.11}$$

Expressing the result of Clausius in Eqs. 9.10 and 9.11 for the two cases of reversible and nonreversible cycles emphasizes the important differences. In Eq. 9.10 all quantities refer to the system itself, and the integral is evaluated for a closed curve or path executed by the system. In Eq. 9.11 everything refers to the auxiliary reservoirs, and the integral is evaluated for a closed range of reservoir temperatures through which incidentally the system is brought back to its initial state.

9.4   Entropy as a Property of a System

Let us now examine the important implications of the vanishing of the Clausius integral for the general reversible cycle. The argument could be carried out for a system with any number of thermodynamic degrees of freedom, but for simplicity let there be two, say, x and y. Then take any two arbitrary curves, C' and C'' (in the x-y plane), which intersect at P_0 and P (Fig. 9.2). The path C' executed from P_0 to P and the path C'' from P to P_0 together constitute a closed cycle. If the system is taken around this loop in a reversible manner, Clausius' equality holds, and

$$\oint \frac{dQ_C}{T} = \int_{P_0}^{P} \frac{dQ_{C'}}{T} + \int_{P}^{P_0} \frac{dQ_{C''}}{T} = 0$$

Since the process is reversible, we may interchange the limits in the last integral by simply reversing the sign of $dQ_{C''}$. Then, since the two integrals cancel, they must be equal; that is,

$$\int_{P_0}^{P} \frac{dQ_{C'}}{T} = \int_{P_0}^{P} \frac{dQ_{C''}}{T}$$

Since C' and C'' are *any* two curves, this result can mean *only* that the integrals are actually independent of the path used. If P_0 is a fixed reference point and P any variable point, the common value of these integrals must be a unique function of the coordinates, x and y, of the variable upper limit. This unique single-valued function of the variables x and y we define as the *entropy* of the

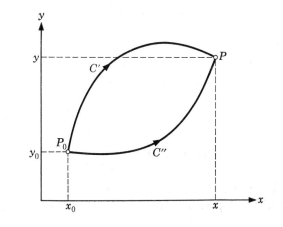

FIGURE **9.2**

system, say, $S(x, y)$, and we have

$$S(x, y) = \int_{x_0, y_0}^{x, y} \left(\frac{dQ_C}{T}\right)_{\text{rev}} \tag{9.12}$$

where C is any reversibly executed path. Note that we now speak of the entropy of *the system*. We can do this because the quantity S is fixed solely by the state of the system and is independent of how the system gets to that state. Thus entropy becomes a calculable thermodynamic function in the same sense that internal energy and enthalpy are. It is, in fact, as definite a property of the system's state as is temperature, pressure, volume, or any other thermodynamic system property.

Since each side of Eq. 9.12 is a function of two variables, we can differentiate each side to obtain

$$dS = \left(\frac{dQ_C}{T}\right)_{\text{rev}} \tag{9.13}$$

Thus the differential change in the entropy of the system is the *reversibly added heat*, dQ_C, *divided by the absolute temperature at which it is added*.

If we now reverse our steps and integrate Eq. 9.13 from P_0 to P along any reversible path, C, we have

$$\int_{P_0}^{P} dS = S(x, y) - S(x_0, y_0) = \int_{P_0}^{P} \left(\frac{dQ_C}{T}\right)_{\text{rev}}$$

or simply
$$\Delta S = S - S_0 = \int_{P_0}^{P} \left(\frac{dQ_C}{T}\right)_{\text{rev}} \tag{9.14}$$

We are thus able to measure (or calculate) only the change in the entropy, $\Delta S = S - S_0$. The value of S_0 remains undetermined. In fact, forming the open integral of Eq. 9.13, we have

$$S = \int \frac{dQ}{T} + \text{constant} \tag{9.15}$$

where the arbitrary constant of integration cannot be evaluated by purely thermodynamic arguments.

Since only *differences* in entropy are experimentally measurable, all entropies are relative to some common reference point. This situation is equivalent to setting S_0 in Eq. 9.14 or the constant in Eq. 9.15 equal to zero. Then

$$S = \Delta S = \int_{P_0}^{P} \left(\frac{dQ_C}{T}\right)_{\text{rev}} \tag{9.16}$$

Since dQ_C depends directly on the mass of the system involved, S is an extensive property along with U, H, and V. It is therefore often convenient to use *specific* entropies and to write

$$S = ms$$

where m is the total mass and s is the entropy of a unit mass, or the specific entropy.

9.5   The Principle of the Increase of Entropy

Consider the two states given by P_1 and P_2 in Fig. 9.3. If the system passes from P_1 to P_2 by a reversible path, C, integration of

$$dS = \frac{dQ_C}{T}$$

for the path gives

$$S_2 = S_1 + \int_{P_1}^{P_2} \frac{dQ_C}{T} \tag{9.17}$$

If, on the other hand, we endeavor to integrate dQ/T for some irreversible process (indicated by the hatched lines) connecting the same points, a quite different result is obtained.

If this irreversible process from P_1 to P_2 is combined with a reversible passage back from P_2 to P_1 along C, the result is an irreversible cycle, for which the inequality of Clausius must hold. In this case the integral breaks up into two parts so that

$$\underbrace{\int_{P_1}^{P_2} \frac{dQ_r}{T_r}}_{\text{irreversible}} + \underbrace{\int_{P_2}^{P_1} \frac{dQ_C}{T}}_{\text{reversible}} = \underbrace{\int_{P_1}^{P_2} \frac{dQ_r}{T_r}}_{\text{irreversible}} - \underbrace{\int_{P_1}^{P_2} \frac{dQ_C}{T}}_{\text{reversible}} < 0$$

The last integral is simply $S_2 - S_1$, as obtained in Eq. 9.17, and, consequently,

$$S_2 > S_1 + \int_{P_1}^{P_2} \frac{dQ_r}{T_r} \tag{9.18}$$

This result applies, of course, to the general irreversible passage from P_1 to P_2 involving the transfer of heat between the various outside auxiliary

FIGURE **9.3**

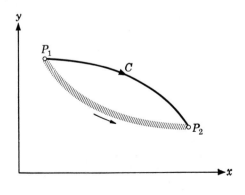

reservoirs and the system. If *the system is isolated thermally* for the irreversible process, so that no heat interchange whatever is possible, then the integral must vanish, and

$$S_2 > S_1$$

In other words, *"any irreversible process that can occur inside a thermally isolated system causes the entropy of the system to increase."* This is the principle of the *increase of entropy* and may be taken as another very useful statement of the second law (form IIG). It applies to all systems that are thermally isolated from the outside world as well as to the more special case of complete isolation. Whatever irreversible processes may occur in such systems must increase entropy. Entropy thus differs fundamentally from internal energy; *it is not conserved simply by isolation of the system from its surroundings.*

The only thermodynamic processes possible in completely isolated systems are *spontaneous* ones. (Note that reversible processes are not spontaneous and require careful guidance from outside the system.) These spontaneous processes include the equalization of pressure and temperature differences, diffusion, dissipation of mechanical energy in various frictional processes, condensation in supersaturated vapors, solidification of supercooled liquids, chemical reactions that proceed of their own accord, and a host of others.[1]

As these more or less violent processes take place, the system comes nearer and nearer to equilibrium, that is, a true stable state of static equilibrium. The entropy correspondingly increases until this final state is reached, after which no further spontaneous changes are possible. The entropy can increase no further and must therefore have attained its maximum value for the system in question, with its given physical makeup and fixed internal energy. The principle of the increase of entropy may then be stated in another instructive form (form IIH):

FIGURE **9.4**

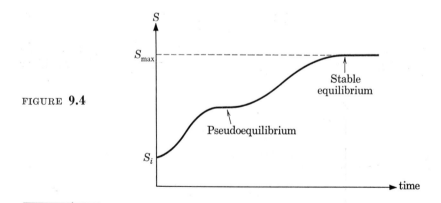

---

[1] Presumably all natural radioactive processes, as well as artificial fusions and fissions, increase entropy as they proceed. At the present time, knowledge as to how they might be carried out reversibly and data for the theoretical calculations are not available, and so the magnitudes of the presumed entropy increases cannot be determined.

"The entropy in an isolated system is a monotonically increasing function of the time."

The relationship is illustrated in Fig. 9.4 by an entropy versus time curve. The curve may reach an intermediate plateau but can never fall. With pseudo-equilibrium we have metastable states, which are apparently stable and which may persist for long periods of time. Some mechanical disturbance or vibration, or perhaps the introduction of a seed crystal into a supersaturated solution or of an appropriate catalyst into a delayed chemical reaction, stimulates the change toward a state of stable equilibrium and greater entropy. Entropy is thus created by the very processes by which equilibrium is attained.

Let us now examine a few important types of spontaneous processes. In natural processes there are usually several of these simple types occurring simultaneously, although, of course, the final result is the same if each simple type is allowed to proceed to completion separately.

9.6 Free Expansion of an Ideal Gas

Any system that is to undergo a spontaneous change must be in a nonequilibrium condition. Consider a gas in a container (Fig. 9.5), separated from an evacuated space by a tight partition. The system is in equilibrium and will remain so indefinitely. If, however, the partition is pulled part of the way out, the equilibrium is upset, and the gas surges into the evacuated space, eventually to reach a stable condition at the larger volume.

Suppose, to make the theorem on the increase of entropy applicable, that the system is isolated thermally. Let the original gas, say, ν moles, occupy volume V_i, and let the total volume of the enclosure be V_e. We know that

$$\Delta S = S_e - S_i > 0$$

for the irreversible or so-called "free" expansion. Since the system performs no external work, the internal energy of the gas must remain a constant. Since the gas is ideal, its temperature must therefore be the same in the initial and final states.

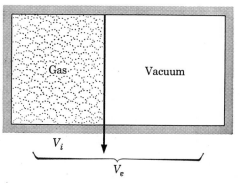

FIGURE **9.5**

To calculate ΔS, we must simply invent a reversible path for taking the gas from the state T_i, V_i to T_e, V_e. The simplest path is, of course, an isothermal expansion during which heat is added to keep the temperature constant (Fig. 9.6).

By the first law

$$dQ_T = dU + p\,dV = p\,dV$$

so that

$$dS = \frac{dQ_T}{T} = p\,\frac{dV}{T} = \nu R\,\frac{dV}{V}$$

Therefore,

$$S_e - S_i = \Delta S = \nu R \int_{V_i}^{V_e} \frac{dV}{V} = \nu R \ln \frac{V_e}{V_i} \tag{9.19}$$

which is surely positive since $V_e > V_i$.

Suppose now that we make up a closed cycle consisting of (1) irreversible expansion $i \rightarrow e$ (gas insulated) and (2) reversible isothermal compression $e \rightarrow i$.

Since this is an irreversible cycle, the inequality of Clausius must hold, and therefore

$$\int_i^e \frac{dQ_r}{T_r} + \int_e^i \frac{dQ_c}{T} < 0$$

or

$$0 + \int_e^i \frac{dQ_c}{T} = -\nu R \ln \frac{V_e}{V_i} \tag{9.20}$$

It is instructive to make up a table in which $\int dQ/T$ is evaluated for the two parts of the cycle and compared with the changes in entropy of the system and its surroundings. These data are given in Table 9.1, where the last column shows the corresponding losses in potentially available work. The bottom row summarizes the quantities for the cycle. Here for simplicity V_e/V_i is taken as 2.

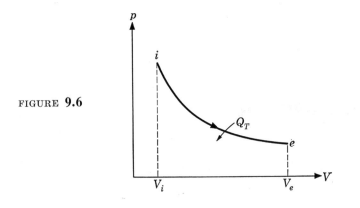

FIGURE **9.6**

TABLE **9.1**

Entropy Changes in Free Expansion from V to 2V

Process	$\int \dfrac{dQ}{T}$	ΔS_{system}	$\Delta S_{\text{surroundings}}$	Loss of potential work
Free expansion	0	$+ \nu R \ln 2$	0	$\nu RT \ln 2$
Isothermal compression	$- \nu R \ln 2$	$- \nu R \ln 2$	$+ \nu R \ln 2$	0
Cycle	$- \nu R \ln 2$	0	$+ \nu R \ln 2$	$\nu RT \ln 2$

The second column indicates the verification of Clausius' inequality, and the third shows that the system, having returned to its initial state, has no net entropy change. The fourth column indicates, however, that the entropy increase, that is, the entropy created by the free expansion, has been passed on to the surroundings. In fact, there is no process known by which the effect of the irreversible free expansion can be entirely obliterated, nor is there any process by which we can recover the net loss of potential work resulting. Thus the *irreversible process has left its indelible mark on the universe*, which will never be the same again. We may take this mark as either the increase, ΔS, in entropy or the loss in potential or originally available work, $\nu RT \ln 2$. The two values are seen to be proportional, the absolute temperature of the system and its surroundings being the proportionality factor.

9.7 Mixing of Gases

The spontaneous mixing of two or more gases represents another essentially irreversible process. Consider ν_A and ν_B moles of two mutually inert ideal gases, A and B. Let them be at temperature T and occupy volumes V_A and V_B (Fig. 9.7). If we pull out the separating wall and allow mixing to occur, the entropy must increase. To calculate the increase, we must, as before, find a reversible way of mixing the two gases.

FIGURE **9.7**

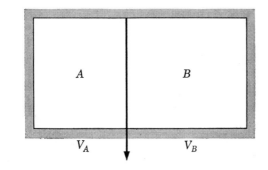

$A \qquad B$

$V_A \qquad V_B$

The simplest way is by the use of two so-called semipermeable pistons (Fig. 9.8). One of these (#1) is freely permeable to gas A but acts as an ordinary piston to gas B. It is thus capable of being pushed back reversibly by gas B, doing work without hindrance from gas A, which passes freely through it. The other piston (#2) is freely permeable to gas B but acts as a piston for gas A. Hence, as A is allowed to expand reversibly from V_A to $V_A + V_B$, it performs work, as does gas B in expanding from V_B to $V_A + V_B$. This reversible expansion of each gas eventually results in the complete mixing of the two. Just as in the last section, heat must be added to keep each process isothermal. The over-all increase of entropy, ΔS, is

$$\Delta S = \int_{V_A}^{V_A + V_B} \frac{dQ_T}{T} + \int_{V_B}^{V_A + V_B} \frac{dQ_T}{T}$$
$$\text{gas } A \qquad\qquad \text{gas } B$$

Each of these integrals is of the type evaluated before for the free expansion and is equal to $\nu R \ln V_e/V_i$. Thus finally we have

$$\Delta S = \nu_A R \ln \frac{V_A + V_B}{V_A} + \nu_B R \ln \frac{V_A + V_B}{V_B} \qquad (9.21)$$

as though we had a free expansion of each of two separate gases from its original volume to the final volume, $V_A + V_B$.

The spontaneous mixing results in a loss of available work equal to the amount of work made available by the reversible mixing. Since in each case the work quantity is obtained by the integration of $p\,dV$, for the reversible mixing it becomes

$$\nu_A R T \ln \frac{V_A + V_B}{V_A} + \nu_B R T \ln \frac{V_A + V_B}{V_B}$$

and is again seen to be proportional to ΔS.

The interdiffusion of two gases is, of course, but a prototype for all cases of spontaneous diffusion. Other important cases involve the interdiffusion of mutually soluble liquids, the diffusion of dissolved substances from regions of

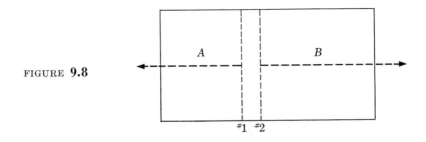

FIGURE **9.8**

high concentration to those of low concentration, and the like. All are irreversible and result in an increase in entropy and a decrease in available work.

A word should be said about semipermeable membranes. Various natural materials, such as a pig's bladder, are permeable to water but not to dissolved salts. Metals such as platinum, if sufficiently hot, are permeable to hydrogen while holding back other gases. Still other semipermeable walls of greater strength can be formed by the precipitation of gelatinous materials in the interstices of unglazed porcelain. It must be stated clearly, however, that pairs of such membranes suitable for separating gases with molecules as much alike as, say, those of oxygen and nitrogen (or, even more alike, the isotopic variations of a given pure elemental gas) are not known. For such gases the idealized apparatus and associated "paper" processes are part of the theoretical framework of the science. These processes are used for calculation purposes only and do not need to be carried out in the laboratory. The only ultimate guide that we have in devising such theoretical processes is that they must never lead to a contradiction of natural law.

9.8 Dissipation of Mechanical and Electrical Energy

The dragging of an object over a rough table top causes the production of heat at the expense of mechanical energy. Reversal of the motion not only fails to reverse this dissipative process but causes more dissipation. In the same way Joulian dissipation of electrical energy in a resistance wire is irreversible—reversing the direction of flow does not convert the heat generated back into electrical form.

To calculate the change in entropy for any such type of dissipation, we must, as before, devise a reversible way of bringing about the same over-all change and integrate dQ_C/T for this process. For definiteness consider the electrical case, and let an amount of electrical energy, $W = Ei\tau/J$, be dissipated in a resistance wire. (Here and throughout, electrical energy stored in whatever form will be regarded as the complete equivalent of the same numerical amount of mechanical energy.) Suppose, as in Fig. 9.9, that the resistance wire is enclosed in some medium that constitutes a system insulated thermally from its surroundings. Let the system be warmed as a result of the dissipation from T_i to T_e at, say, constant pressure. The heat, Q_p, which must be supplied

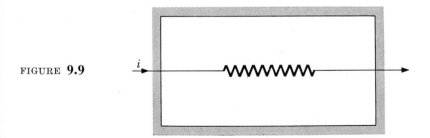

FIGURE **9.9**

to bring this change about thermally, is obtained from the first law as

$$Q_p = \int_i^e dQ_p = \int_{T_i}^{T_e} C_p \, dT = C_p(T_e - T_i) = \frac{Ei\tau}{J}$$

where the heat capacity of the system is treated as a constant.

The corresponding change in entropy for the reversible warming is

$$\Delta S = \int_i^e \frac{dQ_p}{T} = C_p \int_{T_i}^{T_e} \frac{dT}{T} = C_p \ln \frac{T_e}{T_i} \tag{9.22}$$

which is clearly positive, since $T_e > T_i$.

Potential work has, of course, been lost, since the original electrical energy was potentially all available for mechanical use. After the dissipation, however, we have a system only slightly above the temperature of its surroundings. And only a very small part of the energy, $W = Q_p$, is reconvertible into work.

To see just how much of this energy must be rejected to the surroundings as waste heat, arrange a Carnot engine to absorb heat, dQ_p, from the system at T, extract as much work as possible from it, and reject the rest, dQ_p', to the surroundings at T_i. By Carnot's theorem (form IIB)

$$\frac{Q_1}{Q_2} = \frac{T_1}{T_2}$$

which in the present case gives for dQ_p'

$$dQ_p' = \left(\frac{dQ_p}{T}\right) T_i \tag{9.23}$$

where T is the variable temperature of the system, beginning at T_e and ending at T_i when the withdrawal is finished.

If Eq. 9.23 is integrated over the range T_i to T_e, the result gives the total heat rejected as unusable, say, Q_p'. This represents that part of $W = Q_p$ which has been rendered unavailable by the dissipative process. Thus

$$Q_p' = \int_i^e dQ_p' = T_i \int_{T_i}^{T_e} \frac{dQ_p}{T} = T_i \Delta S \tag{9.24}$$

and again we have the direct proportionality between ΔS and the loss in available energy. We may well regard Q_p' as simply an addition to the already unavailable energy of the universe. Thus entropy and unavailable energy increase together. As an example of how very small the recoverable part of Q_p is, see Problem 9.2.

9.9   Temperature Equalization

One of the very important irreversible processes in nature is temperature equalization. Heat is continually being transferred by radiation, conduction, and convection from hot bodies to colder bodies. The flow is always irreversible, and therefore entropy must increase.

Consider two bodies of heat capacities $(C_p)_1$ and $(C_p)_2$, originally at temperatures T_1 and T_2, which, on being placed in thermal contact, arrive eventually at a common equilibrium temperature, say, T_{12}, where $T_1 > T_{12} > T_2$ (Fig. 9.10). To determine the change in entropy, we cool the first body from T_1 to T_{12} and warm the second from T_2 to T_{12}, each process being reversible. The first process causes a fall in entropy, and the second a rise, ΔS being the net change. Thus

$$\Delta S = \int_{T_1}^{T_{12}} \frac{dQ_p}{T} + \int_{T_2}^{T_{12}} \frac{dQ_p}{T} = \int_{T_1}^{T_{12}} \frac{(C_p)_1 \, dT}{T} + \int_{T_2}^{T_{12}} \frac{(C_p)_2 \, dT}{T}$$

Integrating as before gives us

$$\Delta S = (C_p)_1 \ln \frac{T_{12}}{T_1} + (C_p)_2 \ln \frac{T_{12}}{T_2} \qquad (9.25)$$

Since $T_{12} < T_1$, the first term is negative. It can be shown under all circumstances to be less in absolute magnitude than the second term, so that $\Delta S > 0$, as we expect from the increase of entropy principle (form IIG). The direct proof of this relation, as well as the fact that the increase in unavailable energy is $T_0 \Delta S$, is left for the problems (see Problems 9.3 and 9.4). Here T_0 is the temperature of that reservoir in the neighborhood which is at the lowest temperature and which is used as a heat sink.

The same reasoning as that just presented can be extended to any group of n bodies coming to a final equilibrium. If the first two come to equilibrium together, these two as a single body reach equilibrium together with a third, etc., the over-all change is bound to be positive, since it is made up of the individual rises in the $(n - 1)$ equalizations leading to the final state. The over-all change is readily seen to be

$$\Delta S = \sum_{i=1}^{n} (C_p)_i \ln \frac{T_m}{T_i} \qquad (9.26)$$

where T_m is the final mixture temperature.

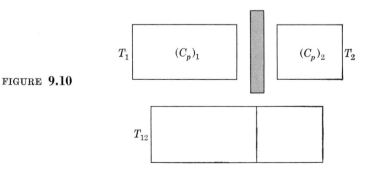

FIGURE **9.10**

9.10   Uses of Entropy

We have established the existence of entropy as a function of the coordinates fixing the state of a system and have examined some of its general properties.

It remains for us to investigate some of the more striking *uses* of this function, not only as a convenient parameter for describing a system in a graphical way, but also as a general mathematical variable on a par with the simpler quantities T, p, and V. This study will lead to a more careful examination of the origin of the function and finally to its interpretation in terms of molecular behavior and probability (Chap. 15).

9.11   Temperature-Entropy Diagram

Once entropy is established as a property of a system, we are free, in principle, to choose it as one of the variables or coordinates in terms of which to describe the system.

Thus if

$$S = S(x, y)$$

and with x and y chosen from the set T, V, and p, there are three new possible variable sets: S and T, S and V, and S and p. Since all systems, whether hydrostatic or not, possess both a temperature and an entropy, the first choice, S and T, is one of quite general applicability.

The use of S and T as variables has a number of advantages. In the first place, since for any reversible process

$$dQ_C = T\,dS \qquad\qquad (9.27)$$

the heat absorption, dQ_C, is graphically represented by the area of the thin strip of height T and width dS under the curve of change, C (Fig. 9.11). To obtain the total amount of heat absorbed, Q_C, in a reversible process, we have

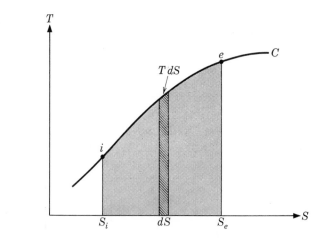

FIGURE **9.11**

merely to integrate $T\,dS$ under the curve in question from the start to the finish. Thus

$$Q_c = \int_i^e T\,dS \qquad (9.28)$$

and is represented by the shaded area in the figure.

Another great advantage of the T-S diagram is that with it the Carnot cycle is always a simple rectangle, irrespective of the working material or its equation of state (Fig. 9.12). Isotherms are horizontal, and adiabatics are vertical. The area of the cycle represents the net heat absorption, which is the net work performed, so that

$$\text{area of cycle} = Q_1 - Q_2 = W$$

The area $S_2 3 4 S_1$ gives the value of the rejected heat, Q_2.

FIGURE **9.12**

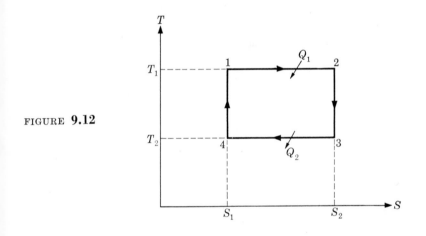

For given values of S_1 and S_2, the cycle area increases as T_1 is raised and T_2 is lowered. Any other cycle inscribed within the rectangle must have a smaller area than the Carnot cycle, even though it uses the same adiabatics (see Problem 9.6). Therefore, any other cycle, such as the Otto cycle or the Diesel cycle, utilizes its heat less efficiently than if it were all absorbed at the maximum temperature and rejected at the minimum temperature.

9.12   *dS* as a Perfect Differential

That dQ_c/T integrated around a reversible cycle always vanishes is, of course, the fundamental fact leading to the invention of the entropy function. From the differential standpoint, this means that although

$$dQ_c = dU - dW_c$$

is *not* a perfect differential, division through by the absolute temperature renders it perfect.

We may then make yet another useful statement of the second law (form IIJ): "The quantity dQ_C/T, where dQ_C is the reversibly added heat, is an exact or perfect differential, dS."

In other words, the discovery of the second law may be regarded as essentially the discovery of an *integrating factor* for the heat differential, dQ_C.

Consider a system describable in terms of the variables T and p. For it

$$dV = \left(\frac{\partial V}{\partial T}\right)_p dT + \left(\frac{\partial V}{\partial p}\right)_T dp$$

and

$$dU = \left(\frac{\partial U}{\partial T}\right)_p dT + \left(\frac{\partial U}{\partial p}\right)_T dp \tag{9.29}$$

and thus by the first law

$$dQ_C = \left[\left(\frac{\partial U}{\partial T}\right)_p + p\left(\frac{\partial V}{\partial T}\right)_p\right] dT + \left[\left(\frac{\partial U}{\partial p}\right)_T + p\left(\frac{\partial V}{\partial p}\right)_T\right] dp \tag{9.30}$$

Dividing this result through by T gives dS as

$$dS = \frac{1}{T}\left[\left(\frac{\partial U}{\partial T}\right)_p + p\left(\frac{\partial V}{\partial T}\right)_p\right] dT + \frac{1}{T}\left[\left(\frac{\partial U}{\partial p}\right)_T + p\left(\frac{\partial V}{\partial p}\right)_T\right] dp \tag{9.31}$$

The right side of each of the last four equations is a first-order linear differential form that can be written formally as

$$M(x,y)\,dx + N(x,y)\,dy \tag{9.32}$$

The first two and the last are *exact* differentials; that is, they represent the total differentials of state functions for the system. The third one is not an exact differential. The integrals of the first two and the last, taken around any closed cycle, are precisely zero. For the third one the result depends on the area enclosed and the curve involved.

Although the integral properties of differential forms are very useful, it is convenient to test for exactness directly without integration. Direct testing is possible by the well-known mathematical theorem stating that the necessary and sufficient condition that the differential form

$$M(x,y)\,dx + N(x,y)\,dy$$

shall be exact is that

$$\left[\frac{\partial M(x,y)}{\partial y}\right]_x = \left[\frac{\partial N(x,y)}{\partial x}\right]_y \tag{9.33}$$

We shall refer to this as the "cross derivative theorem" and shall have occasion to use it repeatedly.

Applying this test to the right of the expression for dU gives

$$\frac{\partial^2 U}{\partial p\,\partial T} = \frac{\partial^2 U}{\partial T\,\partial p} \tag{9.34}$$

a result that we know to be true, since the order of differentiation is immaterial whenever the first and second partial derivatives exist and are continuous. These conditions are amply fulfilled by most functions of physical origin.

For Eq. 9.30, the cross derivatives are clearly unequal since

$$\left(\frac{\partial V}{\partial T}\right)_p + p\,\frac{\partial^2 V}{\partial p\,\partial T} \neq p\,\frac{\partial^2 V}{\partial T\,\partial p} \tag{9.35}$$

After considerable cancellation, the dS expression gives

$$-T\left(\frac{\partial V}{\partial T}\right)_p = \left(\frac{\partial U}{\partial p}\right)_T + p\left(\frac{\partial V}{\partial p}\right)_T \tag{9.36}$$

Returning to Chap. 5, we see that the right side of this result is simply L_p, the latent heat of pressure rise,

$$L_p = \left(\frac{\partial U}{\partial p}\right)_T + p\left(\frac{\partial V}{\partial p}\right)_T \tag{5.28}$$

Consequently,

$$\boxed{L_p = -T\left(\frac{\partial V}{\partial T}\right)_p} \qquad \text{MI}$$

This result is one of an important set of relations first obtained by Maxwell. It is usually referred to (as in Chap. 7) as Maxwell's *first* relation and will be designated as MI.

We see that for the ideal gas, when $V = RT/p$,

$$L_p^\circ = -\frac{TR}{p} = -V$$

which is exactly the result arrived at in Chap. 5 by a special argument. The general form of this Maxwellian relation is now seen to be one of the general consequences of the second law.

The corresponding result for the variables T and V can be obtained by the process just described. It leads directly to Maxwell's *second* relation, giving the latent heat of volume expansion, L_V, as

$$\boxed{L_V = T\left(\frac{\partial p}{\partial T}\right)_V} \qquad \text{MII}$$

Its deduction is left to an exercise (see Problem 9.9) at this point, but it will be obtained by other methods later.

9.13   Heat Capacities as Entropy Derivatives

Another useful analytical property of the entropy function is that the heat capacities can all be written in terms of its partial derivatives.

By definition

$$C_V = \frac{dQ_V}{dT}$$

and since $dQ_C = T\,dS$, $dQ_V = T\,dS_V$, where dS_V is the change in S for a differential isochoric process. Thus

$$C_V = \frac{T\,dS_V}{dT}$$

Since dT is also taken at constant V, this result is the partial derivative of S with respect to T at constant V. Consequently,

$$C_V = T\left(\frac{\partial S}{\partial T}\right)_V \tag{9.37}$$

In general, we have for the heat capacity, $C_x{}^{(y)}$,

$$C_x{}^{(y)} = T\left(\frac{\partial S}{\partial y}\right)_x \tag{9.38}$$

and therefore

$$L_V = T\left(\frac{\partial S}{\partial V}\right)_T \tag{9.39}$$

$$C_p = T\left(\frac{\partial S}{\partial T}\right)_p \tag{9.40}$$

and

$$L_p = T\left(\frac{\partial S}{\partial p}\right)_T \tag{9.41}$$

These are important results and will be used frequently.

As examples, we may utilize them here to obtain the variations of C_V and C_p with volume and pressure, as well as a general relation between C_V and C_p. Consider first the variation of C_V with volume, $(\partial C_V/\partial V)_T$. If we differentiate Eq. 9.37 with respect to V at constant T, we have

$$\left(\frac{\partial C_V}{\partial V}\right)_T = T\frac{\partial^2 S}{\partial V\,\partial T} \tag{9.42}$$

On differentiating Eq. 9.39 with respect to T at constant V, we find, using Eq. 9.42,

$$\left(\frac{\partial L_V}{\partial T}\right)_V = \left(\frac{\partial S}{\partial V}\right)_T + T\frac{\partial^2 S}{\partial T\,\partial V} = \left(\frac{\partial S}{\partial V}\right)_T + \left(\frac{\partial C_V}{\partial V}\right)_T \tag{9.43}$$

whereas on differentiating MII directly, we find

$$\left(\frac{\partial L_V}{\partial T}\right)_V = \left(\frac{\partial p}{\partial T}\right)_V + T\left(\frac{\partial^2 p}{\partial T^2}\right)_V \tag{9.44}$$

A comparison of Eqs. 9.43 and 9.44 and use of MII and Eq. 9.39 give

$$\left(\frac{\partial C_V}{\partial V}\right)_T = T\left(\frac{\partial^2 p}{\partial T^2}\right)_V \tag{9.45}$$

Similarly, calculating $(\partial C_p/\partial p)_T$ from Eq. 9.40 and $(\partial L_p/\partial T)_p$ from Eq. 9.41 and using MI and Eq. 9.41 give

$$\left(\frac{\partial C_p}{\partial p}\right)_T = -T\left(\frac{\partial^2 V}{\partial T^2}\right)_p \tag{9.46}$$

These results show that the rates of change in question are computable directly from the equation of state without any thermal data being required. We note for future reference that neither $(\partial C_V/\partial T)_V$ nor $(\partial C_p/\partial T)_p$ can be determined by this device. They require information not contained in the equation of state.

To find the connection between C_p and C_V, which was anticipated in Chap. 7, Eq. 7.12, we proceed as follows. Since

$$C_p = T\left(\frac{\partial S}{\partial T}\right)_p$$

we express $(\partial S/\partial T)_p$ in terms of dT and dV.

$$C_p = T\left(\frac{\partial S}{\partial T}\right)_V \left(\frac{\partial T}{\partial T}\right)_p + T\left(\frac{\partial S}{\partial V}\right)_T \left(\frac{\partial V}{\partial T}\right)_p$$

where $T(\partial S/\partial T)_V$ is, of course, C_V. With the help of MII this equation can be written

$$C_p = C_V + T\left(\frac{\partial p}{\partial T}\right)_V \left(\frac{\partial V}{\partial T}\right)_p \tag{9.47}$$

Use of the reciprocity relation and the definitions of β_p and κ_T gives finally

$$C_p - C_V = \left(\frac{V\beta_p{}^2 T}{\kappa_T}\right) \tag{7.12}$$

9.14 Entropy of an Ideal Gas

Let us now calculate the entropy of an ideal gas. Since

$$dS = \frac{dQ_C}{T}$$

we may use that dQ_C expression involving the desired independent variables. With T and V, the second dQ_C expression becomes, for a mole of gas,

$$dQ_C = C_V^\circ \, dT + p \, dV = C_V^\circ \, dT + RT \frac{dV}{V}$$

and therefore

$$dS = C_V^\circ \frac{dT}{T} + R \frac{dV}{V} \tag{9.48}$$

This equation is integrable in principle since C_V° is a function of T alone and the variables are separated as they stand.

For the ideal monatomic gas Eq. 9.48 may be integrated directly, since $C_V^\circ = \tfrac{3}{2}R$. For the open integral

$$S^\circ = S^\circ(T, V) = \tfrac{3}{2}R \ln T + R \ln V + S_{0TV} \tag{9.49}$$

where S_{0TV} is the so-called entropy constant, the unknown constant of integration. (Here the subscript TV is needed to identify the variable pair to which the constant is appropriate.) Replacing V by RT/p changes the variables, and

$$S^\circ = S^\circ(T, p) = \tfrac{5}{2}R \ln T - R \ln p + S_{0Tp} \tag{9.50}$$

where $S_{0Tp} = R \ln R + S_{0TV}$ is the appropriate entropy constant for the new variables.

For more complicated ideal gases C_V° may be expressed as a power series for limited temperature ranges. Thus

$$C_V^\circ = C_0 + C_1 T + C_2 T^2 + C_3 T^3 \cdots$$

or simply

$$C_V^\circ = \Sigma C_i T^i \tag{9.51}$$

where $i = 0$, 1, etc. Eq. 9.48 may be integrated between T_0, V_0 and T, V to give

$$\Delta S^\circ = S^\circ - S_0^\circ = \left(\sum \int_{T_0}^{T} C_i T^{i-1} \, dT \right) + R \ln \frac{V}{V_0} \tag{9.52}$$

Here $S_0^\circ = S^\circ(T_0, V_0)$ is the absolute value of the entropy at T_0, V_0. For sufficiently small temperature ranges we can always neglect the variation of C_V°, and the series in Eq. 9.51 therefore reduces to the first term, with $C_0 = C_{V_0}^\circ$. Then

$$S^\circ(T, V) = S_0^\circ(T_0, V_0) + C_{V_0}^\circ \ln \frac{T}{T_0} + R \ln \frac{V}{V_0} \tag{9.53}$$

This equation shows at once why doubling the volume isothermally increases S by $R \ln 2$. The same result was obtained in Sec. 9.6 by the reversible addition of heat and integration of dQ_T/T for the particular process. Now it appears as a special case of the general integral of dS.

Changing the variables in Eq. 9.53 to T and p gives us

$$S°(T, p) = S°(T_0, p_0) + C_{p_0}° \ln \frac{T}{T_0} - R \ln \frac{p}{p_0} \qquad (9.54)$$

where $C_{p_0}° = C_{V_0}° + R$ and $S°(T_0, p_0) = S°(T_0, V_0)$. The latter quantity is the value of the entropy at the standard reference point, and it cannot change with a mere change of variable. Note that this condition is not true for the constants in Eqs. 9.49 and 9.50. (See Problem 9.7.)

Since Eq. 9.49 gives S as a function of T and V, it should represent the equation for the ideal gas adiabatic (with $C_V°$ a constant) when S is constant. Separating out the constant terms in Eq. 9.53 and lumping them together as S_{0TV}, we have

$$S_{0TV} = S°(T_0, V_0) - C_V° \ln T_0 - R \ln V_0$$

and Eq. 9.53 becomes

$$S°(T, V) - S_{0TV} = \ln T^{C_V°} V^R$$

With exponentials this may be written

$$\exp (S° - S_{0TV}) = T^{C_V°} V^R$$

If $S°$ is held constant as a parameter, the left side becomes a constant, and therefore

$$T^{C_V°} V^R = \text{constant}$$

or

$$T V^{R/C_V°} = K \qquad (9.55)$$

where K is a new constant.

With $\gamma = C_p/C_V$, we can always write

$$\gamma_0° - 1 = \frac{R}{C_V°}$$

Hence Eq. 9.55 reduces to

$$T V^{\gamma_0°-1} = K \qquad (9.56)$$

which is essentially the adiabatic law in Eq. 5.62, with $\gamma_0°$ being recognized as the ideal gas value of γ when its temperature variation is neglected. As the value of $S°$ is allowed to change, K alters, and we thus obtain a family of adiabatics covering the T-V plane.

9.15   General Laboratory Equations for *dU*, *dH*, and *dS*

To obtain general equations for the direct calculation of changes in internal energy, enthalpy, and entropy, we need expressions for dU, dH, and dS in terms of directly measurable quantities. Such expressions may be termed "laboratory equations" and may be obtained through the use of MI and MII.

For dU we have merely to rewrite the first law for a hydrostatic system, $dU = dQ_c - p\,dV$. On substitution of the second dQ_c expression and use of MII, we have

$$dQ_c = C_V\,dT + T\left(\frac{\partial p}{\partial T}\right)_V dV \tag{9.57}$$

and therefore

$$dU = C_V\,dT + \left[T\left(\frac{\partial p}{\partial T}\right)_V - p\right]dV \tag{9.58}$$

This is the laboratory equation for dU, since the coefficients of both dT and dV contain quantities that can be measured directly, or calculated from the equation of state.

To obtain the corresponding expression for dH, we proceed as in Chap. 8, writing

$$dH = dU + p\,dV + V\,dp$$

Combining this relation with the first law gives

$$dH = dQ_c + V\,dp$$

Since p is now a naturally indicated independent variable, we turn to the first dQ_c expression and replace L_p by means of MI, to obtain

$$dQ_c = C_p\,dT - T\left(\frac{\partial V}{\partial T}\right)_p dp \tag{9.59}$$

and

$$dH = C_p\,dT + \left[V - T\left(\frac{\partial V}{\partial T}\right)_p\right]dp \tag{9.60}$$

In a similar way division of Eqs. 9.57 and 9.59 by T gives us two equivalent expressions for dS,

$$dS = C_V\frac{dT}{T} + \left(\frac{\partial p}{\partial T}\right)_V dV$$

$$dS = C_p\frac{dT}{T} - \left(\frac{\partial V}{\partial T}\right)_p dp \tag{9.61}$$

These differential equations are the general ones by which changes in the thermodynamic quantities U, H, and S are evaluated. For this evaluation we must select a standard reference level and integrate each expression along a suitable path to any desired variable point. Note that with the value of dH given in Eq. 9.60 we no longer need the approximation made in Sec. 7.12.

9.16   Thermodynamic Potentials

Let us now look at the properties of internal energy, enthalpy, and entropy from a slightly different viewpoint.

   Internal Energy.   Since for any reversible process

$$dU = dQ_c - p\,dV \tag{9.62}$$

for any adiabatic process

$$dQ_{ad} = dQ_S = 0$$

and

$$-dU_S = p\,dV$$

That is, internal energy is such a quantity that its *decrease* during an isentropic process gives the *maximum external work* we can get out of the system.

   For an isochoric process, $dV = 0$, and

$$dU_V = dQ_V$$

so that the increase in U represents the *isochoric heat addition*.

   Enthalpy.   Since

$$dH = dQ_c + V\,dp \tag{9.63}$$

as we have seen so often before,

$$dH_p = dQ_p$$

A change in enthalpy, then, represents the heat absorption in an isobaric process.

   Entropy.   The definition

$$dQ_c = T\,dS$$

suggests that we may rewrite the first law as given in Eqs. 9.62 and 9.63 by eliminating dQ_c entirely. Thus

$$\boxed{dU = T\,dS - p\,dV} \tag{9.64}$$

and

$$\boxed{dH = T\,dS + V\,dp} \tag{9.65}$$

where dU and dH are expressed as the simplest possible linear differential forms of the type of Eq. 9.32. Note that this treatment is possible only if we admit S to the group $T, p,$ and V as a full-fledged thermodynamic variable. For this reason we shall hereafter regard the set $S, T, p,$ and V as so-called *primary* variables and feel free to choose whichever pair is best suited to a given problem.

Since U, H, and S are unique functions of a system's state, they are usually taken together as members of a class of so-called "characteristic functions," "state functions," or *thermodynamic potentials*. Note that the natural variables to be used with U are S and V, whereas H requires the set S and p.

9.17   The Potentials of Helmholtz and Gibbs

If to any thermodynamic potential another single-valued function of the coordinates is added, automatically a new single-valued function (that is, a new potential) is produced. By this method we might invent an infinite number of potentials, although most of them would have little physical significance.

Another technique for creating a potential is to begin with the *differential* of a potential (which by definition is exact) and then to add to it another exact differential. Thus the addition of $d(pV) = p\,dV + V\,dp$ to the right side of Eq. 9.64 gives us the right side of Eq. 9.65, that is, the differential dH. By adding $d(pV)$ we have, in effect, replaced $-p\,dV$ by $V\,dp$ to obtain the new exact differential dH. This type of transformation is known as a *Legendre differential transformation*. The process can be equally well carried out in either direction.

Helmholtz's Potential. Let us now transform Eq. 9.64 by subtracting $d(TS) = T\,dS + S\,dT$. The result is

$$-S\,dT - p\,dV$$

The new potential, of which this is the exact differential, was first investigated by Helmholtz and is usually termed the *free energy* of *Helmholtz* (to differentiate it from other functions that have been given the name free energy). If we designate it by the letter A (from German *Arbeit*)

$$\boxed{dA = -S\,dT - p\,dV} \qquad (9.66)$$

For any reversible isothermal process, A is such a quantity that

$$-dA_T = p\,dV$$

That is, a *decrease* in A represents the *maximum amount of external work* that the system can perform without a change in temperature. (If the change is irreversible, naturally less work is obtained; it may, in fact, vanish as in the case of free expansion and the other spontaneous processes discussed earlier in the chapter.)

To obtain an expression for A itself, we notice that $d(TS)$ was subtracted from dU to get dA and hence that

$$dA = dU - d(TS) = d(U - TS)$$

or

$$\boxed{A = U - TS} \tag{9.67}$$

where the natural variables for the potential A are T and V.

For finite isothermal processes we may write, from Eq. 9.67,

$$\Delta A_T = \Delta U_T - T \Delta S_T = \Delta U_T - \Delta Q_T$$

When ΔA_T is negative, the free energy decreases, the absolute value of the decrease measuring the maximum external work. The internal energy also decreases, but the decrease in U_T, ΔU_T, does not measure the external work as it does in purely mechanical systems. In fact,

$$\text{external work} \gtrless |\Delta U_T|$$

according to whether $\Delta Q_T \gtrless 0$. This relation emphasizes a significant difference between mechanical and thermodynamic systems. Mechanical systems are usually thought of as isolated, whereas thermodynamic ones may or may not be, depending on conditions.

Gibbs' Potential.   If we subject dA to a Legendre transformation by adding $d(pV)$ to the right of Eq. 9.66, we obtain

$$- S\,dT + V\,dp$$

the differential of a potential invented by Gibbs. Designating this new potential by G, we have

$$\boxed{dG = - S\,dT + V\,dp}$$

The advantage of the Gibbs potential is that it alone of the thermodynamic potentials remains unaltered for processes occurring at constant T *and* p, the usual laboratory condition for changes of phase, chemical reactions, etc. Thus Gibbs' potential is of great value in the immense field of heterogeneous changes (whether chemical or physical).

Since dG results from the addition of $d(pV)$ to dA,

$$dG = dA + d(pV) = d(A + pV) \tag{9.68}$$

or

$$\boxed{G = U - TS + pV} \tag{9.69}$$

Attempts to invent more than the four potentials U, H, A, and G by Legendre transformations simply give us members of the same set. Evidently (with the primary variables) this is a closed set as far as Legendre transformations are concerned.

As an example of the behavior of the Gibbs potential, consider the evaporation of a liquid. Here

$$dG_{Tp} = d(U + pV) - T\,dS = dH - T\,dS$$

Since T and p are constant, dG_{Tp} must vanish, and therefore

$$dH = T\,dS$$

or
$$\Delta H = T\,\Delta S$$

which is seen to be true automatically since $\Delta H = \Lambda$ and $\Delta S = \Lambda/T$. In other words, the Gibbs potential of the system does not alter as the *amount* of the two phases present alters. Hence the Gibbs potential of a gram of pure substance in the liquid phase must equal that of a gram of the pure vapor, or, if we are at the triple point, the specific Gibbs' potentials of the three phases are alike, and therefore

$$g' = g'' = g'''$$

9.18   The Clausius Equations

The expressions for dU, dH, dA, and dG given earlier are collected here for reference.

$$dU = T\,dS - p\,dV \qquad\qquad \text{CI}$$
$$dH = T\,dS + V\,dp \qquad\qquad \text{CII}$$
$$dA = -S\,dT - p\,dV \qquad\qquad \text{CIII}$$
$$dG = -S\,dT + V\,dp \qquad\qquad \text{CIV}$$

The first was used by Clausius as an analytical combination of the first and second laws. Since the others are essentially similar combinations in different variables, we shall refer to them hereafter as the *Clausius equations* and designate them simply as CI, CII, CIII, and CIV.

A further interesting and suggestive property of the Clausius equations should be mentioned. Each of the primary variables (S, T, p, and V) can be represented as an appropriate partial derivative obtained from them. Thus we have

$$\left(\frac{\partial U}{\partial S}\right)_V = T = \left(\frac{\partial H}{\partial S}\right)_p$$

$$\left(\frac{\partial U}{\partial V}\right)_S = -p = \left(\frac{\partial A}{\partial V}\right)_T$$

$$\left(\frac{\partial H}{\partial p}\right)_S = V = \left(\frac{\partial G}{\partial p}\right)_T$$

$$\left(\frac{\partial A}{\partial T}\right)_V = -S = \left(\frac{\partial G}{\partial T}\right)_p \qquad\qquad \textbf{(9.70)}$$

In this sense the potentials U, H, A, and G represent a different order or level of physical quantities from that of the *primary* variables T, S, V, and p. For this reason it is convenient to refer to them as *secondary* quantities or variables.

The subject of thermodynamics was begun with the quantities T, p, and V regarded as fundamental. Later entropy was added to this set. From the preceding analysis, however, we may well regard the secondary quantities or potentials as more basic. Thus we may agree to define the absolute temperature, T, as simply the rate of increase of U per unit increase in S (at constant volume) and the absolute pressure, p, as the rate of decrease of U with V at constant S. This possibility becomes of practical importance when later, from purely statistical considerations, we are able to obtain theoretical expressions for U and S. Then T and p may be calculated directly from these theoretical relations for the system in question.

9.19   The Principle of Carathéodory

In the search for a rigorous mathematical basis for the concept of entropy, without recourse to the usual thermodynamic paraphernalia of Carnot engines, closed cycles, and the like, Carathéodory stated the problem thus: "What form must the second law assume in order that the definition of the exact differential dS, as

$$dS = \frac{dQ_C}{T}$$

may follow as a logical mathematical consequence?"

His point of departure is the linear differential form discussed earlier, that is,

$$M(x,y)\, dx + N(x,y)\, dy \tag{9.32}$$

Linear forms in two variables are always integrable directly or may be rendered integrable by multiplication through by a suitable *integrating factor*. This means that if $\rho = \rho(x,y)$ is an integrating factor, then by definition there exists a function, $f(x,y)$, such that

$$\rho M\, dx + \rho N\, dy = df \tag{9.71}$$

Thus $f(x,y)$ is the function of which $\rho M\, dx + \rho N\, dy$ is the exact differential.

If we set $f(x,y) = C$, where C is a parameter, then as C is allowed to vary, there results a family of curves with one curve only passing through any given point in the x-y plane. Since for each such curve $df = 0$, these curves satisfy the differential equation

$$\rho M\, dx + \rho N\, dy = 0 \tag{9.72}$$

and are therefore called *solution curves* of this equation.

Differentially speaking, Eq. 9.72 states that at any point, P, there is a line element of components dx and dy that is *perpendicular* to a vector of components ρM and ρN. The solution curve through P is tangent to this line element and is unique. Since

$$\rho M \, dx + \rho N \, dy$$

is *integrable*, a *single solution* curve passes through any point, P, of the x-y plane.

With three or more variables, the linear form in general is *not* integrable. If we take the three-variable case as typical, this means that the linear form

$$M(x, y, z) \, dx + N(x, y, z) \, dy + O(x, y, z) \, dz \qquad (9.73)$$

in general has *no integrating factor*, and hence no factor $\rho(x, y, z)$ and function $f(x, y, z)$ exist such that

$$\rho M \, dx + \rho N \, dy + \rho O \, dz = df$$

In such a case we can always find a curve through any point, P, that is perpendicular to the vector having the components ρM, ρN, and ρO. But this curve is not unique; in fact, we can pass as many curves as we like through each point. Thus the essence of "being integrable" is the existence of *unique* solution curves, and this property is not possessed in general by differential forms of more than two variables.

We now return to the expressions for dQ_c, which by means of the first law may always be written as a linear differential form in terms of the variables chosen. With a two-variable hydrostatic system and T and V as the indpendent pair,

$$dQ_c = C_V(T, V) \, dT + L_V(T, V) \, dV \qquad (9.74)$$

For a typical three-variable system, such as the surface film under hydrostatic pressure discussed in Sec. 5.13,

$$dQ_c = C_{pA}^{(T)} \, dT + C_{TA}^{(p)} \, dp + C_{Tp}^{(A)} \, dA \qquad (9.75)$$

where the three coefficients are functions of T, p, and A (the area).

Division of these expressions by the absolute temperature renders them integrable, which is tantamount to saying that

$$\frac{C_V \, dT}{T} + \frac{L_V \, dV}{T} = 0$$

and

$$\frac{C_{pA}^{(T)} \, dT}{T} + \frac{C_{TA}^p \, dp}{T} + \frac{C_{Tp}^A \, dA}{T} = 0 \qquad (9.76)$$

are *integrable* and that $1/T$ has the special power of rendering dQ_c an *exact differential, whatever the system and the number of independent variables involved.* This property of $1/T$ must reflect some very special character in the natural world. In particular, the existence of entropy as a solution function for differential equations of the type of Eq. 9.76 must be due to this special property or character of the world in which we live.

Carathéodory felt that this special property should receive a clear statement in a new formulation of the second law—a statement involving provable properties of linear differential forms from which the existence of entropy would follow at once. He reached this new formulation[2] from a general mathematical theorem, which we may now consider.

For purposes of simplicity we confine ourselves again to the case of three variables. Imagine a three-dimensional space with the rectangular coordinates x, y, and z. Let P_0 be any point in this space with coordinates x_0, y_0, and z_0. Then Carathéodory's mathematical theorem is as follows: "There exist points in the neighborhood of P_0 that are *not accessible* from P_0 along solution curves of the equation

$$M\,dx + N\,dy + O\,dz = 0 \qquad (9.77)$$

if, and only if, the equation is integrable."

It is clear that if Eq. 9.77 is integrable, we have a solution curve through point P_0 that is unique. Any points *not on such a curve* through P_0 cannot be reached from P_0 (without moving off the solution curve).

For the physical application we write the first law as

$$dQ_C = M\,dx + N\,dy + O\,dz = \frac{df}{\rho}$$

If $\rho = 1/T$ and $df = dS$, we have the existence of entropy as a direct consequence of the physical fact expressed in Carathéodory's principle. As a result, two entropy curves may never cross; every state has *one* and *only one* value of entropy.

9.20   Natural, Unnatural, and Reversible Processes

If a solution curve of Eq. 9.77 passes through a point, P_0, another solution curve can always pass through a neighboring point, P (see Fig. 9.13). Let the entropies assigned to these two adiabatics be S_0 and S, respectively. For the transition from P_0 to P, the following conditions hold:

1. If $S > S_0$, the transition can always be brought about by a suitable, that is, *irreversible*, process.

2. If $S = S_0$, the transition is possible by means of a *reversible adiabatic* process, and the two curves are identical.

3. If $S < S_0$, the transition is *completely impossible* as long as the system remains isolated.

---

[2] Carathéodory, *Math. Ann.*, **67**, 355 (1909); *Sitzber. preuss Akad. Wiss. Physik.-math. Kl.*, **1925**, 39. See also Buchdahl *Am. J. Phys.*, **17**, 41 (1949), where an excellent discussion of the subject is given; and Turner, *Am. J. Phys.*, **28**, 781 (1960).

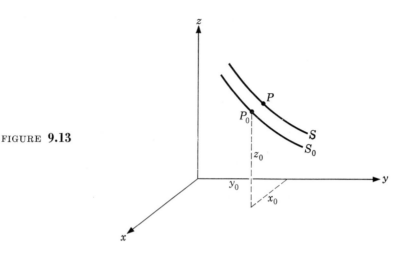

FIGURE **9.13**

In view of these conditions, all conceivable processes can be conveniently divided into three classes:

1. *Natural* processes, for which $\Delta S = S - S_0 > 0$.
2. *Reversible* processes, for which $\Delta S = S - S_0 = 0$.
3. *Unnatural* processes, for which $\Delta S = S - S_0 < 0$.

Natural processes, of course, are the spontaneous, irreversible processes that actually take place in nature. An unnatural process may be thought of as the exact opposite of some natural one. Examples of unnatural processes are the flow of heat from a cold body to a hot body, a gas's compressing itself to a smaller volume, a mixture's separating itself into pure substances, etc. Of course, unnatural processes are unnatural only in closed systems. They can always be brought about artificially, as it were, if outside agents are allowed to act on a system. However, even then they can never involve a net decrease in the total entropy of the universe.

On the basis of the preceding classification, we may write for any isolated system (one therefore with fixed internal energy)

$$\Delta S \gtreqless 0 \tag{9.78}$$

The reversible process thus takes its place as the ideal limiting process, which in the case of isolated systems separates *natural* processes from *unnatural* processes and *possible* processes from *impossible* processes.

The very general limitations on the way in which a system's entropy must behave naturally suggest the search for a general explanation in molecular terms. If the entropy of an isolated system can, at most, increase, this increase must reflect some natural property of particles taken in large numbers. This natural property Boltzmann took to be the tendency for a system to pass from states which were, molecularly speaking, *more ordered* to those showing *less order*, that is, from order to disorder. From the molecular standpoint highly ordered states are not expected to occur very often; they are less *probable* than the highly disordered, chaotic states met with in systems in or near equilibrium. With a gas we might at some instant find all the molecules by chance in the upper half of the vessel, or each having exactly the average molecular speed for the whole gas, or all having velocities parallel to one or the other of the coordinate axes. But such conditions of high molecular order or, better, *low disorder* occur relatively rarely and are thus *low-probability states*. On the other hand, as molecules collide with one another, whatever degree of order may have existed decreases, and the disorder increases. In the final thermodynamic state of equilibrium, the disorder has reached the maximum value possible for the system. This state has a high probability, and if the system could be observed at short intervals (on a molecular level), it would be found to be in this disordered state for an overwhelming majority of the observations. Thus the most disordered state is the state of highest probability. If entropy is regarded as a function of the molecular disorder, which in turn fixes the probability of a state, entropy becomes a function of probability, and the natural increase of entropy in an isolated system becomes understandable. From the molecular standpoint the truth of the second law is a matter of very high probability— not absolute certainty. The entropy of an isolated system may decrease spontaneously, to be sure, but the odds against a decrease are extraordinarily great.

The molecular interpretation of entropy has been a very fruitful idea. It will be developed in detail in Chap. 15 and provide a general approach to the statistics of physical systems.

Problems

9.1 Consider the "truth" of the following statements:
(a) The entropy of the universe must be increasing.
(b) There exists no method whereby the entropy of the universe can be decreased.

9.2 Let 75,000 joules of mechanical energy be dissipated as heat in 3 kg of water originally at 15°C. Assuming that 15°C is also the lowest available temperature, what percentage of this energy is reconvertible into work?

9.3 Prove without appeal to the second law that the expression for the change in entropy when two bodies come to a common temperature must be positive, that is, that

$$\Delta S = (C_p)_1 \ln \frac{T_{12}}{T_1} + (C_p)_2 \ln \frac{T_{12}}{T_2} > 0 \qquad (9.25)$$

(where $T_1 > T_{12} > T_2$) whatever T_1 and T_2 or the heat capacities $(C_p)_1$ and $(C_p)_2$ may be.

9.4 Consider a reservoir at T_0. If $T_0 < T_2$ in Problem 9.3, show that the loss in available energy (that is, energy available for mechanical purposes) due to the process of temperature equalization is given by

$$T_0 \Delta S = T_0 \left[(C_p)_1 \ln \frac{T_{12}}{T_1} + (C_p)_2 \ln \frac{T_{12}}{T_2} \right]$$

9.5 Suppose that N_A molecules of a monatomic gas of type A in volume V_A and N_B molecules of another type, B, in volume V_B are at the same temperature and mix to give a total volume $V_A + V_B$ (at the original temperature). Show that if $\nu R = Nk$, k being Boltzmann's constant, R/N_0, we can write for the pure gases

$$S_A = N_A k(\ln V_A + \ln T^{3\!/\!2} + \ln C_A)$$

and
$$S_B = N_B k(\ln V_B + \ln T^{3\!/\!2} + \ln C_B)$$

where $N_A k \ln C_A$ and $N_B k \ln C_B$ are the appropriate integration constants for these amounts of gas and these variables. If the entropy after mixing is calculated as though each gas existed alone at the volume $V_A + V_B$, we have

$$S_{A+B} = N_A k[\ln (V_A + V_B) + \ln T^{3\!/\!2} + \ln C_A] + N_B k[\ln (V_A + V_B) + \ln T^{3\!/\!2} \times \ln C_B]$$

$V_A + V_B$ being the total volume after mixing, so that the value of ΔS given in Eq. 9.21 results when T is constant.

9.6 Using the equations for the entropy of an ideal gas, sketch the T-S diagram for the following cycles:
(a) Otto,
(b) Sargent,
(c) Diesel, and
(d) Joule.

9.7 How do you reconcile the fact that

$$S_{0T_p} = R \ln R + S_{0TV}$$

with the remarks following Eq. 9.54 in Sec. 9.14?

9.8 The passage from $\Sigma \, \Delta Q_T/T$ to $\int dQ_C/T$ in Clausius' sum theorem may be examined in more detail. Consider a curve of change, C (Fig. 9.14), and a jagged

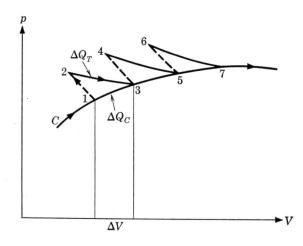

FIGURE **9.14**

curve, 1234567, made up out of alternate adiabatics, $1 \rightarrow 2$, $3 \rightarrow 4$, etc., and isotherms, $2 \rightarrow 3$, $4 \rightarrow 5$, etc. If ΔQ_T and ΔQ_c are heats absorbed along the isothermal sections and along the elements of the curve itself, show by the first law that $\lim \Sigma \Delta Q_T \rightarrow \lim \Sigma \Delta Q_c$ as the points 1, 3, 5, etc., approach one another and therefore that we may write

$$\lim \sum \frac{\Delta Q_T}{T} = \lim \sum \frac{\Delta Q_c}{T} = \int \frac{dQ_c}{T}$$

9.9 Using the cross derivative method on the terms in an expression for dS analogous to Eq. 9.31, but with the independent variables T and V, prove Maxwell's second relation,

$$L_V = T \left(\frac{\partial p}{\partial T} \right)_V$$

CHAPTER TEN

The Steam Engine and the Refrigerator

10.1 Introduction

The early developement of the subject of thermodynamics was closely connected with the behavior of heat engines, in particular the steam engine. We are now in a position to examine the problems posed by heat engines in the light of the general principles outlined in the previous chapters. It was pointed out in Chap. 8 that no actual engine employs the Carnot cycle, or, in fact, any reversible cycle. The justification for discussing quasistatic frictionless cycles is simply that in no other way can we obtain generalized upper limits on the performances of real engines. In this chapter the discussion will be confined largely to steam engines and the simpler types of refrigerators. It will serve as a useful introduction to more technical engineering treatises.

10.2 The Rankine Cycle

Although in principle the reciprocating steam engine could employ the Carnot cycle of Fig. 8.11, in practice it does not. Even if the four steps in this Carnot cycle were carried out in a single cylinder, it would not be practical, for example, to adjust the piston swing so that on adiabatic compression the piston would reach the limit of its swing exactly when the wet mixture was condensed to pure liquid at point 1. With a small error of adjustment, the piston would be forced to compress pure liquid near the end of the stroke with severe mechanical damage to the engine. In practice, therefore, it is more economical to carry out various parts of the cycle in separate units, each designed for the purpose.

In Fig. 10.1 a practical cycle of operations is illustrated schematically. Saturated water is evaporated in the boiler and passes through valve #1 into the cylinder proper, forcing the piston to the right. At an appropriate steam cutoff point, valve #1 closes, and the hot steam expands adiabatically, cooling to the lower temperature (end of power stroke). The piston returns to the left as valve #2 opens, and the exhaust steam is forced into the condenser. Here it condenses to liquid, its latent heat being carried off by cooling water.

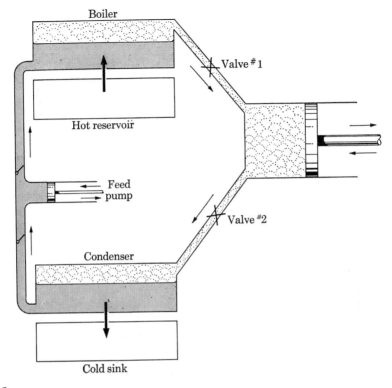

Boiler

Valve #1

Hot reservoir

Feed pump

Valve #2

Condenser

Cold sink

FIGURE **10.1**

The condensed water is thereafter drawn out of the condenser by the feed pump and forced under pressure into the boiler. Here it mixes with the hot boiler water and is warmed to the boiler temperature, and the cycle is completed.

The idealized reversible cycle corresponding to this scheme is called the *Rankine* cycle and is illustrated in Fig. 10.2, where p and the specific volume, v, of a unit mass of water substance are the coordinates. The lightly drawn curve is the saturation curve, and three isotherms are shown as dashed lines: the middle one for T_1, the boiler temperature; the bottom one for T_2, the condenser temperature; and the top one for any superheat temperature, T_3. Since the cycle can be started at any point, we begin with a unit mass of cold saturated liquid in the condenser, point a in the figure, at pressure p_2 and temperature T_2. The Rankine cycle consists of the following five idealized parts:

1. $a \rightarrow b$ Reversible adiabatic compression of the cold condenser water from p_2 to p_1, during which a small but negligible temperature rise occurs.
2. $b \rightarrow c$ Reversible isobaric heating of the compressed feed pump water from T_2 (essentially) to the boiler temperature, T_1.
3. $c \rightarrow d$ Isothermal (and isobaric) evaporation of the water to saturated steam at d, the required heat being taken from the hot reservoir.

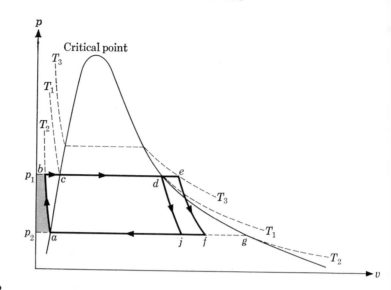

FIGURE **10.2**

4. $d \rightarrow j$ Adiabatic reversible expansion of the steam to a wet mixture of steam and a small percentage of water at T_2 (and p_2). (Here g represents the saturated vapor.)

5. $j \rightarrow a$ Reversible condensation of the steam to saturated liquid, which completes the cycle. The heat is absorbed by the cold reservoir.

It is often desirable to utilize some of the heat of the hot flue gases from the boiler. The saturated steam at d is accordingly piped into the flue, where it is heated further at constant pressure to temperature T_3, at e. The so-called *superheated* (really undersaturated) steam then expands adiabatically to f and is thereafter condensed to the state represented by a, as before.

The Rankine cycle differs from the Carnot cycle basically in that the passage from the lower temperature, T_2, to T_1 is not along an adiabatic. True, the boiler water is compressed adiabatically from p_2 to p_1, but the corresponding temperature rise is quite small (see Problem 10.1). When the cold boiler water is heated in the boiler from T_2 to T_1, a substantial amount of heat is absorbed at temperatures below T_1. In the idealized cycle this heat is envisaged as being supplied in the usual reversible manner by an array of reservoirs with temperatures ranging from T_2 to T_1. Likewise, when superheating takes place, heat is absorbed over a range of temperatures from T_1 to T_3. This heat is used more efficiently than if it were taken in at T_1 but less efficiently than if it were all absorbed at T_3.

10.3   Efficiency of the Rankine Cycle

The efficiency of the Rankine cycle can be expressed very simply in terms of enthalpy. For the cycle with superheating, heat is absorbed at constant pressure along $b \to e$, and the heat absorbed, q_1, is measured directly by the change in enthalpy:

$$q_1 = h_e - h_b$$

The heat rejected, q_2, is all rejected at the constant lower pressure, p_2, along the path $f \to a$, and

$$q_2 = h_f - h_a$$

Therefore, the Rankine efficiency is

$$\eta_{\text{Rankine}} = \frac{q_1 - q_2}{q_1} = \frac{h_e - h_b - h_f + h_a}{h_e - h_b} \tag{10.1}$$

Since h_b, the enthalpy of the compressed condenser water, is not usually recorded in steam tables, the difference $h_b - h_a$ is evaluated as follows. From CII, dh for an adiabatic process is

$$dh = v \, dp$$

Integration from a to b gives

$$h_b - h_a = \int_a^b v \, dp = \overline{v''}(p_1 - p_2) = v''_2(p_1 - p_2)$$

where, owing to the slight compressibility of the liquid, the average value of v'' has been replaced by the specific volume at a, v''_2. The term $v''_2(p_1 - p_2)$ is the so-called feed pump term and is usually quite small. It is represented by the shaded area in Fig. 10.2. Adding $h_b - h_a$ to and subtracting it from the denominator of Eq. 10.1 enables us to write

$$\eta_{\text{Rankine}} = \frac{h_e - h_f - v''_2(p_1 - p_2)}{h_e - h_a - v''_2(p_1 - p_2)} \tag{10.2}$$

10.4   Steam Tables

To facilitate calculations using the results of Sec. 10.3, standard steam tables recording the thermodynamic properties of steam in a useful form have been compiled. These tables give the properties of saturated liquid water, saturated steam, and superheated steam. The saturated steam tables are divided into two parts. The first gives the values of p, v'', v', h'', h', s'', and s' for integral values of temperature (as the independent variable). The second gives the same data recalculated for integral values of pressure. The superheat tables are double-entry ones, since the data for superheated steam must be recorded for suitable ranges of both temperature and pressure as independent variables.

To determine the values of h and s for any particular state of water, we must integrate the corresponding expressions for dh and ds from some satisfactory reference level, say, 0°C and $p = 4$ mm of mercury (the vapor pressure of water at the triple point), to this state. This reference level is indicated by 0 in Fig. 10.3.

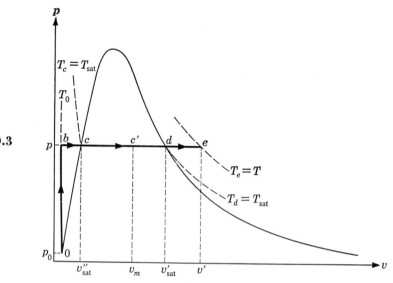

FIGURE **10.3**

Eq. 9.60 gives for dh

$$dh = c_p \, dT + \left[v - T \left(\frac{\partial v}{\partial T} \right)_p \right] dp$$

The value of the enthalpy, h''_{sat}, for any point, c, on the liquid saturation curve is obtained on integration from 0 along the T_0 isotherm to b and then along the isobar $b \rightarrow c$. With $T_b = T_0$ and $T_c = T_{\text{sat}}$,

$$h''_{\text{sat}} = h_c - h_0 = \int_0^b v'' \, dp - T_0 \int_0^b \left(\frac{\partial v''}{\partial T} \right)_p dp + \int_{T_0}^{T_{\text{sat}}} c_p'' \, dT \quad (\textbf{10.3})$$

The value at d is greater than that at c by the latent heat of evaporation, so that

$$h'_{\text{sat}} = h_d - h_0 = h''_{\text{sat}} + \lambda \tag{\textbf{10.4}}$$

For any point, e, in the superheated region (at $T_e = T$, say),

$$h'(T, p) = h_e - h_0 = h'_{\text{sat}} + \int_{T_{\text{sat}}}^{T} c_p' \, dT \tag{\textbf{10.5}}$$

since, of course, $T_d = T_c = T_{\text{sat}}$.

For the entropy of a unit mass, from Eq. 9.61,

$$ds = c_p \frac{dT}{T} - \left(\frac{\partial v}{\partial T} \right)_p dp \tag{\textbf{10.6}}$$

TABLE **10.1**

Properties of Saturated Water and Steam for Integral Temperatures

t, °F	v''_{sat}	v'_{sat}	h''_{sat}	h'_{sat}	s''_{sat}	s'_{sat}	p, lb/in^2
100	0.01613	350.4	67.97	1105.2	0.1295	1.9826	0.9492
200	.01663	33.65	167.99	1145.9	.2938	1.7762	11.526
300	.01745	6.466	269.59	1179.7	.4369	1.6350	67.013
400	.01864	1.8636	374.97	1201.0	.5664	1.5272	247.31
500	.0204	0.6749	478.8	1201.7	.6887	1.4325	680.8
600	.0236	0.2668	617.0	1165.5	.8131	1.3307	1543.9
705.4	.0503	0.0503	902.7	902.7	1.0580	1.0580	3206.2

* Volumes are in ft^3/lb, enthalpies in Btu/lb, and entropies in Btu/lb-deg F.

and the corresponding values of entropy are

$$s''_{\text{sat}} = s_c - s_0 = - \int_{p_0}^{p_{\text{sat}}} \left(\frac{\partial v''}{\partial T} \right)_p dp + \int_{T_0}^{T_{\text{sat}}} c_p'' \, dT \tag{10.7}$$

$$s'_{\text{sat}} = s''_{\text{sat}} + \frac{\lambda}{T_{\text{sat}}} \tag{10.8}$$

$$s'(T, p) = s_e - s_0 = s'_{\text{sat}} + \int_{T_{\text{sat}}}^{T} c_p' \frac{dT}{T} \tag{10.9}$$

Calculation of the values in the tables requires an accurate empirical equation of state for the liquid and the vapor as well as precise data on λ and c_p for both phases.

In English-speaking countries steam tables are usually given in British engineering units, with h in Btu per pound,[1] s in Btu per pound per degree Fahrenheit, etc. Any absolute temperatures occurring in the tables therefore refer to the absolute Fahrenheit or *Rankine* scale designated by R, where

$$T_{\text{Rankine}} = t_{\text{F}} + 459.69°$$

With volume measured in cubic feet and pressure in pounds weight per square inch, the pv product comes out in (lb/in^2)ft^3 and must be multiplied by 144 in^2/ft^2 for conversion to foot-pounds. With the mechanical equivalent as

$$J = 778.26 \text{ ft-lb/Btu}$$

the conversion factor for hydrostatic work terms to Btu is

$$\frac{144}{778.26} pv = 0.18503pv \text{ (Btu)}$$

Table 10.1 gives the properties of saturated steam for a few temperatures from 100°F to the critical point, 705.4°F.[2]

---

[1] The Btu used here is a *mean* Btu; that is, it is $\frac{1}{180}$ of the heat required to warm 1 lb of water from 32 to 212°F.

[2] F. G. Keyes and J. H. Keenan, *Thermodynamic Properties of Steam*, 1st ed., Wiley, New York, 1936.

10.5   Use of Steam Tables

No properties of systems lying within the two-phase (or steam dome) region are recorded in the steam tables. However, such properties may be calculated directly from the saturation values and the so-called *wetness* of the mixture. The latter value is the fraction of the system that is steam. With the wetness being indicated by x, a mixture of unit mass consists of x units of steam and $(1 - x)$ units of water. The volume of steam present is, accordingly, the specific volume of the saturated steam at the temperature considered multiplied by x, whereas that of liquid water is the saturated volume of the liquid multiplied by $1 - x$. Thus the volume of the mixture, v_m, at point, say, c' in Fig. 10.3, becomes

$$v_m = (1 - x)v''_{\text{sat}} + xv'_{\text{sat}} = v''_{\text{sat}} + x(v'_{\text{sat}} - v''_{\text{sat}}) \tag{10.10}$$

In the same way the values for enthalpy and entropy can be written down at once as

$$h_m = h''_{\text{sat}} + x(h'_{\text{sat}} - h''_{\text{sat}}) = h''_{\text{sat}} + x\lambda \tag{10.11}$$

and
$$s_m = s''_{\text{sat}} + x(s'_{\text{sat}} - s''_{\text{sat}}) = s''_{\text{sat}} + \frac{x\lambda}{T} \tag{10.12}$$

To find the volume or enthalpy of any point in the steam dome, such as j of Fig. 10.2, we must first find the richness, x. Since j lies on an adiabatic through d,

$$s_j = s_d$$

and therefore

$$s_j = s_a + x(s_g - s_a) = s_d$$

on use of Eq. 10.12. Since s_d, s_a, and s_g are all saturation values, they are recorded in the steam tables, and the unknown x can be calculated. With x known and the saturation values at the temperature given in the steam tables, v_j and h_j can be obtained at once from Eqs. 10.10 and 10.11.

As an example, suppose that it is desirable to find the efficiency of a Rankine cycle with the upper and lower temperatures 400°F and 100°F, respectively (and without superheat). With subscripts 1 and 2 to refer to saturated values at the upper and lower temperatures, respectively, of Fig. 10.2.

$$h_e = h_d = h'_1$$
$$h_f = h_j$$
$$h_a = h''_2$$

and Eq. 10.2 becomes

$$\eta_{\text{Rankine}} = \frac{h'_1 - h_j - v''_2(p_1 - p_2)}{h'_1 - h''_2 - v''_2(p_1 - p_2)}$$

Here all the quantities involved are saturation values except h_j, which refers to a mixture of unknown richness, x_j.

To find x_j, we use the equality of entropy at d and j, where

$$s_j = s''_2 + x_j(s'_2 - s''_2) = s_d$$

From Table 10.1

$$s_d = s'_1 = 1.5272 = s_j \qquad\qquad s'_2 = 1.9826$$

$$s_a = s''_2 = \underline{0.1295} \qquad\qquad\qquad s''_2 = \underline{0.1295}$$

$$s_j - s''_2 = 1.3977 \qquad\qquad s'_2 - s''_2 = 1.8531$$

and thus

$$x_j = \frac{1.3977}{1.8531} = 0.7543$$

We may now find h_j by using Eq. 10.11.

$$h_j = h''_2 + 0.7543(h'_2 - h''_2) = 67.97 + 0.7543(1105.2 - 67.97) = 850.3$$

The feed pump term is

$$v''_2(p_1 - p_2) = 0.01613(247.31 - 0.95) \times 0.1850\ \text{Btu} = 0.7\ \text{Btu}$$

Thus $$\eta_{\text{Rankine}} = \frac{1201.0 - 850.3 - 0.7}{1201.0 - 68.0 - 0.7} = \frac{350.0}{1132.3} = 30.9\%$$

The corresponding Carnot efficiency with

$$T_1 = 400 + 459.7 = 859.7°\text{R}$$

and

$$T_2 = 100 + 459.7 = 559.7°\text{R}$$

is $$\eta_{\text{Carnot}} = \frac{T_1 - T_2}{T_1} = \frac{300}{859.7} = 34.9\%$$

which is considerably larger than the Rankine efficiency, as is to be expected. The lower efficiency of the Rankine cycle is, of course, due to the heat taken in along $b \to c$ at temperatures varying from 100 to 400°F. Since this amounts to nearly 307 Btu, it is an appreciable fraction of the total heat (1132 Btu) absorbed along $b \to d$. The efficiency of the Rankine cycle may be improved by the use of superheating. (See Problem 10.3.)

10.6   The Steam Dome in the *p-v* Plane

The curves of Figs. 10.2 and 10.3 were drawn for ease of discussion but are in fact highly schematic. In actuality the specific volumes of saturated liquid water are so nearly constant that the saturation curve rises almost vertically to the critical point. Moreover, these volumes are so small compared to the volumes of saturated steam that no scale is adequate to show both curves except for temperatures well above usual condenser temperatures. Thus in Fig. 10.4 the lower left-hand curve represents the data from the critical point down to the temperature of about 216°F, where $v' = 25\ \text{ft}^3/\text{lb}$. In the insert

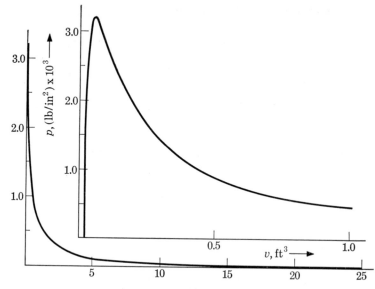

FIGURE **10.4**

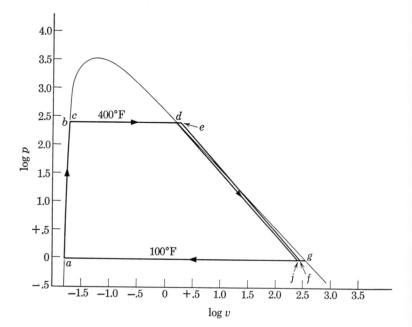

FIGURE **10.5**

the volume scale has been expanded by 20 to 1, and no steam volumes below about 450°F can be included.

Resort to a logarithmic scale along each axis gives the steam dome shown in Fig. 10.5. Data down to the triple point can readily be included in this figure, and the saturation curves for both liquid and vapor are substantially linear. The Rankine cycle of Fig. 10.2 has been drawn in for the special case of $t_1 = 400°F$ and $t_2 = 100°F$, and the near linearity of the adiabatics $d \rightarrow j$ and $e \rightarrow f$ is to be noted.

Unfortunately the right-hand side of the cycle is much too cramped for convenience. In addition, the significance of areas in the plot varies from region to region—a distinct drawback.

10.7   The *T-s*, *h-s*, and *p-s* Diagrams

The difficulties arising in the *p-v* diagram are largely absent in the thermo-dynamically more meaningful charts to be considered here.

Of these the *T-s* diagram is both convenient and highly satisfactory for most purposes. It is given in Fig. 10.6 for the Rankine cycle shown in Fig. 10.5. The new diagram shows a and b as coincident, whereas the large separation of b and c indicates the large thermal difference between these two states. Since the entropy of a wet mixture is linearly proportional to the wetness, x, the relative wetness of any mixture, such as j or f, is clearly indicated by its nearness to g, the saturation point where $x = 1$. As in the *p-v* diagram, areas have the dimensions of energy, and the area of a cycle is a direct measure of the heat energy convertible into work by the idealized cycle.

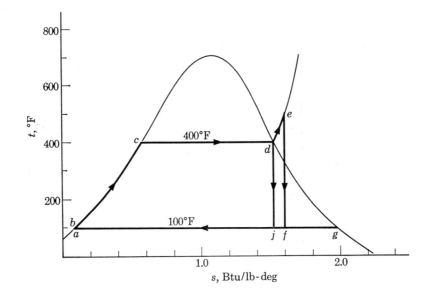

FIGURE **10.6**

Of even more convenience in practice is the h-s diagram, due to the German engineer Mollier and shown in Fig. 10.7. In principle, all the data needed for efficiency calculations can be read directly from this chart, without reference to steam tables. In practice, with small-scale diagrams the points a and b are essentially coincident, and the feed pump term must be calculated. When a and b are coincident, the heating curve, $b \rightarrow c$, coincides with the liquid saturation curve, just as in the T-s diagram.

A most important property of the Mollier diagram follows from Clausius' second equation. For unit mass this equation becomes

$$dh = T\,ds + v\,dp$$

and thus for a constant pressure change

$$dh = T\,ds$$

or
$$\left(\frac{\partial h}{\partial s}\right)_p = T$$

This means that the slope of an isobar always gives the absolute temperature of the system at that point. As a result, the upper and lower isotherms of a Rankine (or Carnot) cycle are straight lines with slopes T_1 and T_2, respectively. For isobars such as $d \rightarrow e$ in the superheat region, the slope must, of course, increase as the temperature rises, and the isobars are, accordingly, concave upward.

Owing to the shape of the steam dome in the h-s diagram, any Rankine cycle tends to be crowded into a rather small fraction of the total area of the chart. Another diagram—also due to Mollier—avoids this difficulty by using

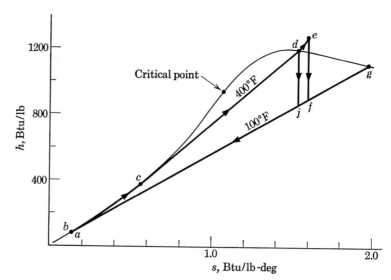

FIGURE **10.7**

pressure and enthalpy as coordinates. Such a p-h diagram is shown in Fig. 10.8, where, however, the vertical axis is log p instead of p itself (p is expressed in pounds per square inch). The resulting diagram is open and easy to read, and with isoentropic curves drawn in, it is easy to use. The cycle of Fig. 10.7 has been inserted for comparison. The horizontal lines (dashed and solid) indicate the regular spacing of the isobars for temperatures in 100°F steps.

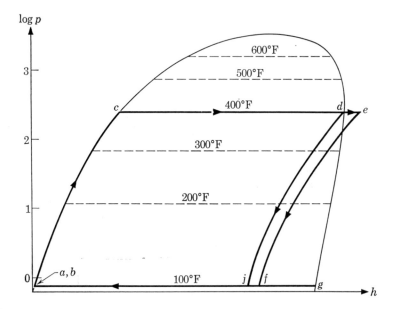

FIGURE **10.8**

10.8 Improvements in the Utilization of Steam

Although the first recorded use of steam to produce mechanical motion was undoubtedly by Hero of Alexandria (c. 130 B.C.), his device must be regarded as essentially a toy. Except for brief descriptions of designs by Giambattista della Porta (1601) and the second Marquis of Worcester (1665), the history of the steam engine is blank from the time of Hero to 1698. At that time Thomas Savery, in France, received a patent for a steam-operated water pump. Savery's engine used steam to displace water from a tank, the direct pressure of the steam acting on the water surface to force it to the desired height. Aside from the serious troubles encountered in generating enough steam pressure (pressures up to 150 lb/in² were used without safety valves), the system was prodigal in its fuel consumption. No data exist from which the performance of the original Savery engines can be computed. Smeaton, however, in 1774, many years after Savery's death, built an improved model that developed 2.65 hp and performed 62,500 ft-lb of work per pound of fuel consumed. With 1 lb of coal taken as equivalent to 12,000 Btu, the performance coefficient in modern terms is about 500 kBtu/kw-hr. The original engines probably required considerably more, say, 600 kBtu/kw-hr, corresponding to a thermal efficiency of about 0.6%.

During the two and a half centuries since Savery's patent, the performance ratio (see Fig. 10.14) has decreased from 600 to around 10 kBtu/kw-hr, a ratio of 60 to 1. This progress has been due to a small army of mechanics, inventors, and engineers, and only a few of the major improvements can be cited here.

The Newcomen Atmospheric Engine.   Thomas Newcomen (1663–1729), an English contemporary of Savery, introduced two major improvements. He prevented the live steam from coming in contact with the water being pumped and eliminated the necessity for high pressures. He brought about the first improvement by allowing the steam to act on the lower face of a piston in a vertical cylinder. When the cylinder was full of steam, jets of water produced condensation and a vacuum in the cylinder, whereupon the atmosphere pushed the piston down to its starting position. The piston rod was connected to a heavy rocker arm, which in turn operated a water lift pump. Since the steam cylinder could be made of large diameter, a large total force could be produced, enough, in fact, to raise water several hundred feet. Newcomen thereby neatly avoided the dangers of the high pressures that Savery required.

James Watt's Contributions.   It is to the genius, driving energy, and scientific approach of James Watt (1736–1819) that we owe the reciprocating steam engine in essentially its present form. Watt introduced the vacuum condenser, steam-jacketed the cylinder, made the engine double-acting by allowing steam to work alternately on each face of the piston, introduced the adiabatic expansion of the steam after cutoff, and invented the centrifugal governor and throttle valve, a host of mechanical linkages for opening and closing valves, etc. He found the device a slow, unreliable steam pump and left it a high-speed, efficient steam engine.

Multiple-Expansion Engines.   As more substantial steam boilers were designed, higher steam pressures became feasible, and by the 1850's the use of 50 to 60 lb/in² was common practice. But as boiler temperatures were raised, the heat loss to cylinder walls became increasingly important. Recourse was

TABLE **10.2***

Type	Date	Pressure, lb/in²	Weight, lb/hp	Performance, kBtu/kw-hr
Simple	1870	50	500	36.5
Compound	1880	75	480	31.3
Triple	1890	180	400	22.6
Quadruple	1900	225	350	19.2

*From R. H. Thurston, *History of the Growth of the Steam Engine*, Cornell Univ. Press, Ithaca, N.Y., 1939.

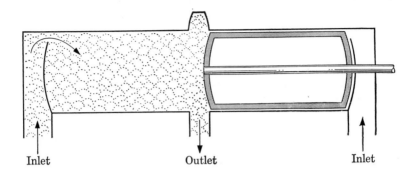

Inlet   Outlet   Inlet

FIGURE **10.9**

accordingly had to a modification introduced by Jonathan Hornblower as early as 1781. His engines used two cylinders of unequal size. The high-pressure steam entered the smaller one, where some work was extracted. The exhaust steam then entered the larger one, where it was expanded to the condenser pressure and temperature. Since the range of fluctuation of temperature in each cylinder was decreased, the consequent loss of heat to the walls was reduced, with improvement in the over-all performance. In triple- and quadruple-expansion engines the process is carried even further. Table 10.2 gives some of the pertinent data on typical marine installations between 1870 and 1900. The steady decrease in the ratio kiloBtu to kilowatt-hour is striking.

The Uniflow Engine. Reduction of the loss due to rapid heating and cooling of the cylinder walls was later (1910) attained more economically than with multiple-expansion engines by the so-called *uniflow* engine. In this type of engine (see Fig. 10.9), the hot steam enters alternately at the right and left ends of the cylinder (which are therefore always hot). At the end of each stroke, the large hollow piston uncovers the exhaust port at the center of the cylinder (which is therefore kept relatively cold).

10.9   The Steam Turbine

Significant competition with reciprocating engines did not arise until the great work of Dr. Gustaf de Laval (1845–1913) and Sir Charles Parsons (1854–1931) on steam turbines.

Steam turbines are basically of two types, the *impulse* (or velocity) turbine and the *reaction* turbine. In the impulse turbine high-pressure steam passing through a nozzle suffers a large drop in enthalpy and acquires a high speed. The high-speed steam then strikes the curved blades of a Pelton water-wheel type of rotor, which is given a high speed of rotation.

In the reaction turbine steam at relatively low speed strikes a series of radial blades so formed that the passage between the blades is itself nozzle-shaped. The steam is thus accelerated and reacts back upon the blades, causing them to spin in the opposite direction. (Hence the name *reaction* turbine, although it must be remembered that the names *impulse* and *reaction* as applied to turbines are purely conventional and must not be interpreted too literally or exclusively.)

De Laval devoted himself primarily to the impulse turbine, beginning with the design of the nozzle, which he was the first to analyze scientifically. It is clear that, for optimum transfer of energy from the high-speed steam jet to the moving turbine blades, the exhaust steam should have a speed as near zero as possible. It can be shown readily that this condition requires ideally that the turbine blades have just one half the speed of the entering steam. (See Problem 10.6 and Fig. 10.23, which shows a radial cross section of the cupped blades.) Since this speed condition may require tangential blade tip speeds of 1500 to 2000 ft/sec, the problem of suitable reduction gears becomes serious for most applications.

Parsons was the inventor of the compound or multiple-expansion reaction turbine. In this turbine the pressure drop, instead of taking place in one step in the steam nozzle, as in a de Laval turbine, takes place in a series of small steps from one end of the turbine to the other. Each section of the turbine consists of sets of radial blades, one set fixed to the turbine casing and the next to the rotating shaft. The blades are so contoured that the space between them decreases from the inlet to the outlet side, producing a nozzle effect. As Fig. 10.10 illustrates, the steam passing through the fixed blade system is deflected and acquires a certain speed at the expense of a small pressure drop. On entering the moving blade system, it is accelerated again and in turn reacts back upon the blades to give them a rotary motion in the opposite direction. The steam then passes through the next set of fixed blades, etc. As the pressure of the steam falls, its specific volume increases, and the radial blades are made of larger radius to provide the needed volume. Although the temperature falls

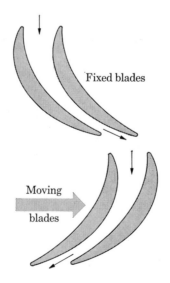

Fixed blades

FIGURE **10.10**

Moving

blades

from one end of the turbine to the other, each section remains at a stable operating value. The compound turbine is thus superior to the multiple-expansion or the uniflow reciprocating engine. At the same time, by having the pressure drop in many stages, it avoids the high speeds of the de Laval type. The compound steam turbine, whether of the pure reaction type or involving impulse stages as well, represents the major improvement in the use of steam during the nineteenth and early twentieth centuries.

10.10   Superpressure Turbines[3]

In the attempt to use ever higher temperatures, it became clear that pressures greater than the critical pressure (3205 lb/in²) would be desirable. In this superpressure region, as it is called, ordinary steel blades are rapidly eroded by steam, although temperatures of 1100°F are feasible if the pressure is kept below 3500 lb/in². With steam at 5000 lb/in², it is necessary to employ stainless steel (austenite) throughout; and since in this region water passes into steam directly without boiling, the ordinary impurities in boiler water must be removed with great care.

To understand the implications of superpressure turbines, consider Figs. 10.11, 10.12, and 10.13, T-s diagrams with temperatures on the Rankine scale.

FIGURE **10.11**

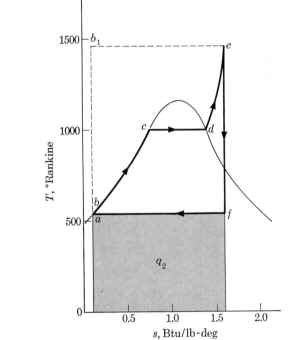

---

[3] Condensed from *Research and Develop.* (Westinghouse Electric Co.), Letter No. 7 (April–May, 1959).

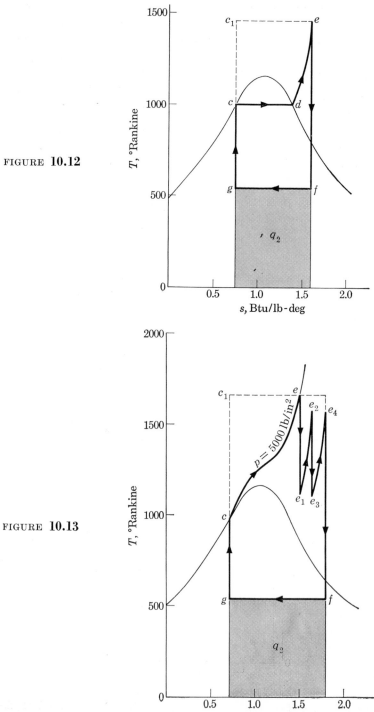

FIGURE **10.12**

FIGURE **10.13**

Fig. 10.11 shows the ordinary Rankine cycle, with a boiler at 1000°R and superheating to 1460°R. The Rankine cycle is seen to include a considerably smaller area than the Carnot cycle, bb_1ef, although each has the same minimum waste heat, q_2, indicated by the shaded area. The least efficiently utilized heat is that absorbed by the feed pump water along $b \rightarrow c$.

In the so-called regenerative cycle (Fig. 10.12), the left-hand part of the Rankine cycle is effectively removed by the bleeding of steam from the turbine to heat the water from the condenser. The work out and the heat rejection are both reduced. The area of the regenerative cycle ($gcdef$) is a larger fraction of the Carnot area (gc_1ef) than is the area of the ordinary Rankine cycle, and the over-all efficiency is improved.

Fig. 10.13 shows the *superpressure regenerative* cycle with two stages of reheating. The expansion $e \rightarrow e_1$ takes place in a superpressure stellite turbine. The partially expanded steam is then reheated, $e_1 \rightarrow e_2$, and further expanded, $e_2 \rightarrow e_3$, in an ordinary steel turbine. It is reheated once more, $e_3 \rightarrow e_4$, and after final expansion in the turbine, $e_4 \rightarrow f$, goes to the condenser. Again, for a given loss, q_2, the new cycle represents a larger fraction of the Carnot rectangle than

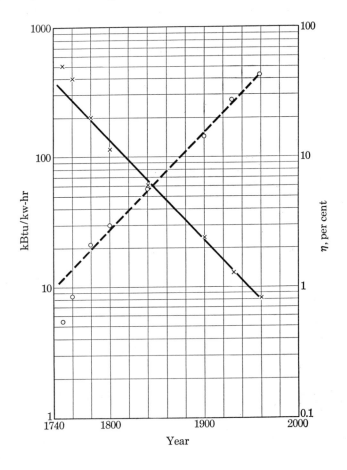

FIGURE **10.14**

does the cycle of Fig. 10.11. The new cycle, in fact, gives an output of 1 kw-hr for 8 kBtu, corresponding to a thermal efficiency of 42.5%. This is an efficiency that can be pushed higher only with greatly increased construction costs. Nor do more than two reheatings seem practical at the present stage of development.

Fig. 10.14 shows the historic improvement in the utilization of steam during the last two centuries. The solid curve represents kiloBtu per kilowatt-hour, and the dashed curve the thermal efficiency, η, in per cent, for the best technical practice at each date. As in many other areas of technical development, the points lie very close to a straight line when plotted on semilog paper.

10.11   The Refrigerator

In Sec. 8.12 the coefficient of performance of a refrigerator, K_{ref}, was defined as

$$K_{ref} = \frac{q_2}{W} = \frac{q_2}{q_1 - q_2}$$

where q_2 is the heat extracted from the cold source, W is the work required per cycle, and q_1 and q_2 refer to a unit mass of working substance. For the Carnot refrigerator operating between T_2 and T_1,

$$(K_{ref})_{\text{Carnot}} = \frac{T_2}{T_1 - T_2}$$

Although no actual refrigerator uses a reversed Carnot cycle, the theoretical Carnot relation serves, just as in the case of heat engines, as the ultimate criterion, and practical refrigerating devices must be judged on the basis of their approach to this ideal.

A refrigerator using a liquid-vapor working cycle is shown schematically in Fig. 10.15. Vapor compressed in a compressor passes into a condenser, where it condenses to the liquid state, the liberated heat flowing into a warm reservoir. The warm compressed liquid then collects in a liquid storage tank and passes through a throttle valve, emerging as a mixture of vapor and liquid droplets, with large decreases in pressure and temperature occurring. The remaining liquid then vaporizes in an evaporator, the required heat being taken from a cold reservoir. Although the cycle would more nearly approach the Carnot cycle if the irreversible expansion through the throttle valve were replaced by a working (adiabatic) expansion against a piston, the improvement in over-all efficiency is seldom worth the extra mechanical complication.

Owing to the irreversible throttling process, the idealized refrigeration cycle is quasistatic (and reversible) only in part and must be represented as in Fig. 10.16. The various steps are as follows, beginning with the warm saturated liquid at a:

$a \rightarrow c$ Irreversible throttling, with a pressure drop from p_1 to p_2. Some evaporation occurs, and the temperature falls from T_1 to T_2.

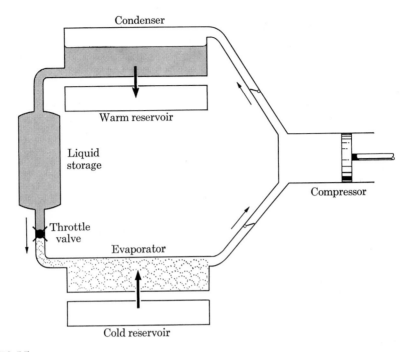

FIGURE **10.15**

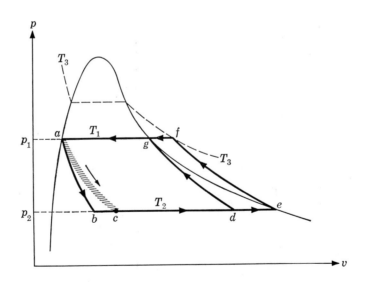

FIGURE **10.16**

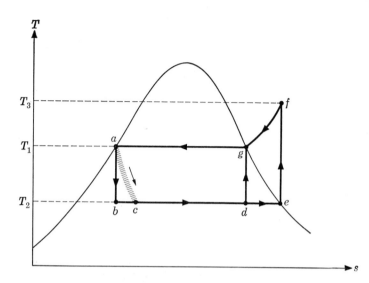

FIGURE **10.17**

$c \to e$ Reversible evaporation of the droplets in the wet mixture in the evaporator at T_2 (and p_2) to saturated vapor, with absorption of heat from the cold reservoir.

$e \to f$ Adiabatic and reversible compression of the saturated vapor to the superheat temperature, T_3.

$f \to g$ Isobaric "desuperheating" from T_3 to T_1.

$g \to a$ Reversible isobaric condensation to the saturated liquid. Heat is rejected to the warm reservoir during the last two processes.

This cycle is called the *simple saturation* cycle. A variation involves compression of the wet mixture at d directly to the saturated liquid at g. This modification reduces the over-all refrigeration effect but raises the coefficient of performance since no heat is rejected above T_1. If the throttling process is replaced by a reversible adiabatic expansion, the section $a \to c$ is replaced by $a \to b$ and $b \to c$, with a further improvement in performance.

The refrigeration cycles have been redrawn in Figs. 10.17 and 10.18 as T-s and p-h diagrams. It should be noted that $h_a = h_c$, since throttling leaves enthalpy unaltered, whereas $s_c > s_a$, owing to the irreversibility of the process. Likewise, $s_a = s_b$, but $h_b < h_a$.

The coefficient of performance, K_{ref}, can be written down at once. For the simple saturation cycle,

$$K_{\text{ref}} = \frac{q_2}{q_1 - q_2} = \frac{h_e - h_c}{h_f - h_a - (h_e - h_c)} = \frac{h_e - h_a}{h_f - h_e} \qquad (10.13)$$

since $h_a = h_c$. For the cycle with adiabatic expansion,

$$K_{\text{ref}} = \frac{h_e - h_b}{h_f - h_a - (h_e - h_b)} \qquad (10.14)$$

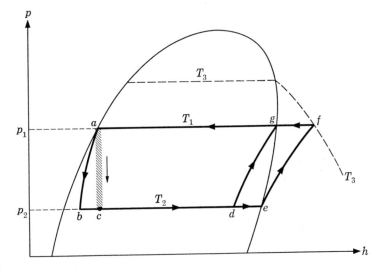

This is larger than the first result since the difference $h_a - h_b$ is added to the numerator but subtracted from the denominator of Eq. 10.13.

10.12   Common Refrigerants

A great many materials are available as working substances in refrigeration cycles, and the best choice for a particular use requires careful study. In addition to questions of toxicity, corrosiveness, inflammability, etc., there are many purely thermodynamic considerations. For a given pair of temperatures, T_1 and T_2, the higher pressure must not be so high, nor the lower so low, that excessive volumes are needed for the evaporator. It is further desirable to have both a large specific heat for the vapor and a large latent heat of evaporation. In order that as large a value of K_{ref} as possible may be obtained, it is also desirable to have h_f in Eq. 10.13 as close to h_e as possible. This means that in the p-h plane adiabatics in the vapor region should lie as close to the vapor saturation curve as possible.

Fig. 10.19 shows saturation curves in the p-h plane for a few common refrigerants. In each case the width of the loop at any pressure is the latent heat of vaporization. The segments of dashed lines at the lower right of each vapor saturation curve are portions of constant-entropy curves. For water and ammonia, with their large values of latent heat, these curves make large angles with the saturation curves. To the left in the figure the isoentropic curves become increasingly closer to the corresponding saturation curves, but the latent heats unfortunately diminish rapidly as well.

To get an idea of the relative behavior of different refrigerants, consider a simple saturation cycle with

$$t_1 = 80°\text{F} \ (T_1 = 540°\text{R})$$

and

$$t_2 = 10°\text{F} \ (T_2 = 470°\text{R})$$

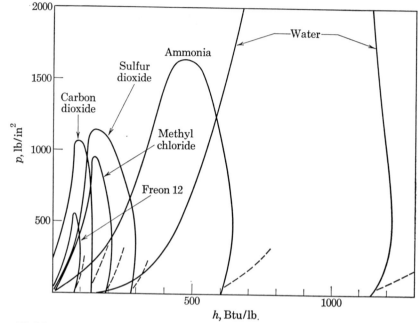

FIGURE **10.19**

Then for a Carnot refrigerator using these temperatures,

$$(K_{ref})_{Carnot} = \frac{T_2}{T_1 - T_2} = 6.72$$

The values of K_{ref} for a simple saturation cycle with these same temperatures are given in column 3 of Table 10.3.

TABLE **10.3**

Coefficients of Performance for Various Refrigerants*

Refrigerant	Formula	K_{ref}	% of Carnot
Methyl chloride	CH_3Cl	5.7	84
Ammonia	NH_3	5.5	82
Sulfur dioxide	SO_2	5.8	87
Freon 12	CCl_2F_2	4.7	69
Carbon dioxide	CO_2	3.8	57

* For a simple saturation cycle with $t_1 = 80°F$ and $t_2 = 10°F$.

The last column gives the percentage of the Carnot coefficient. Since the values of K_{ref} often change rapidly with small alterations in temperature, the results of Table 10.3 cannot be given too much weight without examination of a range of values for t_1 and t_2.

10.13   The Heat Pump

When refrigerators are used as heat pumps, Q_1, the heat pumped into the upper reservoir, is more important than Q_2, that extracted from the lower one. Accordingly, the coefficient of performance as a heat pump, K_{hp}, becomes of interest. This is larger by unity than K_{ref}, as we see from the definition

$$K_{hp} = \frac{Q_1}{Q_1 - Q_2} = \frac{Q_2}{Q_1 - Q_2} + \frac{W}{Q_1 - Q_2} = K_{ref} + 1$$

If, for purposes of argument, we take the value of $K_{ref} = 5$ in round numbers, then $K_{hp} = 6$, and for each unit of work employed, 6 units of heat can be pumped into the space to be heated.

As Kelvin envisioned the scheme of thermodynamic house heating described in Sec. 8.13, work was to be obtained from a local heat engine utilizing the heat of combustion of fuel that would otherwise have been burned directly. The machinery necessary for such a process is usually too expensive and requires too much attention for local installations. It is more feasible to buy electric power and use electric motors to drive heat pumps. Where average outdoor temperatures are not too low or local power rates too high, this adaptation offers a distinct improvement over present heating methods.

Since the mild climates for which this type of house heating is suitable usually require air conditioning in the summer, two purposes can be served with the same installation. A typical schematic arrangement is shown in Fig. 10.20. In winter the master valve is set for heating, and the compressor forces compressed and warmed refrigerant into finned pipes within the house, where condensation occurs, the liberated heat being carried into the house by fan-driven air. The condensed fluid then passes through the throttle valve from right to left into another set of finned pipes, which act as the evaporator. The heat of evaporation is supplied by the cold outdoor air circulated by another set of fans.

In summer the master valve is rotated to the "cool" position, and, with the compressor operating in the same direction as before, the circulation in the system is reversed. The outside finned pipes now constitute the condenser, and the inside ones become the evaporator. Thus in winter the apparatus heats the house by *cooling* the cold outside air further, whereas in summer it refrigerates the house by *heating* the warm outside air even warmer. For clarity, the high-pressure part of each cycle is shown in black up to the throttle valve, and the air-circulating fans have been omitted.

Other quite different methods of refrigeration are also available. With the improvement in thermocouple materials, it is possible to produce local heating

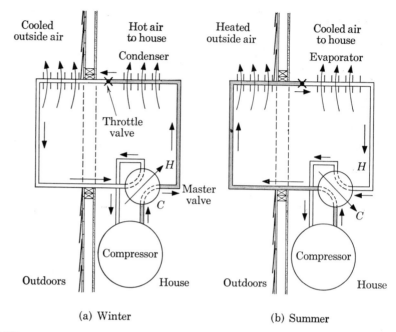

(a) Winter   (b) Summer

FIGURE **10.20**

and cooling efficiently by use of the reversible Peltier effect. If two conductors, A and B (Fig. 10.21), are such that a current, i, flowing to the right causes the absorption of heat, Q, the rate of heat absorption is proportional to i. Thus we write

$$\frac{dQ}{d\tau} = \Pi i$$

where Π is the Peltier coefficient. On reversal of the current, heat is evolved at the junction. This is the Peltier effect. It represents a strictly reversible effect and can therefore be used to produce local refrigeration. For practical experiments in house heating and cooling, see the work of Penrod and his co-workers,[4] as well as the Kaye and Welsh reference at the end of the chapter.

FIGURE **10.21**

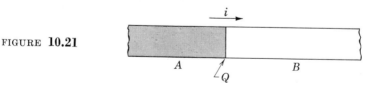

---

[4] Penrod, *Kentucky Univ. Eng. Exp. Sta. Bull.*, No. 4 (1947); *Trans. Kentucky Acad. Sci.*, 13 (1949); and Penrod, Gard, Jones, Collier, and Patey, *Kentucky Univ. Eng. Exp. Sta. Bull.*, No. 14 (1949).

10.14   The Electrolux Refrigerator

Many other refrigeration schemes are in operation, including in particular the ammonia absorption process, which makes use of the fact that heat is absorbed when ammonia is evaporated from an aqueous solution and rejected when it is redissolved in the water.

An interesting and ingenious variation of the ammonia absorption process was devised by two young Swedish engineers. It enables the Electrolux refrigerator to operate without moving mechanical parts. The refrigerant, ammonia, is circulated through a cycle that includes parts of two subcycles involving hydrogen gas and water. Since the pressure is made up of the partial pressures of ammonia gas, hydrogen, and water vapor or steam, the total pressure is everywhere the same, and no valves are needed.

The operation is best understood from Fig. 10.22. Circulation is maintained by a gas burner (or electrical heater) at the lower right, which draws con-

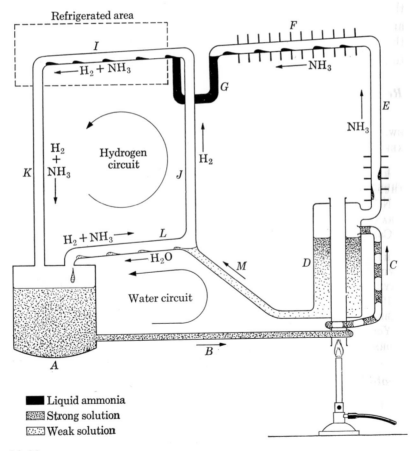

FIGURE **10.22**

centrated ammonia solution from a storage tank at A through tube B by means of a liquid lift at C. This lift operates much as a coffee percolator; bubbles of vapor interspersed with sections of liquid rise, owing to their low average density, and run into the top of a distillation vessel, D. From this vessel the vapor, a mixture of ammonia and a small amount of steam, rises through a fractionating column, E. Fins in the column produce air-cooling, which condenses the steam to water. The water drips back into the distillation vessel, leaving almost pure ammonia vapor to enter the condenser at F. Here a further provision of fins causes further heat removal, resulting in a condensation of the ammonia, the liquid ammonia collecting in a U-tube, G. Once G is filled, further addition of liquid from F causes the ammonia to drain into tube I, where a stream of hydrogen gas from a vertical riser, J, sweeps over it and aids its evaporation. I thus becomes the refrigeration unit. The vaporized ammonia and hydrogen gas, being a heavy mixture, flow down tube K through the top of the storage tank into an absorber, L. Here the ammonia meets a downcoming trickle of dilute aqueous solution, which is the overflow from tube M. The ammonia is rapidly absorbed, freeing the hydrogen, which, owing to its lightness, is forced up through J again. The enriched ammonia solution drips into the tank, A, and is ready to begin the cycle once more. Since concentrated ammonia solutions are less dense than dilute ones, the weaker solution falls to the bottom of the distillation vessel, D, and therefore fills tube M and is ready to enter the absorber for enriching.

References

GENERAL

EWING, J. A., *Thermodynamics for Engineers*, Cambridge Univ. Press, Cambridge, 1936.

KEENAN, J. H., *Thermodynamics*, Wiley, New York, 1941.

ENGINES

THURSTON, R. H., *History of the Growth of the Steam Engine*, Cornell Univ. Press, Ithaca, N.Y., 1939.

WRANGHAM, D. A., *Theory and Practice of Heat Engines*, 2nd ed., Cambridge Univ. Press, Cambridge, 1948.

HEATING AND REFRIGERATION

EWING, J. A., *Mechanical Production of Cold*, Cambridge Univ. Press, Cambridge, 1921,

KAYE, J., and J. H. WELSH, *Direct Conversion of Heat to Electricity*, Wiley, New York. 1960.

RABER, B. F., and F. W. HUTCHINSON, *Refrigeration and Air Conditioning*, Wiley, New York, 1945.

SPORN, P., E. R. AMBROSE, and T. BAUMEISTER, *Heat Pumps*, Wiley, New York, 1947.

Problems

10.1   We have written the first dQ_C expression in the light of Maxwell's first relation as

$$dQ_C = C_p dT - T\left(\frac{\partial V}{\partial T}\right)_p dp$$

For an adiabatic process, $dQ_{ad} = 0$, and

$$dTs = \frac{T}{C_p}\left(\frac{\partial V}{\partial T}\right)_p dp = \frac{TV\beta_p}{C_p} dp$$

Integrate this equation for a pressure change from p_2 to a high pressure, p_1, to obtain an expression for the adiabatic temperature rise of cold condenser water in a feed pump (Sec. 10.2). The coefficient of dp may be treated as essentially constant. What is the rise in temperature if $p_2 = 1$ and $p_1 = 300$ lb/in²?

10.2 If the compression in Problem 10.1 were treated as isothermal (that is, along the liquid isotherm at T_2), what would be the heat loss in Btu per pound of water?

10.3 Calculate the Rankine efficiency to be expected for the case discussed in Sec. 10.5 where $t_1 = 400°F$ and $t_2 = 100°F$ if superheating to $t_3 = 450°F$ (at $p = 247.3$ lb/in²) is included in the cycle.

10.4 Using steam tables, find u_m, h_m, and s_m for a mixture of richness $x = 0.60$ at $t = 400°F$.

10.5 Determine the values of v, u, h, and s for a water system of mass 1 lb when
(a) $p = 60$ lb/in², $x = 0.87$; and
(b) $p = 135$ lb/in², $t = 460°F$.

10.6 Obtain the Carnot and Rankine efficiencies for a steam engine with $t_1 = 350°F$ and $t_2 = 110°F$. What improvement results in the Rankine cycle if 50° of superheat is used? Plot each cycle in a T-s diagram.

10.7 Suppose that the velocities of the steam before and after striking the curved blades in an impulse turbine are $\mathscr{V}_i$ and $\mathscr{V}_f$, respectively. Let the tangential velocity of the blades be $\mathscr{V}_B$ (as in Fig. 10.23). The smaller $\mathscr{V}_f$ can be made, the greater the degree of conversion of kinetic energy of the steam into kinetic energy of the blades. Optimum performance results when $\mathscr{V}_f = 0$. For simplicity take $\mathscr{V}_i$ to be parallel to $\mathscr{V}_B$, and show that for optimum performance $\mathscr{V}_B = \frac{1}{2}\mathscr{V}_i$. (*Hint:* Refer all velocities to the blade as a reference point.)

10.8 Using thermodynamic charts for carbon dioxide and Freon 12 (see the Raber and Hutchinson reference at the end of the chapter) determine the value of K_{ref} for simple saturation cycles with $t_1 = 86°F$ and $t_2 = 0°F$. What improvement results on replacement of the irreversible throttle expansion by a reversible adiabatic one?

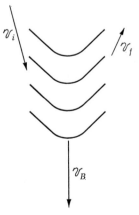

FIGURE **10.23**

CHAPTER ELEVEN

Thermodynamic Methods

11.1 Introduction

Many examples of the methods used for deducing results from the laws of thermodynamics have been given in the previous chapters. Since these results can not only be expressed in a variety of ways but can also be obtained by apparently quite different procedures, this chapter will be devoted to a general study of thermodynamic methods.

The results of the two laws of thermodynamics can always be expressed in either integral or differential form. Kirchhoff's equation for the heat of sublimation of a monatomic solid,

$$\Lambda = \Lambda_0 + \int_0^T (C_p^\circ - C_p''') \, dT \qquad (7.40)$$

is an example of the former, whereas Maxwell's first and second relations,

$$\frac{L_p}{T} = - \left(\frac{\partial V}{\partial T} \right)_p$$

and

$$\frac{L_V}{T} = \left(\frac{\partial p}{\partial T} \right)_V$$

are examples of the latter. In general, the truths of thermodynamics are more useful when expressed in terms of derivatives than when expressed in terms of integrals. Derivatives are readily changed to forms involving other variables and may, of course, be integrated when desired. The relations among two or more derivatives are termed the *general relations* of thermodynamics, and their deduction and transformation will receive a good share of our attention.

11.2 Thermodynamic Methods

There are many methods for applying the truths contained in the first and second laws, as is evident from the many results derived up to this point. It is none the less worthwhile, at the risk of a certain amount of repetition, to

292

attempt a classification of the methods available. Such a classification not only aids in presenting a true picture of the structure of the science but is of practical importance in giving the user confidence in results that he may deduce in a variety of ways.

All methods must start with the laws expressed in convenient forms. These we repeat here for ready reference.

$$\left.\begin{aligned} dU &= dQ_c - p\,dV \\ dQ_c &= C_V\,dT + L_V\,dV \\ dQ_c &= C_p\,dT + L_p\,dp \end{aligned}\right\} \quad \text{first law}$$

$$dS = \frac{dQ_c}{T} \qquad \text{second law}$$

$$\left.\begin{aligned} dU &= T\,dS - p\,dV \\ dH &= T\,dS + V\,dp \\ dA &= -S\,dT - p\,dV \\ dG &= -S\,dT + V\,dp \end{aligned}\right\} \quad \text{first and second laws combined}$$

In some cases we may want to apply each law separately, and in others we may make no attempt to keep the deductions from each law separate.

The numerous methods available fall into two classes. The first class we call *cyclic* and the second, for lack of a better name, *analytic*.

The Cyclic Method.   The cyclic method makes use of the fact that all state functions or thermodynamic potentials undergo a net change of zero when a system is taken through any cyclic process. Stated in an equivalent way, when a system is taken from one state to another by two different paths, the net change in any potential is the same for both paths.

Except that the cycles are always reversible, they may be quite diverse in details. They may be *finite* or *infinitesimal* cycles. (See Fig.11.1.)

Finite Cycles.   Although any closed curve in a suitable plane may be used, ease of calculation always dictates cycles made up of segments of isobars, adiabatics, and the like.

Infinitesimal Cycles.   When we allow infinitesimal changes in *one* variable, a first-order infinitesimal cycle results, whereas infinitesimal changes in both variables produce a second-order differential cycle.

In all such cycles direct use of the first and second laws demands that

$$\oint dU = 0$$

and
$$\oint dS = 0 \qquad\qquad\qquad \textbf{(11.1)}$$

For finite cycles the integrals are broken up into readily evaluated parts, one for each segment of the cycle. The summations for infinitesimal cycles of the first order involve integrals along the finite portions and the addition of differentials along the rest. For second-order differential cycles the summations reduce to the addition of differential quantities alone.

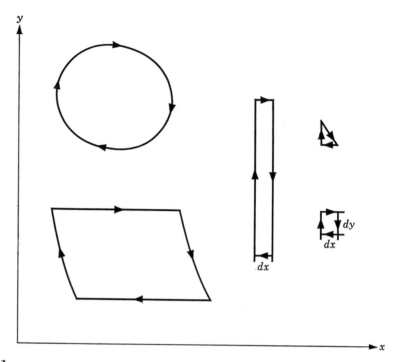

FIGURE **11.1**

The most useful of all cycles is, of course, the Carnot cycle. Particularly useful is the Carnot cycle reduced to a first-order differential one, the temperature change being differential. Such a cycle is shown in Fig. 11.2, with the temperature difference between the two isotherms taken as ΔT. In the limit as $\Delta T \to 0$, this becomes a differential Carnot cycle. From the vanishing of $\oint dU$, the first law gives

$$\oint dQ_C = -\oint dW_C$$

or, since the cycle is small,

$$\Delta Q_{\text{cyc}} = -\Delta W_{\text{cyc}} = \text{area of rectangle} \qquad (11.2)$$

The second law gives

$$\oint dS = 0 = \int_1^2 \frac{dQ_T}{T} + \int_3^4 \frac{dQ_T}{T} = \frac{Q_1}{T_1} - \frac{Q_2}{T_2}$$

which we rewrite as

$$\frac{Q_1 - Q_2}{Q_1} = \frac{T_1 - T_2}{T_2}$$

or, for the small cycle,

$$\frac{\Delta Q_{\text{cyc}}}{Q} = \frac{\Delta T}{T} \qquad (11.3)$$

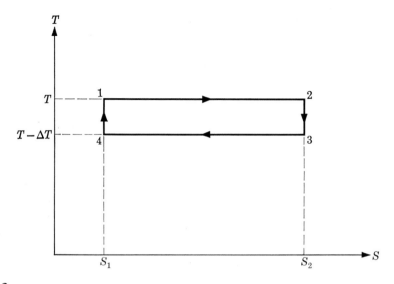

FIGURE **11.2**

where Q refers to heat absorbed at temperature T. In the limit as $\Delta T \to 0$, Eqs. 11.2 and 11.3 become

$$dQ_{\text{cyc}} = -dW_{\text{cyc}} \tag{11.4}$$

and

$$\frac{dQ_{\text{cyc}}}{dT} = \frac{Q}{T} \tag{11.5}$$

or, on combination,

$$\boxed{\frac{-dW_{\text{cyc}}}{dT} = \frac{Q}{T}} \tag{11.6}$$

This is the Carnot restriction on a differential Carnot cycle.

Analytic Methods. All other methods we classify as analytic. They involve analytic operations on the basic equations and are too diverse in character to be further subdivided in any rigorous way. Nevertheless, several particular methods should be mentioned.

The Cross Derivative Theorem. Given any exact differential written as

$$M\,dx + N\,dy$$

we can always write

$$\left(\frac{\partial M}{\partial y}\right)_x = \left(\frac{\partial N}{\partial x}\right)_y$$

Applied to a particular case such as dU or dS, this gives the differential equivalent of the finite cycle result in Eq. 11.1. In fact, the analytical results must in general be equivalent to the cyclic ones; the method is simply a matter of convenience and approach.

Partial Derivatives from Differentials.   It is not necessary to keep the two laws separate—only to combine the consequences of each later. The equations of Clausius involve both laws, and use of them gives us our final results in one step. Thus if we take CI,

$$dU = T\,dS - p\,dV$$

divide by dx,

$$\frac{dU}{dx} = \frac{T\,dS}{dx} - \frac{p\,dV}{dx}$$

and envisage this change in x as taking place at constant y, we obtain $(dU/dx)_y$ as

$$\left(\frac{\partial U}{\partial x}\right)_y = T\left(\frac{\partial S}{\partial x}\right)_y - p\left(\frac{\partial V}{\partial x}\right)_y$$

On selecting x and y, we then have an equation expressing a general relation among three partial derivatives (that is, a *general relation* of thermodynamics).

Change of Variable.   A desired result can often be obtained by an appropriate change of variable. Here we use the general formulas of differential calculus for calculating partial derivatives in terms of the new variables. For conciseness these formulas will be termed the "function of a function" theorems or simply the composite-function theorems. For a statement see Problem 11.10.

In other cases there may be two equivalent expressions for the same quantity (as the two dQ_C expressions). Changing variables in one and equating coefficients in the two identical expressions give useful new relations. (See, for example, Sec. 5.11.)

Use of Special Properties of Potentials.   A powerful method that produces results in a direct and simple manner makes use of a special property of a potential to give an equation that may be manipulated. As an example, consider entropy. On evaporation the entropy change is λ/T, and therefore

$$s' - s'' = \frac{\lambda}{T}$$

Differentiation gives us an important relation between the heat capacities of the saturated vapor and the rate of change of the latent heat with temperature (see Sec. 11.7).

Cyclic methods were used historically for the deduction of many of the most important relations in thermodynamics. They are always instructive and usually give a clear idea of the physical processes involved. Appropriate cycles are, however, often difficult to devise, and in inexpert hands they may lead to false results due to omitted terms or lack of closure of the cycle.

Analytic methods are in a majority of cases direct, concise, and less subject to the error of "neglected terms." They are, of course, not picturesque and always require careful attention to the independence of the variables employed and to the adequacy of the variable set chosen in the first place.

In what follows a number of examples of these various methods will be given. The reader can with profit classify the methods used in previous chapters according to the present scheme.

11.3   The Clausius-Clapeyron Equation (Cyclic Method)

One of the most useful general relations is the so-called Clausius-Clapeyron equation. It connects the slope of the equilibrium curve between any pair of phases with the temperature and the latent heat of the transition.

Let us deduce this result for the liquid-vapor case, using the cyclic method. First we must discover a cycle involving the change from liquid to vapor. The differential Carnot cycle is ideal for our purpose. We accordingly need two isotherms differing in temperature by dT and two adiabatics to make up the cycle. Consider now the finite cycle illustrated in Fig. 11.3. It requires that a unit mass of material be taken reversibly around the cycle 12341, where points 1 and 4 are on the saturated *liquid* curve and 2 and 3 on the saturated *vapor* curve. The steps are as follows:

$1 \rightarrow 2$ Isothermal *absorption* of the latent heat, λ, as saturated liquid of volume v'' evaporates to saturated vapor of volume v'.

$2 \rightarrow 3$ Cooling of vapor along the saturation curve from T to $T - \Delta T$. If the specific heat of the saturated vapor is c', then

$$\text{heat gain} = -c' \Delta T$$

$3 \rightarrow 4$ Isothermal condensation of vapor to saturated liquid at $T - \Delta T$.

$$\text{heat gain} = - (\lambda - \Delta\lambda)$$

$4 \rightarrow 1$ Warming of liquid along the saturation curve from $T - \Delta T$ to T.

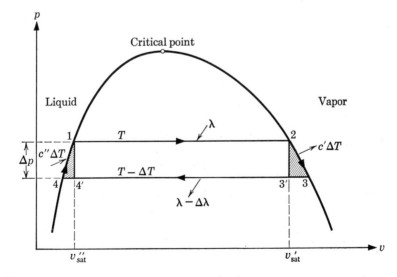

FIGURE **11.3**

With c'' the specific heat of the saturated liquid,

$$\text{heat gain} = c'' \Delta T$$

For this cycle the first law requires that

$$\Sigma \Delta U = 0$$

and hence that $\Sigma \Delta Q_c{}^i = - \Delta W_{\text{cyc}} = \text{area of cycle}$

where $\Delta Q_c{}^i$ is the heat absorbed along the ith stage of the cycle. Here $-\Delta W_{\text{cyc}}$ is the work lost by the system, which in this plane is equal to the area of the cycle. Thus we write, beginning at point 1,

$$\lambda - c'\Delta T - (\lambda - \Delta\lambda) + c''\Delta T = (v' - v'')\,\Delta p$$
$$+ \text{ area } 144' + \text{ area } 233' \quad \textbf{(11.7)}$$

The areas 144' and 233' are shaded in the figure. Their sizes depend not only on Δp but also on the changes, $\Delta v'$ and $\Delta v''$, in the saturated volumes, v' and v''. We can, in fact, always write

$$\text{area } 144' = \tfrac{1}{2}\Delta p\,\Delta v'' + \cdots$$

and

$$\text{area } 233' = \tfrac{1}{2}\Delta p\,\Delta v' + \cdots$$

where terms due to the curvature of the saturation curves involve higher powers than the second, in Δp and Δv, and are indicated by dots. Thus Eq. 11.7 becomes

$$\Delta\lambda = (c' - c'')\,\Delta T + (v' - v'')\,\Delta p + \tfrac{1}{2}(\Delta v' + \Delta v'')\,\Delta p + \cdots$$

On dividing by ΔT and taking the limit as $\Delta T \to 0$, we have

$$\lim_{\Delta T \to 0} \frac{\Delta\lambda}{\Delta T} = (c' - c'') + (v' - v'') \lim_{\Delta T \to 0} \frac{\Delta p}{\Delta T}$$

since all the higher-order terms vanish. Hence finally

$$\frac{d\lambda}{dT} = (c' - c'') + (v' - v'') \frac{dp}{dT} \quad \textbf{(11.8)}$$

We must remember that c', c'', v', and v'' are all saturation values; when doubt might arise, we should write them with subscripts. Writing $c'_{\text{sat}} - c''_{\text{sat}}$ as Δc_{sat} and $v'_{\text{sat}} - v''_{\text{sat}}$ as Δv_{sat}, we have the concise result

$$\frac{d\lambda}{dT} = \Delta c_{\text{sat}} + \Delta v_{\text{sat}} \frac{dp}{dT} \quad \textbf{(11.9)}$$

which connects the rate of change of the latent heat, λ, with the slope of the vapor pressure curve. Since this curve is the liquid-vapor equilibrium curve, Eq. 11.9 connects the temperature derivative of the latent heat of phase transition with the slope of the two-phase equilibrium curve.

To apply the second law correctly, we must be sure that the cycle is in reality a Carnot cycle. As it stands, with ΔT finite, it is clearly not, since

$2 \to 3$ and $4 \to 1$ are not adiabatics. We notice, however, that as $\Delta T \to 0$, the heat absorbed at T remains finite and constant, while that absorbed along the two small segments becomes infinitesimal and hence can be neglected in comparison. Therefore, the limit cycle is to all intents and purposes a differential Carnot cycle, and Eq. 11.6 may safely be used.[1] Thus

$$-dW_{\text{cyc}} = \frac{\lambda}{T} dT$$

or, since
$$-dW_{\text{cyc}} = (v' - v'') dp$$

$$\frac{dp}{dT} = \frac{\lambda}{T(v' - v'')} \qquad (11.10)$$

This is the famous equation of Clausius-Clapeyron. It shows that dp/dT varies directly with λ/T and inversely with $v' - v'' = \Delta v_{\text{sat}}$, the change in specific volume on evaporation. Since $v' > v''$, the slope is always positive, that is, the vapor pressure always *increases* with T. We may rewrite this result more specifically as

$$\frac{dp_{21}}{dT} = \frac{\lambda_{21}}{T \Delta v_{21}} \qquad (11.11)$$

where now everything refers to the equilibrium between phases 2 and 1 as differentiated from the other two possibilities.

Inserting Eq. 11.11 in Eq. 11.9 gives

$$c'_{\text{sat}} - c''_{\text{sat}} = \Delta c_{\text{sat}} = \Delta c_{21} = \frac{T d}{dT}\left(\frac{\lambda_{21}}{T}\right) \cdots \qquad (11.12)$$

See Problem 11.6, where another method of using the second law is suggested.

11.4   The Clausius-Clapeyron Equation in General

Although the preceding argument was based solely on the liquid-vapor equilibrium, nothing in the reasoning prevents its application to any equilibrium between two phases, i and j. We thus write Eq. 11.11 in general as

$$\frac{dp_{ij}}{dT} = \frac{\lambda_{ij}}{T \Delta v_{ij}} \qquad (11.13)$$

where p_{ij} is the equilibrium pressure for the ith and jth phases (the latter being the one stable at the *higher* temperature) and the other symbols have their

---

[1] It should be noted that although $c' dT$ and $c'' dT$ are negligible compared with λ, they are not so compared with $d\lambda$. Thus with the first law the net heat absorption is $d\lambda + (c' - c'') dT$, not simply $d\lambda$ itself.

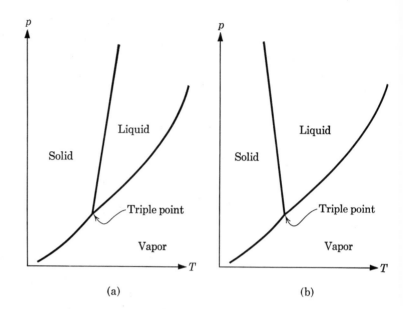

FIGURE 11.4

usual meanings. The equilibrium curve must rise with temperature as long as $\Delta v_{ij} > 0$, or as long as the system expands when heat is absorbed.

Given the three normal phases, with volumes v', v'', and v''', respectively, the three slopes are

$$\text{(liquid-vapor)} \qquad \frac{dp_{21}}{dT} = \frac{\lambda_{21}}{T(v' - v'')}$$

$$\text{(solid-vapor)} \qquad \frac{dp_{31}}{dT} = \frac{\lambda_{31}}{T(v' - v''')}$$

$$\text{(solid-liquid)} \qquad \frac{dp_{32}}{dT} = \frac{\lambda_{32}}{T(v'' - v''')} \qquad \textbf{(11.14)}$$

For normal substances the right sides of these equations are always positive, and hence the equilibrium curves all slope toward the right [Fig. 11.4(a)]. For water substance $v'' - v''' < 0$, and the ice-water curve has a negative slope [Fig. 11.4(b)].

At the triple point the heat of sublimation, λ_{31}, must be the same whether we measure it directly or by first melting the solid and then vaporizing the liquid. Thus

$$\lambda_{31} = \lambda_{32} + \lambda_{21}$$

and since the temperature is common,

$$(v' - v''')\frac{dp_{31}}{dT} = (v'' - v''')\frac{dp_{32}}{dT} + (v' - v'')\frac{dp_{21}}{dT}$$

Equilibrium curves also have an important bearing on the relative stabilities of phases placed side by side at a common temperature. Let the curves each be extended beyond the triple point as indicated by dashed lines in Fig. 11.5. The dashed lines represent regions of *instability* for the phases concerned.

Suppose, for example, that a liquid is supercooled to T_1 ($T_1 < T_{tr}$). It will tend to evaporate until the system exerts a pressure corresponding to point a on the p_{21} curve. We thus have liquid and vapor in the region of stable existence of the solid. The vapor therefore condenses as solid. Since this condensation liberates more heat than was required to vaporize the liquid, the system is warmed. This process continues either until all the liquid is gone (when the vapor pressure falls to a point on the p_{31} curve) or until the triple point is reached, where all three phases may coexist.

A similar situation would arise if a solid-vapor system could be superheated to, say, point c at T_2, above the triple point. In this case the solid would vaporize, and the vapor would condense as liquid. Since these changes would result in the *absorption* of heat, the system would cool, and, as before, the process would continue until the more unstable phase had disappeared or the triple point had been reached.

We can readily predict the sequence of events should a liquid-solid system (such as ice-water) be taken into the region of stability of the vapor. It should be remarked that such discussions are rather academic, when temperatures above the triple point are involved, since attempts to superheat solids invariably result in melting.

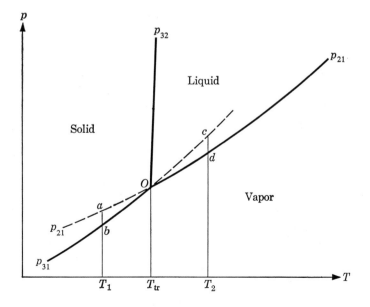

FIGURE **11.5**

11.5   Maxwell's Relations (Cross Derivative Method)

Starting with the Clausius equations, which we now regard as being essentially equivalent equations with different independent variables, we have

$$
\begin{array}{llll}
dU = T\,dS - p\,dV & S, V & \text{CI} \\
dH = T\,dS + V\,dp & S, p & \text{CII} \\
dA = -S\,dT - p\,dV & T, V & \text{CIII} \\
dG = -S\,dT + V\,dp & T, p & \text{CIV} & \textbf{(11.15)}
\end{array}
$$

Applying the cross derivative theorem to these relations, we obtain for CIV, which has the independent variables T and p,

$$
\left(\frac{\partial S}{\partial p}\right)_T = -\left(\frac{\partial V}{\partial T}\right)_p
\qquad\text{MI}
$$

Since
$$
\left(\frac{\partial S}{\partial p}\right)_T = \frac{1}{T}\frac{dQ_T}{dp} = \frac{L_p}{T}
$$

this is simply Maxwell's first relation.

Similarly, from CIII,

$$
\left(\frac{\partial S}{\partial V}\right)_T = \left(\frac{\partial p}{\partial T}\right)_V
\qquad\text{MII}
$$

which, since

$$
\left(\frac{\partial S}{\partial V}\right)_T = \frac{L_V}{T}
$$

is Maxwell II.

From CII we obtain

$$
\left(\frac{\partial T}{\partial p}\right)_S = \left(\frac{\partial V}{\partial S}\right)_p
$$

which is best rewritten with the reciprocals of each side to give

$$
\left(\frac{\partial p}{\partial T}\right)_S = \left(\frac{\partial S}{\partial V}\right)_p
\qquad\text{MIII}
$$

This result was also obtained by Maxwell, and we refer to it as Maxwell III.

Maxwell's fourth relation comes from CI, which we also take for convenience of interpretation in the reciprocal form; that is,

$$
\left(\frac{\partial S}{\partial p}\right)_V = -\left(\frac{\partial V}{\partial T}\right)_S
\qquad\text{MIV}
$$

These four relations are thus the direct result of the exactness of dG, dA, dH, and dU

$$T, p \qquad \left(\frac{\partial S}{\partial p}\right)_T = -\left(\frac{\partial V}{\partial T}\right)_p \qquad \text{MI}$$

$$T, V \qquad \left(\frac{\partial S}{\partial V}\right)_T = \left(\frac{\partial p}{\partial T}\right)_V \qquad \text{MII}$$

$$S, p \qquad \left(\frac{\partial S}{\partial V}\right)_p = \left(\frac{\partial p}{\partial T}\right)_S \qquad \text{MIII}$$

$$S, V \qquad \left(\frac{\partial S}{\partial p}\right)_V = -\left(\frac{\partial V}{\partial T}\right)_S \qquad \text{MIV} \qquad (11.16)$$

On the left of each of them is an entropy derivative. Each is therefore proportional to a rate of heat absorption. On the right is a temperature derivative. In other words, Maxwell's relations equate a *calorimetric* property of a system to a *thermometric* property.

Calorimetric properties are very difficult to measure experimentally. Maxwell's relations permit their calculation from quantities that can be measured directly, often with considerable precision.

11.6   Maxwell's Relations and Multiphase Systems

In the deduction of Maxwell's relations in Sec. 11.5, no assumptions were made about the system other than that it was the usual hydrostatic one. As a result, the relations should apply to a vapor, a liquid, or a solid system, since in any of these cases the four choices of independent variable pairs $(T, p; T, V; S, p;$ and $S, V)$ are all possible.

In the same way application of Maxwell's relations to two-phase systems should be possible, provided those equations are selected which involve permissible variable pairs. Since now $p = p(T)$, MI is clearly not applicable, although the other three are.

To apply MII, for example, we must choose the variable pair T, V. Since $p = p(T)$, the partial derivative $(\partial p/\partial T)_V$ becomes the ordinary derivative dp/dT, the slope of the two-phase equilibrium curve. Moreover, $(\partial S/\partial V)_T = L_V/T$. If a unit mass changes from phase 2 to phase 1 with absorption of latent heat, λ, then the heat absorbed per unit volume expansion becomes

$$L_V = \frac{\lambda}{v' - v''}$$

and MII reduces to

$$\frac{dp}{dT} = \frac{\lambda}{T(v' - v'')} \qquad (11.17)$$

which is simply the Clausius-Clapeyron equation. This was obtained in Sec. 11.3 by a cyclic method but now is seen to be simply a special case of MII.

In the same way, MIII reduces directly to Eq. 11.17, as does MIV after some transformation (see Problem 11.8).

None of the four Maxwellian relations is applicable to a three-phase system, since for it both T and p are fixed.

11.7 Specific Heats of Saturated Phases

In Sec. 11.3 the relation

$$\Delta c_{21} = c'_{\text{sat}} - c''_{\text{sat}} = \frac{T\,d}{dT}\left(\frac{\lambda_{21}}{T}\right) \qquad (11.12)$$

was obtained by the cyclic method. Before examining the saturation heats in more detail, let us see how the same result may be obtained by the analytic method. Probably the simplest process uses an appropriate potential function (Sec. 11.2), and the heat capacities involved suggest entropy as this function. Reversible evaporation results in an entropy change of λ/T, and thus we start with

$$\frac{\lambda}{T} = s'_{\text{sat}} - s''_{\text{sat}} \qquad (11.18)$$

On differentiation by T and multiplication through by T, we have

$$\frac{T\,d}{dT}\left(\frac{\lambda}{T}\right) = \frac{T\,ds'_{\text{sat}}}{dT} - \frac{T\,ds''_{\text{sat}}}{dT}$$

Since

$$\frac{T\,ds_{\text{sat}}}{dT} = c_{\text{sat}}$$

the desired result follows at once,

$$\frac{T\,d}{dT}\left(\frac{\lambda}{T}\right) = c'_{\text{sat}} - c''_{\text{sat}}$$

The directness of this method contrasts with the length of the cyclic approach.

Since

$$c_{\text{sat}} = \frac{T\,ds_{\text{sat}}}{dT} = T\left(\frac{ds}{dT}\right)_{\text{sat}}$$

the saturation heat capacity of a given phase is fixed by the slope (dT/ds) of the corresponding saturation curve in the T-s plane. In Fig. 11.6 saturation curves for the liquid and vapor are drawn to illustrate three typical cases. In each case, of course, the liquid and vapor curves join at the critical point to form a continuous curve separating the two-phase region of existence from the regions of single-phase stability. Furthermore, in each of the three cases the slope of the liquid curve is *positive* throughout its length. Thus c''_{sat} is a positive quantity as are ordinary specific heats.

The right, or vapor, section, however, shows marked variations. In Fig. 11.6(a) its slope (except for the critical point) is always *negative*. Therefore, for water, carbon dioxide, and ammonia, for example, for which this shape is typical, c'_{sat} is *negative*, and heat is absorbed as the saturated vapor has its temperature lowered. This novel and unexpected behavior is due to the fact that as the saturated vapor falls in temperature, it must expand so much to avoid supersaturation that the external work performed *exceeds* the drop in internal energy. As a result, heat must be absorbed to make up the difference. In other cases the vapor curve has one or more vertical tangents, at which points the slope, and hence c'_{sat}, changes sign. Fig. 11.6(b), drawn for ether, has two such sign changes; Fig. 11.6(c), drawn for acetic acid, has but one and that near the critical point.

It is convenient to express the saturation specific heats of the two phases in terms of the ordinary specific heats of the phases, c_p' and c_p''. To do this, we make use of the fact that the difference in entropy between two points on the

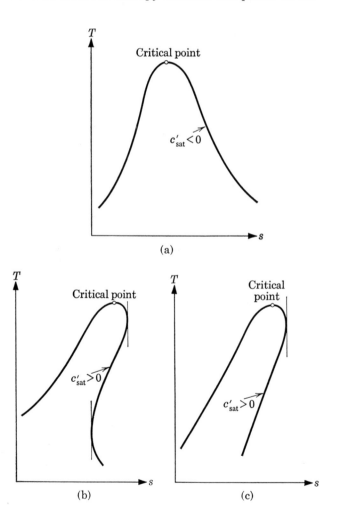

(a)

(b)

(c)

FIGURE **11.6**

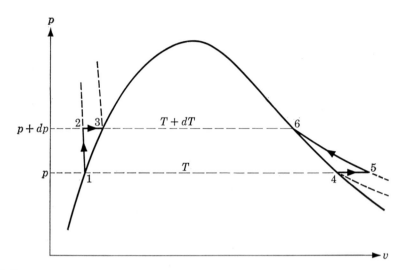

FIGURE **11.7**

saturation curve is independent of how the system is taken from one point to the other (see the the method for infinitesimal cycles, Sec. 11.2). Thus in Fig. 11.7 consider points 1 and 4 on the liquid and vapor curves, respectively, at pressure p and temperature T. Taking the liquid case first, we note that the entropy change, ds''_{sat}, between 1 and 3 is the same whether we move along the saturation curve or along the elbow path 123. This latter path is entirely in the liquid region, where

$$s'' = s''(p, T)$$

and hence

$$ds''_{\text{sat}} = ds'' = \left(\frac{\partial s''}{\partial p}\right)_T dp + \left(\frac{\partial s''}{\partial T}\right)_p dT$$

Multiplying through by T/dT and using MI, we obtain

$$\frac{T\, ds''_{\text{sat}}}{dT} = -T\left(\frac{\partial v''}{\partial T}\right)_p \frac{dp}{dT} + T\left(\frac{\partial s''}{\partial T}\right)_p$$

Replacing the entropy derivatives by their equivalent specific heats and using the Clausius-Clapeyron relation give

$$c''_{\text{sat}} = -\frac{\lambda}{v' - v''}\left(\frac{\partial v''}{\partial T}\right)_p + c_p'' \tag{11.19}$$

This is the exact relation between c''_{sat} and c_p''. We can see that the negative term is quite small, however, as long as we stay a reasonable distance from the critical point. Thus when $v' \gg v''$, and v'' is neglected in comparison, this term becomes

$$-\frac{\lambda \beta_p''}{\dfrac{v'}{v''}}$$

where $\beta_p{}''$ is the coefficient of thermal expansion for the liquid and is small. Since the ratio v'/v'' is large, this term is usually very small and therefore may usually be neglected, so that

$$c''_{\text{sat}} \approx c_p{}''$$ (11.20)

The same considerations apply to the passage $4 \to 6$; ds'_{sat} is the same whether we use the saturation path or the isobaric-isothermal path 456. As before,

$$\frac{T \, ds'_{\text{sat}}}{dT} = T \left(\frac{\partial s'}{\partial T}\right)_p - \frac{\lambda}{v'_{\text{sat}} - v''_{\text{sat}}} \left(\frac{\partial v'}{\partial T}\right)_p$$

or

$$c'_{\text{sat}} = c_p{}' - \frac{\lambda}{v'_{\text{sat}} - v''_{\text{sat}}} \left(\frac{\partial v'}{\partial T}\right)_p$$ (11.21)

Here the negative term is much larger than in Eq. 11.19, since now $(\partial v'/\partial T)_p$ is much greater. If we use the perfect gas law for the vapor and neglect v'' as before, this term reduces to λ/T, and

thus

$$c'_{\text{sat}} \approx c_p{}' - \frac{\lambda}{T}$$ (11.22)

This expression is *negative* as long as λ/T exceeds the ordinary specific heat of the vapor, $c_p{}'$, which it does whenever the slope of the curve of Fig. 11.6 is negative.

Insertion of Eqs. 11.20 and 11.22 in Eq. 11.12 gives

$$\frac{d\lambda}{dT} \approx \Delta c_p = (c_p{}' - c_p{}'') + \cdots$$ (11.23)

which is the approximate relation of Kirchhoff, Eq. 7.44, obtained in Sec. 7.15. It is often given as an exact thermodynamic result, although it is reliable only under the assumptions just made. The precise relation results on insertion of Eqs. 11.19 and 11.21 in Eq. 11.12.

$$\frac{d\lambda}{dT} = \Delta c_p + \frac{\lambda}{T} - \frac{\lambda}{\Delta v_{\text{sat}}} \left[\left(\frac{\partial v'}{\partial T}\right)_p - \left(\frac{\partial v''}{\partial T}\right)_p \right]$$ (11.24)

Although Δv_{sat} refers to the saturation volumes, $(\partial v'/\partial T)_p$ and $(\partial v''/\partial T)_p$ refer to the pure phases and not to the slopes of the saturation curves in the T-v plane. (These would be ordinary derivatives.)

We note that $\lambda/\Delta v_{\text{sat}} = T \, dp/dT$ by the Clausius-Clapeyron relation and therefore that $d\lambda/dT$ is expressed in terms of specific heats, $(\partial v/\partial T)_p$, and dp/dT, the three basic derivative types for the problem.

11.8 Gibbs' Potential

Gibbs' potential has a number of very striking uses, a few examples of which will be given in the next two sections.

From CIV

$$dG = -S \, dT + V \, dp$$

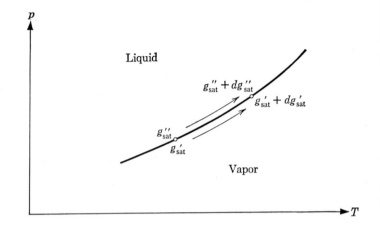

FIGURE 11-8

and Gibbs' potential is such a function that it remains unchanged for all processes at constant temperature and pressure. Since change of phase is just such a process, this equation leads to the equality of the specific Gibbs' potentials for all phases in equilibrium (as we saw in Sec. 9.17). Thus if we have, say, a liquid in equilibrium with its vapor,

$$g''_{sat} = g'_{sat}$$

If we move along the equilibrium curve of Fig. 11.8, the same relation must hold at a neighboring point, and therefore

$$dg''_{sat} = dg'_{sat}$$

Use of CIV gives

$$-s''_{sat} dT + v''_{sat} dp = -s'_{sat} dT + v'_{sat} dp$$

or

$$\frac{dp}{dT} = \frac{s'_{sat} - s''_{sat}}{v'_{sat} - v''_{sat}} = \frac{\lambda_{21}}{T \Delta v_{21}}$$

which is the equation of Clausius-Clapeyron once more. It is thus the direct result of the equality of the specific Gibbs' functions, g'' and g', along the equilibrium curve.

11.9   Relation of the Triple Point to the Ice Point

The fact that the triple point of water is different from the ice point (which defines 0° on the Celsius scale) was emphasized in Sec. 2.2. Although the temperature difference is not large, about 0.0098°C, investigation of the reason for the difference reveals some very interesting thermodynamic information.

At the triple point ice, liquid water, and pure vapor exist in equilibrium together under the pressure, say, p_{321}, of the triple point [Fig. 11.9(a)]. At the ice point the system exists under a total pressure equal to that of the atmosphere, which is roughly 165 times as great as p_{321}. In this case, moreover, the gaseous phase is made up of air saturated with water vapor, and the liquid is a saturated solution of air in water [see Fig. 11.9(b), where small circles are used to indicate the added air]. This situation offers such a good example of the use of the Gibbs' function that it is appropriate to discuss it here, despite the fact that the water-air system contains more than one chemical substance or component and therefore is strictly outside the province of this chapter. As a consequence, we must draw on the future for a generalization of the behavior of Gibbs' potential in such systems. In Chapter 13 it is shown that in the equilibrium of a general polyphase, multicomponent system, the same criterion holds as for a single-component system. The specific Gibbs' potential of a given component *always has the same value* in all the phases in which it is found. Thus the equality for water substance,

$$g_{sat}''' = g_{sat}'' = g_{sat}'$$

for the system in Fig. 11.9(a) can be carried over directly to the system in Fig. 11.9(b).

When a foreign gas is pumped into a system with both ice and liquid water present, there are two different effects. Since they are small, we suppose that each may be treated independently of the other. A discussion of these effects follows.

Solubility Effect.   Air dissolves in water to form a saturated solution of air in water. It is a common property of all dissolved substances to produce a

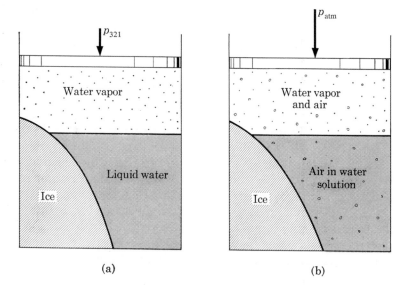

(a)   (b)

FIGURE **11.9**

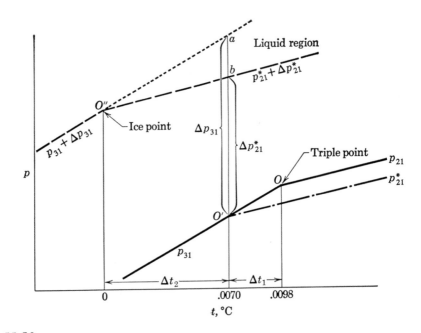

FIGURE **11.10**

reduction in the vapor pressure of the solvent. In Fig. 11.10 the vapor pressure of pure water is indicated by the solid line p_{21} (since the scale is large, all vapor pressure curves are drawn as straight lines). The reduced vapor pressure of the water saturated with air is shown by the broken line marked p_{21}^*. The original triple point of the three pure phases, O, is now shifted to O', with a corresponding drop in temperature, $\Delta t_1 = 0.0028°C$.

Direct Pressure Effect.   The added external pressure on each condensed phase increases its vapor pressure above the normal value. At the temperature of O' we suppose this increase in vapor pressure to be Δp_{31} for the ice phase and Δp_{21}^* for the saturated liquid phase. The vapor pressure of the ice phase is thus raised to point a on the dotted (unstable) portion of the (dashed) ice-vapor curve. The vapor pressure of the saturated solution rises from O' to b, a point on the new (dashed) vapor pressure curve for the solution under pressure. These last two lines are marked $p_{31} + \Delta p_{31}$ and $p_{21}^* + \Delta p_{21}^*$, respectively. They intersect at O'', which is the ice point, to which by definition we assign the temperature 0°C. The corresponding shift in temperature, Δt_2, from O' is 0.0070°C, a little over twice the first lowering, Δt_1.

To understand the pressure effect and the reason for the further temperature lowering, we must examine the equilibrium from the standpoint of Gibbs' potential. Considering the solution-water vapor equilibrium first, at any point on the equilibrium curve for these phases, we have

$$g_{\text{sat}}''^* = g_{\text{sat}}'$$

(11.25)

where g''^*_{sat} refers to the water in the solution and g'_{sat} to the water in the gaseous phase. For any change in T and p,

$$dg = -s\,dT + v\,dp$$

or, if T is constant,

$$dg_T = v\,dp \tag{11.26}$$

Thus if, while the solution is saturated with air, we increase the total pressure on its surface by dp, we must write, from Eqs. 11.25 and 11.26,

$$v''^*_{\text{sat}}\,dp = v'_{\text{sat}}\,dp^*_{21}$$

where now dp^*_{21} is the corresponding increase in the partial pressure of the water vapor in the vapor phase. For a small finite increase, Δp,

$$\Delta p^*_{21} = \left(\frac{v''^*_{\text{sat}}}{v'_{\text{sat}}}\right)\Delta p \tag{11.27}$$

If v''^*_{sat} is taken as v''_{sat}, the saturated volume of pure water, the ratio on the right is very small indeed (about 4.8×10^{-5}). Therefore, a large increase, Δp, produces a modest rise, Δp^*_{21}.

Exactly the same reasoning applies to an increase in the total pressure on the ice-vapor system. The corresponding rise, Δp_{31}, is, accordingly,

$$\Delta p_{31} = \left(\frac{v'''_{\text{sat}}}{v'_{\text{sat}}}\right)\Delta p \tag{11.28}$$

Since ice contracts on melting, $v'''_{\text{sat}} > v''_{\text{sat}}$, and

$$\Delta p_{31} > \Delta p^*_{21}$$

This is why a lies above b in the figure. Since this situation renders the ice unstable with respect to the liquid phase, ice melts. The melting lowers the temperature of the system, just as in the simple system of Sec. 11.4, to the new, stable three-phase equilibrium point, O''. Thus the ice point is a stable point as long as some ice is present. These results also emphasize the necessity of seeing that the water is saturated with air; otherwise, the ice point might be a sizable fraction of $0.0028°$ too high, even though, of course, still well below the triple point temperature.

11.10   The Six General Relations of Maxwell

Use of the four Clausius equations gave us four Maxwellian relations. With the primary variable set (T, p, V, and S), there are two remaining pairs of independent variables, namely, T, S and p, V, for which similar equations could be written. However, since the set of Clausius equations is a closed set, these two cases must be approached in some other way. We saw in Sec. 11.6 that for two-phase systems at least, one Maxwellian relation could be transformed into another by a suitable change of variable. This treatment is applicable to Maxwellian relations in general. Maxwell's four relations as given in Eq. 11.16

do not make four independent statements about hydrostatic systems; they are simply equivalent statements expressed in terms of four different sets of independent variables.

Examination of the four relations of Eq. 11.16 shows that no single derivative occurs more than once. Therefore, regarded as algebraic equations in partial derivatives, Maxwell's relations are essentially independent; none can be deduced from the others by purely algebraic eliminations.

With differentiation, however, any one can be deduced from any of the rest by a change of variables. Thus we take MI and change the independent variable pair from T, p to T, V. Transforming the left side first, we obtain

$$\left(\frac{\partial S}{\partial V}\right)_T \left(\frac{\partial V}{\partial p}\right)_T = -\left(\frac{\partial V}{\partial T}\right)_p$$

or

$$\left(\frac{\partial S}{\partial V}\right)_T = -\left(\frac{\partial V}{\partial T}\right)_p \left(\frac{\partial p}{\partial V}\right)_T = \left(\frac{\partial p}{\partial T}\right)_V$$

by the reciprocity theorem. This is just MII. In the same manner it can be transformed into each of the remaining two Maxwellian relations.

Starting with, say, MI,

$$\left(\frac{\partial S}{\partial p}\right)_T = -\left(\frac{\partial V}{\partial T}\right)_p \tag{11.29}$$

let us transform to the new variable pair T, S. We leave the left side as it is because it is the reciprocal of $(\partial p/\partial S)_T$, which is already in the correct form. Using the composite-function theorem on the right side, we obtain

$$\left(\frac{\partial S}{\partial p}\right)_T = -\left(\frac{\partial V}{\partial T}\right)_S \left(\frac{\partial T}{\partial T}\right)_p - \left(\frac{\partial V}{\partial S}\right)_T \left(\frac{\partial S}{\partial T}\right)_p$$

or

$$\left(\frac{\partial S}{\partial p}\right)_T = -\left(\frac{\partial V}{\partial T}\right)_S - \left(\frac{\partial V}{\partial S}\right)_T \left(\frac{\partial S}{\partial T}\right)_p \qquad \text{MV} \tag{11.30}$$

This is a new relation that contains the new derivative $(\partial S/\partial T)_p$.

Similarly, changing to the pair $p, \bar{V}$ in MI gives

$$\left(\frac{\partial S}{\partial p}\right)_V = -\left(\frac{\partial V}{\partial T}\right)_p - \left(\frac{\partial S}{\partial V}\right)_p \left(\frac{\partial V}{\partial p}\right)_T \qquad \text{MVI} \tag{11.31}$$

Here the new derivative is $(\partial V/\partial p)_T$. This completes the set of six Maxwellian relations.

11.11   The Three Independent or Basic Derivatives

We must now examine the general problem of calculating any desired derivative. First we must answer two questions:

1. How many partial derivatives of the type occurring in Maxwell's relations do we have?

2. How many (algebraically) independent relations exist among these derivatives?

The difference between these two numbers fixes the number of derivatives that are *undeterminable* or, what is the same thing, *arbitrary* as far as the laws of thermodynamics and mathematics are concerned. Since each partial derivative represents some measurable physical property of the system, the difference fixes the *irreducible minimum* of properties we must measure. With these properties measured, all the others may be calculated as needed.

The answer to the first question naturally depends upon how many *variables* we wish to include. Since the six Maxwellian relations involve only the primaries (S, T, p, and V), we begin by confining ourselves to derivations involving these alone. The general derivative of this type involves three different variables and may be written

$$\left(\frac{\partial x_1}{\partial x_2}\right)_{x_3}$$

The variable x_1 may be chosen in four ways, x_2 in three ways, and x_3 in two ways, so that

$$\begin{pmatrix}\text{number of first-order}\\ \text{partial derivatives}\\ \text{with four variables}\end{pmatrix} = 4 \times 3 \times 2 = 24$$

This number fortunately can be cut in half by the reciprocal theorem, since

$$\left(\frac{\partial x_1}{\partial x_2}\right)_{x_3} = \frac{1}{\left(\dfrac{\partial x_2}{\partial x_1}\right)_{x_3}}$$

There are thus twelve reciprocal pairs, and we need consider only *twelve derivatives* as actually different.

To answer question number two, we must write down in addition to Maxwell's relations all the purely mathematical relations that exist among the partial derivatives. These new relations come from the reciprocity theorem, which applies to the three variables, say, x_1, x_2, and x_3, connected by a functional relation of the form

$$F(x_1, x_2, x_3) = 0$$

In this case

$$\left(\frac{\partial x_1}{\partial x_2}\right)_{x_3}\left(\frac{\partial x_3}{\partial x_1}\right)_{x_2}\left(\frac{\partial x_2}{\partial x_3}\right)_{x_1} = -1 \tag{11.32}$$

Since there are four variables to choose from, there are $\dfrac{4 \times 3 \times 2}{3!} = 4$ ways of selecting sets of 3 (when order is immaterial). There are therefore four new equations of the form of Eq. 11.32. These are written out as follows, with the functional relation from which each comes indicated at the left:

$$F_1(T, p, V) \qquad \left(\frac{\partial T}{\partial p}\right)_V \left(\frac{\partial V}{\partial T}\right)_p \left(\frac{\partial p}{\partial V}\right)_T = -1$$

$$F_2(S, T, p) \qquad \left(\frac{\partial S}{\partial T}\right)_p \left(\frac{\partial p}{\partial S}\right)_T \left(\frac{\partial T}{\partial p}\right)_S = -1$$

$$F_3(S, T, V) \qquad \left(\frac{\partial S}{\partial T}\right)_V \left(\frac{\partial V}{\partial S}\right)_T \left(\frac{\partial T}{\partial V}\right)_S = -1$$

$$F_4(S, p, V) \qquad \left(\frac{\partial S}{\partial p}\right)_V \left(\frac{\partial V}{\partial S}\right)_p \left(\frac{\partial p}{\partial V}\right)_S = -1 \qquad \textbf{(11.33)}$$

Examination shows that the twelve derivatives present are all different, and hence these new equations are algebraically independent. Moreover, we find by trial that none of the four can be transformed into any other of the set by the use of MI to MV. Thus nine equations, Maxwell's first *five* and the *four* in Eq. 11.33, are algebraically *independent*.

This algebraic independence does not hold if we include MVI. To demonstrate this fact, we write out the twelve derivatives in what we may call their standard forms. Thus $(\partial V/\partial T)_p$ is used in place of $(\partial T/\partial V)_p$, $(\partial S/\partial T)_p$ in place of $(\partial T/\partial S)_p$, etc. The standard forms are grouped for easy reference in a rectangular array in Table 11.1, where all derivatives in a column have a common variable held constant.

It can be shown readily that use of MI to MIV and the four reciprocity relations in Eq. 11.33 makes possible the transformation of MV into MVI (or vice versa). Since this is purely an algebraic process, it is left as an exercise (see Problem 11.5).

TABLE **11.1**

The Twelve Primary Partial Derivatives in S, T, p, and V*

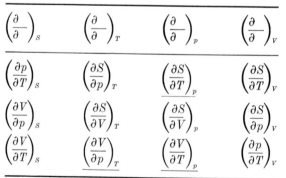

$\left(\dfrac{\partial}{\partial}\right)_S$	$\left(\dfrac{\partial}{\partial}\right)_T$	$\left(\dfrac{\partial}{\partial}\right)_p$	$\left(\dfrac{\partial}{\partial}\right)_V$
$\left(\dfrac{\partial p}{\partial T}\right)_S$	$\left(\dfrac{\partial S}{\partial p}\right)_T$	$\left(\dfrac{\partial S}{\partial T}\right)_p$	$\left(\dfrac{\partial S}{\partial T}\right)_V$
$\left(\dfrac{\partial V}{\partial p}\right)_S$	$\left(\dfrac{\partial S}{\partial V}\right)_T$	$\left(\dfrac{\partial S}{\partial V}\right)_p$	$\left(\dfrac{\partial S}{\partial p}\right)_V$
$\left(\dfrac{\partial V}{\partial T}\right)_S$	$\left(\dfrac{\partial V}{\partial p}\right)_T$	$\left(\dfrac{\partial V}{\partial T}\right)_p$	$\left(\dfrac{\partial p}{\partial T}\right)_V$

* Those underlined form the basic set of three usually chosen as independent.

The conclusion, of course, is that only five of the six Maxwellian relations are algebraically independent. Since these and Eq. 11.33 give us nine independent relations and twelve derivatives, there are $12 - 9 = 3$ *independent* or, mathematically speaking, *arbitrary* derivatives. This means that there are three derivatives that cannot be calculated from the laws of thermodynamics or the theorems of mathematics. They must be measured *experimentally*. Once this is done, all the others are, in principle, fixed and may be calculated by use of the preceding ten equations or by other convenient means.

The choice of the basic set of three must be consistent with the nine independent equations and at the same time must include only those derivatives that are most readily and accurately measured experimentally. The most suitable set for most purposes is

$$\left(\frac{\partial V}{\partial T}\right)_p \qquad \left(\frac{\partial V}{\partial p}\right)_T \qquad \left(\frac{\partial S}{\partial T}\right)_p$$

Since each of these in turn is related directly to the experimental coefficients β_p, κ_T, and C_p by the expressions

$$\beta_p = \frac{1}{V}\left(\frac{\partial V}{\partial T}\right)_p \qquad \kappa_T = -\frac{1}{V}\left(\frac{\partial V}{\partial p}\right)_T \qquad C_p = T\left(\frac{\partial S}{\partial T}\right)_p$$

we may take either the three *derivatives* or the three *coefficients* as the basic data for calculating the other nine derivatives.

11.12   Derivatives in Terms of the Basic Three

Having selected our basic three derivatives, we must now express the remaining nine primary derivatives in terms of these three. The equations resulting from such calculations are collected for reference in Table 11.2, where the three basic derivatives are shown in square frames and the derivatives are listed in the order of the columns of Table 11.1.

With the data of Table 11.2 it is possible to express any partial derivative of U, H, A, or G in terms of the basic three. To find $(\partial U/\partial T)_p$, for example, we begin with CI,

$$dU = T\,dS - p\,dV$$

and obtain by the method of partial derivatives from differentials (Sec. 11.2)

$$\left(\frac{\partial U}{\partial T}\right)_p = T\left(\frac{\partial S}{\partial T}\right)_p - p\left(\frac{\partial V}{\partial T}\right)_p$$

where now none but basic derivatives appear on the right. Other more complicated derivatives can be found readily by use of the usual theorems of partial differentiation.

The total number of general relations that can be formed with the variables S, T, p, V, U, H, A, and G, that is, both *primary* and *secondary* variables, is huge. Although only a few of these relations need ever be used in practice, it is

TABLE **11.2**

The Primary Derivatives in Terms of the Basic Three

(1) $\left(\dfrac{\partial p}{\partial T}\right)_S = \dfrac{\left(\dfrac{\partial S}{\partial T}\right)_p}{\left(\dfrac{\partial V}{\partial T}\right)_p}$

(7) $\boxed{\left(\dfrac{\partial S}{\partial T}\right)_p = \dfrac{C_p}{T}}$

(2) $\left(\dfrac{\partial V}{\partial p}\right)_S = \dfrac{\left(\dfrac{\partial V}{\partial T}\right)_p^2}{\left(\dfrac{\partial S}{\partial T}\right)_p} + \left(\dfrac{\partial V}{\partial p}\right)_T$

(8) $\left(\dfrac{\partial S}{\partial V}\right)_p = \dfrac{\left(\dfrac{\partial S}{\partial T}\right)_p}{\left(\dfrac{\partial V}{\partial T}\right)_p}$

(3) $\left(\dfrac{\partial V}{\partial T}\right)_S = \left(\dfrac{\partial V}{\partial T}\right)_p + \dfrac{\left(\dfrac{\partial V}{\partial p}\right)_T \left(\dfrac{\partial S}{\partial T}\right)_p}{\left(\dfrac{\partial V}{\partial T}\right)_p}$

(9) $\boxed{\left(\dfrac{\partial V}{\partial T}\right)_p = V\beta_p}$

(4) $\left(\dfrac{\partial S}{\partial p}\right)_T = -\left(\dfrac{\partial V}{\partial T}\right)_p$

(10) $\left(\dfrac{\partial S}{\partial T}\right)_V = \left(\dfrac{\partial S}{\partial T}\right)_p + \dfrac{\left(\dfrac{\partial V}{\partial T}\right)_p^2}{\left(\dfrac{\partial V}{\partial p}\right)_T}$

(5) $\left(\dfrac{\partial S}{\partial V}\right)_T = \dfrac{-\left(\dfrac{\partial V}{\partial T}\right)_p}{\left(\dfrac{\partial V}{\partial p}\right)_T}$

(11) $\left(\dfrac{\partial S}{\partial p}\right)_V = \dfrac{\left(\dfrac{\partial S}{\partial T}\right)_p \left(\dfrac{\partial V}{\partial p}\right)_T}{-\left(\dfrac{\partial V}{\partial T}\right)_p} - \left(\dfrac{\partial V}{\partial T}\right)_p$

(6) $\boxed{\left(\dfrac{\partial V}{\partial p}\right)_T = -V\kappa_T}$

(12) $\left(\dfrac{\partial p}{\partial T}\right)_V = \dfrac{-\left(\dfrac{\partial V}{\partial T}\right)_p}{\left(\dfrac{\partial V}{\partial p}\right)_T}$

interesting to determine just how many there are. Selecting the three variables entering into a partial derivative, just as before, and dividing by two to take account of reciprocals, we find

$$\left[\begin{array}{c} \text{number of first-} \\ \text{order derivatives} \\ \text{(with eight variables)} \end{array}\right] = \frac{8 \times 7 \times 6}{2} = 168$$

We have seen that with $n = 2$ no general relations need contain more than four derivatives, that is, one derivative expressed in terms of three others. Of course, many of these relations are degenerate and contain only two or three derivatives. In any event, we can obtain an upper limit on the total number of possible relations by calculating the number of four derivative expressions conceivable. This is simply the number of ways of combining 168 derivatives four at a time (the order being immaterial). The result is

$$\left(\begin{array}{c}\text{maximum number of}\\ \text{general first-order relations}\end{array}\right) = \frac{168 \times 167 \times 166 \times 165}{4!} = 3.5 \times 10^7$$

Obviously a shorter method is needed for calculating the few relations that we may want. The method of algebraic elimination requires too many intermediate equations and is tedious to carry out. Bridgman[2] discovered by inspection a method of writing each derivative as a ratio of two quantities, selected in a simple manner from a tabular array. Further discussion of this method will be postponed until after the general Jacobian method has been developed in the following sections.

11.13   Jacobians

We have seen that it is possible to express any thermodynamic derivative for a system with $n = 2$ in terms of three basic derivatives. However, the calculation is often laborious, and so it is desirable to have a method at once rapid and direct. This method is provided by the use of Jacobians.

Jacobians are simply determinants in which the partial derivatives of two or more dependent variables are arranged in a particular way. Thus, to consider a second-order Jacobian, take two nonrelated quantities, X and Y, where

$$X = X(A, B)$$

and
$$Y = Y(A, B)$$

A and B being two independent variables. The Jacobian of X and Y, $J(X, Y)$, is written as

$$J(X, Y) = \begin{vmatrix} \left(\dfrac{\partial X}{\partial A}\right)_B & \left(\dfrac{\partial Y}{\partial A}\right)_B \\ \left(\dfrac{\partial X}{\partial B}\right)_A & \left(\dfrac{\partial Y}{\partial B}\right)_A \end{vmatrix}$$

or, on expansion, $J(X, Y) = \left(\dfrac{\partial X}{\partial A}\right)_B \left(\dfrac{\partial Y}{\partial B}\right)_A - \left(\dfrac{\partial X}{\partial B}\right)_A \left(\dfrac{\partial Y}{\partial A}\right)_B$

The notation $J(X, Y)$ has the advantage of brevity but does not indicate the independent variables. A much more meaningful notation, devised by Jacobi, indicates these variables and also suggests a generalization of a partial derivative. We write

$$J(X, Y) = \frac{\partial(X, Y)}{\partial(A, B)}$$

This notation is particularly useful for the following special cases.

---

[2] P. W. Bridgman, *A Condensed Collection of Thermodynamic Formulas*, Harvard Univ. Press, Cambridge, Mass., 1925.

1. $Y = B$ (direct cancellation). We have

$$\frac{\partial(X, B)}{\partial(A, B)} = \left(\frac{\partial X}{\partial A}\right)_B \left(\frac{\partial B}{\partial B}\right)_A - \left(\frac{\partial X}{\partial B}\right)_A \left(\frac{\partial B}{\partial A}\right)_B$$

Since the last derivative is zero, this reduces to a single derivative, $(\partial X/\partial A)_B$. In other words, formally we may cancel a variable when it occurs in the numerator and directly beneath in the denominator. The canceled variable then goes outside as the variable held constant. Thus

$$\frac{\partial(X, \not{B})}{\partial(A, \not{B})_B} = \left(\frac{\partial X}{\partial A}\right)_B$$

and the Jacobian has been reduced to a partial derivative.

This process can be carried out in the opposite direction. Therefore, we can always write a partial derivative as a Jacobian, with the variable held constant appearing in both the numerator and the denominator. This possibility is the basis for the expression of a derivative as a Jacobian, the so-called expanded Jacobian. Using the general transformation properties of Jacobians, we are able to convert the expanded Jacobian (really the expanded derivative) into terms of new variables directly and simply. This transformation requires a general theorem on Jacobians, derived in the next section.

2. $X = B$ (cross cancellation). In this case the first term in the expansion is zero, and the Jacobian reduces to a partial derivative with a negative sign; that is,

$$\frac{\partial(B, Y)}{\partial(A, B)} = \frac{\partial(\not{B}, Y)}{\partial(A, \not{B})_B} = -\left(\frac{\partial Y}{\partial A}\right)_B$$

as though we canceled the B's above and below and introduced the minus sign to compensate for what we shall call cross cancellation.

3. $X = A$ and $Y = B$. In this case the Jacobian reduces to unity.

$$\frac{\partial(A, B)}{\partial(A, B)} = 1$$

4. Interchange of order of the variables. If the order of the independent variables in a second-order Jacobian is reversed, the two columns are changed, and the sign of the Jacobian is reversed. Subsequent reversal of the order of the dependent variables results in the interchange of the two original rows and another sign change. Thus

$$\frac{\partial(A, B)}{\partial(X, Y)} = -\frac{\partial(B, A)}{\partial(X, Y)} = +\frac{\partial(B, A)}{\partial(Y, X)}$$

The same rule can be extended to a Jacobian of the nth order. The interchange of two variables, whether neighbors or not, always involves an odd number of interchanges of neighbors and hence introduces a minus sign. The proof of this behavior is left as an exercise (Problem 11.13).

11.14 The Reciprocity Theorem for Jacobians

Most of the useful transformation properties of Jacobians related to change of variables in derivatives can be obtained from the following general theorem. Suppose that we are given two independent quantities, X and Y, as in Sec. 11.13, where

$$X = X(A, B)$$

and
$$Y = Y(A, B)$$

Suppose further that A and B are functions of x and y and that the relations can be inverted to give x and y as functions of X and Y. Then the theorem states that

$$\left[\frac{\partial(X, Y)}{\partial(A, B)} \right] \left[\frac{\partial(A, B)}{\partial(x, y)} \right] \left[\frac{\partial(x, y)}{\partial(X, Y)} \right] = 1 \qquad (11.34)$$

This symmetric result can be proved readily by use of the rules for multiplying determinants (see Appendix 11.1) and, because of its resemblance to the simple reciprocity theorem for partial derivatives, may be called the *reciprocity theorem for Jacobians*. Although it is proved in the appendix for $n = 2$, it retains the same form for any value of n, each Jacobian being of the nth order.

Most of the transformation formulas of partial differential calculus can be obtained as special cases of this general theorem (see Problems 11.9, 11.10, and 11.11 for examples). To arrive at the special case required here, first let $x = X$ and $y = Y$. Then the third Jacobian reduces to unity, and Eq. 11.34 becomes

$$\left[\frac{\partial(X, Y)}{\partial(A, B)} \right] \left[\frac{\partial(A, B)}{\partial(X, Y)} \right] = 1$$

or
$$\boxed{\frac{\partial(X, Y)}{\partial(A, B)} = \frac{1}{\dfrac{\partial(A, B)}{\partial(X, Y)}}} \qquad (11.35)$$

This is the *reciprocal theorem for Jacobians*. It shows that the reciprocal of any Jacobian (as with partial derivatives) results on interchange of the dependent and independent variables.

Use of the reciprocal theorem on the first Jacobian of Eq. 11.34 gives

$$\frac{\partial(A, B)}{\partial(X, Y)} = \left[\frac{\partial(A, B)}{\partial(x, y)} \right] \left[\frac{\partial(x, y)}{\partial(X, Y)} \right] \qquad (11.36)$$

Finally, application of the reciprocal theorem again, this time to the last Jacobian, gives

$$\frac{\partial(A, B)}{\partial(X, Y)} = \frac{\dfrac{\partial(A, B)}{\partial(x, y)}}{\dfrac{\partial(X, Y)}{\partial(x, y)}} \qquad (11.37)$$

In this result a Jacobian with X, Y as the independent variable set is expressed as the ratio of two new Jacobians, in each of which all derivatives are with respect to a *new variable set* (x, y). Special forms of this relation give us the results we need for transforming any desired derivatives. With $B = Y$ (or $A = Y$) the left side of Eq. 11.37 reduces to a partial derivative in terms of the independent variable set X, Y and the right side involves derivatives with the new variable set, x, y. Thus, for $B = Y$

$$\frac{\partial(A, Y)}{\partial(X, Y)} = \left(\frac{\partial A}{\partial X}\right)_Y = \frac{\dfrac{\partial(A, Y)}{\partial(x, y)}}{\dfrac{\partial(X, Y)}{\partial(x, y)}} \qquad (11.38)$$

and the desired derivative is expressed as the ratio of two independently calculable Jacobians having a common dependent variable, Y.

As an example of the general usefulness of the transformation theorem given in Eq. 11.38, suppose that we wish to express $(\partial p/\partial T)_S$ in terms of derivatives in which a new set of independent variables, T, p, replaces the old set, T, S. With X, Y equal to T, S and x, y equal to T, p, we write, from Eq. 11.38,

$$\left(\frac{\partial p}{\partial T}\right)_S = \frac{\partial(p, S)}{\partial(T, S)} = \frac{\dfrac{\partial(p, S)}{\partial(T, p)}}{\dfrac{\partial(T, S)}{\partial(T, p)}} = \frac{-\left(\dfrac{\partial S}{\partial T}\right)_p}{\left(\dfrac{\partial S}{\partial p}\right)_T} \qquad (11.39)$$

where the reduction results from the cancellation of common variables.

Other general Jacobian theorems may be used as the starting points for such calculations, but the approach just illustrated is at once simple and direct, and the formulas are easy to remember and to write down.[3] Furthermore, no derivatives other than those with the desired independent variables (x and y) occur on the right side of Eq. 11.38. The truth of this formula is the

---

[3] See, for example, Shaw, *Phil. Trans. Roy. Soc. London*, **A234**, 299 (1935), where a more general theorem is used; unfortunately, it is hard to remember and more general than is necessary for most cases. For more details see Crawford, *Am. J. Phys.*, **17**, 1 (1949) (hydrostatic case); *Proc. Am. Acad. Arts Sci.*, **78**, 165 (1950) (*n*-variable case, Part I, Physical Systems); **83**, 191 (1955) (*n*-variable case, Part II, Chemical Systems). See also Einbinder, *J. Chem. Phys.*, **21**, 2134 (1953), where Shaw's method is extended to the calculation of second derivatives and interesting examples of the utility of these derivatives are given.

basis of Bridgman's tables (Sec. 11.12). Each of his entries is a Jacobian with the independent variables p and T.

11.15   Maxwell's Relations in Jacobian Form

We are now ready to apply the results obtained in the preceding sections to thermodynamics. Beginning with CI,

$$dU = T\,dS - p\,dV$$

and using the cross derivative theorem, we obtain

$$\left(\frac{\partial T}{\partial V}\right)_S = -\left(\frac{\partial p}{\partial S}\right)_V \qquad\qquad \text{MIV}$$

We transform this relation by the method of the last section, first expanding each derivative as a Jacobian and then, by means of Eq. 11.38, expressing it as the ratio of two Jacobians with the general independent variables x and y. Working from each end, we have

$$\left(\frac{\partial T}{\partial V}\right)_S = \frac{\partial(T,S)}{\partial(V,S)} = \frac{\dfrac{\partial(T,S)}{\partial(x,y)}}{\dfrac{\partial(V,S)}{\partial(x,y)}} = -\frac{\dfrac{\partial(p,V)}{\partial(x,y)}}{\dfrac{\partial(S,V)}{\partial(x,y)}} = -\frac{\partial(p,V)}{\partial(S,V)} = -\left(\frac{\partial p}{\partial S}\right)_V$$

In the two fractions in the center, $J(V,S) = -J(S,V)$. Since S and V are not functionally related by the result cited in Problem 11.14, neither Jacobian vanishes. They thus may safely be canceled on introduction of a minus sign. The cancellation leaves us

$$\boxed{\frac{\partial(T,S)}{\partial(x,y)} = \frac{\partial(p,V)}{\partial(x,y)}} \qquad\qquad \textbf{(11.40)}$$

This is Maxwell's relation in its most general form, ready to be specialized by the choice of x, y.

If we place both terms of Eq. 11.40 on the same side of the equation, it is clear that the application of the cross derivative theorem to

$$dU = T\,dS - p\,dV$$

gives us

$$\frac{\partial(T,S)}{\partial(x,y)} - \frac{\partial(p,V)}{\partial(x,y)} = 0 \qquad\qquad \textbf{(11.41)}$$

This is a form readily remembered since we have merely to write down the dependent variable pairs (T, S and p, V) in the order and with the signs occurring in CI.

Taking the six possible choices of x, y from the primary set $(S, T, p,$ and $V)$ gives the special cases of Eq. 11.40.

T, p $\dfrac{\partial(\cancel{T}, S)}{\partial(\cancel{T}, p)} = \dfrac{\partial(\cancel{p}, V)}{\partial(T, \cancel{p})}$ or $\left(\dfrac{\partial S}{\partial p}\right)_T = -\left(\dfrac{\partial V}{\partial T}\right)_p$ MI

T, V $\dfrac{\partial(\cancel{T}, S)}{\partial(\cancel{T}, V)} = \dfrac{\partial(p, \cancel{V})}{\partial(T, \cancel{V})}$ or $\left(\dfrac{\partial S}{\partial V}\right)_T = \left(\dfrac{\partial p}{\partial T}\right)_V$ MII

S, p $\dfrac{\partial(T, \cancel{S})}{\partial(\cancel{S}, p)} = \dfrac{\partial(\cancel{p}, V)}{\partial(S, \cancel{p})}$ or, on inversion, $\left(\dfrac{\partial p}{\partial T}\right)_S = \left(\dfrac{\partial S}{\partial V}\right)_p$ MIII

S, V $\dfrac{\partial(T, \cancel{S})}{\partial(\cancel{S}, V)} = \dfrac{\partial(p, \cancel{V})}{\partial(S, \cancel{V})}$ or, on inversion, $\left(\dfrac{\partial V}{\partial T}\right)_S = -\left(\dfrac{\partial S}{\partial p}\right)_V$ MIV

T, S $\dfrac{\partial(T, S)}{\partial(T, S)} = \dfrac{\partial(p, V)}{\partial(T, S)}$ or $\dfrac{\partial(p, V)}{\partial(T, S)} = 1$ MV

p, V $\dfrac{\partial(T, S)}{\partial(p, V)} = \dfrac{\partial(p, V)}{\partial(p, V)}$ or $\dfrac{\partial(T, S)}{\partial(p, V)} = 1$ MVI

It is clear at once why MV and MVI are not analytically independent; one transforms into the other by the Jacobian reciprocal theorem. Their algebraic equivalence is also very readily shown. Expanding MV gives

$$\left(\frac{\partial p}{\partial T}\right)_S \left(\frac{\partial V}{\partial S}\right)_T - \left(\frac{\partial p}{\partial S}\right)_T \left(\frac{\partial V}{\partial T}\right)_S = 1 \qquad (11.42)$$

On use of MIII, MII, MI, and MIV in that order, Eq. 11.42 becomes

$$\left(\frac{\partial T}{\partial p}\right)_V \left(\frac{\partial S}{\partial V}\right)_p - \left(\frac{\partial T}{\partial V}\right)_p \left(\frac{\partial S}{\partial p}\right)_V = 1 \qquad (11.43)$$

which is MVI. (Note that the early forms obtained in Sec. 11.10, although less symmetrical, are essentially equivalent to these.) Thus MVI is algebraically dependent on the first five Maxwellian relations. The much greater ease of this proof as compared with that in Sec. 11.10 depends on the fact that the Jacobian theorem does not give us "mixed formulas," that is, formulas with different sets of independent variables. This troublesome mixing of derivatives always occurs when the composite-function theorem is used to calculate partial derivatives.

Another striking feature of the new technique is this: if we apply it to CII,

$$dH = T\, dS + V\, dp$$

we obtain $\dfrac{\partial(T, S)}{\partial(x, y)} + \dfrac{\partial(V, p)}{\partial(x, y)} = 0$

which becomes Eq. 11.41 on interchange of V and p. Similar results follow from CIII and CIV. It thus appears that the Jacobian relation in Eq. 11.41

is a unique expression of the exactness of the differential of any of the thermodynamic potentials U, H, A, or G.

11.16   General Derivatives by Jacobians

Any desired derivative may now be calculated, the result being simplified by the use of the corresponding Maxwellian equation for the particular variables.

Suppose that we wish to express $(\partial V/\partial T)_S$ in terms of derivatives involving T and p only. We proceed as in Sec. 11.14, with x, y replaced by T, p.

$$\left(\frac{\partial V}{\partial T}\right)_S = \frac{\partial(V,S)}{\partial(T,S)} = \frac{\dfrac{\partial(V,S)}{\partial(T,p)}}{\dfrac{\partial(T,S)}{\partial(T,p)}} = \frac{\left(\dfrac{\partial V}{\partial T}\right)_p \left(\dfrac{\partial S}{\partial p}\right)_T - \left(\dfrac{\partial V}{\partial p}\right)_T \left(\dfrac{\partial S}{\partial T}\right)_p}{\left(\dfrac{\partial S}{\partial p}\right)_T}$$

or

$$\left(\frac{\partial V}{\partial T}\right)_S = \left(\frac{\partial V}{\partial T}\right)_p - \frac{\left(\dfrac{\partial V}{\partial p}\right)_T \left(\dfrac{\partial S}{\partial T}\right)_p}{\left(\dfrac{\partial S}{\partial p}\right)_T}$$

Since with these variables MI holds, the derivative $(\partial S/\partial p)_T$ is replaced by $-(\partial V/\partial T)_p$, and finally

$$\left(\frac{\partial V}{\partial T}\right)_S = \left(\frac{\partial V}{\partial T}\right)_p + \frac{\left(\dfrac{\partial V}{\partial p}\right)_T \left(\dfrac{\partial S}{\partial T}\right)_p}{\left(\dfrac{\partial V}{\partial T}\right)_p} \tag{11.44}$$

Thus a given derivative is expressed in terms of the *basic three* for a given choice of independent variables. The only intermediate equation is the appropriate Maxwellian relation.

Derivatives involving secondary quantities are almost as readily obtained; the only difference is that one or more of the basic equations of Clausius must be used in the reduction of the final result (see Problem 11.15).

11.17   The Fundamental Jacobian

The general Jacobian procedure can be shortened somewhat by the following device. Starting with CI,

$$dU = T\,dS - p\,dV$$

we select the independent variables desired, say, T and p as before. Then we define the *fundamental Jacobian*, J_0, for the problem as

$$J_0 = \frac{\partial(S,V)}{\partial(T,p)} = \begin{vmatrix} \left(\dfrac{\partial S}{\partial T}\right)_p & \left(\dfrac{\partial V}{\partial T}\right)_p \\ \left(\dfrac{\partial S}{\partial p}\right)_T & \left(\dfrac{\partial V}{\partial p}\right)_T \end{vmatrix} = \begin{vmatrix} a & b \\ d & c \end{vmatrix} \tag{11.45}$$

This contains the derivatives in terms of which the Jacobian method will express *all other derivatives*. A general primary derivative will be of the form

$$\left(\frac{\partial X}{\partial Y}\right)_Z$$

so that

$$\left(\frac{\partial X}{\partial Y}\right)_Z = \frac{\partial(X, Z)}{\partial(Y, Z)} = \frac{\dfrac{\partial(X, Z)}{\partial(T, p)}}{\dfrac{\partial(Y, Z)}{\partial(T, p)}} = \frac{J(X, Z)}{J(Y, Z)} \tag{11.46}$$

Since X, Y, and Z must be chosen from the set S, T, p, and V, at least *one* will be T or p. Thus both dependent variables, S and V, can occur at most in *one* of the Jacobians, $J(X, Z)$ or $J(Y, Z)$. If one Jacobian in Eq. 11.46 contains the four partial derivatives

$$\left(\frac{\partial S}{\partial T}\right)_p, \qquad \left(\frac{\partial S}{\partial p}\right)_T, \qquad \left(\frac{\partial V}{\partial T}\right)_p, \qquad \left(\frac{\partial V}{\partial p}\right)_T$$

given in the fundamental Jacobian, J_0, the other must reduce to some *single* derivative of the set. In other cases more cancellation occurs, and each of the Jacobians in Eq. 11.46 reduces to a single one of the set of four. This behavior is the mathematical reason for our being able to express any primary derivative in terms of four derivatives, one of which may then be eliminated by the use of the appropriate Maxwellian relation.

We note that with the independent variables T and p, since

$$\left(\frac{\partial S}{\partial p}\right)_T = -\left(\frac{\partial V}{\partial T}\right)_p \qquad \text{or} \qquad d = -b$$

the fundamental Jacobian, J_0, is *antisymmetric* around the main diagonal. If we modified J_0 properly, we could obtain a symmetric Jacobian, so that *writing down the equality of the terms symmetric about the main diagonal would give Maxwell's relation at once*. Such a Jacobian we call the *modified* Jacobian, J_0', for the problem. Here

$$J_0' = \frac{\partial(S, -V)}{\partial(T, p)} = \begin{vmatrix} \left(\dfrac{\partial S}{\partial T}\right)_p & -\left(\dfrac{\partial V}{\partial T}\right)_p \\ \left(\dfrac{\partial S}{\partial p}\right)_T & -\left(\dfrac{\partial V}{\partial p}\right)_T \end{vmatrix} = \begin{vmatrix} a & -b \\ -b & -c \end{vmatrix} \tag{11.47}$$

The rules for arriving at the modified Jacobian are very simple. We write down the expression for dU,

$$dU = T\,dS - p\,dV \tag{11.48}$$

and select the independent variables. Then we set up the fundamental Jacobian with the *other* variables in the numerator. If the independent variables are selected in the *same* order (that is, each from the *first* of its parent term in Eq. 11.48, as in the present case, or from the last of its parent term, as S and V), then each *dependent variable in J_0' receives the sign of the parent term*. Thus we write $+S$ and $-V$ in Eq. 11.47. If we select x and then select y in a *different* order, we compensate by introducing an extra minus sign before the dependent variable *conjugate* to y in J_0'.

As an example, suppose that we wish to use as x, y the pair T, V. From

$$dU = T\,dS - p\,dV$$

we have selected T as x and then reversed the order by selecting V as y. Hence J_0' is set up with two minus signs in front of p, so that

$$J_0' = \frac{\partial(S, p)}{\partial(T, V)} = \begin{vmatrix} \left(\dfrac{\partial S}{\partial T}\right)_V & \left(\dfrac{\partial p}{\partial T}\right)_V \\ \left(\dfrac{\partial S}{\partial V}\right)_T & \left(\dfrac{\partial p}{\partial V}\right)_T \end{vmatrix} \qquad (11.49)$$

Since this Jacobian must be symmetric, the symmetry gives

$$\left(\frac{\partial S}{\partial V}\right)_T = \left(\frac{\partial p}{\partial T}\right)_V$$

which is, of course, Maxwell's relation for this choice of x, y (that is, MII).

Similar remarks apply to any other nonconjugate selection of x, y, that is, to any selection in which x and y are not taken from the *same* parent term in the expression for dU.

When x and y are conjugate pairs, as T, S or p, V, the fundamental Jacobian is neither symmetric nor antisymmetric, and it cannot be made symmetric since Maxwell's relation demands that the whole Jacobian must be equal to unity. None the less, even here J_0 contains the four derivatives in terms of which all other derivatives are expressible.

When the present methods are extended to systems of more than two variables, much use will be made of the symmetric modified Jacobian, J_0'. For such systems, therefore, all independent variable sets will be chosen to be nonconjugate. (See Sec. 13.1.)

Problems

11.1 For a system with $n > 2$, advantage may be taken of the fact that since $\int dU = 0$ for a closed cycle, $\oint dQ_C = \oint dW_C$. Since for an isothermal cycle form IID of the second law states that no work can be extracted, we must set

$$\oint dW_T = 0$$

Thus dW_T must be the exact differential of an isothermal work function, W_T. A similar relation, of course, holds for dQ_T. Apply these results to a system with surface area A under hydrostatic pressure, where CI is

$$dU = T\,dS - p\,dV + \mathscr{S}\,dA$$

11.2   Show that Eq. 11.12,

$$c'_{\text{sat}} - c''_{\text{sat}} = \frac{T\,d}{dT}\left(\frac{\lambda}{T}\right) \tag{11.12}$$

can be deduced directly from the Clausius-Clapeyron equation.

11.3   Apply Eq. 11.19,

$$c''_{\text{sat}} = -\frac{\lambda}{v' - v''}\left(\frac{\partial v''}{\partial T}\right)_p + c_p'' \tag{11.19}$$

to saturated water, and show that $c''_{\text{sat}} \approx c_p''$.

11.4   Using Eq. 11.22,

$$c'_{\text{sat}} \approx c_p' - \frac{\lambda}{T} \tag{11.22}$$

show that the specific heat of saturated steam is in fact negative.

11.5   Using Maxwell's relations MI to MIV and the four reciprocal relations, Eq. 11.33, prove that MV and MVI (Eqs. 11.30 and 11.31) are algebraically equivalent. (*Hint:* Represent the derivatives in Table 11.1 by the letters a, b, c, etc.)

11.6   For a Carnot cycle

$$\oint \frac{dQ_c}{T} = 0$$

Apply this relation by summing the entropy changes around the cycle discussed in Sec. 11.3. Show that in the differential limit cycle Eq. 11.12 results, that is,

$$\frac{T\,d}{dT}\left(\frac{\lambda}{T}\right) = c'_{\text{sat}} - c''_{\text{sat}}$$

11.7   Since

$$\lambda = h'_{\text{sat}} - h''_{\text{sat}}$$

show that differentiation through by T leads to a result equivalent to Eq. 11.12 once more.

11.8   Show that MIV, in the case of a two-phase system, can be reduced to the Clausius-Clapeyron equation.

11.9   Show that

$$\left[\frac{\partial(X, Y)}{\partial(A, B)}\right]\left[\frac{\partial(A, B)}{\partial(x, y)}\right]\left[\frac{\partial(x, y)}{\partial(X, Y)}\right] = 1$$

becomes the reciprocity theorem for partial derivatives if the six variables are reduced to three in a suitable way (several selections are possible).

11.10   Using Eq. 11.36, we may write

$$\left(\frac{\partial U}{\partial X}\right)_Y = \frac{\partial(U, Y)}{\partial(X, Y)} = \left[\frac{\partial(U, Y)}{\partial(x, y)}\right]\left[\frac{\partial(x, y)}{\partial(X, Y)}\right]$$

Show that on proper transformation this leads to the composite-function theorem,

$$\left(\frac{\partial U}{\partial X}\right)_Y = \left(\frac{\partial U}{\partial x}\right)_y\left(\frac{\partial x}{\partial X}\right)_Y + \left(\frac{\partial U}{\partial y}\right)_x\left(\frac{\partial y}{\partial X}\right)_Y$$

11.11 Show from Eq. 11.37 that if $B = Y = y$,

$$\left(\frac{\partial A}{\partial X}\right)_y = \frac{\left(\dfrac{\partial A}{\partial x}\right)_y}{\left(\dfrac{\partial X}{\partial x}\right)_y}$$

11.12 Verify the equations of Table 11.2 by the Jacobian method.

11.13 Given the general Jacobian

$$\frac{\partial(A, B, C, D, \ldots)}{\partial(X, Y, Z, W, \ldots)}$$

show that interchange of any pair of dependent variables involves an odd number of interchanges of neighbors and must therefore always reverse the sign of the Jacobian. (Accordingly, interchanges of two dependent variables *and* of two independent variables leave the sign unchanged.)

11.14 Given two functions, U and V, related in such a way that

$$U = f(V)$$
$$V = F(U)$$

or

show that

$$J(U, V) \equiv 0$$

Conversely, it can be shown that the vanishing of $J(U, V)$ is both a necessary and a sufficient condition for the existence of a functional connection between U and V. (See, for example, E. Goursat, *Mathematical Analysis*, trans. by E. Hedrick, Ginn, Boston, 1904, Vol. I, p. 52.)

11.15 Using the Jacobian method and the abbreviations of Sec. 11.17, show that the derivative $(\partial U/\partial T)_H$ can be written in the form

$$\left(\frac{\partial U}{\partial T}\right)_H = \frac{V(aT - bp) + pT(ac + b^2)}{V - bT}$$

11.16 Set up the modified Jacobian, J_0', for the independent variables S and p, and show that the symmetry of J_0' gives MIII,

$$\left(\frac{\partial p}{\partial T}\right)_S = \left(\frac{\partial S}{\partial V}\right)_p$$

CHAPTER TWELVE

Applications of the General Relations

12.1 Introduction

Most thermodynamic arguments begin with the use of one or more of the general relations, a few of which were obtained in the last chapter. Let us now examine some of the problems that can be answered directly by use of the appropriate general relations. A few numerical illustrations will be presented in this section, and examples of a more involved character will be taken up later.

Suppose that a gram-mole of copper is compressed isothermally to 1000 atm. What is the heat evolved, and what part of it is due to the work of compression? What would be the temperature rise if the compression were adiabatic instead of isothermal?

1. For the first question we are interested in the derivative dQ_T/dp, which we write with the help of MI as

$$\frac{dQ_T}{dp} = T \left(\frac{\partial S}{\partial p} \right)_T = -T \left(\frac{\partial V}{\partial T} \right)_p$$

The heat absorbed, Q_T, is therefore

$$Q_T = \int_{p_0}^{p} \frac{dQ_T}{dp} \, dp = -T \int_{p_0}^{p} \left(\frac{\partial V}{\partial T} \right)_p dp$$

and is seen to be negative, since normally $(\partial V/\partial T)_p > 0$. Thus heat is evolved in the compression. Since this partial derivative is relatively insensitive to pressure, we may take it out of the integral and write

$$Q_T = -T \left(\frac{\partial V}{\partial T} \right)_p (p - p_0)$$

or

$$Q_T = -\frac{TM\beta_p}{\rho} (p - p_0) \tag{12.1}$$

where ρ, β_p, and M are the density, coefficient of expansion, and atomic weight of the copper, respectively. With the following data, $\rho = 8.8 \, \text{g/cm}^3$, $M = 63.54 \, \text{g}$,

328

$\beta_p = 50.0 \times 10^{-6}$ deg^{-1}, and $p_0 = 0$, we have for 0°C

$$Q_T = -\frac{273 \times 63.54 \times 50.0 \times 10^{-6} \times 10^3 \times 1.01 \times 10^6}{8.8 \times 4.18 \times 10^7}$$

$$= -2.37 \text{ cal/mole}$$

the factor 1.01×10^6 being necessary to reduce atmospheres to absolute cgs units.

2. To find the part of the heat evolved that results from the work of hydrostatic compression, we write

$$W_T = + \int_{p_0}^p \frac{dW_T}{dp} \, dp = - \int_{p_0}^p p \left(\frac{\partial V}{\partial p}\right)_T dp$$

or

$$W_T = - \left(\frac{\partial V}{\partial p}\right)_T \left(\frac{p^2 - p_0^2}{2}\right) = \frac{\kappa_T M (p^2 - p_0^2)}{2\rho} \qquad (12.2)$$

where again the compressibility, κ_T, is taken as approximately its low-pressure value. With $\kappa_T = 79.7 \times 10^{-8}$ atm^{-1} and $p_0 = 0$ as before,

$$W_T = \frac{79.7 \times 10^{-8} \times 63.54 \times 10^6 \times 1.01 \times 10^6}{2 \times 8.8 \times 4.18 \times 10^7}$$

$$= 0.0695 \text{ cal/mole}$$

and the heat evolved is actually over thirty times the work done on the metal.

3. We now seek the temperature rise that could be expected if the compression were adiabatic. In this case we need the derivative $(\partial T/\partial p)_S$ when

$$dT_S = \left(\frac{\partial T}{\partial p}\right)_S dp$$

To find this derivative, we proceed as usual.

$$\left(\frac{\partial T}{\partial p}\right)_S = \frac{\partial(T, S)}{\partial(p, S)} = \frac{\dfrac{\partial(T, S)}{\partial(T, p)}}{\dfrac{\partial(p, S)}{\partial(T, p)}} = -\frac{\left(\dfrac{\partial S}{\partial p}\right)_T}{\left(\dfrac{\partial S}{\partial T}\right)_p} = \frac{T\left(\dfrac{\partial V}{\partial T}\right)_p}{C_p}$$

or

$$\left(\frac{\partial T}{\partial p}\right)_S = \frac{TV\beta_p}{C_p} = \frac{T\beta_p}{\rho c_p}$$

Thus

$$\Delta T = \int_{p_0}^p dT_S = \int_{p_0}^p \frac{T\beta_p}{\rho c_p} \, dp = \frac{\beta_p \bar{T}}{\rho c_p} (p - p_0) \qquad (12.3)$$

where the quantities β_p, ρ, and c_p are insensitive to pressure and $\bar{T}$ is the average temperature during the compression. With this taken as approximately the original temperature, say, 273°C, and $c_p = 0.10$ cal/g,

$$\Delta T = \frac{50.0 \times 10^{-6} \times 273 \times 10^3 \times 1.01 \times 10^6}{8.8 \times 0.10 \times 4.18 \times 10^7} = 0.375°C$$

12.2   Internal Energy, Enthalpy, and Entropy for Condensed Phases

Our next problem is the calculation of internal energy, enthalpy, and entropy when no equation of state exists. According to the laboratory equations for dU, dH, and dS obtained in Sec. 9.15, volume and its derivatives must be expressed in terms of the experimental quantities β_p and κ_T. Collecting the earlier equations for convenience, we have

$$dU = C_V \, dT + \left[T \left(\frac{\partial p}{\partial T} \right)_V - p \right] dV \tag{12.4}$$

$$dH = C_p \, dT + \left[V - T \left(\frac{\partial V}{\partial T} \right)_p \right] dp \tag{12.5}$$

$$dS = C_V \frac{dT}{T} + \left(\frac{\partial p}{dT} \right)_V dV \tag{12.6}$$

and
$$dS = C_p \frac{dT}{T} - \left(\frac{\partial V}{\partial T} \right)_p dp \tag{12.7}$$

We begin with enthalpy, since T and p are the variables in terms of which β_p and κ_T are defined.

To obtain an expression for enthalpy, we integrate dH along a convenient elbow path from a standard reference state (T_0, p_0) to any other state (T, p). Taking the path abc in Fig. 12.1, we obtain

$$H - H(T_0, p_0) = \int_{T_0, p_0}^{T_0, p} \left[V - T \left(\frac{\partial V}{\partial T} \right)_p \right] dp + \int_{T_0, p}^{T, p} C_p \, dT \tag{12.8}$$

Numerically the last term is the important one, the second being simply a small pressure correction term, in the evaluation of which considerable approximation is permissible.

From the definition of κ_T we have

$$dV = \left(\frac{\partial V}{\partial p} \right)_T dp = -V \kappa_T \, dp$$

and thus for an isothermal pressure change, $\Delta p = p - p_0$,

$$\Delta V = V - V_0 \approx -V \kappa_T \, \Delta p \approx -V_0 \kappa_T (p - p_0)$$

or
$$V \approx V_0 - V_0 \kappa_T (p - p_0) \tag{12.9}$$

with
$$\left(\frac{\partial V}{\partial T} \right)_p = V \beta_p \approx V_0 \beta_p \tag{12.10}$$

since β_p itself is small.

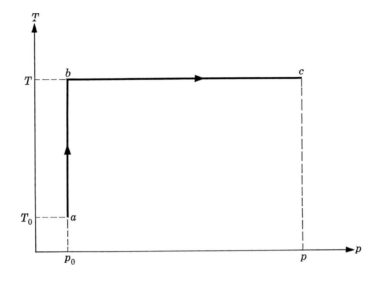

FIGURE **12.1**

Inserting Eqs. 12.9 and 12.10 in Eq. 12.8 and neglecting the variation of κ_T and β_p with pressure, we have finally

$$H - H(T_0, p_0) = \int_{T_0}^{T} C_p(T)\, dT + V_0(p - p_0)\left[1 - \beta_p T_0 - \kappa_T\left(\frac{p - p_0}{2}\right)\right]$$
$$(12.11)$$

In this integral C_p in fact depends on the value of the pressure, p, but can normally be taken to be a function of T only.

In the special case, of interest chiefly for solids, where $T_0 = 0°K$ and $p_0 = 0$, Eq. 12.11 reduces to

$$H''' = -\Lambda_0 + \int_0^{T} C_p'''(T)\, dT + V_0'''p \qquad (12.12)$$

since $H'''(T_0 = 0°K, p_0 = 0) = -\Lambda_0$, the sublimation heat at $0°K$. For low values of p the last term is also quite small (see Problem 12.1).

Since $U = H - pV$, the corresponding expression for internal energy is

$$U''' = -\Lambda_0 + \int_0^{T} C_p'''\, dT + (V_0 - V)p \qquad (12.13)$$

To obtain an expression for the entropy, we simplify Eq. 12.7 in a similar way and, integrating along the same path in Fig. 12.1, find

$$S''' = S'''(T_0, p_0) + \int_{T_0}^{T} C_p'''(p, T)\frac{dT}{T} - V_0'''\beta_p(p - p_0) \qquad (12.14)$$

For future use (Sec. 12.18) it is convenient to write down the open integral of Eq. 12.7 suitable for low-temperature regions where $(\partial V/\partial T)_p = V\beta_p$ is quite negligible. This is

$$S''' = S_0''' + \int C_p''' \frac{dT}{T} \qquad (12.15)$$

Here S_0''' is the constant of integration, or the "entropy constant for the solid" and is arbitrary as far as thermodynamics is concerned.

12.3   Thermodynamic Functions for Ideal Gases

In Chap. 5 we saw how the work of Joule and Kelvin on gases leads to the definition of an ideal gas by the relations

$$pV = RT$$

and
$$\left(\frac{\partial U}{\partial V}\right)_T = 0$$

Since U is a function of T and V in general, this definition is equivalent to

$$pV = RT$$
and
$$U° = U°(T)$$

It is customarily stated that the second part of the definition, that is, $(\partial U/\partial V)_T = 0$ or $U° = U°(T)$, can be dropped as soon as results deducible from the second law are available. From CI we can write

$$\left(\frac{\partial U}{\partial V}\right)_T = T\left(\frac{\partial p}{\partial T}\right)_V - p\left(\frac{\partial V}{\partial V}\right)_T$$

which, with $pV = RT$ given, also reduces to zero. We must not infer from this situation that the fact that U is independent of V is a deduction from the second law. It is simply a statement *consistent* with the second law.

As Miller and Dennis have noted,[1] when the original Carnot cycle is carried out with an ideal gas for proof of the second law (form IIB), the explicit assumption is made (and is necessary) that $U° = U°(T)$. Since $H° = U°(T) + RT$, this assumption is equivalent to postulating that $H° = H°(T)$ also.

Thus when we apply the definitions of C_V and C_p,

$$C_V = \left(\frac{\partial U}{\partial T}\right)_V$$

and
$$C_p = \left(\frac{\partial H}{\partial T}\right)_p$$

to an ideal gas, it is clear at once that

$$C_V° = C_V°(T)$$
and
$$C_p° = C_p°(T)$$

---

[1] Miller and Dennis, *Am. J. Phys.*, **28**, 796 (1960).

and hence that

$$\left(\frac{\partial C_V^\circ}{\partial V}\right)_T = 0$$

and

$$\left(\frac{\partial C_p^\circ}{\partial p}\right)_T = 0$$

These results must be consistent with other general relations deduced from the laws of thermodynamics. Take, for example, the relations obtained in Chap. 9, that is, Eqs. 9.45 and 9.46,

$$\left(\frac{\partial C_V}{\partial V}\right)_T = T\left(\frac{\partial^2 p}{\partial T^2}\right)_V \tag{12.16}$$

and

$$\left(\frac{\partial C_p}{\partial p}\right)_T = -T\left(\frac{\partial^2 V}{\partial T^2}\right)_p \tag{12.17}$$

Here the ideal gas equation of state is of just the right form to reduce the right side of each equation to zero.

In the general laboratory equations for dU and dH, the ideal gas law is again of just the proper form to reduce the bracketed term in each equation to zero, leaving simply

$$dU^\circ = C_V^\circ(T)\, dT$$

and

$$dH^\circ = C_p^\circ(T)\, dT$$

Therefore, when we obtain on integration

$$U^\circ - U^\circ(T_0) = \int_{T_0}^T C_V^\circ(T)\, dT \tag{12.18}$$

and

$$H^\circ - H^\circ(T_0) = \int_{T_0}^T C_p^\circ(T)\, dT \tag{12.19}$$

we have merely more explicit statements of the functional relations already *assumed*.

The analogous expressions for entropy result as

$$S^\circ(T, V) - S^\circ(T_0, V_0) = \int_{T_0}^T C_V^\circ(T)\frac{dT}{T} + R \ln \frac{V}{V_0} \tag{12.20}$$

and

$$S^\circ(T, p) - S^\circ(T_0, p_0) = \int_{T_0}^T C_p^\circ(T)\frac{dT}{T} - R \ln \frac{p}{p_0} \tag{12.21}$$

In these equations $S^\circ(T_0, V_0)$ and $S^\circ(T_0, p_0)$ are the values of entropy at the fixed reference points.

For use in the discussion of vapor pressure in Sec. 12.18, the open integral equivalents of Eqs. 12.20 and 12.21 are

$$S^\circ(T, V) = \int C_V^\circ \frac{dT}{T} + R \ln V + S_{0TV}^\circ \tag{12.22}$$

and

$$S^\circ(T, p) = \int C_p^\circ \frac{dT}{T} - R \ln p + S_{0Tp}^\circ \tag{12.23}$$

where, as we saw in Sec. 9.14, the entropy constants from Eqs. 9.49 and 9.50 are related by

$$S_{0Tp}^{\circ} = R \ln R + S_{0TV}$$

Formally, with ideal gases for which C_V° is constant, S_{0TV} is the entropy of the gas when the gas is under the artificial conditions of $T = 1°K$ and $V =$ unity. The values of $A°$ and $G°$ may be written from the preceding results as

$$A° = U°(T_0) + \int_{T_0}^{T} C_V^{\circ} dT - T \int_{T_0}^{T} C_V^{\circ} \frac{dT}{T} - RT \ln \frac{V}{V_0} \qquad (12.24)$$

and

$$G° = H°(T_0) + \int_{T_0}^{T} C_p^{\circ} dT - T \int_{T_0}^{T} C_p^{\circ} \frac{dT}{T} + RT \ln \frac{p}{p_0} \qquad (12.25)$$

These ideal functions for a monatomic gas have been drawn in Fig. 12.2. Since only $U°$ and $H°$ are functions of T alone, $S°$, $A°$, and $G°$ are plotted for $p = p_0$ and with all constants of integration set equal to zero.

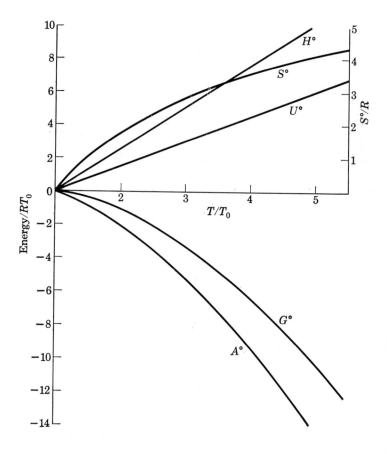

FIGURE **12.2**

Division of Eq. 12.21 by R gives a dimensionless quantity, $S°/R$, which is plotted on the vertical scale at the right as a function of the ratio T/T_0. Division of the remaining quantities by RT_0 renders them likewise dimensionless functions of the same ratio, T/T_0.

12.4   The van der Waals Gas

The equation of state for a van der Waals gas can be written

$$p = \frac{RT}{V - b} - \frac{a}{V^2} \tag{12.26}$$

Since $p = p(T, V)$, it is natural to use T and V rather than T and p as independent variables. We thus begin with Eq. 12.4,

$$dU = C_V \, dT + \left[T \left(\frac{\partial p}{\partial T} \right)_V - p \right] dV$$

Here $(\partial p/\partial T)_V$ and $(\partial^2 p/\partial T^2)_V$ are both required, and from Eq. 12.26

$$\left(\frac{\partial p}{\partial T} \right)_p = \frac{R}{V - b}$$

and

$$\left(\frac{\partial^2 p}{\partial T^2} \right)_V = 0$$

This means that for a van der Waals gas $C_V = C_V° = C_V°(T)$ just as for the ideal case.

Insertion of these results in Eq. 12.4 gives

$$dU = C_V° \, dT + \frac{a}{V^2} dV$$

or

$$U = U_0 + \int_{T_0}^{T} C_V° \, dT - a \left(\frac{1}{V} - \frac{1}{V_0} \right) \tag{12.27}$$

In this expression the term a/V is a correction term for the lack of perfection of a van der Waals gas. If V is allowed to become large,

$$U = U_0 + \int_{T_0}^{T} C_V° \, dT + \frac{a}{V_0}$$

which must coincide with the ideal gas expression in Eq. 12.18. Comparison shows that $U_0 = U°(T_0) - (a/V_0)$, and Eq. 12.27 becomes

$$U = U°(T) - \frac{a}{V} \tag{12.28}$$

The enthalpy expression results on the addition of pV.

$$H = U°(T) + RT + pb - \frac{2a}{V} + \frac{ab}{V^2} \tag{12.29}$$

This result involves T, p, and V on the right, where only two are independent. For H in terms of T and p only, see Problem 12.8.

To find the entropy, we naturally use the laboratory equation Eq. 12.6, which becomes

$$dS = C_V° \frac{dT}{T} + \frac{R\,dV}{V-b}$$

or

$$S = S(T_0, V_0) + \int_{T_0}^{T} C_V° \frac{dT}{T} + R \ln \frac{V-b}{V_0 - b} \tag{12.30}$$

The last term may be written

$$R \ln \frac{1 - \dfrac{b}{V}}{1 - \dfrac{b}{V_0}} + R \ln \frac{V}{V_0}$$

Consequently, the expression for $S°$ from Eq. 12.20 and the limit of Eq. 12.30 at large volumes must be identical. This condition holds only if $S(T_0, V_0)$ in Eq. 12.30 is identified as

$$S(T_0, V_0) = S°(T_0, V_0) + R \ln \left(1 - \frac{b}{V_0} \right)$$

In other words, $R \ln [1 - (b/V)]$ is the van der Waals correction for the ideal gas entropy, and Eq. 12.30 becomes

$$S = S°(T, V) + R \ln \left(1 - \frac{b}{V} \right) \tag{12.31}$$

Use of Eqs. 12.28 and 12.31 gives for the Helmholtz free energy

$$A = A°(T, V) - \frac{a}{V} - RT \ln \left(1 - \frac{b}{V} \right) \tag{12.32}$$

The Gibbs function is more useful as a function of T and p and may be so obtained when needed (see Problem 12.9).

12.5 The Adiabatic Law for a van der Waals Gas

The equation for an adiabatic follows from the equation for entropy when the entropy is set equal to a constant. In the case of Eq. 12.30, the integral must be evaluated first. If C_V is written as

$$C_V = c_0 + c_1 T + c_2 T^2 + \cdots \tag{12.33}$$

then $\quad \displaystyle\int_{T_0}^{T} C_V \frac{dT}{T} = \ln\left(\frac{T}{T_0}\right)^{c_0} + c_1(T - T_0) + \frac{c_2}{2}(T^2 - T_0^2) + \cdots$

Eq. 12.30 becomes, with S_0 for $S(T_0, V_0)$,

$$S - S_0 = \ln\left(\frac{T}{T_0}\right)^{c_0}\left(\frac{V - b}{V_0 - b}\right)^{R} + c_1(T - T_0) + \frac{c_2}{2}(T^2 - T_0^2) + \cdots$$

or

$$\exp \frac{S - S_0}{c_0} = \left(\frac{T}{T_0}\right)\left(\frac{V - b}{V_0 - b}\right)^{R/c_0} \exp \frac{c_1}{c_0}(T - T_0) \exp \frac{c_2}{2c_0}(T^2 - T_0^2) + \cdots$$

Collecting all the constant terms on one side and fixing S give finally

$$T(V - b)^{R/c_0} \exp \frac{c_1 T}{c_0} \exp \frac{c_2 T^2}{2c_0} \cdots = \text{constant}$$

or, with $R/c_0 = n$, $c_1/c_0 = \alpha$, $c_2/2c_0 = \beta$, etc.,

$$T(V - b)^n e^{\alpha T} e^{\beta T^2} \cdots = \text{constant}$$

Elimination of the first T by use of the original equation of state gives

$$\left(p + \frac{a}{V^2}\right)(V - b)^{n+1} e^{\alpha T} e^{\beta T^2} \cdots = \text{constant}$$

The last two results are analogs of the ideal gas equations

$$(TV)^{\gamma-1} = \text{constant}$$

and $\qquad\qquad pV^\gamma = \text{constant}$

obtained on the assumption of *constant* heat capacities.

For temperature ranges for which α, β, etc., are very small compared to unity, the exponentials reduce to unity, and the more convenient approximate forms are

$$T(V - b)^n = \text{constant} \tag{12.34}$$

and $\qquad \displaystyle\left(p + \frac{a}{V^2}\right)(V - b)^{n+1} = \text{constant} \tag{12.35}$

Here c_0 is not the value of C_V° at T_0, say, $C_{V_0}^\circ$. In general, if we write

$$C_V = C_{V_0}^\circ + c_1'(T - T_0) + c_2'(T^2 - T_0^2) + \cdots \tag{12.36}$$

and collect the constant terms,

$$c_0 = C_{V_0}^\circ - c_1' T_0 - c_2' T_0^2 + \cdots$$

as is seen on comparison with Eq. 12.33.

It can be shown (Problem 12.7) that for the van der Waals gas C_p (unlike C_V) varies with both p and T. Hence the ratio $\gamma = C_p/C_V^\circ$ is not a constant even when T is fixed. The quantities n, α, β, etc., are, however, constants.

The results of this section can be used to show that a Carnot cycle with a van der Waals gas has the same efficiency as the cycle with the ideal gas (see Problem 12.16).

12.6   Internal Energy, Enthalpy, and Entropy for Real Gases

To the extent that real gases may be approximated by van der Waals' equation, the expressions obtained in the last section are simple and easy to use. In a similar way other equations of state that are solvable directly to give p as an explicit function of T and V lead to closed expressions for the thermodynamic functions.

For more exact calculations it is necessary to use equations of the Onnes type, in which as many terms as are needed may be retained. From the two alternate forms,

$$pV = RT + \mathcal{B}_1 \frac{1}{V} + \mathcal{B}_2 \frac{1}{V^2} + \cdots \tag{12.37}$$

and

$$pV = RT + B_1 p + B_2 p^2 + \cdots \tag{12.38}$$

the necessary derivatives may be written down at once.

With T and p as independent variables,

$$\left(\frac{\partial V}{\partial T}\right)_p = \frac{R}{p} + B_1' + B_2' p + \cdots \tag{12.39}$$

and

$$\left(\frac{\partial^2 V}{\partial T^2}\right)_p = B_1'' + B_2'' p + \cdots \tag{12.40}$$

where the primes indicate temperature derivatives. Use of Eq. 12.17 to obtain the rate of variation of C_p with pressure leads to

$$\left(\frac{\partial C_p}{\partial p}\right)_T = -T\left(\frac{\partial^2 V}{\partial T^2}\right)_p = -B_1'' T - B_2'' T p + \cdots$$

Multiplication of this result through by dp and integration (at fixed T) from $p = 0$ to p gives

$$C_p = C_p^\circ - B_1'' T p - \frac{B_2''}{2} T p^2 + \cdots \tag{12.41}$$

Use of Eqs. 12.38, 12.39, and 12.41 in the expression for dH, Eq. 12.5, gives, on rearrangement of terms,

$$dH = C_p^\circ dT - B_1'' T p \, dT + (B_1 - B_1' T) \, dp - \frac{B_2''}{2} T p^2 \, dT + (B_2 - B_2' T) p \, dp$$

Since dH is a perfect differential, and so is $C_p^o \, dT$, we see that the rest of the expression must be, also. In fact, the remaining terms combine pairwise to give

$$dH = C_p^o \, dT + d\left[(B_1 - B_1'T)p + (B_2 - B_2'T)\frac{p^2}{2} + \cdots \right] \quad (12.42)$$

A similar use of the equation of state in powers of $1/V$ leads to

$$dU = C_V^o \, dT + d\left[(\mathcal{B}_1 - \mathcal{B}_1'T)\frac{1}{V} + (\mathcal{B}_2 - \mathcal{B}_2'T)\frac{1}{2V^2} + \cdots \right] \quad (12.43)$$

The two alternate expressions for dS resulting from Eqs. 12.6 and 12.7 are

$$dS = C_V^o \frac{dT}{T} + R\frac{dV}{V} - d\left(\frac{\mathcal{B}_1'}{V} + \frac{\mathcal{B}_2'}{2V^2} + \cdots \right) \quad (12.44)$$

and

$$dS = C_p^o \frac{dT}{T} - R\frac{dp}{p} - d\left(B_1'p + \frac{B_2'}{2}p^2 + \cdots \right) \quad (12.45)$$

The last term in each of these equations is the correction to be applied to the appropriate ideal gas equation.

Direct integration of the preceding equations leads to the following expressions:

$$U = U^\circ(T) + (\mathcal{B}_1 - \mathcal{B}_1'T)\frac{1}{V} + (\mathcal{B}_2 - \mathcal{B}_2'T)\frac{1}{2V_2} + \cdots + C_1$$

$$H = H^\circ(T) + (B_1 - B_1'T)p + (B_2 - B_2'T)\frac{p^2}{2} + \cdots \quad + C_2$$

$$S = S^\circ(T, V) - \frac{\mathcal{B}_1'}{V} - \frac{\mathcal{B}_2'}{2V^2} + \cdots \quad + C_3$$

$$S = S^\circ(T, p) - B_1'p - \frac{B_2'}{2}p^2 + \cdots \quad + C_4 \quad (12.46)$$

In these equations $U^\circ(T)$, $H^\circ(T)$, $S^\circ(T, V)$, and $S^\circ(T, p)$ are given by the ideal gas equations (Eqs. 12.18 to 12.21). The constants C_1 to C_4 result on substitution of the initial coordinates into the correction terms.

The results of this section are useful for any equation of state that can be expanded in the virial form. As an example of their use, suppose that we consider Eq. 12.41. This gives $C_p - C_p^o = \Delta C_p{}^{imp}$, the molar contribution to the heat capacity at constant pressure due to gas imperfections, as

$$\Delta C_p{}^{imp} = -B_1''Tp - \frac{B_2''}{2}Tp^2 + \cdots$$

Each of the equations of state—van der Waals', Berthelot's, Dieterici's, and Wohl's, for example—can be thrown into the virial form in powers of p. Since the constants for each of these simple equations can be calculated in terms of the critical quantities, T_c and p_c, the results can always be given in reduced coordinates θ and π.

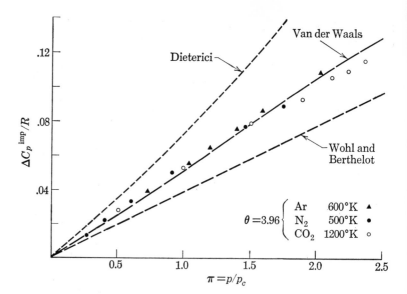

FIGURE **12.3**

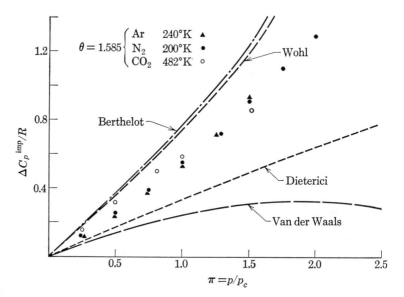

FIGURE **12.4**

For van der Waals' equation we find

$$pV = RT + \left(b - \frac{a}{RT}\right)p + \frac{a}{R^2T^2}\left(2b - \frac{a}{RT}\right)p^2 + \cdots$$

Use of the values of a and b in terms of the critical constants, as given in Eqs. 3.22 and 3.23, permits us to rewrite Eq. 12.41 in the dimensionless form,

$$\frac{\Delta C_p{}^{imp}}{R} = \frac{27}{32}\frac{\pi}{\theta^2}\left[1 - \frac{3\pi}{8\theta}\left(1 - \frac{27}{8\theta}\right) + \cdots\right] \qquad (12.47)$$

retaining no terms beyond those in π^2. Similar results have been obtained for the other three equations (see Problem 12.5) and are shown graphically in the accompanying figures. In each case the points marked "observed" have been

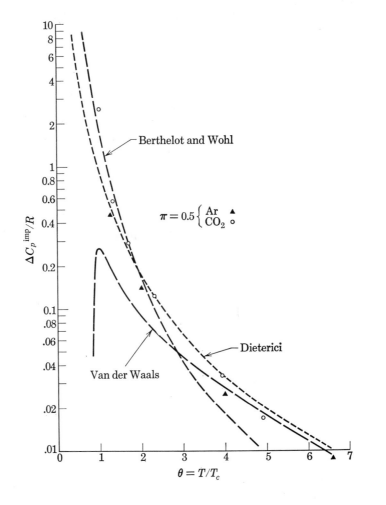

FIGURE **12.5**

calculated from Eq. 12.41 and include data for three different types of gas, monatomic (argon), diatomic nonpolar (N_2), and triatomic highly polar (CO_2). In Fig. 12.3 the temperature of each gas has been selected so that the common reduced temperature is $\theta = 3.96$. At such relatively high temperatures the values of ΔC_p of imperfection are small, and the van der Waals equation is definitely the best of the four. Fig. 12.4 is drawn for $\theta = 1.585$. At this much lower reduced temperature ΔC_p is about ten times as large as in Fig. 12.3, and all four equations give large deviations, van der Waals' equation now being the worst. In Fig. 12.5 $\Delta C_p^{\text{imp}}/R$ is shown as a function of θ at $\pi = 0.5$. The Berthelot and Wohl equations (coincident to this degree of expansion) are the best at low values of θ, and the other two at high values.

The Dieterici, Wohl, and Beattie-Bridgeman equations are all of a form permitting p to be expressed explicitly as a function of T and V. Consequently, the internal energy can be calculated in closed form for each of these, just as was done in Sec. 12.4 for the van der Waals equation. If we define the internal energy of gas imperfection, ΔU^{imp}, by

$$\Delta U^{\text{imp}} = U - U^\circ$$

it can be expressed as a closed function of T and V. This has been done, and the results in dimensionless form for argon and CO_2 are shown in Figs. 12.6

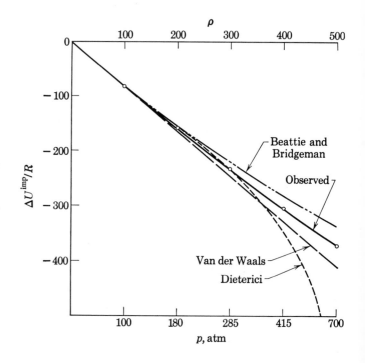

FIGURE **12.6**

and 12.7. These figures are modified from Hirschfelder[2] and show $\Delta U^{imp}/R$ plotted versus, not $1/V$, but ρ, the Amagat density. Since this is simply the density expressed as a multiple of the density at 0°C and 1 atm, it is proportional to $1/V$. The curves for argon are drawn for 273°K ($\theta = 1.81$) and show that for this monatomic noble gas even at extreme densities the equations of Beattie-Bridgeman and van der Waals give fairly close representations of the rigorous virial equation (curve marked "observed").

For the highly polar gas CO_2 ($T = 423°K$, $\theta = 1.395$), the Dieterici and Beattie-Bridgeman results begin to depart from the observed ones at around $\rho = 100$ and $\rho = 200$, respectively, The Wohl equation is fairly good to the highest ρ values (where $p \approx 1400$ atm). Although van der Waals' equation exhibits steady deviation from the start, it is remarkably good, considering its extreme simplicity. It must be remembered that this procedure represents an unduly severe test of these equations. The simpler ones were intended to take into account only small departures from the ideal state, and even the Beattie-

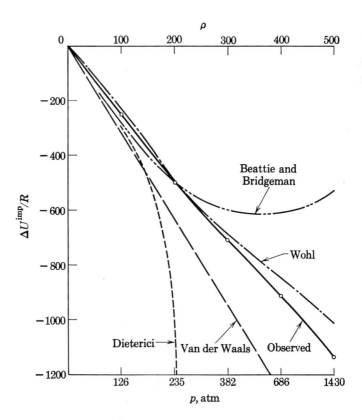

FIGURE **12.7**

[2] J. O. Hirschfelder, C. F. Curtis, and R. B. Bird, *The Molecular Theory of Gases and Liquids,* Wiley, New York, 1954.

Bridgeman equation is not suitable for densities above the critical density. (In the figures the critical density is reached around $\rho = 300$ for argon and $\rho = 235$ for CO_2.)

12.7   The Joule-Kelvin Effect

The Joule-Kelvin (or Joule-Thomson) experiments, as we saw in Sec. 5.14, were important in the study of real gases and led to the thermodynamic concept of the ideal gas. The constant streaming of the gas through a porous plug was a special case of the general first law with mass flow and, as we noted in Sec. 7.16, was a constant-enthalpy process, that is, one in which

$$h_1 = h_2$$

h_1 and h_2 being the specific enthalpies before and after passage through the plug.

It will be remembered that Joule found the temperature change brought about by passage of the gas through the plug to be usually negative. We are now in a position to obtain a general expression for this temperature change and thus to understand the reason for his results.

To begin with, let us define a quantity μ, the so-called *differential Joule-Kelvin coefficient*, as

$$\mu = \lim_{p \to 0} \frac{\Delta T}{\Delta p} = \left(\frac{\partial T}{\partial p} \right)_h \qquad (12.48)$$

It represents the ratio of the temperature change to the pressure change when the latter is differentially small. To find μ in terms of the basic three derivatives, we proceed as before and write

$$\mu = \left(\frac{\partial T}{\partial p} \right)_h = \frac{\partial(T, h)}{\partial(p, h)} = \frac{\frac{\partial(T, h)}{\partial(T, p)}}{\frac{\partial(p, h)}{\partial(T, p)}} = - \frac{\left(\frac{\partial h}{\partial p} \right)_T}{\left(\frac{\partial h}{\partial T} \right)_p} \qquad (12.49)$$

From CII and MI

$$\left(\frac{\partial h}{\partial p} \right)_T = - T \left(\frac{\partial v}{\partial T} \right)_p + v$$

and since $(\partial h / \partial T)_p = c_p$, μ is given as

$$\mu = \frac{T \left(\frac{\partial v}{\partial T} \right)_p - v}{c_p} = \frac{T \left(\frac{\partial V}{\partial T} \right)_p - V}{C_p} \qquad (12.50)$$

where specific or gram-molar quantities may be used as desired. Since the heat capacity is always positive, μ is *positive*, *zero*, or *negative* according to whether

$$T \left(\frac{\partial V}{\partial T} \right)_p - V \gtreqless 0 \qquad (12.51)$$

The physical reason for the temperature change on Joule-Kelvin streaming can best be understood from Eq. 12.49. With molar quantities and $H = U + pV$, this becomes

$$\mu = \left(\frac{\partial T}{\partial p}\right)_H = \frac{-\left(\frac{\partial U}{\partial p}\right)_T - \left[\frac{\partial(pV)}{\partial p}\right]_T}{C_p} \qquad (12.52)$$

Since $C_p > 0$, the sign of μ is fixed by the two terms in the numerator.

The first term is the change in internal energy per unit pressure drop (the minus sign being taken into account). The second term, also per unit pressure drop, is the excess of the work done on the gas on the *high*-pressure side of the porous plug (per mole streaming through) over that lost by the gas on the low-pressure side. For the ideal gas each term vanishes, and no temperature change is produced. For small pressures the molecules moving through the plug acquire larger separations, and $-(\partial U/\partial p)_T$ is positive (see, for example, Fig. 16.4, where decreasing pressure is associated with increasing distance between the molecular pairs). Thus the first term contributes a cooling effect, since the molecules moving in an attractive field increase their potential energy at the expense of their kinetic energy. The second term is the negative of the slope of a pV isotherm plotted versus p (see Fig. 3.9, for example). For low values of p (and not too high values of T), this term is therefore also *positive* and contributes a further cooling effect. With a rise in pressure the term becomes zero and eventually negative. At a certain pressure the two terms cancel, and μ vanishes. For higher pressures the second term dominates, and only heating can occur. (The first term also eventually becomes negative but only at very high pressures.)

12.8   The Inversion Curve

The locus of points for which $\mu = 0$, that is,

$$V = T\left(\frac{\partial V}{\partial T}\right)_p \qquad (12.53)$$

is called the *inversion curve*. It is a curve that in the T-p plane separates the regions where μ is positive from those in which it is negative.[3] In Fig. 12.8 curves of constant h have been drawn in the T-p plane. The inversion curve is simply the locus of points for which

$$\mu = \left(\frac{\partial T}{\partial p}\right)_h = 0$$

and is therefore a curve through the maxima of the curves of constant enthalpy. This curve, a dashed line in the figure, separates the regions where $(\partial T/\partial p)_h$ is positive from those in which it is negative. The change in pressure must

---

[3] Notice that from the laboratory equation for dH, $dH = C_p\,dT + [V - T(\partial V/\partial T)_p]\,dp$, the only way we can have a differential process with $dH = dT = 0$ and at the same time have an actual flow ($dp > 0$) is for the coefficient of dp to vanish; this is just the condition of Eq. 12.53.

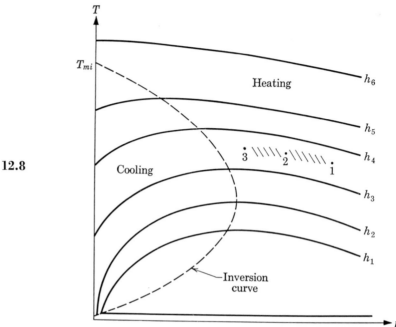

FIGURE **12.8**

always be negative for streaming to occur, and therefore cooling occurs *within* the inversion curve, and heating at all points *outside* it. The point at which the inversion curve cuts the T axis ($p = 0$) is called the maximum inversion temperature, say, T_{mi}. At any temperature above T_{mi}, the h curves have no maxima but exhibit a negative slope for all pressures. Thus any gas above its maximum inversion temperature is always warmed by expansion through a porous plug, whatever the pressure differences employed.

To obtain a constant-enthalpy curve experimentally, we start at some point, say, p_1, T_1, allow the gas to expand through a nozzle (which is usually employed in place of a porous plug) to a lower pressure, p_2, and measure the new temperature, T_2. The gas is then further expanded to p_3, T_3 is measured, etc. Smooth curves drawn through these isolated experimental points give one of the isoenthalpic curves of the figure. The values of μ may be determined as desired from the slopes of the smoothed curves of constant h.

Actually the temperatures in such experiments are usually measured on the Celsius scale, although we have defined μ in terms of the Kelvin scale only. If the coefficients for these two scales are indicated by μ' and μ, respectively, we have

$$\mu' = \left(\frac{\partial t}{\partial p}\right)_h$$

and

$$\mu = \left(\frac{\partial T}{\partial p}\right)_h$$

Whatever the assumed relation between t and T, we can always write from Eq. 12.49

$$\left(\frac{\partial T}{\partial p}\right)_h \left(\frac{\partial h}{\partial T}\right)_p = -\left(\frac{\partial h}{\partial p}\right)_T$$

or

$$\mu c_p = -\left(\frac{\partial h}{\partial p}\right)_T \qquad (12.54)$$

Likewise, for the Celsius scale,

$$\left(\frac{\partial t}{\partial p}\right)_h \left(\frac{\partial h}{\partial t}\right)_p = -\left(\frac{\partial h}{\partial p}\right)_t$$

or

$$\mu' c_p' = -\left(\frac{\partial h}{\partial p}\right)_t \qquad (12.55)$$

Of course, $(\partial h/\partial p)_T = (\partial h/\partial p)_t$, since the *constancy* of the temperature is not influenced by the relation of t to T. Hence

$$\mu' c_p' = \mu c_p = T\left(\frac{\partial v}{\partial T}\right)_p - v \qquad (12.56)$$

The experimental values of $\mu' c_p'$ can therefore always be used in place of μc_p in theoretical formulas.[4]

The isoenthalpic curves of Fig. 12.8 are simply curves of the relation

$$h(t, p) = \text{constant}$$

and do not represent curves of Joule-Kelvin streaming. The gas has no thermodynamic coordinates as it flows through the plug or throttle valve from $1 \rightarrow 2$ or $2 \rightarrow 3$. The process is irreversible, and the smooth curves represent equilibrium states between which flow can occur with no change in h.

12.9   Joule-Kelvin Cooling

Historically the Joule-Kelvin throttling process has offered one of the most valuable methods for chilling gases to temperatures at which liquefaction will occur. A schematic diagram of a device using this principle is given in Fig. 12.9. High-pressure gas coming from a compressing pump rises through a spiral in a liquid cooling bath and passes down another spiral (within a spiral) in the insulated chamber on the right. At the bottom it flows through a throttling valve, and the pressure falls to around atmospheric pressure. The cooled gas then rises through the outer spiral and eventually is drawn down to the low-pressure side of the compressor. Of course, as the expanded and cooled gas rises, it cools the descending stream of high-pressure gas still further, and eventually, after several circuits, the expansion at the throttle valve produces partial liquefaction. The resulting liquid collects at the bottom of a collecting

---

[4] For the use of Joule-Kelvin coefficients in determination of the absolute value of the ice point, see Hoxton, *Phys. Rev.*, **13**, 438 (1919).

vessel and may be drawn off, while the uncondensed vapor rises and repeats the process. At the steady state a constant fraction of each gram of expanding gas, say, y, condenses, the remainder, $1 - y$, returning to the compressor, where it mixes with fresh gas from the supply tank. Since the system at the right of the figure is well insulated and no external work is performed, the flow between point 1 in the figure and point 3 (just before re-entry to the compressor) is adiabatic and isoenthalpic.

If

$$h'_1 = \text{enthalpy of gas entering at 1 } (T_1, p_1)$$
$$h''_2 = \text{enthalpy of liquid at 2 } (T_2, p_2)$$

and

$$h'_3 = \text{enthalpy of gas leaving at 3 } (T_e, p_e)$$

we can write for the over-all process

$$h'_1 = (1 - y)h'_3 + yh''_2$$

and thus for the steady state

$$y = \frac{h'_3 - h'_1}{h'_3 - h''_2}$$

At the steady state all of these quantities take on constant values. Thus h''_2 is fixed by p_2, the pressure on the liquid that fixes T_2. The gas leaving at point 3 is at pressure p_e (slightly below p_2 owing to friction in the return pipes) while its temperature, T_e, is higher than T_2, owing to the heat interchange with the descending gas, but still well below T_1. Therefore, p_i is the only variable at our

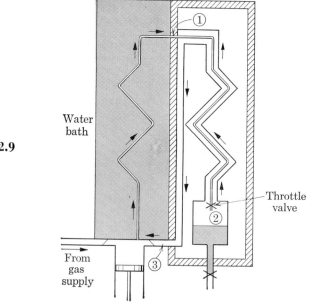

FIGURE **12.9**

Water bath

Throttle valve

From gas supply

disposal, and it should be chosen to make y, the fraction condensed, as high as possible. A maximum of y requires a minimum of h'_1, and at this point

$$\left(\frac{\partial h}{\partial p}\right)_{T=T_1} = 0$$

Since, as we have just seen, in general

$$\left(\frac{\partial h}{\partial p}\right)_T = -\mu c_p \tag{12.54}$$

and since $c_p > 0$, this condition requires that $\mu = 0$. This means that for the maximum fraction to liquefy, T_i, p_i should be chosen on the inversion curve. This point is also the initial state, which produces the maximum cooling on expansion through the throttle valve.

12.10 The Maximum Inversion Temperature

When hydrogen was circulated in an apparatus like that in Sec. 12.9, it was found to be hotter after circulation than before. The reason, of course, was that the initial temperature, T_i, was above T_{mi}, the maximum inversion temperature, and under such circumstances only heating could result. T_{mi} for hydrogen is about 202°K or −71°C, and the gas had to be precooled below this temperature, say, by a liquid air bath, before it could be liquefied successfully. For helium T_{mi} is much lower, about 34°K. Hence the liquefaction of helium required the production of liquid hydrogen and precooling of the compressed helium with the liquid hydrogen before any further cooling on throttling could be expected.

It is of interest to see how the maximum inversion temperature may be estimated. Since by definition it is fixed by the intersection of the inversion curve with the T axis, we first need the inversion curve. This is given by Eq. 12.53 as

$$V = T\left(\frac{\partial V}{\partial T}\right)_p$$

With
$$pV = RT + B_1p + B_2p^2 + B_3p^3$$

$$\left(\frac{\partial V}{\partial T}\right)_p = \frac{R}{p} + B_1'p + B_2'p^2 + B_3'p^3$$

and the equation for the inversion curve becomes

$$(B_1 - B_1'T) + (B_2 - B_2'T)p + (B_3 - B_3'T)p^2 + \cdots = 0$$

Although calculation of the inversion curve from this equation is quite tedious, the maximum inversion temperature is defined by the limit of the curve as $p \to 0$. This gives

$$B_1 = B_1'T$$

TABLE **12.1**

Maximum Inversion Temperatures

Gas	T_c	Observed	T_{mi} Holborn and Otto	Beattie-Bridgeman
He	5.20	34	43	44
H$_2$	33.2	202	207	231
Ne	44.5		219	253
N$_2$	126.3	625	592	651
Air	132.6	603		691
Ar	150.7	723	784	811

which should be written

$$B_1(T_{mi}) = B_2'(T_{mi})T_{mi}$$

In the case of the Onnes type of equation of state, values of B_1 are given by Holborn and Otto (see Chap. 2, footnote 7; see also Appendix 2.1) in the form

$$B_1 \times 10^5 = a + 10^{-2}bT + \frac{10^2c}{T} + \frac{10^6d}{T^3}$$

from which we obtain for the maximum inversion temperature the condition

$$a + \frac{2 \times 10^2c}{T_{mi}} + \frac{4 \times 10^6d}{T_{mi}^3} = 0$$

Since the last term on the left side is rather small, this equation may be solved readily by successive approximations for T_{mi}. The same calculations may be carried out for the Beattie-Bridgeman equation, in which the second virial

TABLE **12.2**

Equation of state	Value of K in Eq. 12.57
Van der Waals	$27/4 = 6.75$
Berthelot	$9/\sqrt{8} = 3.18$
Berthelot (modified)	$\sqrt{18} = 4.24$
Dieterici ($n = 1.27$)	$4(n + 1)^{1/n} = 5.69$
Wohl	$\sqrt{96/5} = 4.38$

coefficient has the value

$$B_1(T) = B_0 - \frac{A_0}{RT} - \frac{c}{T^3}$$

Measured values of T_{mi} are obtained by projecting the experimental inversion curves to the $p = 0$ axis. Table 12.1 includes results for a few gases. The third column gives the observed values (where available), and the fourth and fifth give values as estimated from the Holborn and Otto equation and the Beattie-Bridgeman equation, respectively. (Values of T_c, the critical temperature, appear in column 2.) Since the values of T_{mi} are often outside the temperature range for which the original values of B_1 were determined, the agreements are probably all that such extrapolations would warrant.

In the case of the simpler equations of state, $B_1 = B_1'T$ requires that T_{mi}

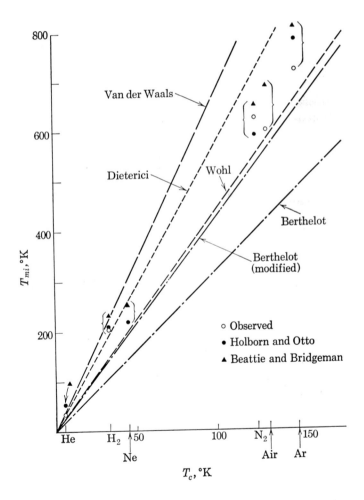

FIGURE **12.10**

be proportional to T_c, that is,

$$T_{mi} = KT_c \tag{12.57}$$

The values of this constant are given in Table 12.2, and the predictions are shown as straight lines in Fig. 12.10, which is a plot of T_{mi} versus T_c. The data of Table 12.1 are plotted as individual points.

12.11   Integration of the Clausius-Clapeyron Equation

Let us now return to the Clausius-Clapeyron equation for the cases in which one phase is a vapor. Using gram-molar quantities, we have

$$(\text{liquid-vapor}) \qquad \frac{dp_{21}}{dT} = \frac{\Lambda_{21}}{T(V' - V'')}$$

$$(\text{solid-vapor}) \qquad \frac{dp_{31}}{dT} = \frac{\Lambda_{31}}{T(V' - V''')}$$

As long as we stay away from the critical point, $V' \gg V''$, and $V' \gg V'''$. Under these circumstances the relation

$$dp = \frac{\Lambda \, dT}{TV} \tag{12.58}$$

(where the primes have been omitted) refers to either case, since only the volume of the vapor phase is involved. Dividing both sides of Eq. 12.58 by p gives

$$d \ln p = \frac{\Lambda \, dT}{pVT} \tag{12.59}$$

If the pressure is never allowed to be too great, pV can be written

$$pV = RT + B_1 p + \cdots$$

and thus

$$d \ln p = \frac{\Lambda \, dT}{RT^2 \left(1 + \dfrac{B_1 p}{RT} + \cdots\right)} \tag{12.60}$$

12.12   The Ideal Gas Approximation

The simplest result is obtained when the vapor is assumed dilute enough for the ideal gas law to apply. Then Eq. 12.60 reduces to

$$d \ln p = \frac{\Lambda \, dT}{RT^2} \tag{12.61}$$

or

$$\frac{d \ln p}{d \left(\dfrac{1}{T}\right)} = -\frac{\Lambda}{R} \tag{12.62}$$

This way of writing the result shows that if we plot the logarithm of the vapor pressure versus the reciprocal of the absolute temperature, the slope at any point will be $-\Lambda/R$. (If we use semilog paper and therefore common logarithms, the slope will, of course, be $-\Lambda/2.3026R$.)

In Fig. 12.11 data for the vapor pressure of water and ice are plotted on semilog paper versus $1/T$. The tangent to the liquid curve at 0°C is drawn as a dashed line to emphasize the curvature of the curve at the high-temperature end.

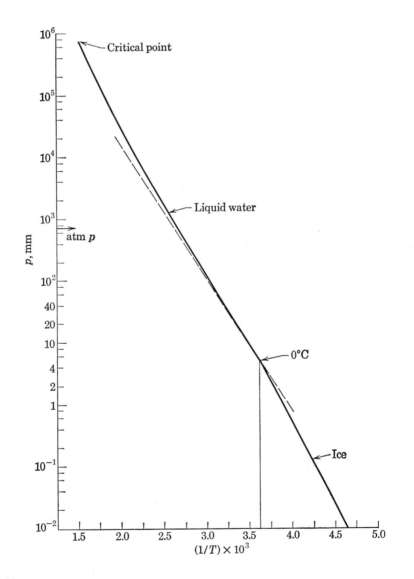

FIGURE **12.11**

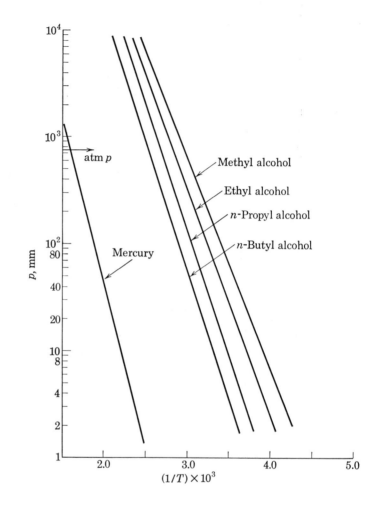

FIGURE **12.12**

Similar curves are given in Fig. 12.12 for mercury and the first four members of the series of alcohols beginning with methyl alcohol. Although the range of pressures is smaller than in Fig. 12.11, the almost exact linearity of the curves is to be noted. Since the vapor pressure curves of a great many substances are nearly linear in such graphs, determination of the slope of the curve at any point offers a direct method of measuring the latent heat, Λ. This method is particularly useful for metals and other stable solids for which the smallness of the vapor pressure would preclude the usual direct calorimetric measurement.

Integration of Eq. 12.61, with Λ being treated as a constant, gives

$$\ln p = -\frac{\Lambda}{RT} + \text{constant} \qquad (12.63)$$

This is of the general two-constant form

$$\ln p = A - \frac{B}{T} \tag{12.64}$$

where the constants A and B naturally depend on the units employed as well as the substance. Dividing through by 2.3026 to convert to common logarithms, with $R = 1.987$ cal/mole and p in millimeters of mercury, we have

$$\log p \text{ (mm)} = -\frac{\Lambda \text{ (cal/mole)}}{(2.3062 \times 1.987)T} + A \text{ (mm)}$$

or

$$\log p \text{ (mm)} = -\frac{218.6\Lambda \text{ (kcal)}}{T} + A \text{ (mm)} \tag{12.65}$$

where Λ is in kilocalories, or

$$\log p \text{ (mm)} = -\frac{52.23\Lambda \text{ (kjoule)}}{T} + A \text{ (mm)} \tag{12.66}$$

with Λ in kilojoules per mole.

When we wish to change to another pressure unit, we must change the constant A (mm) to its proper value in the new system. To do this, we must subtract from A (mm) the logarithm of the number of millimeters of mercury in the new pressure unit. In general, this means that the new A is

$$A \text{ (mm)} - \log \frac{\text{size of new unit}}{\text{size of old unit}}$$

Thus, for conversion to atmospheres,

$$A \text{ (atm)} = A \text{ (mm)} - \log \frac{760}{1} = A \text{ (mm)} - 2.8808$$

whereas for conversion to dynes per square centimeter, the correction is $+ \log 1.333 \times 10^3 = 3.1248$ with the numerical values from Sec. 3.3.

TABLE **12.3**

Empirical Vapor Pressure Constants

Substance	State	Λ, kcal	A, mm	Range of validity, °C
Cadmium	Solid	26.8	8.56	150–320.9 (mp)
Cesium	Liquid	17.5	6.95	200–350
Copper	Liquid	111.0	12.34	2100–2310 (bp)
Mercury	Solid	17.4	10.38	−80−−38.87 (mp)
Magnesium	Liquid	32.6	7.45	400–1300
Potassium	Liquid	20.3	7.18	260–760 (bp)
Silver	Liquid	60.0	8.76	1650–1950
Sodium	Liquid	24.8	7.553	180–880
Rubidium	Liquid	18.2	6.98	250–370
Zinc	Solid	31.8	9.20	250–419.1 (mp)
	Liquid	28.2	8.11	600–985

The values of Λ and A for a few typical metals are given in Table 12.3, Λ being in kilocalories and A in millimeters of mercury. This data is taken chiefly from the work of Egerton and his co-workers.[5] Usually the uncertainty in the latent heats varies from $+0.15$ to ± 0.75 kcal.

12.13   The General Vapor Pressure Equation of Kirchhoff

Although the simple two-constant vapor pressure formula is of great value, a result valid over a large range of temperature requires taking into account the variation of Λ with T. Thus if Λ_1 is the value of Λ at any temperature T_1, we can always write

$$\Lambda = \Lambda_1 + a_1(T - T_1) + a_2(T - T_1)^2 + \cdots \qquad (12.67)$$

where a, a_2, etc., are empirical constants usually decreasing rapidly in size as the series progresses. Expanding and rearranging the terms in the usual way, we have the more convenient power series in T,

$$\Lambda = b_0 + b_1 T + b_2 T^2 + b_3 T^3 + \cdots \qquad (12.68)$$

where
$$b_0 = \Lambda_1 - a_1 T_1 + a_2 T_1^2 + \cdots$$
$$b_1 = a_1 - 2a_2 T_1 + 3a_3 T_1^2 + \cdots$$
$$b_2 = a_2 - 3a_3 T_1 + \cdots$$

Since Λ usually diminishes with temperature, b_1 is normally negative. Insertion of Eq. 12.68 in Eq. 12.61 and integration give

$$\ln p = -\frac{b_0}{RT} + \frac{b_1}{R} \ln T + \frac{b_2}{R} T + \frac{b_3 T^2}{2R} + \cdots + \text{constant}$$

which we can write

$$\boxed{\ln p = A - \frac{B}{T} - C \ln T + DT + ET^2 + \cdots} \qquad (12.69)$$

This is the general vapor pressure equation obtained by Kirchhoff. In it the constant B is always positive, and the constant C normally so. The constant A can always be written as

$$A = \ln p_1 + \frac{B}{T_1} + C \ln T_1 - DT_1 - ET_1^2 + \cdots$$

where p_1 is the measured value of the vapor pressure at T_1. In principle, therefore, all the constants in Eq. 12.69 can be evaluated from a single vapor pressure measurement. Actually, however, the data for Λ at various temperatures are

---

[5] Egerton, *Proc. Phys. Soc.* (*London*), **37**, 73 (1925) (resumé); Edmondson and Egerton, *Proc. Roy. Soc.* (*London*), **A113**, 520 (1926–7).

seldom sufficient for a reliable expansion, and the constants A, B, C, etc., must be evaluated to give the best empirical fit for the vapor pressure data.

It must be remembered that although Eq. 12.69 is a much better approximation to vapor pressure than the two-constant formula (Eq. 12.64), it is still based on the perfect gas law. Thus B and C are normally positive and much larger than D, E, etc. Hence on the usual plotting of $\ln p$ versus $1/T$, the curve would be expected to be concave upward. In practice, at high pressures (as the critical point is approached) the $\log p$ curves may actually curve downward or have a slight S shape. This may be taken as an indication of the failure of the ideal gas law approximation as well as the result of neglecting the volume of the liquid compared with that of the vapor.

Using a van der Waals approximation, Frost and Kalkwarf[6] obtained a vapor pressure equation of the form

$$\ln p = A - \frac{B}{T} - C \ln T + \frac{Dp}{T^2} + \cdots \tag{12.70}$$

where A, B, C, and D are all positive (see Problem 12.14). Although the last term contains both p and T, it is small, and the value of p can be calculated readily by successive approximation. Such a formula was found to fit the vapor pressure data of water, CO_2, and the first eight members of the methane series of hydrocarbons, methane to n-octane. The average deviation, from the melting point of the solid to the critical point, between the measured values and those calculated from Eq. 12.70 was about $\pm 0.31\%$.

12.14 Kirchhoff's Formula for Latent Heat of Sublimation

Another approach to the problem of expressing Λ in a form suitable for insertion in the Clausius-Clapeyron equation depends on the properties of the enthalpy function as used earlier in Sec. 7.12. Starting with the relation

$$\Lambda_{31} = H' - H''' \tag{12.71}$$

we arrived (after approximations made necessary by the lack of the second law) at Eq. 7.40,

$$\Lambda_{31} = \Lambda_0 + \int_0^T (C_p^\circ - C_p''') \, dT \tag{12.72}$$

Λ_0 being the heat of sublimation at $0°K$. We can now obtain a precise result, using the laboratory equation for dH.

We begin by writing Eq. 12.71 as

$$\Lambda = \Lambda_T = H' - H''' \tag{12.73}$$

and thus for any fixed temperature, T_1,

$$\Lambda_1 = \Lambda_{T_1} = H'_1 - H'''_1 \tag{12.74}$$

[6] Frost and Kalkwarf, *J. Chem. Phys.*, **21**, 265 (1953).

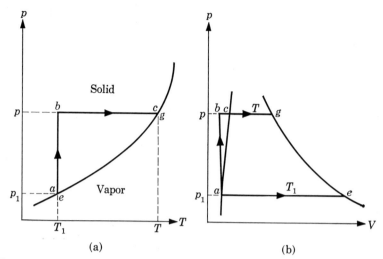

FIGURE **12.13**

Subtracting Eq. 12.74 from Eq. 12.73 gives

$$\Lambda = \Lambda_1 + (H' - H'_1) - (H''' - H'''_1) \tag{12.75}$$

Consider now a portion of the equilibrium curve for the solid and vapor shown in Fig. 12.13(a). Let p and p_1 be the pressures at, respectively, T and T_1, the temperatures at two points on the solid-vapor equilibrium curve. Here the states a and c refer to the solid, and e and g to the vapor, at the two temperatures [Fig. 12.13(b)]. Then

$$H_c - H_a = H''' - H'''_1$$

and

$$H_g - H_e = H' - H'_1$$

Applying the enthalpy equation from Eqs. 12.46 to the vapor with $T_0 = T_1$ and $p_0 = p_1$, we have

$$H' - H'_1 = \int_{T_1}^{T} C_p^\circ(T)\, dT + [B_1(T) - B_1'(T)T]p$$
$$- [B_1(T_1) - B_1'(T_1)T_1]p_1 \tag{12.76}$$

retaining only linear terms in pressure.

In the same way Eq. 12.11 gives for the solid

$$H''' - H'''_1 = \int_{T_1}^{T} C_p'''(T)\, dT + V_1(p - p_1)\left[1 - T_1\beta_p - \kappa_T\left(\frac{p - p_1}{2}\right)\right] \tag{12.77}$$

Combining these with Eq. 12.75 gives

$$\Lambda = \Lambda_1 + \int_{T_1}^{T} [C_p^\circ(T) - C_p'''(T)]\, dT + \text{correction term} \tag{12.78}$$

where the correction term is

$$[B_1(T) - B_1'(T)T]_p - [B_1(T_1) - B_1'(T_1)T_1]p_1$$
$$- V_1(p - p_1)\left[1 - T_1\beta_p - \kappa_T\left(\frac{p - p_1}{2}\right)\right]$$

Since C_p^o is the ideal gas heat capacity, it can always be split into the value for the monatomic gas and the correction term, say, C_{int}^o, due to internal degrees of freedom; that is,

$$C_p^o = \tfrac{5}{2}R + C_{int}^o$$

Then the integral in Eq. 12.78 becomes

$$\tfrac{5}{2}R(T - T_1) - \int_{T_1}^T (C_p''' - C_{int}^o)\,dT$$

and $\Lambda = \Lambda_1 + \tfrac{5}{2}R(T - T_1)$
$$- \int_{T_1}^T (C_p''' - C_{int}^o)\,dT + \text{correction term}   \textbf{(12.79)}$$

This is the general Kirchhoff sublimation formula.

12.15   The Vapor Pressure Formula for a Solid (Ideal Vapor)

We may now use the new general relation for Λ instead of the series formula (Eq. 12.68) to integrate the Clausius-Clapeyron equation in another form. We must be sure, of course, that no solid transitions occur in the range T_1 to T. If, further, none occur between T_1 and $0°K$, we may allow T_1 to approach zero when $\Lambda_1 = \Lambda_0$. Since $p_1 = 0$ at $0°K$, the gas must be infinitely dispersed and thus ideal. Therefore, all terms in p_1 vanish, and the correction term of Eq. 12.78 becomes considerably simpler. Thus Eq. 12.79 reduces to

$$\Lambda = \Lambda_0 + \frac{5}{2}RT - \int_0^T (C_p''' - C_{int}^o)\,dT$$
$$+ [B_1(T) - B_1'(T)T]p - V_0'''p\left(1 - \kappa_T\frac{p}{2}\right)   \textbf{(12.80)}$$

If we choose T so low that p is always small, the vapor may, to a very high degree of approximation, be treated as ideal at T, also, and, since V_0''' is the molar volume of the solid, pV_0''' becomes very small numerically. Thus the last two terms may be dropped, and the result is the useful approximation also given by Kirchhoff,

$$\boxed{\Lambda = \Lambda_0 + \tfrac{5}{2}RT - \int_0^T (C_p''' - C_{int}^o)\,dT}   \textbf{(12.81)}$$

Inserting this in the Clausius-Clapeyron equation, Eq. 12.61, as written for the ideal gas, gives

$$d\ln p = \frac{\Lambda_0}{RT^2}\,dT + \frac{5}{2}\frac{dT}{T} - \frac{dT}{RT^2}\int_0^T (C_p''' - C_{int}^o)\,dT$$

If we integrate this as an open integral and call the constant of integration i_p, we obtain

$$\ln p = -\frac{\Lambda_0}{RT} + \ln T^{5/2} - \int \frac{dT}{RT^2} \int_0^T (C_p''' - C_{\text{int}}^{\circ})\, dT + i_p \qquad (12.82)$$

where the double integral is an iterated integral. This is the new vapor pressure equation, i_p being the *absolute vapor pressure* constant. Once i_p has been determined, say, by an accurate measurement of the vapor pressure at a single temperature, then the vapor pressure can be calculated for the entire range of validity of Eq. 12.82.

It must be remembered that this result holds only when no transitions occur in the solid between $0°K$ and T and when the pressure is low enough for the ideal gas approximation to be a good one. Moreover, the constant i_p must not be identified with the constant A in such relations as Eqs. 12.64 and 12.69. Those equations are valid for limited temperature ranges, also, but the ranges usually lie far above the low temperatures to which the new result is restricted.

12.16   Latent Heat of Sublimation of a Monatomic Solid

A special case of great theoretical interest is that of solids with strictly monatomic vapors. For this situation Eq. 12.81 reduces to

$$\Lambda = \Lambda_0 + \tfrac{5}{2}RT - \int_0^T C_p''' \, dT \qquad (12.83)$$

since for such gases $C_{\text{int}}^{\circ} = 0$. This is Kirchhoff's sublimation formula for the monatomic solid, obtained by more special reasoning in Sec. 7.12 as Eq. 7.39. As we saw there, if the internal energy of the ideal vapor at $0°K$ (and $p = 0$) is taken arbitrarily to be zero, since $H = U + pV$,

$$H°(T = 0) = U°(T = 0) + 0 = 0$$

and H' and U' for the vapor are measured from a common zero. Then we must write for the solid at $0°K$

$$H'''(T = 0) = H_0''' = -\Lambda_0$$

and Eq. 12.77 for the enthalpy of the solid (with $T_1 = 0$ and $p_1 = 0$) reduces to

$$H''' = -\Lambda_0 + \int_0^T C_p''' \, dT + pV_0 \left(1 - \kappa_T \frac{p}{2}\right)$$

where the small correction term may usually be neglected.

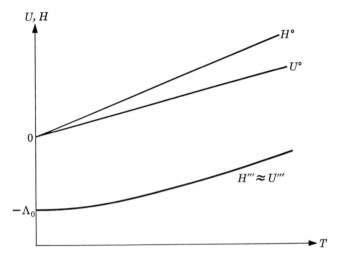

FIGURE **12.14**

Typical behavior of U and H at low temperatures is indicated in Fig. 12.14. The difference between U''' and H''' is too small to show. This figure should be compared with Figs. 7.12 and 7.13, which are drawn for a constant over-all pressure equal to atmospheric pressure and which include the effects of changes of phase at the standard pressure. In Fig. 12.14 $p = p(T)$ and increases from 0 at 0°K.

Evaluation of the important quantity Λ_0 requires the determination of Λ at some temperature, T, and the values of C_p''' from T down to 0°K. The first quantity is found by plotting $\log p$ versus $1/T$ and determining the slope as in Sec. 12.12. The temperature chosen must be high enough to lie in a range where the vapor pressure can be measured accurately and yet not so high that the ideal gas approximation is invalidated. For evaluation of the heat capacity integral, the experimental data are extrapolated to 0°K by the Debye cube law, and the area under the curve is found graphically.

Column 2 of Table 12.4 gives values of Λ_0, as calculated from Eq. 12.83,

$$\Lambda_0 = \Lambda_T - \tfrac{5}{2}RT + \int_0^T C_p''' \, dT \qquad (12.83)$$

TABLE **12.4**

Heats of Sublimation of Monatomic Solids (cal/mole)

Substance	Λ_0	Λ_T	T, °K	$\tfrac{5}{2}RT$	$\int_0^T C_p''' \, dT$
Sodium	25,803	25,629	371	1843	2017
Potassium	21,441	21,789	336.7	1672	1995
Zinc	31,330	30,871	691	3410	3869
Mercury	15,530	15,416	234.2	1160	1274

for a few monatomic metals. The values of Λ_T and the temperatures at which they were measured are given in columns 3 and 4. The last two columns indicate the relative importance of the last two terms in Eq. 12.83. It is noteworthy that Λ_T changes quite slowly as the temperature rises from 0°K.

12.17   Vapor Pressure of a Monatomic Solid

For the special case of a solid with a monatomic vapor, Eq. 12.82 reduces to

$$\ln p = -\frac{\Lambda_0}{RT} + \ln T^{5/2} - \int \frac{dT}{RT^2} \int_0^T C_p''' \, dT + i_p \qquad (12.84)$$

Extensive tests of this important relation have been carried out by a great many observers.

To put Eq. 12.84 in practical form, we convert it to common logarithms and express the pressure in atmospheres rather than absolute units. If we write

$$p \text{ (cgs)} = p_0 \text{ (cgs)} P \text{ (atm)}$$

where p_0 is the value of 1 atm in cgs units and P is the pressure in atmospheres, the equation becomes

$$\log P \text{ (atm)} = -\frac{\Lambda_0}{2.30RT} + \frac{5}{2} \log T - \frac{1}{2.30R} \int \frac{dT}{T^2} \int_0^T C''' \, dT + \frac{i_p}{2.30}$$
$$- \log p_0 \quad (12.85)$$

We now set $p_0 = 1.013 \times 10^6$ dynes/cm² and write

$$i_p' = \frac{i_p}{2.30} - \log 1.013 \times 10^6 = \frac{i_p}{2.30} - 6.0052$$

where i_p' is the so-called *conventional vapor pressure* constant. Then, indicating the integral term by $I(T)$ and expressing Λ_0 in kilocalories, we obtain

$$\log P \text{ (atm)} = -\frac{218.6\Lambda_0}{T} \text{ (kcal)} + \log T^{5/2} - I(T) + i_p' \quad (12.86)$$

Although in theory a value of i_p' could be determined from a measurement of p at a single value of T, a more reliable value is determined from the best data for as wide a range of temperatures as possible. From the form of Eq. 12.86, it is clear that we may regard i_p' as the following limit:

$$i_p' = \lim_{T \to \infty} \left[\log \frac{P}{T^{5/2}} + \frac{218.6\Lambda_0}{T} + I(T) \right]$$

As $T \to \infty$, the middle term reduces to zero, and

$$i_p' = \lim_{T \to \infty} \left[\log \frac{P}{T^{5/2}} + I(T) \right] = \lim_{T \to \infty} y$$

where y is an abbreviation for the term in brackets. If Eq. 12.86 is rewritten in terms of y, we have

$$y = -\frac{218.6\Lambda_0}{T} + i_p' \tag{12.87}$$

and $y = \log P/T^{5/2} + I(T)$ is a linear function of $1/T$ for which the slope is $-218.6\Lambda_0$ and the intercept as $T \to \infty$ (and $1/T \to 0$) is the desired vapor pressure constant, i_p'. See Fig. 12.15, where the dashed extension of the experimental curve represents the extrapolation to $1/T = 0$.

Experimental values of the conventional vapor pressure constant, i_p', have been obtained by many observers.[7] A number of the results, for solids with strictly monatomic vapors, are given in Table 12.5. Measurements of small vapor pressures at low temperatures are fraught with many difficulties, and the experimental errors are considerably larger than the approximations made in arriving at the final expression of Eq. 12.84. The results of low-temperature measurements on the vapor pressure of solid H_2 are included in the table, since at low enough temperatures the vapor behaves essentially as a monatomic gas.[8]

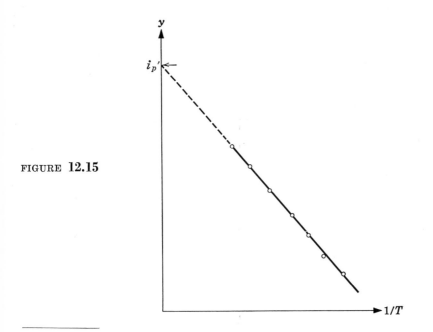

FIGURE **12.15**

---

[7] See in particular Coleman and Egerton, *Phil. Trans. Roy. Soc. London*, **A237**, 177 (1935); Clusius, Kruis, and Konnertz, *Ann. Physik*, **33**, 642 (1938); and Simon and Bleaney, *Trans. Faraday Soc.*, **35**, 1205 (1939).

[8] In the case of helium, the result refers to the liquid since the solid melts at $p < 25$ atm.

TABLE **12.5**

**Conventional Vapor Pressure Constants
for Solids with Monatomic Vapors**

Gas	Mol wt	i_p'
(H₂)	2.016	$-1.09 \pm .02$
(He)	4.00	$-0.68 \pm .01$
Ne	20.18	$0.39 \pm .04$
Ar	39.9	$0.81 \pm .02$
Kr	83.7	$1.29 \pm .02$
Xe	131.03	$1.60 \pm .02$
Mg	24.32	$0.47 \pm .02$
Zn	65.38	$1.21 \pm .15$
Cd	112.4	$1.45 \pm .1$
		1.57
Hg	200.6	$1.85 \pm .06$
Pb	207.2	$1.8 \ \pm .2$

12.18 Entropy and the Vapor Pressure Constant

The great theoretical importance of the absolute vapor pressure constant, i_p, lies in its connection with basic entropy constants for the solid and vapor phases. To find this connection, we utilize Gibbs' potential and state its equality for the two equilibrium phases, solid and vapor; that is,

$$G''' = G' = G°$$

Specific equations for enthalpy and entropy were obtained in Secs. 12.2 and 12.3, and we may use them to write out each side of this relation in detail.

Beginning with the solid, since

$$G''' = H''' - TS'''$$

we insert the appropriate values from Eqs. 12.12 and 12.15. In this case the small term $V_0'''p$ may safely be ignored, so that

$$G''' = - \Lambda_0 + \int_0^T C_p''' \, dT - T \int C_p''' \frac{dT}{T} - TS_0'''$$

The corresponding value for the ideal vapor requires the use of Eqs. 12.19 and 12.23, with $C_p° = \frac{5}{2}R$, $T_0 = 0°K$, and $H°(T_0)$ set equal to 0. The result is

$$G° = \frac{5}{2}RT - \frac{5}{2}RT \ln T + RT \ln p - TS_{0Tp}°$$

Equating these values of Gibbs' potential and solving for $\ln p$ give

$$\ln p = -\frac{\Lambda_0}{RT} + \ln T^{5/2} + \frac{1}{RT}\int_0^T C_p{}'''\,dT - \frac{1}{R}\int C_p{}'''\frac{dT}{T} + \frac{S_{0Tp}^\circ - S_0{}'''}{R} - \frac{5}{2}$$

The two integrals can be combined since integration by parts shows that

$$-\int \frac{dT}{RT^2}\int_0^T C_p{}'''\,dT = \frac{1}{RT}\int_0^T C_p{}'''\,dT - \frac{1}{R}\int C_p{}'''\frac{dT}{T}$$

Finally, then,

$$\ln p = -\frac{\Lambda_0}{RT} + \ln T^{5/2} - \int \frac{dT}{RT^2}\int_0^T C_p{}'''\,dT + \frac{S_{0Tp}^\circ - S_0{}'''}{R} - \frac{5}{2} \quad \textbf{(12.88)}$$

This result is identical with the original vapor pressure formula (Eq. 12.84) if we identify the constant terms. Thus

$$i_p = \frac{S_{0Tp}^\circ}{R} - \frac{S_0{}'''}{R} - \frac{5}{2} \quad \textbf{(12.89)}$$

This shows that the absolute vapor pressure constant is fixed by the absolute entropy constants of the vapor and solid. Of course, from the point of view of classical thermodynamics, we have no "absolute" entropy constants. They are simply arbitrary integration constants and are not unique. On the other hand, as we shall see in Chap. 17, statistical mechanics with the help of quantum theory does enable us to calculate values for the entropy constants so that the difference, $S_{0Tp}^\circ - S_0{}'''$, is unique.[9]

The right side of Eq. 12.89 can be expressed very simply in terms of the molecular weight, M, of the gas. In fact, as we shall see (Eq. 17.5)

$$i_p = \text{constant} + \ln M^{3/2} \quad \textbf{(12.90)}$$

Here the constant term contains only universal constants as long as the atoms involved have no spin or angular momentum in their ground states (whether in the condensed or vapor state). The substances listed in Table 12.5 are all in this category. The values of $i_p{}'$ are thus related in a linear fashion to $\log M$. Accordingly, the values of $\log M$ are plotted versus the experimental values of

---

[9] It is perhaps more accurate to say that neither classical thermodynamics nor quantum statistics can fix an absolute value of entropy. If the latter study fixes values for $S_0{}'''$ and S_{0pT}° in Eqs. 12.15 and 12.23, then we are free to add any constant to each. At any finite temperature, however, $S^\circ - S'''$ must be equal to Λ/T, and since this value is unique, if a constant, say, K, is added to the right of Eq. 12.15, the same one must be added to the right of Eq. 12.23. Thus when Eq. 12.88 is arrived at, the K's cancel, making the difference in Eq. 12.88 unique.

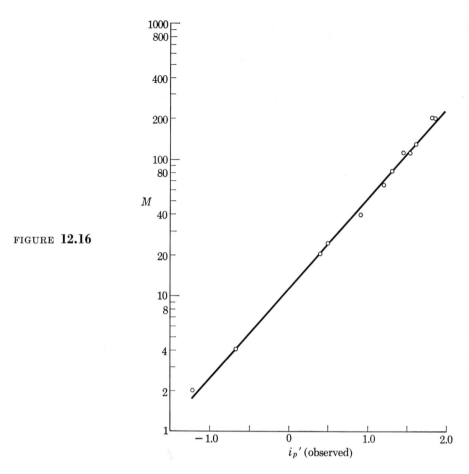

FIGURE **12.16**

i_p' from Table 12.5 in Fig. 12.16. The points lie very close to a straight line over the entire mass range of over 100:1. The reciprocal slope of this line is found to be almost exactly the predicted value of $\frac{3}{2}$.

Problems

12.1 Consider a mole of copper at 0°K. The correction term in Eq. 12.11 for the enthalpy is, with $p_0 = 0$ and $T_0 = 0°K$,

$$V_0'''p\left[1 - \kappa_T \frac{p}{2}\right]$$

Calculate this term in calories per mole for $p = 1$ atm. Here an upper limit for V_0''' is obtained from the ordinary values of the molar volume. See also Fig. 3.14. What is the approximate difference between H''' and U''' for this metal?

12.2 Using the relation

$$C_p = C_V + \frac{TV\beta_p{}^2}{\kappa_T}$$

calculate the difference between C_p and C_V for molar quantities of
(a) metallic copper,
(b) water at 4°C, and
(c) a van der Waals gas.

12.3 In the discussion of Sec. 12.1 the work performed was small compared to the heat loss in the isothermal compression. Since the former is a quadratic function of pressure rise and the latter is only a linear one, the two should attain equality at some high pressure. What must the pressure be for copper?

12.4 Write out the free energy (Helmholtz) equation for a van der Waals gas from the results of Sec. 12.4, and verify that

$$\left(\frac{\partial A}{\partial V}\right)_T = p = \frac{RT}{V-b} - \frac{a}{V^2}$$

12.5 Expand the state equations of Berthelot, Dieterici, and Wohl in their virial forms in powers of p, and show that, with the critical constant relations given in Secs. 3.10 and 3.11 and Problem 3.11,

$$\frac{\Delta C_p{}^{\text{imp}}}{R} = \frac{81\pi}{32\theta^3}\left[1 - \frac{9\pi}{64\theta}\left(1 - \frac{15}{2\theta^2}\right) + \cdots\right] \quad \text{Berthelot}$$

$$\frac{\Delta C_p{}^{\text{imp}}}{R} = \frac{11.53\pi}{e^2\theta^{n+1}}\left[1 - \frac{1.29\pi}{e^2\theta}\left(1 - \frac{4.32}{\theta^n}\right) + \cdots\right] \quad n = 1.27 \quad \text{Dieterici}$$

$$\frac{\Delta C_p{}^{\text{imp}}}{R} = \frac{64\pi}{25\theta^3}\left[1 - \frac{\pi}{15\theta}\left(1 + \frac{5 \times 52}{81\theta^{1/3}} - \frac{16}{\theta^2}\right) + \cdots\right] \quad \text{Wohl}$$

12.6 Show that van der Waals' equation may be thrown into the two virial forms

$$pV = RT + (RTb - a)\frac{1}{V} + RTb^2\frac{1}{V^2} + \cdots$$

and $$pV = RT + \left(b - \frac{a}{RT}\right)p + \frac{a}{R^2T^2}\left(2b - \frac{a}{RT}\right)p^2 + \cdots$$

12.7 Using the second virial approximation from Problem 12.6, show that for a van der Waals gas

$$C_p = C_p^\circ + \frac{2ap}{RT^2} - \frac{6a}{R^2T^3}\left(b - \frac{a}{RT}\right)p^2 + \cdots$$

12.8 With the expression just given for C_p and the general laboratory equation for dH, show that for the van der Waals gas

$$H = H^\circ + bp - \frac{2a}{RT}p + \frac{a}{R^2T^2}\left(3b - \frac{2a}{RT}\right)p^2 + \cdots$$

12.9 Show that the corresponding entropy expression for a van der Waals gas in terms of the variables T and p is

$$S = S^\circ - \frac{ap}{RT^2} + \frac{2a}{R^2T^2}\left(\frac{b}{T} - \frac{3a}{4RT^2}\right)p^2 + \cdots$$

and that the Gibbs function with the same variables is

$$G = G^\circ + \left(b - \frac{a}{RT}\right)p + \frac{a}{R^2T^2}\left(b - \frac{a}{2RT}\right)p^2 + \cdots$$

12.10 Show that for a van der Waals gas the inversion curve defined by

$$V = T\left(\frac{\partial V}{\partial T}\right)_p$$

can be put in parametric form as

$$p = \frac{a}{bV}\left(2 - \frac{3b}{V}\right)$$

$$T = \frac{2a}{Rb}\left(1 - \frac{b}{V}\right)^2$$

12.11 Using the critical constant relations for a van der Waals gas given in Chap. 3,

$$V_c = 3b \qquad p_c = \frac{a}{27b^2} \qquad T_c = \frac{8a}{27Rb} \tag{3.22}$$

and

$$a = \frac{27}{64}\frac{R^2T_c^2}{p_c} \qquad b = \frac{RT_c}{8p_c} \tag{3.23}$$

show that the parametric equations for the inversion curve obtained in Problem 12.10 assume the reduced form,

$$\pi = \frac{9}{\phi}\left(2 - \frac{1}{\phi}\right)$$

$$\theta = \frac{27}{4}\left(1 - \frac{1}{3\phi}\right)^2$$

Sketch this result in the θ-π plane.

12.12 Starting with the modified form of Berthelot's equation of state,

$$pV = RT + b'p - \frac{a'p}{RT^2}$$

show that the temperature change, ΔT, in a gas on passage through a Joule-Kelvin porous plug can be written

$$\Delta T = \frac{3a'}{C_p^\circ R}\left[\frac{p_1}{T_1^2} - \frac{p_2}{(T_1 + \Delta T)^2}\right] - \frac{b'}{C_p^\circ}(p_1 - p_2) + \cdots$$

where C_p° is the ideal heat capacity of the gas, T_1 and p_1 are the initial coordinates of the gas, and $T_1 + \Delta T$ and p_2 are the final coordinates. (*Hint:* First obtain an expression for the enthalpy of the gas.)

12.13 A Joule-Kelvin expansion is carried out with pure nitrogen under the following conditions: $p_1 = 100$ atm, $T_1 = 300°K$, and $p_2 = 1$ atm. Using the result of Problem 12.12, estimate the final temperature, T_2, of the gas after a single expansion.

12.14 Show that van der Waals' equation can be put in the approximate form

$$p(V - b) = RT\left(1 - \frac{ap}{R^2T^2} + \cdots\right)$$

Then, assuming that

$$V - b \approx V' - V''$$

and

$$\Lambda = \Lambda_0 - b_1 T \qquad (b_1 > 0)$$

show that the integral of the Clausius-Clapeyron equation takes the form of Eq. 12.70,

$$\ln p = A - \frac{B}{T} - C \ln T + \frac{Dp}{T^2}$$

where $B = \Lambda_0/R$, $C = b_1/R$, and $D = a/R^2$ (see footnote 6 in the chapter).

12.15 Show that for the general Wohl equation the laboratory equation for dU becomes

$$dU = C_V^\circ \, dT + d\left[\frac{2a}{bT}\ln\left(1 - \frac{b}{V}\right) + \frac{(n+1)c}{2T^nV^2}\right]$$

and hence that

$$U = U^\circ + \frac{2a}{bT}\ln\left(1 - \frac{b}{V}\right) + \frac{7c}{6T^{4/3}V^2}$$

12.16 The arguments of Sec. 12.5 show that a van der Waals gas with $C_V = C_V(T)$ is a special case of a more general class for which the equation of state and the adiabatic equation, respectively, may be written

$$p = \frac{RT}{V - b} + f(V)$$

and

$$T(V - b)^n F(T) = C$$

where $f(V)$ and $F(T)$ are independent functions. Show that if such a gas is used in a Carnot cycle, the same efficiency results as for the ideal gas,

$$\eta_R = \frac{T_1 - T_2}{T_1}$$

CHAPTER THIRTEEN

Applications
to Various Systems

13.1   The n-Variable Thermodynamic System

In this chapter applications of the laws of thermodynamics to a variety of systems will be considered. The systems studied will include those acted on by forces other than or in addition to hydrostatic ones. Among them are rods under pressure and tension, electric cells, black body radiation, stressed dielectrics in electric fields, and chemical systems. All these different systems cannot, of course, be treated exhaustively, and the discussion will therefore be confined to a few of the many aspects each presents.

To understand how each fits into the over-all framework, we return to the general case with n independent variables discussed in Sec. 5.6. There the first law was written (Eq. 5.19) in the general form

$$dU = dQ_c + \sum_{i=1}^{n-1} F_i \, d\theta_i \tag{13.1}$$

where $F_1, F_2, \ldots, F_{n-1}$ are the generalized forces and $d\theta_1, d\theta_2, \ldots, d\theta_{n-1}$ the increments of the conjugate geometric variables.

Use of the second law gives the general form of CI as

$$dU = T \, dS + \sum_{i=1}^{n-1} F_i \, d\theta_i \tag{13.2}$$

Since we may regard T as the generalized force conjugate to the generalized geometric variable S, it is convenient to consider $T = F_1$ and $S = \theta_1$ and rewrite Eq. 13.2 as

$$dU = T \, dS + \sum_{i=2}^{n} F_i \, d\theta_i \tag{13.3}$$

The general Jacobian treatment of such a system fortunately follows the pattern of the simple case with $n = 2$. It is shown in Appendix 13.1 for the case of $n = 3$, and the proof is readily generalized, that Maxwell's relations always contain only two derivatives each under certain conditions.[1] These conditions are that the independent variables $(x_1, x_2, \ldots, x_n)$, which we call an x set, are always chosen (1) from the $2n$ primaries on the right of Eq. 13.3 and (2) contain no conjugate pairs (that is, no pairs such as T and S or F_i and θ_i). These restrictions actually are not very severe; in fact, we shall in many cases be satisfied with an x set containing only force variables such as T, $F_2, \ldots, F_n$. With a nonconjugate x set the fundamental Jacobian can always be modified, for the case when $n \geq 2$, so that the modified Jacobian, J_0', is symmetric about the positive diagonal. This symmetry leads to the Maxwellian relations for the problem in terms of the given x set.

To illustrate the form of the results, we now set up the modified Jacobian, J_0', for an x set made up of force variables only. The variables chosen for the x set are underlined. Thus, starting with

$$dU = \underline{T}\, dS + \underline{F}_2\, d\theta_2 + \underline{F}_3\, d\theta_3 + \cdots + \underline{F}_n\, d\theta_n$$

we write by definition

$$J_0' = \frac{\partial(S, \theta_2, \theta_3, \ldots, \theta_n)}{\partial(T, F_2, F_3, \ldots, F_n)}$$

$$= \begin{vmatrix} \dfrac{\partial S}{\partial T} & \dfrac{\partial \theta_2}{\partial T} & \dfrac{\partial \theta_3}{\partial T} & \cdots & \dfrac{\partial \theta_n}{\partial T} \\[2mm] \dfrac{\partial S}{\partial F_1} & \dfrac{\partial \theta_2}{\partial F_1} & \dfrac{\partial \theta_3}{\partial F_1} & \cdots & \dfrac{\partial \theta_n}{\partial F_1} \\[2mm] \dfrac{\partial S}{\partial F_2} & \dfrac{\partial \theta_2}{\partial F_2} & \dfrac{\partial \theta_3}{\partial F_2} & \cdots & \dfrac{\partial \theta_n}{\partial F_2} \\[2mm] \cdot & \cdot & \cdot & \cdots & \cdot \\ \cdot & \cdot & \cdot & \cdots & \cdot \\[2mm] \dfrac{\partial S}{\partial F_n} & \dfrac{\partial \theta_2}{\partial F_n} & \dfrac{\partial \theta_3}{\partial F_n} & \cdots & \dfrac{\partial \theta_n}{\partial F_n} \end{vmatrix} = \begin{vmatrix} a_0 & a_1 & a_2 & \cdots & a_n \\[2mm] a_1 & b_{11} & b_{12} & \cdots & b_{1n} \\[2mm] a_2 & b_{12} & b_{22} & \cdots & b_{2n} \\[2mm] \cdot & \cdot & \cdot & \cdots & \cdot \\ \cdot & \cdot & \cdot & \cdots & \cdot \\[2mm] a_n & b_{1n} & b_{2n} & \cdots & b_{nn} \end{vmatrix}$$

The derivatives in J_0' have been abbreviated in the determinant by n^2 letters a_0 to b_{nn}. Here $a_0, \ldots, a_n$ are, as we see from the top row of J_0', all temperature derivatives, whereas $b_{11}, \ldots, b_{nn}$ are *isothermal* derivatives or coefficients. The n^2 derivatives are those in terms of which any arbitrary derivatives can be expressed.

The symmetry of J_0' reduces the independent derivatives to those *on* and *above the positive diagonal*. In other words, the number of Maxwellian relations is equal to the number of derivatives above (but not counting) the main diagonal. Thus

$$\begin{pmatrix} \text{number of Maxwellian} \\ \text{relations} \end{pmatrix} = (n-1) + (n-2) + \cdots + 1 = \frac{n}{2}(n-1)$$

---

[1] The general n-variable case is discussed in detail in Crawford, *Proc. Am. Acad. Arts Sci.*, **78**, 165 (1950).

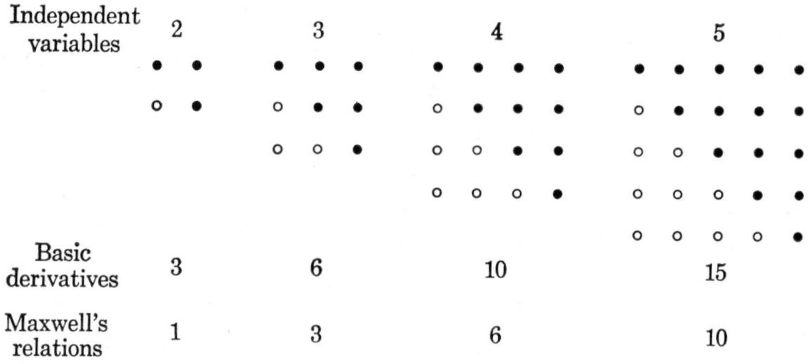

Independent variables	2	3	4	5
	• •	• • •	• • • •	• • • • •
	o •	o • •	o • • •	o • • • •
		o o •	o o • •	o o • • •
			o o o •	o o o • •
				o o o o •
Basic derivatives	3	6	10	15
Maxwell's relations	1	3	6	10

FIGURE **13.1**

The number of derivatives that are independent and therefore constitute a *basic set* of derivatives is the number *on* and *above* the main diagonal. Since this is just n greater than the first number, we have

$$\begin{pmatrix}\text{number of independent} \\ \text{derivatives in the} \\ \text{basic set}\end{pmatrix} = \frac{n}{2}(n-1) + n = \frac{n}{2}(n+1) \qquad (13.4)$$

These results are shown symbolically in Fig. 13.1 for the cases $n = 2$ to $n = 5$. The n^2 elements of J_0' are the small circles. The black dots constitute the *basic set*. The number of circles gives the number of simultaneous Maxwellian relations for the problem.

13.2   Restricted and Unrestricted Systems

Because of the general nature of the thermodynamic results indicated in the previous section, we are able to translate them into their appropriate form for any particular system. In other words, if we deduce a result for, say, a single-phase system under hydrostatic pressure, it can immediately be translated into the proper form for any other system with $n = 2$. Given CI as

$$dU = \underline{T}\,dS - \underline{p}\,dV$$

we know that with T and p for the x set MI becomes

$$\left(\frac{\partial S}{\partial p}\right)_T = -\left(\frac{\partial V}{\partial T}\right)_p \qquad (13.5)$$

Then for any system for which CI is of the form

$$dU = T\,dS + F\,d\theta \qquad (13.6)$$

if we write $p = -F$ and $V = \theta$, Eq. 13.5 becomes

$$\left(\frac{\partial S}{\partial F}\right)_T = \left(\frac{\partial \theta}{\partial T}\right)_F \qquad (13.7)$$

which is MI for the new system. Or again, if we take C_p, which by definition is

$$C_p = T \left(\frac{\partial S}{\partial T} \right)_p$$

we have

$$C_F = T \left(\frac{\partial S}{\partial T} \right)_F$$

the heat capacity at constant F.

All results so translated may be used without separate proof with one proviso. Eq. 13.5 was deduced for a system in which the x set (T and p) was a possible one. If, however, in the system to which Eq. 13.6 applies, it happens that $F = F(T)$, Eq. 13.7 is meaningless, because we are trying to translate results from one class of thermodynamic systems to an entirely different class.

Examination shows that equilibrium thermodynamic systems can be grouped in two general categories, which we call (1) restricted systems and (2) unrestricted systems. The familiar example of a restricted system is that of water and steam, for which $p = p(T)$. The choice of variables for an x set is *restricted* by one or more conditions. The system for which $F = F(T)$ is likewise restricted—in fact, in exactly the same way. In general, we may translate thermodynamic equations *freely for systems with equivalent restrictions*. The case of the force variable as a function of T is a common type, and we often refer to all such systems as *two-phase-type systems*.

Of course, other types of restrictions exist. In a three-phase system with a single pure substance, we have $T = T_{tr}$ and $p = p_{tr}$, and neither T nor p can be included in the x set.

In contrast, *unrestricted* systems are those in which, in principle, *any n variables* from the primary set ($T, S, F_2, \theta_2, \ldots, F_n, \theta_n$) may be chosen as the independent x set. Convenience alone dictates the choice. Consequently, translation of results from one unrestricted system to another is always possible.

TABLE **13.1**

Restricted and Unrestricted Systems

System	n	CI	Restrictions
Two-phase hydrostatic system	2	$T\,dS - p\,dV$	$p = p(T)$
Reversible electric cell	3	$T\,dS - p\,dV + E\,dz$	$E = E(T)$
Black body radiation	2	$T\,dS - p\,dV$	$p = p(T)$
Surface under pressure	3	$T\,dS - p\,dV + \mathcal{S}\,dA$	$\mathcal{S} = (T, p)$
Chemical system, two components	4	$T\,dS - p\,dV +$ $\mu_1\,dm_1 + \mu_2\,dm_2$	$\mu_1 = \mu_1(T, p, c_1)$ $\mu_2 = \mu_2(T, p, c_1)$
Single-phase hydrostatic system	2	$T\,dS - p\,dV$	None
Tensed filament	2	$T\,dS + F\,dL$	None
Dielectric in an electric field	3	$T\,dS + F\,dL + \mathcal{E}\,dM'$	None
Paramagnetic solid	2	$T\,dS + \mathcal{H}\,dM'$	None

Fortunately, owing to the directness and speed with which thermodynamic formulas may be deduced by the Jacobian method, it is usually preferable to calculate the formula we want directly, once CI or its equivalent is available.

Table 13.1 includes most of the systems of interest in this and the next chapter. Column 2 gives the value of n, column 3 the form of CI, and the last column the restriction, if any. The notation will be explained in the appropriate section. The particular value of n chosen can always be reduced by dropping out an appropriate work term in CI, and so the number of terms in the table is rather arbitrary. It must be re-emphasized that space forbids giving more than a few basic results for such a wide variety of systems.

13.3   Tensed Filament or Uniform Rod

For a uniform filament under a stretching force, F, CI takes the simple form

$$dU = \underline{T}\,dS + \underline{F}\,dL$$

We could readily translate any of the general relations for the single-phase system under hydrostatic pressure to the proper form for this case. It is instructive, however, to treat the system as an example of the use of the general Jacobian method as given in Sec. 13.1.

With T and F as the x set, the modified Jacobian is

$$J_0' = \frac{\partial(S, L)}{\partial(T, F)} = \begin{vmatrix} \left(\dfrac{\partial S}{\partial T}\right)_F & \left(\dfrac{\partial L}{\partial T}\right)_F \\ \left(\dfrac{\partial S}{\partial F}\right)_T & \left(\dfrac{\partial L}{\partial F}\right)_T \end{vmatrix} = \begin{vmatrix} a_0 & a_1 \\ a_1 & b_{11} \end{vmatrix}$$

The single Maxwellian relation we write down from the symmetry of J_0' as

$$\left(\frac{\partial S}{\partial F}\right)_T = \left(\frac{\partial L}{\partial T}\right)_F$$

where $(\partial L/\partial T)_F$ is determined from the coefficient of linear expansion, say, α_F, where

$$\alpha_F = \frac{1}{L}\left(\frac{\partial L}{\partial T}\right)_F = \frac{a_1}{L}$$

or
$$a_1 = \alpha_F L \qquad\qquad (13.8)$$

The heat capacity at constant force, C_F, is defined by

$$C_F = T\left(\frac{\partial S}{\partial T}\right)_F = a_0 T$$

or
$$a_0 = \frac{C_F}{T} \qquad\qquad (13.9)$$

Finally, $(\partial L/\partial F)_T$, which is an isothermal elastic quantity, is related to the isothermal Young's modulus, Y_T. This is defined as

$$Y_T = \lim_{\Delta F \to 0} \frac{\dfrac{\Delta F_T}{A}}{\dfrac{\Delta L_T}{L}} = \frac{L}{A}\left(\frac{\partial F}{\partial L}\right)_T = \frac{L}{Ab_{11}}$$

so that

$$b_{11} = \frac{L}{A Y_T} \tag{13.10}$$

As a result, any derivative we need can be expressed in terms of the three basic derivatives

$$\left(\frac{\partial S}{\partial T}\right)_F = a_0$$

$$\left(\frac{\partial L}{\partial T}\right)_F = a_1$$

$$\left(\frac{\partial L}{\partial F}\right)_T = b_{11}$$

or their equivalents. Examples follow.

*Temperature Change on Stretching (**Adiabatic**).*   To answer the question as to whether stretching changes the temperature of a filament, we need a derivative such as, say, $(\partial T/\partial F)_S$. This we calculate as

$$\left(\frac{\partial T}{\partial F}\right)_S = \frac{\partial(T,S)}{\partial(F,S)} = \frac{\dfrac{\partial(T,S)}{\partial(T,F)}}{\dfrac{\partial(F,S)}{\partial(T,F)}} = -\frac{a_1}{a_0} = -\frac{\alpha_F LT}{C_F} \tag{13.11}$$

(The direct calculation with Jacobians is usually faster than finding the analogous formula from the hydrostatic case and translating it.)

This equation shows that for a small adiabatic increase in force, ΔF, the temperature change, ΔT, is given as

$$\Delta T = \left(\frac{\partial T}{\partial F}\right)_S \Delta F = -\frac{a_1}{a_0}\Delta F = -\frac{\alpha_F LT}{C_F}\Delta F \tag{13.12}$$

Since $C_F > 0$ for all substances (and is roughly equal to C_p) and L and T are certainly positive, the sign of ΔT is always negative as long as $\alpha_F > 0$. Since this is true for most solids, we expect normally to find a *cooling* on stretching. An exception is rubber, which *warms* on stretching (touch a rubber band to your lips as you stretch it slowly) and for which, therefore, α_F must be *negative*.

Heating a Stiff Rod at Constant Length.   Consider a rod of length L and cross section A of sufficient size to prevent its buckling under compression. Suppose that it is confined between heavy supports at either end so that

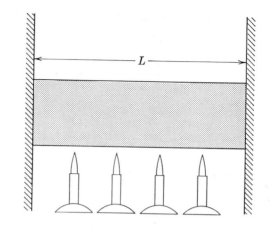

FIGURE **13.2**

on heating its length remains constant (Fig. 13.2). What is the maximum force exerted by the rod on a rise of temperature, ΔT?

In this case we are interested in $(\partial F/\partial T)_L$ since

$$\Delta F = \left(\frac{\partial F}{\partial T}\right)_L \Delta T$$

Here

$$\left(\frac{\partial F}{\partial T}\right)_L = \frac{\partial(F, L)}{\partial(T, L)} = \frac{\frac{\partial(F, L)}{\partial(T, F)}}{\frac{\partial(T, L)}{\partial(T, F)}} = -\frac{\left(\frac{\partial L}{\partial T}\right)_F}{\left(\frac{\partial L}{\partial F}\right)_T} = -\frac{a_1}{b_{11}} = -\alpha_F A Y_T \quad \textbf{(13.13)}$$

and since we are interested not in the force, ΔF, exerted on the rod by the end supports but its negative, the extensive force exerted by the rod, we have

$$-|\Delta F| = \alpha_F A Y_T \Delta T \quad \textbf{(13.14)}$$

Notice that this force is independent of the length of the rod but increases directly with the cross section, A. How do you account for this?

13.4   Reversible Electric Cell

Although the dry cell and the lead storage cell are far from reversible, there are many electric cells in which the chemical reaction on discharge is exactly reversed on charge. These are termed *reversible cells*. If charge is allowed to flow in (or out) at an infinitesimal rate (as was shown in Sec. 5.4), the irreversible Joulian heating may be neglected. Furthermore, if all solutions are kept saturated, as in a Daniel cell or standard Clark cell, the emf, E, is independent of the state of charge or discharge, that is, how much charge has flowed in or out. Thus, instead of having an equation of state,

$$E = E(T, z)$$

we have simply

$$E = E(T)$$

Such cells represent *restricted* systems.

With CI as

$$dU = T\,dS + E\,dz \qquad (13.15)$$

dz is regarded as positive for charge (work added) and negative for discharge when the cell does external electrical work. Fig. 13.3 is a sketch of a Daniel cell, with two compartments separated by a porous partition that reduces interdiffusion of the copper sulfate solution on the right into the zinc sulfate solution on the left. The two electrodes are connected to a potentiometer so that the cell can be either charged or discharged at an infinitely slow rate. An excess of the salt in the form of solid crystals is at the bottom of each compartment, to ensure saturation at all times.

In solution the salts are ionized into doubly charged positive metal ions and the doubly charged negative sulfate ion. On charging, the conventional current flows into the copper electrode, which dissolves to form more Cu^{++} ions, while on the other side Zn^{++} ions are discharged from solution (by the excess electrons coming in) to produce more neutral zinc. On discharge the process is reversed. Thus charging consists basically of the ionization of neutral atoms at the positive electrode and vice versa at the negative electrode. If we indicate the size of a faraday of electricity (96,519 coul/mole) by $\mathbf{F}$ and the number of faradays required to dissolve a gram-mole at one electrode and deposit the equivalent at the other by j, we can write

$$j\mathbf{F} + Cu + Zn^{++} \rightleftharpoons Cu^{++} + Zn \qquad (13.16)$$

where $j = 2$ and the upper arrow refers to charging.

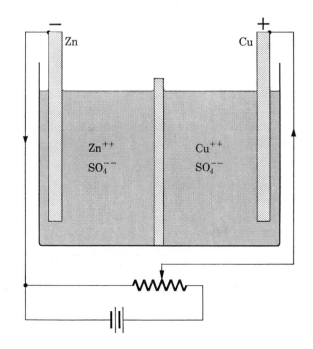

FIGURE **13.3**

In this particular cell no gas is evolved, and so the hydrostatic work done by the atmosphere is negligible. This situation is not true of all cases, however. If a hydrostatic work term is included, Eq. 13.15 becomes

$$dU = T\,dS - p\,dV + E\,dz \tag{13.17}$$

Since we are normally interested in processes at constant pressure, enthalpy is of more direct interest than internal energy. With

$$H = U + dV$$
$$dH = dU + p\,dV + V\,dp \tag{13.18}$$

and therefore Eq. 13.17 transforms to CII for the cell under pressure,

$$dH = \underline{T}\,dS + V\,d\underline{p} + E\,d\underline{z} \tag{13.19}$$

We now set up the symmetric Jacobian, $J_0{}'$, for the problem. Since in this case $E = E(T, p)$, an all force x set is impossible. Taking the underlined variables T, p, and z, we have for $J_0{}'$

$$J_0{}' = \frac{\partial(S, -V, -E)}{\partial(T, p, z)}$$

Since this requires minus signs in front of six of the nine elements, an equivalent form with minus signs before only three is obtained by reversing all signs in the numerator. We take for $J_0{}'$, accordingly,

$$J_0{}' = \frac{\partial(-S, V, E)}{\partial(T, p, z)} = \begin{vmatrix} -\dfrac{\partial S}{\partial T} & \dfrac{\partial V}{\partial T} & \dfrac{\partial E}{\partial T} \\[2mm] -\dfrac{\partial S}{\partial p} & \dfrac{\partial V}{\partial p} & \dfrac{\partial E}{\partial p} \\[2mm] -\dfrac{\partial S}{\partial z} & \dfrac{\partial V}{\partial z} & 0 \end{vmatrix} = \begin{vmatrix} a_0 & a_1 & a_2 \\ a_1 & b_{11} & b_{12} \\ a_2 & b_{12} & 0 \end{vmatrix}$$

Here a zero occurs in the lower right corner because $(\partial E/\partial z)_{Tp}$ must vanish. Writing down the necessary conditions for the symmetry of $J_0{}'$ gives the three simultaneous Maxwellian relations for this particular choice of independent variables:

$$-\left(\frac{\partial S}{\partial p}\right)_{Tz} = \left(\frac{\partial V}{\partial T}\right)_{pz} = a_1$$

$$-\left(\frac{\partial S}{\partial z}\right)_{Tp} = \left(\frac{\partial E}{\partial T}\right)_{p} = a_2$$

$$\left(\frac{\partial V}{\partial z}\right)_{Tp} = \left(\frac{\partial E}{\partial p}\right)_{T} = b_{12} \tag{13.20}$$

The first is the analog of MI for the hydrostatic case; the second and third are new. The second fixes the heat absorbed per unit charge passed into the cell in terms of the temperature coefficient of emf, $(\partial E/\partial T)_p$. The last shows that the volume change per unit charge passed in is fixed by the pressure coefficient of emf, $(\partial E/\partial p)_T$. If volume changes are negligible on charge or discharge, then the emf may be taken as essentially independent of p. This is the case for the Daniel cell and others in which no gases are evolved during the cell's operation.

Let us now rewrite the expression for dH, Eq. 13.19, in terms of entropy. For changes dT, dp, and dz we have

$$T\,dS = T\left(\frac{\partial S}{\partial T}\right)_{pz} dT + T\left(\frac{\partial S}{\partial p}\right)_{Tz} dp + T\left(\frac{\partial S}{\partial z}\right)_{Tp} dz$$

and substitution in Eq. 13.19 gives

$$dH = T\left(\frac{\partial S}{\partial T}\right)_{pz} dT + \left[V + T\left(\frac{\partial S}{\partial p}\right)_{Tz}\right] dp + \left[E + T\left(\frac{\partial S}{\partial z}\right)_{Tp}\right] dz$$

For any charge flow at constant T and p, therefore,

$$dH_{Tp} = \left[E + T\left(\frac{\partial S}{\partial z}\right)_{Tp}\right] dz$$

or for a finite charge flow, Δz,

$$\Delta H_{Tp} = E\,\Delta z + T\left(\frac{\partial S}{\partial z}\right)_{Tp} \Delta z$$

The term $T(\partial S/\partial z)_{Tp}$ is a sort of latent heat of charging and represents heat absorbed from the surroundings as the cell is charged. Calling it L_z,

$$L_z = T\left(\frac{\partial S}{\partial z}\right)_{Tp}$$

and setting $\Delta z = j\mathbf{F}$, we have

$$Ej\mathbf{F} + j\mathbf{F}L_z = \Delta H_{Tp} \tag{13.21}$$

If $L_z > 0$, $j\mathbf{F}L_z$ is energy *absorbed* from the surroundings on charge and *rejected* to the surroundings on discharge. By the second of the Maxwellian relations in Eq. 13.20,

$$L_z = T\left(\frac{\partial S}{\partial z}\right)_{Tp} = -T\left(\frac{\partial E}{\partial T}\right)_p$$

and is thus negative for cells for which $(\partial E/\partial T)_p > 0$. Fig. 13.4 illustrates the possible situations, as follows:

1. When $(\partial E/\partial T)_p > 0$, L_z is negative, and on discharge the cell *absorbs* energy from the surroundings. This is converted into electrical energy along with ΔH_{Tp} from the chemical reaction. This case is shown in Fig. 13.4(a).

2. When $(\partial E/\partial T)_p = 0$, $L_z = 0$, and

$$jE\mathbf{F} = \Delta H_{Tp}$$

This case is shown in Fig. 13.4(b).

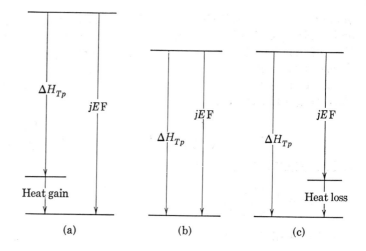

FIGURE **13.4**   (a)   (b)   (c)

3. When $(\partial E/\partial T)_p < 0$, L_z is *positive*, and on discharge some of the heat of the reaction is rejected as lost heat rather than transformed into usable electrical energy. This case is shown in Fig. 13.4(c).

Data for a few reactions are given in Table 13.2. With E in volts and $\mathbf{F}$ in coulombs per mole, we divide by $J \times 10^3$ to convert the electrical terms in Eq. 13.21 to kilocalories per mole.

The primary use of such measurements so far has been to provide a precise way of determining ΔH through the electrical determination of the other two terms. The calorimetric measurement of ΔH for the Daniel cell results in a value of 56.19 kcal/mole, which is not as reliable as the 56.175 from Table 13.2 but agrees well with it.

Great interest has been developing in the fuel cell and the conditions under which various fuels may be oxidized in high-temperature cells to provide

TABLE **13.2**

Reaction in cell ($\rightarrow$ charge, $j = 2$)	$\left(\dfrac{\partial E}{\partial T}\right)_p$, mv	$\dfrac{jT\mathbf{F}'}{J \times 10^3}$, kcal/mole	$\dfrac{-jT\left(\dfrac{\partial E}{\partial T}\right)_p}{J \times 10^3}$, kcal/mole	ΔH_{Tp}
Pb + HgCl$_2 \rightarrow$ 2Hg + PbCl$_2$ at $T = 298°$K, $E = 0.5356$ v	0.145	29.70	-2.00	27.20
Cu + ZnSO$_4 \rightarrow$ Zn + CuSO$_4$ at $T = 273°$K, $E = 1.0934$ v	-0.4533	50.46	5.715	56.175
2Ag + ZnCl$_2 \rightarrow$ 2AgCl + Zn at $T = 298°$K, $E = 1.005$ v	-0.400	46.14	5.50	51.87

electrical energy directly. For the oxidation of graphite to CO and to CO_2, $(\partial E/\partial T)_p$ is positive, and the terms in Eq. 13.21 (for the case of charge) for the CO fuel cell are

$$32.81 - 6.39 = 26.4 \text{ kcal/mole}$$

and for the CO_2 fuel cell

$$94.26 - 0.21 = 94.05 \text{ kcal/mole}$$

Of course, it would be uneconomical to burn carbon to CO, and in the conversion to CO_2 the gain in the second term is negligible. Regardless of this factor, however, the possibilities are intriguing since the conversion would result directly in electrical energy and would not entail the use of the much less efficient heat engine. The chief disadvantages are the cost of the cells and the cost of the chemicals used to supply the required oxygen.[2]

13.5   The Cavity Radiator and Black Body Radiation

One of the great triumphs of classical thermodynamics was its application to so-called black body radiation. This is the radiation from an ideal black body or, better, since truly black surfaces are impossible to make, the radiation from a small hole in the wall of a cavity with walls at a uniform temperature, T (Fig. 13.5). This radiation we call *cavity radiation*. Before attempting to apply thermodynamic reasoning to radiation of this or any other type, we need to know a few basic properties of radiation from surfaces, etc.

   Radiancy of a Surface or Cavity.   In speaking of the radiation from any surface, as in Fig. 13.6, we call the total upward power radiated from all points

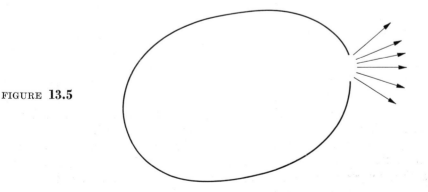

FIGURE **13.5**

---

[2] For further details and references see J. Kaye and J. A. Welsh, *Direct Conversion of Heat into Electricity*, Wiley, New York, 1960.

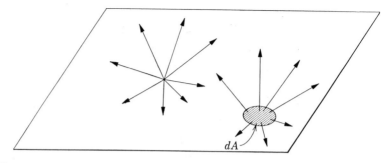

FIGURE **13.6**

of the surface the radiant *flux* and indicate it by ψ. Then the total flux from any small area, dA, is $d\psi$, and the ratio $d\psi/dA$ is the *radiancy*, R, of the surface. Thus

$$\frac{d\psi}{dA} = R = \text{power radiated from the surface per unit area}$$

or
$$d\psi = R\, dA$$

The Cavity Radiator. The definition of radiancy applies to the flux from any surface. If we use it with the cavity of Fig. 13.5, $d\psi$ is the flux of cavity radiation from an area, dA, of the opening to the cavity. In this case we write

$$d\psi = R_c\, dA$$

where R_c is the radiancy (radiant energy per unit time per unit area) of a cavity at temperature T.

In general, the radiancy of a surface depends on the nature of the surface as well as its temperature. However, the radiancy of a cavity, R_c, can be shown to be a function of T only. It is entirely independent of the size or shape of the cavity, of the material of its walls, or of the presence or absence of material objects in the cavity.

As an example, imagine two cavities (Fig. 13.7) of differing size, shape, wall materials, etc., but in equilibrium at a common temperature, T. Let them be connected by a small opening covered by a thin shutter.

Now suppose that the radiancy of the larger cavity is greater than that of the smaller one. Let the shutter be opened for a length of time and then closed. By hypothesis the smaller cavity will gain energy at the expense of the larger one. It will therefore warm somewhat, and the other will cool.

Without performing any work on the radiation or the cavities, we thus produce a finite temperature difference in an isothermal system. By the second law such a process is impossible even in principle. Therefore, the radiancies of the two cavities must be alike and can depend only on their common temperature, T; that is,

$$R_c = R_c(T)$$

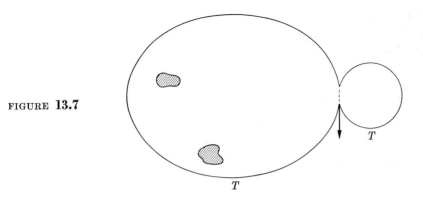

FIGURE **13.7**

This means that the total flux per unit area *arriving from the interior* at the opening, or at any other area in the cavity for that matter, must be exactly equal to R_c and be fixed by T only. It is this fact that prevents the foreign bodies in a cavity or the nature or shape of the walls from having any effect on R_c.

Properties of Surfaces.   Imagine a thin slab of some material at equilibrium in a cavity (Fig. 13.8). The flux traveling in an upward direction from its surface in general consists of three parts: (1) the energy actually emitted by the surface, (2) the energy reflected upward, and (3) the energy transmitted from below (if the slab is not entirely opaque).

Let the radiancy of the surface, which cannot exceed R_c, as an argument analogous to the preceding one can show, be written as a fraction of R_c. That is, write

$$\frac{R}{R_c} = e_r$$

or

$$R = e_r R_c$$

where e_r is the so-called *relative emissive power* of the surface. Here $0 \leq e_r \leq 1$. When $e_r = 1$, the surface radiates like an opening into a cavity, whereas when

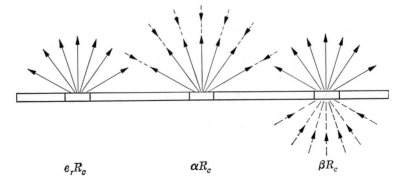

$$e_r R_c \qquad\qquad \alpha R_c \qquad\qquad \beta R_c$$

FIGURE **13.8**

$e_r = 0$, it can only reflect or transmit radiation. Similarly, define a reflection coefficient, α, as the fraction of the energy incident on an area that is reflected, the rest, $1 - \alpha$, being absorbed or transmitted. Further, let a transmission coefficient be defined as the fraction, β, of the total flux arriving from below that is transmitted through the slab.

Then we can write for the energy balance for a unit area of the surface

$$\begin{pmatrix} \text{total flux} \\ \text{arriving from above} \end{pmatrix} = \begin{pmatrix} \text{total flux} \\ \text{leaving in an upward direction} \end{pmatrix}$$

From the preceding considerations this becomes

$$R_c = e_r R_c + \alpha R_c + \beta R_c$$

and so

$$1 = e_r + \alpha + \beta$$

If the body is perfectly transparent, $\beta = 1$, and $e_r = \alpha = 0$, and it can neither radiate nor absorb. On the other hand, if it is perfectly opaque, $\beta = 0$, and

$$e_r + \alpha = 1$$

In this case suppose that the body is a *perfect absorber*. Then it can reflect nothing, and $\alpha = 0$, and $e_r = 1$. Such a body normally appears perfectly *black*, and since it has the same radiancy as the *opening into a cavity*, we equate a cavity radiator with a perfectly black body. We are thus able to identify black body radiation as cavity radiation and R_c as the radiancy of a perfectly black body. Since it is impossible to construct, even by depositing dull soot from a flame, a surface that reflects no energy at some part or other of the spectrum, truly black surfaces do not exist. In practice we replace them by the equivalent cavity radiator, and any wall materials may be used, provided true temperature equilibrium exists within the cavity.

13.6   Radiation Density and Radiancy

In order to establish a connection between the radiancy, R_c, of a black body radiator and another important quantity, the energy density in a cavity, we need to know a number of geometric properties of radiating surfaces.

Directional Radiancy.   The radiancy, R, of any surface may be regarded as a summation over the hemisphere above the surface of the directional radiancy, say, R_ω. This gives the flux per unit area per unit solid angle (that is, per stere) in a direction θ, ϕ. In Fig. 13.9 a polar coordinate system is set up with its origin in the area dA of the surface in question and with the z axis normal to it. Let the total flux from all points in dA, which passes through the area dA', normal to the direction θ, ϕ, be indicated by $d^2\psi$. Then we define R_ω by

$$\frac{d^2\psi}{dA \, d\omega} = R_\omega$$

or

$$d^2\psi = R_\omega \, dA \, d\omega \tag{13.22}$$

where it is assumed that dA' subtends the same solid angle, $d\omega$, for all points in dA.

Parallel Beam Radiancy.   Whenever a surface is viewed (by the eye or by an instrument), a parallel beam is involved. The flux included in the directional radiancy, R_ω, is diverging, parallel, or converging according to the relative size of dA and dA'. Suppose that we make dA' of such size as to be the exact projection of dA normal to the direction θ, ϕ. In this case we have a *parallel beam* from dA, and the parallel beam radiancy, $R_\parallel$, is defined as the flux per stere per unit *area of the beam;* that is,

$$\frac{d^2\psi}{d\omega\,dA'} = R_\parallel$$

Since

$$dA' = \cos\theta\,dA$$

we have

$$d^2\psi = R_\parallel \cos\theta\,dA\,d\omega \tag{13.23}$$

Comparison with Eq. 13.22 gives

$$\boxed{R_\omega = R_\parallel \cos\theta} \tag{13.24}$$

This relation is the basis for Lambert's law, which may be stated thus: "The parallel beam radiancy from an extended isotropic surface at temperature T is independent of the direction (θ, ϕ) from which it is observed." The directional radiancy being referred to a constant area, dA, gets smaller as θ increases until at glancing angle $R_\omega = 0$. When we use the parallel beam radiancy, the flux is

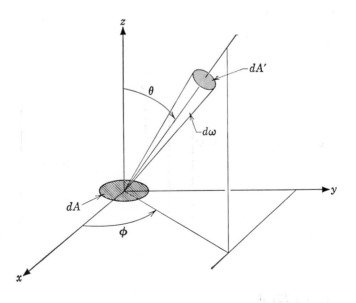

FIGURE **13.9**

calculated in terms of dA'. As θ increases, flux is included from a larger and larger area of the radiator and compensates for the reduction in R_ω. (See Fig. 13.10.) (This is the basic reason, for example, for the sun's appearing as a flat disk rather than a rounded surface.)

Relation of R to $R_{\parallel}$. To obtain the connection between the total radiancy and $R_{\parallel}$, the parallel beam radiancy, it is simply necessary to integrate Eq. 13.23 over the hemisphere above dA. Thus R becomes

$$R = \frac{d\psi}{dA} = \frac{1}{dA} \int d^2\psi = \int_{\text{hemi}} R_{\parallel} \cos \theta \, d\omega$$

Since $d\omega = \sin \theta \, d\theta \, d\phi$ and $R_{\parallel}$ is independent of θ or ϕ, this becomes

$$R = R_{\parallel} \int_0^{2\pi} d\phi \int_0^{\pi/2} \cos \theta \sin \theta \, d\theta$$

or

$$\boxed{R = \pi R_{\parallel}} \qquad (13.25)$$

and $R_{\parallel}$ is twice the average radiancy per stere over the hemisphere.

Relation of R_c to the Energy Density. To find the relation between R_c and the energy density, u, in a cavity at temperature T, we proceed as follows. In a cavity, $R_{\parallel}$ from the walls takes on the value for a truly black radiator since what the walls fail to radiate is made up for by reflection. Since $R_{\parallel}$ is the value of R_ω in a direction normal to the surface, we arrange a cavity with walls in the form of a sphere of very large radius, say, r_0 (Fig. 13.11).

Now consider flux from an area, dA, of the walls to a small volume, of size v, around the center of the sphere. If v is small, θ is essentially zero for all flux

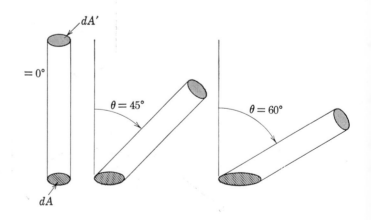

FIGURE **13.10**

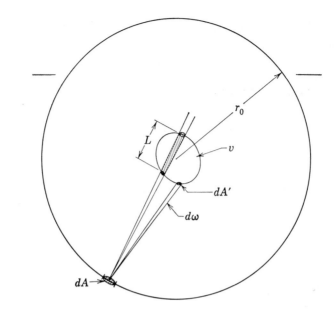

FIGURE **13.11**

from dA, and we write for this normal flux

$$d^2\psi = R_{\parallel}(T)\,d\omega\,dA \qquad (13.26)$$

where $R_{\parallel}$ is the parallel beam radiancy of a black body at temperature T. In a time τ, radiation into v from dA is

$$\tau\,d^2\psi$$

or $$R_{\parallel}\tau\,d\omega\,dA = R_{\parallel}\frac{L}{c}\,d\omega\,dA \qquad (13.27)$$

where L is the length of the cone of solid angle $d\omega$ cut off by the volume, v, and c is the speed of light. This radiation is somewhere within v during the time τ. Now replace $d\omega$ by dA'/r^2, dA' being the area subtended on the surface of the volume, v, by the small cone of solid angle $d\omega$. Inserting the new expression in Eq. 13.27 and summing over all cones cutting the volume v gives

$$\sum \frac{R_{\parallel}\,dA'\,L\,dA}{cr^2} = \frac{R_{\parallel}}{c}\sum \frac{L\,dA'}{r^2}\,dA$$

If we replace the variable, r, by the constant, r_0, $\Sigma L\,dA'$ is just v, the size of the small volume. Integrating over the entire inner area of the large sphere gives the total radiant energy in the volume, v, from the entire wall area. Thus

$$\text{total energy in } v = \frac{R_{\parallel}v}{c}\int \frac{dA}{r_0^2} = \frac{4\pi R_{\parallel}v}{c}$$

Dividing through by v gives the energy density, u, and therefore

$$u = \frac{4\pi R_{\parallel}}{c} = \frac{4R_c}{c} \tag{13.28}$$

from Eq. 13.25. Finally

$$R_c = \frac{uc}{4} \tag{13.29}$$

Thus the energy density in a cavity at T filled with equilibrium radiation is proportional to the radiancy, R_c, of a black body radiator. Since R_c is a function of T, so is u.

13.7   Pressure of Radiation

Imagine a parallel beam of radiant energy arriving on an element, dA, of a perfect absorber. Both the classical theory and the quantum theory of radiation predict that a force will be exerted on the absorber. This force is due to the momentum inherent in the radiation, and this momentum is equal to the amount of energy involved divided by c, the speed of light. If the element of the absorber, dA, is in a cavity, we know that the flux arriving is equal to the flux leaving, and therefore the flux arriving for any direction θ, ϕ is, by Eq. 13.23,

$$d^2\psi = R_{\parallel} \cos \theta \, d\omega \, dA$$

which Eq. 13.28 reduces to

$$\frac{d^2\psi}{dA} = \frac{uc}{4\pi} \cos \theta \, d\omega$$

The term $d^2\psi/dA$ represents energy arriving per second per unit area, and thus $(1/c) \, d^2\psi/dA$ is *momentum* arriving per second per unit area. The component of this momentum normal to the surface contributes to the pressure of the diffuse radiation in the cavity an element, say, dp, where

$$dp = \frac{u}{4\pi} \cos^2 \theta \, d\omega$$

Before summing to get the total pressure due to flux from all directions, we write $d\omega = \sin \theta \, d\theta \, d\phi$ when

$$p = \int dp = \frac{u}{4\pi} \int_0^{2\pi} d\phi \int_0^{\pi/2} \cos^2 \theta \sin \theta \, d\theta$$

or

$$p = \frac{1}{2}\frac{u}{3} \tag{13.30}$$

If the same argument is carried out for a totally reflecting wall, the result is simply doubled, and we have

$$p = \tfrac{1}{3}u \qquad (13.31)$$

This is the mechanical pressure exerted on a reflecting surface by the equilibrium radiation in a cavity. Actually this value applies for the black wall area as well, since the result in Eq. 13.30 is just doubled when the reaction due to re-emission of radiation is taken into account. The same result holds also for nonblack walls in cavities since flux from a wall area is independent of whether it is all emitted or part emitted and part reflected. This important theoretical finding was first verified experimentally by Lebedew and shortly thereafter and independently by Nichols and Hull.[3]

13.8   The Stefan-Boltzmann Total Radiation Law

We can now apply thermodynamic reasoning to a system involving cavity radiation. Let us imagine, with Boltzmann, a cylinder and piston such as we have used for simple hydrostatic systems (Fig. 13.12). Suppose, however, that

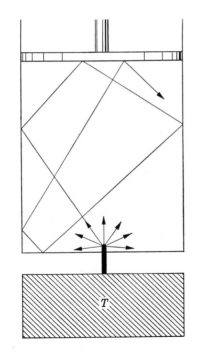

FIGURE **13.12**

[3] Lebedew, *Ann. Physik*, **6**, 413 (1901); Nichols and Hull, *Phys. Rev.*, **13**, 307 (1901); and Hull, *Phys. Rev.*, **20**, 188, 292 (1905).

its walls are perfectly reflecting mirrors and that it is filled with equilibrium radiation from a cavity at temperature T.[4]

To do work on the system, it is necessary only to push the piston down slowly against the pressure of the contained radiation. To add heat, we insert a small rod with a speck of black material on its end and touch it to the heat reservoir below. Heat then flows in and is radiated into the enclosure. The black speck also ensures at all times preservation of the proper wave length distribution for black body radiation.

We write the first law in the form

$$dQ_c = dU + p\,dV$$

where, since $p = \frac{1}{3}u(T)$, $p = p(T)$ and the system is a *restricted* one of the two-phase type. Since $U = Vu$ and $p = \frac{1}{3}u$, dQ_c may be written out in terms of u and V as

$$dQ_c = V\,du + \tfrac{4}{3}u\,dV \tag{13.32}$$

If the heat addition and compression are carried out reversibly, the entropy change becomes

$$dS = \frac{dQ_c}{T} = \frac{V\,du}{T} + \frac{4}{3}\frac{u}{T}dV$$

or since

$$du = \frac{du}{dT}dT$$

$$dS = \frac{V}{T}\frac{du}{dT}dT + \frac{4}{3}\frac{u}{T}dV$$

where T and V are the independent variables. Using the cross derivative theorem on this exact differential gives the simple result

$$\frac{du}{u} = 4\frac{dT}{T}$$

which integrates to

$$\boxed{u = aT^4} \tag{13.33}$$

In other words, the energy density in a cavity increases extremely rapidly with T; doubling T increases u sixteenfold.

Combining Eq. 13.33 with Eq. 13.29 gives the Stefan-Boltzmann total radiation law,

$$R_c = \frac{uc}{4} = \frac{ac}{4}T^4$$

or

$$\boxed{R_c = \sigma T^4} \tag{13.34}$$

---

[4] The walls need not be perfect specular reflectors. They may be perfectly diffusing (white) walls or anything in between.

where $\sigma = ac/4$ is the Stefan-Boltzmann radiation constant. This law gives the total radiant power emitted in all directions from a unit area of a black body radiator (or from a unit opening into a black body cavity) in terms of the Stefan-Boltzmann constant, σ. The value of this constant is

$$\sigma = 5.69 \times 10^{-5} \text{ erg/cm}^2\text{-sec-deg}^4$$

It measures the radiancy of a black body at 1°K. We shall later be able to calculate the absolute value of σ with the help of statistics and the quantum theory. (See Sec. 19.4.)

For surfaces that are not perfectly black, the temperature radiation follows a fourth-power law, but the constant is less than that for a black body in the ratio of $e_r:1$. Thus Eq. 13.34 takes on the general form

$$R = e_r \sigma T^4 \tag{13.35}$$

where $0 \le e_r \le 1$.

Returning to Eq. 13.32, if dQ_C is set equal to zero, we have the differential equation for the adiabatic,

$$V\, du + \tfrac{4}{3} u\, dV = 0$$

This integrates to

$$u V^{4/3} = C$$

which can be thrown at once into the equivalent forms

$$pV^{4/3} = C' \tag{13.36}$$

and

$$TV^{1/3} = C'' \tag{13.37}$$

The similarity to the adiabatic laws for ideal gases is striking (note that the power of V in Eq. 13.36 is just greater by unity than it is in Eq. 13.27; see in this connection Problem 13.7).

13.9   Surface Tension

For the sake of generality let us consider a surface film subject to an external hydrostatic pressure so that CI becomes

$$dU = \underline{T}\, dS - \underline{p}\, dV + \underline{\mathscr{S}}\, d\underline{A} \tag{13.38}$$

Ordinarily $\mathscr{S} = \mathscr{S}(T)$, but in this case we write $\mathscr{S} = \mathscr{S}(T, p)$ and we still have a restricted system. With the underlined variables as the x set, the symmetric Jacobian is

$$J_0' = \frac{(S, -V, -\mathscr{S})}{(T, p, A)} = \begin{vmatrix} \left(\dfrac{\partial S}{\partial T}\right)_{pA} & -\left(\dfrac{\partial V}{\partial T}\right)_{pA} & -\left(\dfrac{\partial \mathscr{S}}{\partial T}\right)_{p} \\[2ex] \left(\dfrac{\partial S}{\partial p}\right)_{TA} & -\left(\dfrac{\partial V}{\partial p}\right)_{TA} & -\left(\dfrac{\partial \mathscr{S}}{\partial p}\right)_{T} \\[2ex] \left(\dfrac{\partial S}{\partial A}\right)_{Tp} & -\left(\dfrac{\partial V}{\partial A}\right)_{Tp} & 0 \end{vmatrix}$$

a result similar in form to J_0' for the electric cell. Maxwell's relations are

$$\left(\frac{\partial S}{\partial p}\right)_{TA} = -\left(\frac{\partial V}{\partial T}\right)_{pA} \tag{13.39}$$

$$\left(\frac{\partial S}{\partial A}\right)_{Tp} = -\left(\frac{\partial \mathcal{S}}{\partial T}\right)_{p} \tag{13.40}$$

$$\left(\frac{\partial V}{\partial A}\right)_{Tp} = \left(\frac{\partial \mathcal{S}}{\partial p}\right)_{T} \tag{13.41}$$

For a system at constant temperature and pressure and for which volume changes are negligible, we may write $T\,dS$ in Eq. 13.38 as

$$TdS = T\left(\frac{\partial S}{\partial A}\right)_{Tp} dA = -T\left(\frac{\partial \mathcal{S}}{\partial T}\right)_{p} dA$$

Thus Eq. 13.38 becomes

$$dU_{Tp} = \left[\mathcal{S} - T\left(\frac{\partial \mathcal{S}}{\partial T}\right)_{p}\right] dA$$

Integration (at constant T and p) from a state in which surface area is so small that U has essentially its ordinary value, U_0, gives

$$\frac{U - U_0}{A} = \mathcal{S} - T\left(\frac{\partial \mathcal{S}}{\partial T}\right)_{p} = u'$$

where u' is the surface energy density for the system. Since $\mathcal{S}$ decreases with T, to vanish at the critical point, u' is always positive. It eventually vanishes at $T = T_c$, also.

Turning to the third Maxwellian relation, Eq. 13.41, we have

$$\left(\frac{\partial V}{\partial A}\right)_{Tp} = \left(\frac{\partial \mathcal{S}}{\partial p}\right)_{T}$$

Just what causes V to depend on A in the first place? Clearly, when this derivative has a value different from zero, the assumption can only be that as molecules move from the interior to the free surface, they occupy a different average volume from that they occupied in the interior of the liquid. Thus suppose that

$$\left(\frac{\partial V}{\partial A}\right)_{Tp} < 0$$

This indicates that the molecules are more crowded near the surface than in the interior. In any volume the density of matter is greater near the surface,

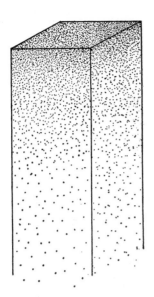

FIGURE **13.13**

and we have what is called *positive surface adsorption*. Since then $(\partial \mathscr{S}/\partial p)_T$ is also negative, increasing the pressure reduces the surface tension. Thus positive surface adsorption always causes a reduction in surface energy density. This positive adsorption occurs because migration to the surface, where surface forces cause dense packing, tends to mitigate the pressure increase that normally causes a reduction in the volume of a system. Similar remarks apply when there is negative adsorption; the molecules move in such a way as to tend to relieve the pressure increase.

This reasoning is not confined to pure liquids. If we have a dissolved substance that affects surface tension—and most dissolved substances have very marked effects on surface tension—the effects due to surface adsorption of the foreign substance are much more important than those due to so-called self-adsorption.

Suppose that we have a column of unit cross section perpendicular to the liquid surface (Fig. 13.13). Let us call the excess of material in the column over what would be present in the same volume of the interior the *surface mass excess*, say, σ_{ex}. Here the column is of unspecified length but long enough, perhaps a few hundredths of a millimeter at most, to include all the adsorbed excess. For the whole system of area A,

$$\text{total mass excess} = \sigma_{ex}A$$

If we let ρ_i = normal mass density in the *interior*, then

$$m = \rho_i V + \sigma_{ex}A$$

or

$$V = \frac{m - \sigma_{ex}A}{\rho_i} = \frac{m}{\rho_i} - \frac{\sigma_{ex}A}{\rho_i}$$

For small changes in A, ρ_i may be taken as sensibly constant, and differentiation gives

$$\left(\frac{\partial V}{\partial A}\right)_{Tp} = -\frac{\sigma_{\text{ex}}}{\rho} = \left(\frac{\partial \mathscr{S}}{\partial p}\right)_T \tag{13.42}$$

where ρ is the ordinary density of the system, m/V. Thus when $\mathscr{S}$ decreases with pressure, $\sigma_{\text{ex}} > 0$, and there is positive adsorption.

Actually, with dissolved materials it is necessary to include concentration as one of the independent variables in Eq. 13.38, and a term similar to Eq. 13.42 arises from its effect on $\mathscr{S}$. Common impurities in water tend to reduce $\mathscr{S}$. They concentrate at the surface and are the direct cause of the conflicting data on the surface tension of this liquid obtained by different observers.

13.10 Stressed Dielectrics in an Electric Field

Consider a dielectric filling the space between the plates of a parallel plate condenser across which an emf, E, is applied from a suitable potentiometer (Fig. 13.14). As we saw in Chap. 5, if the charge on the plates is increased by dz, the work done on the system is

$$dW = E\,dz$$

Here the work done on the system is divided between increasing the electric field between the plates and thus storing energy in the field and increasing the electric polarization in the dielectric. This latter work we naturally assign to the physical system, the dielectric.

Indicating the electric field by $\mathscr{E}$, we have

$$E = \mathscr{E}L$$
and
$$z = CE$$

where C is the capacitance of the parallel plate condenser. With A the area, L

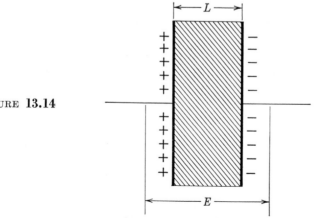

FIGURE **13.14**

the plate separation, and K the dielectric capacity,

$$C = \frac{KA}{4\pi L}$$

This gives for the charge z

$$z = \frac{KAE}{4\pi L} = \frac{A}{4\pi} D \qquad\qquad (13.43)$$

since the electric displacement, D, is

$$D = K\mathcal{E} = K\frac{E}{L}$$

The value D is also connected with the electric moment per unit volume, $\mathbf{M}'/V$, by

$$D = \mathcal{E} + \frac{4\pi\mathbf{M}'}{V}$$

whence, from Eq. 13.43,

$$z = \frac{A\mathcal{E}}{4\pi} + \frac{\mathbf{M}'}{L}$$

Differentiation of this relation, with small changes in V and L being neglected, gives

$$dz = \frac{A}{4\pi}d\mathcal{E} + \frac{d\mathbf{M}'}{L}$$

which combined with $dW = \mathcal{E}L\,dz$ gives

$$dW = V\frac{\mathcal{E}\,d\mathcal{E}}{4\pi} + \mathcal{E}\,d\mathbf{M}' \qquad\qquad (13.44)$$

In this expression the first term integrates to $V\dfrac{\mathcal{E}^2}{8\pi}$, the energy in the electric field. This leaves $\mathcal{E}\,d\mathbf{M}'$ as the work added to the dielectric proper as the applied electric field increases the total electric moment by $d\mathbf{M}'$. This is the energy that goes into polarizing the medium, and, just as in the discussion of the paramagnetic substance in the magnetic field, this is the term that we want.

If now we confine ourselves to a system of *unit volume*, since P', the electric polarization, is simply the electric moment per unit volume,

$$\frac{\mathbf{M}'}{V} = P'$$

we may replace $\mathcal{E}\,d\mathbf{M}'$ by $\mathcal{E}\,dP'$. Thus CI for a *unit volume* of a dielectric becomes

$$dU = \underline{T}\,dS + \mathcal{E}\,dP' \qquad\qquad (13.45)$$

In this case, of course, $\mathcal{E}$ and P' are related through the electric susceptibility, ϵ, by the relation

$$P' = \epsilon \mathcal{E}$$

If, in addition, we imagine the dielectric to be acted on by a stretching force, $\underline{F}$ (say, along $\mathcal{E}$), Eq. 13.45 is replaced by

$$dU = \underline{T}\,dS + \underline{F}\,dL + \underline{\mathcal{E}}\,dP' \tag{13.46}$$

and with the x set indicated, J_0' for the problem is given as

$$J_0' = \frac{\partial(S, L, P')}{\partial(T, F, \mathcal{E})} = \begin{vmatrix} \dfrac{\partial S}{\partial T} & \dfrac{\partial L}{\partial T} & \dfrac{\partial P'}{\partial T} \\[2mm] \dfrac{\partial S}{\partial F} & \dfrac{\partial L}{\partial F} & \dfrac{\partial P'}{\partial F} \\[2mm] \dfrac{\partial S}{\partial \mathcal{E}} & \dfrac{\partial L}{\partial \mathcal{E}} & \dfrac{\partial P'}{\partial \mathcal{E}} \end{vmatrix} = \begin{vmatrix} a_0 & a_1 & a_2 \\ a_1 & b_{11} & b_{12} \\ a_2 & b_{12} & b_{22} \end{vmatrix} \tag{13.47}$$

Of the nine derivatives involved, only the six in the triangular array on and above the diagonal are independent. These six constitute the basic derivatives for the problem. Of these, a_0, a_1, and b_{11} are the constant-field analogs of the coefficients for the tensed filament discussed in Sec. 13.3. The remaining three are new. Thus $a_2 = (\partial P'/\partial T)_{F\mathcal{E}}$ measures an increase in polarization due to a temperature rise and is a so-called *pyroelectric* coefficient; $b_{12} = (\partial P'/\partial F)_{T\mathcal{E}}$ measures an increase in polarization due solely to an increase in mechanical stretching force and is a so-called *piezoelectric* coefficient; and, as we have seen, $\epsilon = b_{22} = (\partial P'/\partial \mathcal{E})_{TF}$ is the *electric susceptibility*.

This case has been artificially simplified since an ordinary noncrystalline dielectric shows no pyroelectric or piezoelectric effects. For these effects we need crystals having a rather great lack of symmetry, such as quartz or Rochelle salts. In such crystals each component of the electric field produces polarization in each of the other directions as well as in its own. Indicating the three components of polarization by P'_1, P'_2, and P'_3, we can write

$$\begin{aligned} P'_1 &= \epsilon_{11}\mathcal{E}_1 + \epsilon_{12}\mathcal{E}_2 + \epsilon_{13}\mathcal{E}_3 \\ P'_2 &= \epsilon_{21}\mathcal{E}_1 + \epsilon_{22}\mathcal{E}_2 + \epsilon_{23}\mathcal{E}_3 \\ P'_3 &= \epsilon_{31}\mathcal{E}_1 + \epsilon_{32}\mathcal{E}_2 + \epsilon_{33}\mathcal{E}_3 \end{aligned} \tag{13.48}$$

where $\mathcal{E}_1$, $\mathcal{E}_2$, and $\mathcal{E}_3$ are the three normal components of the applied electric field. The nine constants ϵ_{11} to ϵ_{33} are the appropriate isothermal susceptibility constants for the general crystal. For such a crystal we must add a term of the form $\mathcal{E}\,dP'$ for each of the components of $\mathcal{E}$ to give CI as

$$dU = \underline{T}\,dS + \underline{\mathcal{E}}_1\,dP'_1 + \underline{\mathcal{E}}_2\,dP'_2 + \underline{\mathcal{E}}_3\,dP'_3$$

Here $n = 4$, and if the underlined force set is chosen as the x set, J_0' contains sixteen elements. We have, in fact,

$$J_0' = \frac{\partial(S, P'_1, P'_2, P'_3)}{\partial(T_1, \mathcal{E}_1, \mathcal{E}_2, \mathcal{E}_3)}$$

$$= \begin{vmatrix} \dfrac{\partial S}{\partial T} & \dfrac{\partial P'_1}{\partial T} & \dfrac{\partial P'_2}{\partial T} & \dfrac{\partial P'_3}{\partial T} \\[2mm] \dfrac{\partial S}{\partial \mathcal{E}_1} & \dfrac{\partial P'_1}{\partial \mathcal{E}_1} & \dfrac{\partial P'_2}{\partial \mathcal{E}_1} & \dfrac{\partial P'_3}{\partial \mathcal{E}_1} \\[2mm] \dfrac{\partial S}{\partial \mathcal{E}_2} & \dfrac{\partial P'_1}{\partial \mathcal{E}_2} & \dfrac{\partial P'_2}{\partial \mathcal{E}_2} & \dfrac{\partial P'_3}{\partial \mathcal{E}_2} \\[2mm] \dfrac{\partial S}{\partial \mathcal{E}_3} & \dfrac{\partial P'_1}{\partial \mathcal{E}_3} & \dfrac{\partial P'_2}{\partial \mathcal{E}_3} & \dfrac{\partial P'_3}{\partial \mathcal{E}_3} \end{vmatrix} = \begin{vmatrix} a_0 & a_1 & a_2 & a_3 \\[2mm] a_1 & \epsilon_{11} & \epsilon_{12} & \epsilon_{13} \\[2mm] a_2 & \epsilon_{12} & \epsilon_{22} & \epsilon_{23} \\[2mm] a_3 & \epsilon_{13} & \epsilon_{23} & \epsilon_{33} \end{vmatrix} \qquad (13.49)$$

where the symmetry of J_0' has reduced the sixteen independent constants to ten. Of these ten, a_1, a_2, and a_3 are pyroelectric coefficients analogous to a_2 in Eq. 13.47, whereas the six constants ϵ_{11}, . . . , ϵ_{33} come from the use of Eqs. 13.48 and replace the single susceptibility constant, ϵ, of the simpler system. Other choices of independent variables are possible and are frequently used. As long as the choice is nonconjugate, the modified Jacobian gives us the basic set of derivatives and the appropriate Maxwellian relations in the same compact form.

13.11 Behavior of Entropy and Helmholtz's and Gibbs' Potentials on Approach to Equilibrium

We must now examine the general problem of equilibrium in physical and chemical systems from the standpoint of the known behavior of entropy. We begin by considering a general system, heterogeneous or homogeneous, containing various substances that can interact chemically. Let us suppose that the system has already attained equality of temperature and pressure throughout. Therefore, it is in thermal and mechanical equilibrium but not in chemical or phase equilibrium.

Now suppose that the system receives a quantity of heat, dQc, from the surroundings. If nothing but reversible processes take place in the surroundings, the change in entropy there is

$$dS_0 = \frac{-dQc}{T}$$

This heat flowing into the system may cause various chemical and phase changes for which the entropy change is dS. Thus, for the system and its surroundings taken together, we can write

$$dS + dS_0 \geq 0$$

by the principle of the increase of entropy. By the first law

$$dQ_C = dU + p\,dV = -T\,dS_0$$

where dU and $-p\,dV$ refer to the system, and therefore

$$dS - \left(\frac{dU + p\,dV}{T}\right) \geq 0$$

or

$$\boxed{dU + p\,dV - T\,dS \leq 0} \qquad \textbf{(13.50)}$$

becomes the general condition that applies as the system reacts to and with its surroundings. Here the equality sign holds if the system is already in complete equilibrium, and the inequality sign if it is not. This condition applies to any infinitesimal process and thus eventually to any finite process that the system undergoes. It is, however, too general to be useful without more specific restrictions. These we now impose.

Adiabatic Processes.   For adiabatic processes

$$dQ_C = 0$$

and therefore

$$dU = -p\,dV$$

As we expect, Eq. 13.50 reduces to

$$dS \geq 0$$

That is, the entropy can only increase, or at most remain constant, if the system is already in equilibrium at the start.

Of course, adiabatic processes may be either *isochoric* or *isobaric*. If they are isochoric,

$$dV = dU = 0$$

and we write, as equilibrium ensues,

$$\boxed{S \to S_{\max} \qquad U \text{ and } V \text{ constant}} \qquad \textbf{(13.51)}$$

If p is constant,

$$dU = -p\,dV = -d(pV)$$

or

$$d(U + pV) = dH = 0$$

and the inference is that

$$\boxed{S \to S_{\max} \qquad H \text{ and } p \text{ constant}} \qquad \textbf{(13.52)}$$

Isothermal Processes. For isothermal processes Eq. 13.50 may be written

$$d(U - TS) \leq - p \, dV = dW_T$$

or

$$dA \leq dW_T$$

In other words, the change in Helmholtz's free energy is always less than or equal to the work done on the system. If V is kept constant, this work vanishes, and A can only decrease or remain constant. The condition follows that

$$A \to A_{\min} \qquad T \text{ and } V \text{ constant} \qquad\qquad \textbf{(13.53)}$$

and A must always *decrease* until its equilibrium value is reached.

If p is kept constant as well as T, then, as before,

$$dW_p = - p \, dV = - d(pV)$$

and the general condition may be written

$$d(U - TS + pV) \leq 0$$

or

$$dG \leq 0$$

in which case G must *decrease* for any nonequilibrium process, and thus

$$G \to G_{\min} \qquad T \text{ and } p \text{ constant} \qquad\qquad \textbf{(13.54)}$$

13.12   Conditions for Stable Equilibrium

Suppose now that a system has attained a state of true stable equilibrium. Then any conceivable process that can take place must be a *reversible* one. If it were irreversible, entropy would increase, and it is already at its maximum value.

If we indicate any imaginable or *virtual* change by a δ, then at equilibrium, since all processes must be reversible, the general condition of Eq. 13.50 must be written with the equality sign to give

$$\delta U + p \, \delta V - T \, \delta S = 0 \qquad\qquad \textbf{(13.55)}$$

as the general criterion for equilibrium. If we follow the same arguments as in the previous section, this equation for the four cases governed by Eqs. 13.51

to 13.54 leads us to the following equivalent criteria for stable equilibrium:

$$\begin{array}{lll}
\delta U = 0 & \delta V = 0 & \delta S = 0 \\
\delta H = 0 & \delta p = 0 & \delta S = 0 \\
\delta T = 0 & \delta V = 0 & \delta A = 0 \\
\delta T = 0 & \delta p = 0 & \delta G = 0
\end{array} \qquad (13.56)$$

13.13   The Electrochemical Potential

Thus far we have considered systems of constant mass only. Suppose that the mass is allowed to vary, as well as, for example, T and p. In this case the Gibbs potential for the system must be regarded as a function of the three variables, T, p, and m; that is,

$$G = G(T, p, m)$$

On differentiation

$$dG = \left(\frac{\partial G}{\partial T}\right)_{pm} dT + \left(\frac{\partial G}{\partial p}\right)_{Tm} dp + \left(\frac{\partial G}{\partial m}\right)_{Tp} dm \qquad (13.57)$$

Of course, with m constant we have CIV,

$$dG = -S\,dT + V\,dp$$

$$\left(\frac{\partial G}{\partial T}\right)_{pm} = -S$$

and

$$\left(\frac{\partial G}{\partial p}\right)_{Tm} = V$$

Since $G = mg$, where g is the specific Gibbs potential,

$$g = u + pv - Ts = g(T, p)$$

and

$$\left(\frac{\partial G}{\partial m}\right)_{Tp} = g$$

Therefore, we write Eq. 13.57 as

$$\boxed{dG = -S\,dT + V\,dp + g\,dm} \qquad (13.58)$$

This is the form of CIV for a system made up of a pure substance of variable mass, and g is called the *chemical potential* of the substance.

Subjecting dG to the usual Legendre transformations gives

$$dA = -S\,dT - p\,dV + g\,dm$$
$$dH = T\,dS + V\,dp + g\,dm$$

and

$$dU = T\,dS - p\,dV + g\,dm \qquad (13.59)$$

From these relations it follows that

$$g = \left(\frac{\partial G}{\partial m}\right)_{Tp} = \left(\frac{\partial A}{\partial m}\right)_{TV} = \left(\frac{\partial H}{\partial m}\right)_{Sp} = \left(\frac{\partial U}{\partial m}\right)_{SV}$$

This is the remarkable quantity that Gibbs generalized and made the basis for a discussion of equilibrium in physicochemical systems.

13.14 Multicomponent Systems

Suppose that we have a system made up not of a single pure substance but containing a number of different ones. There are two possible situations according to whether these substances are *inert* or *react chemically* with one another.

In the first case, if we regard the mass of the system as not fixed, the mass of each of the substances present can be varied independently of the others. Each of these substances we call a *component of the system*. If there are c substances, we have a c-component system.

A gaseous mixture of argon and nitrogen is a two-component single-phase system. A system made up of liquid water, granite, and, say, helium constitutes a three-component system that, in this case, exists in three phases. The solid phase is pure granite, and the other two phases each contain a mixture of the other two components.

When the substances react chemically, the number of substances that we must fix to determine the composition of a system (or a phase, if more than one exists) is also called the number of components. However, in this case the number of components is in general smaller than the number of chemical substances present. Thus if we put H_2 and O_2 gas together in a vessel at high temperature, the reaction

$$H_2 + O_2 \rightarrow 2H_2O$$

proceeds to an equilibrium point, and although there are three types of molecules present, the mass of each is fixed when we know, say, how many gram-atoms of O and H are present (irrespective of the state of combination). Here $c = 2$, fixed by the nature of the system and the conditions that we impose (total mass variable). Just which combination of molecular species we choose is, of course, a matter of convenience. We might choose O and H, or H_2 and O_2, or H_2 and H_2O, etc.

Consider an aqueous solution of HCl in the presence of vapor. The atomic species present are H, Cl, and O. If we take H and Cl as components, the mass of each phase is fixed once the amount of each component is given. Again $c = 2$. For the two components we might select HCl and H_2O, even though the first is ionized in solution (and the ions are largely hydrated) and water molecules are associated in various polymolecular clusters.

To determine the thermodynamic state of a phase, we must fix the mass of the components (this operation fixes the total mass and the composition).

Since it is a homogeneous system, two other coordinates are needed, which may be selected at our convenience from the set T, p, V, S, and U.

If, for example, we select T and p, the Gibbs function becomes the basic function and is regarded as a function of the variables $(T, p, m_1, m_2, \ldots, m_c)$; that is, we assume

$$G = G(T, p, m_1, m_2, \ldots, m_c)$$

Thus
$$dG = \left(\frac{\partial G}{\partial T}\right)_{pm_i} dT + \left(\frac{\partial G}{\partial p}\right)_{Tm_i} dp + \sum_{j=1}^{c} \left(\frac{\partial G}{\partial m_j}\right)_{Tpm_i} dm_j \qquad \textbf{(13.60)}$$

where m_i outside the first two parentheses indicates that all masses are held constant and m_i in the summation indicates that all masses save m_j are so treated. The derivatives in the sum are seen to be generalizations of the derivative $(\partial G/\partial m)_{Tp}$ of Eq. 13.57 and are called *partial potentials*. They are designated as $\mu_1, \mu_2, \ldots, \mu_c$, where

$$\mu_j = \left(\frac{\partial G}{\partial m_j}\right)_{Tpm_i}$$

is the partial (chemical) potential of the jth component and reduces to g when the other components are missing. Since as in Eq. 13.57 the first two derivatives in Eq. 13.60 can be replaced by $-S$ and V, respectively, we write finally

$$dG = -S\,dT + V\,dp + \sum_{j=1}^{c} \mu_j\,dm_j \qquad \textbf{(13.61)}$$

Here each μ depends only on T, p, and the composition of the phase and is unaffected by the presence or absence of other phases. Thus the μ's are *intensive* properties as in the case where $c = 1$. This circumstance makes all chemical systems *restricted* systems in the sense used earlier.

13.15 Heterogeneous Equilibrium and the Phase Rule

If a system has more than one phase, the total Gibbs potential is the sum of the Gibbs potentials for each phase. For a system with ϕ phases

$$G = G^1 + G^2 + \cdots + G^\phi = \sum_{\alpha=1}^{\Phi} G^\alpha$$

where the α refers to the αth phase.

We saw in Sec. 13.12 that the conditions for stable equilibrium with T and p constant were

$$\delta T = 0 \qquad \delta p = 0 \qquad \delta G = 0$$

Thus for the polyphase system

$$\delta G = \Sigma \delta G^\alpha = 0$$

where δG^α has the form of Eq. 13.61 for each α, with δ's replacing the d's.

Now take two phases, say, the αth and βth, and allow a small mass of the jth component to pass from the αth phase to the βth phase, keeping all other masses constant. Then the condition for equilibrium for these phases is

$$\delta G^\alpha + \delta G^\beta = (- S^\alpha - S^\beta) \delta T + (V^\alpha + V^\beta) \delta p + \mu_j{}^\alpha dm_j{}^\alpha + \mu_j{}^\beta dm_j{}^\beta = 0$$

Since $\delta T = \delta p = 0$ and conservation of mass require

$$dm_j{}^\alpha = - dm_j{}^\beta$$

this reduces to

$$\boxed{\mu_j{}^\alpha = \mu_j{}^\beta}$$

This reasoning can be extended to each component in every pair of phases, and the conclusion is that at equilibrium at constant T and p the partial potential of *any given component must have a common value in all phases.* Therefore,

$$\mu_j{}^1 = \mu_j{}^2 = \ldots = \mu_j{}^\phi \qquad j = 1, 2, \ldots, c \qquad (13.62)$$

a total of $(\phi - 1)c$ general conditions of equilibrium.

Gibbs' Phase Rule. Consider now the question of the total number of variables involved in describing an equilibrium system of ϕ phases with c components. The necessary variables are grouped in Table 13.3 in three groups. Group I gives the component masses in each phase $(m_j{}^\alpha)$, the phase masses and volumes (m^α, V^α), the component masses (m_j), and the system mass and volume (m and V). These are all extensive variables.

Group II contains, besides T and p, the phase concentrations of each component $(c_j{}^\alpha)$, and group III includes the partial potentials, $\mu_j{}^\alpha$. These two groups are all intensive.

Adding the quantities in the third column gives the total number of variables, n_{var}, as

$$n_{var} = 3\phi c + 2\phi + c + 4$$

The equations connecting these variables are given in Table 13.4 and are self-explanatory.

TABLE **13.3**

Group	Variables		Number
I (extensive)	$m_j{}^\alpha$	$\alpha = 1, \ldots, \phi; j = 1, \ldots, c$	ϕc
	m^α	$\alpha = 1, \ldots, \phi$	ϕ
	m_j	$j = 1, \ldots, c$	c
	V^α	$\alpha = 1, \ldots, \phi$	ϕ
	m, V		2
II (intensive)	$c_j{}^\alpha$	$\alpha = 1, \ldots, \phi; j = 1, \ldots, c$	ϕc
	T, p		2
III (intensive)	$\mu_j{}^\alpha$	$\alpha = 1, \ldots, \phi; j = 1, \ldots, c$	ϕc

TABLE **13.4**

Equations Connecting Variables in Multicomponent Polyphase Systems

Group		Equations		Number
Mass and volume sums	(1)	$\sum_j m_i^\alpha = m^\alpha$	$\alpha = 1, \ldots, \phi$	ϕ
	(2)	$\sum_\alpha m_i^\alpha = m_j$	$j = 1, \ldots, c$	c
	(3)	$\sum \sum m_i^\alpha = m \qquad \sum V^\alpha = V$		2
Equations of state	(4)	$V^\alpha = V^\alpha(T, p, m_j)$	$\alpha = 1, \ldots, \phi$	ϕ
Definitions of	(5)	$c_j^\alpha = m_j^\alpha / m^\alpha$	(j, α)	ϕc
and conditions on	(6)	$\sum_j c_j^\alpha = 1$	$\alpha = 1, \ldots, \phi$	(ϕ)
concentrations				
Nature of μ's	(7)	$\mu_j^\alpha = \mu_j^\alpha(T, p, c_j)$	(j, α)	ϕc
Gibbs' criterion	(8)	$\mu_j^1 = \mu_j^2 = \ldots = \mu_j^\Phi$	(j)	$c(\phi - 1)$

In finding the total number of equations, we must be careful not to include both 1 and 6, since they are not independent.[5] Thus

$$n_{eq} = 3\phi c + 2\phi + 2$$

and the total number of independent variables becomes

$$\boxed{n = n_{var} - n_{eq} = c + 2} \qquad \textbf{(13.63)}$$

This result shows that all the properties of this complicated system are fixed by $c + 2$ variables and furnishes in the last analysis the justification of the form of Eq. 13.61 for dG.

In case a given component is missing from a phase, its mass, concentration, and partial potential drop out of Table 13.3. However, one equation is also lost from each of Eqs. 5, 7, and 8 of Table 13.4, the difference remains $c + 2$, and n is unchanged. If other outside forces, such as electric and magnetic fields, are applied to the system, they must be added to group II in Table 13.3, and n accordingly increases.

As for the *intensive* variables, groups II and III of Table 13.3 give for their number

$$2\phi c + 2$$

---

[5] Eq. 6 was unfortunately omitted from Table II in Crawford, *Proc. Am. Acad. Arts Sci.*, **83**, 191 (1955).

The corresponding equations come from the last three rows of Table 13.4 and number

$$2\phi c - c + \phi$$

The difference is n_{int}, the maximum number of intensive variables that remain arbitrary.

$$n_{\text{int}} = c - \phi + 2 \qquad (13.64)$$

This is *Gibbs' phase rule* for multiphase polycomponent systems. Since n_{int} can never be negative, its smallest value is zero. Accordingly, the maximum number of phases that can coexist stably is

$$\phi_{\text{max}} = c + 2$$

This explains why no more than three phases of a pure substance can coexist and why, when $c = 2$, the possible number goes up to four. (See Problem 13.9.)

Gibbs' phase rule gives only the maximum number of intensive variables that can be included in an independent set. In general,

$$n \geq n_{\text{int}}$$

and we may include as many intensive variables as we like up to the maximum number allowed by Eq. 13.64.

13.16   Chemical Systems of Two Components

As an example of the application of the general analysis of this chapter to chemical systems, consider a two-component system with a single phase. In this case Eq. 13.61 becomes

$$dG = -S\,dT + V\,dp + \mu_1\,dm_1 + \mu_2\,dm_2$$

It is convenient to write

$$m_1 + m_2 = m$$

and

$$c_2 = 1 - c_1 = 1 - \frac{m_1}{m}$$

in which case $$dG = -S\,dT + V\,dp + \beta_1\,dc_1 + \beta_2\,dm \qquad (13.65)$$

where $\beta_1 = m(\mu_1 - \mu_2)$ and $\beta_2 = (\mu_1 - \mu_2)c_1 + \mu_1$. Thus

$$\beta_1 = \beta_1(T, p, c_1, m)$$

and
$$\beta_2 = \beta_2(T, p, c)$$

so that β_2 depends only on intensive variables. Here J_0' becomes

$$J_0' = \frac{\partial(-S, V, \beta_1, \beta_2)}{\partial(T, p, c_1, m)} = \begin{vmatrix} -\dfrac{\partial S}{\partial T} & \dfrac{\partial V}{\partial T} & \dfrac{\partial \beta_1}{\partial T} & \dfrac{\partial \beta_2}{\partial T} \\[2mm] -\dfrac{\partial S}{\partial p} & \dfrac{\partial V}{\partial p} & \dfrac{\partial \beta_1}{\partial p} & \dfrac{\partial \beta_2}{\partial p} \\[2mm] -\dfrac{\partial S}{\partial c_1} & \dfrac{\partial V}{\partial c_1} & \dfrac{\partial \beta_1}{\partial c_1} & \dfrac{\partial \beta_2}{\partial c_1} \\[2mm] -\dfrac{\partial S}{\partial m} & \dfrac{\partial V}{\partial m} & \dfrac{\partial \beta_1}{\partial m} & 0 \end{vmatrix}$$

and there are nine rather than ten basic derivatives for the system. For a few of the many interesting applications of these results, the reader is referred to the original papers.[6]

13.17   The Thermocouple

Although the thermocouple provided an early example of the application of thermodynamics to electric currents, it was not included in Table 13.1 because it does not belong to the class of equilibrium systems. When two dissimilar metals, A and B (Fig. 13.15) are joined to form an electrical circuit and the two junctions are maintained at two different temperatures, T_1 (hot) and T_2 (cold), an electromotive force, E, the so-called thermal emf, is set up in the circuit. This is the effect discovered by Seebeck (1826), who found E to be a function of T_1 and T_2 and, of course, dependent on the metals, A and B. When it is necessary here to indicate the metals involved, the subscripts A and B will be used, E_{AB} indicating an emf driving current in the direction from A to B at the hot junction.

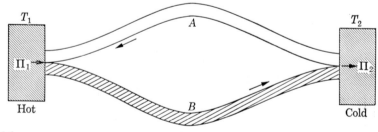

FIGURE **13.15**

---

[6] Shaw, *Phil. Trans. Roy. Soc. London*, **A234**, 299 (1935); Crawford, *Am. J. Phys.*, **17**, 1 (1949); *Proc. Am. Acad. Arts Sci.*, **78**, 165 (1950); **83**, 191 (1955); Einbinder, *J. Chem. Phys.*, **21**, 2134 (1953); and Manning and Manning, *J. Chem. Phys.*, **33**, 1554 (1960). See also F. G. Donnan and A. Haas, eds., *A Commentary on the Writings of J. Willard Gibbs*, Yale Univ. Press. New Haven, Conn., 1936, Vol. I (especially Parts D and G). For easy translation of the notation there, $\epsilon \equiv U$, $\chi \equiv H$, $\eta \equiv S$, $\psi \equiv A$, and $\zeta \equiv G$.

In case T_1 and T_2 are kept fixed, a steady state is reached in which a constant current, determined by E and the resistance, flows in the circuit. At this time two irreversible processes are in progress, a flow of heat down the wires from the hot to the cold junction and the Joulian heat production due to the electrical resistance of the wires. Peltier (1834) found also that whenever current flows across a junction, a *reversible* heat absorption occurs, the rate, as we saw in Chap. 10, being proportional to the current. If a charge passes, say, from A to B at T_1, we have

$$dQ_T = \Pi_{AB}\,dz$$

where Π_{AB} is the Peltier coefficient for the flow A to B and may be regarded as an emf originating at the junction. The heat absorption is required to compensate for the electrical work performed on the charge and to preserve the constancy of the temperature.

It is found experimentally, as we noted in Sec. 2.15, that if one junction is kept at a fixed temperature, say, at 0°C, and the other at a variable temperature, t, E can always be expressed as

$$E = E_{AB} = a_1 t + a_2 t^2 + a_3 t^3 + \cdots \tag{13.66}$$

where the constants a_1, a_2, and a_3 are characteristic of the materials A and B. It is found also that if the temperature of the cold junction is changed to, say, t_1, the new emf can be written as

$$E - E_1 = a_1 t + a_2 t^2 + a_3 t^3 + (a_1 t_1 - a_2 t_2^2 + a_3 t_3^3) \tag{13.67}$$

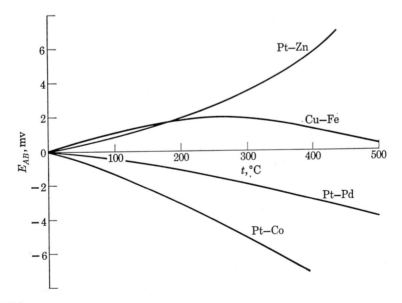

FIGURE **13.16**

Since the term in brackets is a constant, the same value for dE/dt, the so-called thermoelectric *power* of the couple, is obtained from Eq. 13.66 or Eq. 13.67. Thus the thermoelectric power may be written

$$\frac{dE}{dt} = \frac{dE}{dT} = a_1 + 2a_2t + 3a_3t^2 \tag{13.68}$$

and is fixed by the temperature of the hot junction alone. Fig. 13.16 shows the behavior of E versus t for a few typical thermocouple combinations.

13.18   Kelvin's Treatment of the Thermocouple

Lord Kelvin (then Professor William Thomson) was the first investigator to treat the thermodynamics of a thermocouple. He showed that if all but reversible phenomena were ignored, the resulting formulas agreed with the facts of experiment. He began by demonstrating that the Peltier heat alone was inadequate to account for the phenomena observed.

His argument follows. Since the Peltier effect is reversible, the thermocouple is essentially a heat engine absorbing heat, Π_1, at T_1 and rejecting Π_2 at T_2 (each per unit charge passed), so that from Carnot's theorem,

$$\frac{\Pi_1}{T_1} = \frac{\Pi_2}{T_2}$$

By the first law the energy supplied to a charge, dz, by the emf's at the junctions must equal the energy supplied to the outside world; that is,

$$(\Pi_1 - \Pi_2)\, dz = E\, dz \tag{13.69}$$

and
$$E = \frac{\Pi_2}{T_2}\,(T_1 - T_2) \tag{13.70}$$

If T_2 is kept constant, Π_2 is fixed, and E is a *linear* function of T_1 (and hence also of t_1). This result contradicts the form of E in Eq. 13.66. Thus the Peltier heat alone is inadequate to account for the results of experiment.

Kelvin went on to show that a new and hitherto unsuspected heat absorption is always present in any conductor carrying a current and at the same time having a temperature gradient along its length. If a current flows up a gradient in wire A from a point at temperature T to one at $T + dT$, there is another emf, called, after him, the Thomson emf, given by

$$\sigma_A\, dT$$

σ_A being the *Thomson coefficient* for substance A. If σ_A is positive and charge moves *up* the temperature gradient, then an equivalent amount of heat, the Thomson heat, is *absorbed* by the wire from its surroundings. This Thomson heat is strictly reversible, as is the Peltier heat, and may be written

$$\sigma_A\, dT\, dz$$

for the passage of a charge dz.

Kelvin then applied the laws of thermodynamics to the Peltier and Thomson heats, ignoring the irreversible effects entirely. To follow his reasoning most readily, let us consider the differential emf, dE_{AB}, produced when the two junctions of Fig. 13.15 are at T and $T + dT$, respectively. In this case let $\Pi + d\Pi$ and Π be the Peltier coefficients for these junctions. For a small charge, dz, circulated in the direction of normal flow, the heat interchanges are

$(\Pi + d\Pi)\,dz$	absorbed at warm junction at $T + dT$
$\Pi\,dz$	rejected at cool junction at T
$\sigma_A\,dT\,dz$	absorbed by wire A from surroundings
$\sigma_B\,dT\,dz$	rejected by wire B to surroundings

The first law requires that

$$dE\,dz = (\Pi + d\Pi)\,dz - \Pi\,dz + (\sigma_A - \sigma_B)\,dT\,dz$$

This can be rewritten more specifically as

$$\frac{dE_{AB}}{dT} = \frac{d\Pi_{AB}}{dT} + (\sigma_A - \sigma_B) \tag{13.71}$$

This gives the value of the thermoelectric power to be expected. If we integrate this equation from T_1 to T_2, we obtain the total emf in the form

$$E_{AB} = \Pi_{AB}(T_1) - \Pi_{AB}(T_2) + \int_{T_2}^{T_1} (\sigma_A - \sigma_B)\,dT \tag{13.72}$$

where the integral term, although much smaller than the first, is new.

To apply the second law, we sum the entropy changes arising from the reversible heat interchanges and set the result equal to zero. For this purpose the average temperature at which the Thomson heats are absorbed and rejected may be taken as $T + \tfrac{1}{2}\,dT$. Omitting the common factor, dz, gives

$$\frac{\Pi + d\Pi}{T + dT} - \frac{\Pi}{T} + \frac{\sigma_A\,dT}{T + \dfrac{dT}{2}} - \frac{\sigma_B\,dT}{T + \dfrac{dT}{2}} = 0$$

With only terms in differentials that are of the first order being retained, this reduces to

$$\frac{d\Pi_{AB}}{dT} = \frac{\Pi_{AB}}{T} - (\sigma_A - \sigma_B) \tag{13.73}$$

Insertion of this in Eq. 13.71 gives

$$\boxed{\frac{dE_{AB}}{dT} = \frac{\Pi_{AB}}{T}} \tag{13.74}$$

If this is differentiated once with respect to T and Eq. 13.73 is used once more, the result is

$$\frac{d^2 E_{AB}}{dT^2} = -\frac{(\sigma_A - \sigma_B)}{T} \tag{13.75}$$

These are the two Kelvin differential equations giving the first and second temperature derivatives of E_{AB} in terms of the appropriate thermoelectric coefficients.

Use of Eq. 13.66 and its temperature derivatives shows that

and
$$(\sigma_A - \sigma_B) = -2T(a_2 + 3a_3t)$$
$$\Pi_{AB} = T(a_1 + 2a_2t + 3a_3t^2) \tag{13.76}$$

where a_1, a_2, and a_3 are empirically determined coefficients. Since the Peltier and Thomson coefficients can be measured directly by passing currents through junctions and along wires with known temperature gradients, comparison of the results of experiment and the predictions of Eq. 13.76 are possible. The agreement can hardly leave doubt as to the basic correctness of the results given in Eqs. 13.74 and 13.75.

A more satisfactory approach to the theory of the thermocouple requires taking into account the irreversible as well as reversible effects. The thermodynamics of irreversible phenomena is a new, although rapidly growing, subject and uses ideas and techniques peculiar to itself. For details the reader is referred to De Groot and Callen, as well as to the earlier discussion of the subject by Bridgman.[7]

Problems

13.1 Apply Eq. 13.12 to the case of a thin steel wire of radius 0.025 cm when ΔF is 10 kg. What is the change in temperature?

13.2 If such a large stress as that in the preceding problem could be applied to rubber, what would you expect ΔT to be?

13.3 Write down the hydrostatic analogs of Eqs. 13.11 and 13.13.

13.4 Use Eq. 13.14 to find the maximum outward force exerted by a steel rod of cross section 20 cm² when $\Delta T = 100°C$.

13.5 Obtain expressions for a thin rod under tension corresponding to Eqs. 12.1, 12.2, and 12.3 in Sec. 12.1 for a solid under bulk compression.

---

[7] H. B. Callen, *Thermodynamics*, Wiley, New York, 1960, Chap. 17; *Phys. Rev.*, **73**, 1349 (1948); R. De Groot, *Thermodynamics of Irreversible Processes*, Interscience, New York, 1951; and P. W. Bridgman, *Thermodynamics of Electrical Phenomena in Metals*, Macmillan, New York, 1934, Chap. 2. See also Gross, *Am. J. Phys.*, **29**, 729 (1961), for a general discussion of the efficiency of thermoelectric devices.

13.6 Show that the derivative $(\partial L/\partial T)_S$ can be put in the form

$$\left(\frac{\partial L}{\partial T}\right)_S = L\left(\alpha_F - \frac{\rho c_F}{Y_T \alpha_F T}\right)$$

where ρ is the density and c_F the specific heat at constant force.

13.7 Eqs. 13.36 and 13.37 giving the adiabatic law for radiation are suggestive of the same laws for an ideal gas. Does this mean that we can define γ for black body radiation as C_p/C_V and say that $\gamma = \frac{4}{3}$? Examine this question in the light of the results of Secs. 13.6 and 13.7.

13.8 Calculate the total radiation received per second on an area of 1 cm^2 that is normal to the beam and 1 meter from a black body radiator of 2 cm^2 area. Suppose that the body is at $2000°$K and that the beam is radiated at an angle of $30°$ to the normal to the hot surface.

13.9 Return to Problem 1.6(d), and discuss the various polyphase systems and the values of n and n_{int} that these two-component systems possess.

13.10 Prove directly from the expression

$$dU = T\,dS - p\,dV + g\,dm \qquad\qquad \textbf{(13.59)}$$

that indeed $$g = \left(\frac{\partial U}{\partial m}\right)_{SV} = u + pv - Ts$$

13.11 In the case of a thermocouple made up of platinum and gold, the coefficients of Eq. 13.66 with E in volts are given as $a_1 = -5.991 \times 10^{-6}$, $a_2 = -0.0180 \times 10^{-6}$, and $a_3 = -0.2 \times 10^{-11}$. Using these values and the relation obtained in Sec. 13.18, calculate the two contributions to the emf on the right of Eq. 13.72,

$$E_{AB} = \Pi_{AB}(T_1) - \Pi_{AB}(T_2) + \int_{T_2}^{T_1} (\sigma_A - \sigma_B)\,dT$$

when $T_1 = 373°$K and $T_2 = 273°$K.

13.12 In a reversible electric cell with $(\partial E/\partial T)_p > 0$, heat is absorbed from the surroundings and converted into useful electrical energy. If such a cell is placed in an isothermal reservoir, why is the second law not contradicted?

13.13 Take the simple case of the prototype stressed dielectric in an electric field where

$$dU = T\,dS + F\,dL + \mathcal{E}\,dP' \qquad\qquad \textbf{(13.46)}$$

and suppose that we wish to calculate the heat capacity at constant L and P', say, $C_{LP'}$. We can write

$$T\left(\frac{\partial S}{\partial T}\right)_{LP'} = T\frac{\partial(S,L,P')}{\partial(T,L,P')} = T\frac{\dfrac{\partial(S,L,P')}{\partial(T,F,\mathcal{E})}}{\dfrac{\partial(T,L,P')}{\partial(T,F,\mathcal{E})}} = \frac{J_0' T}{\begin{vmatrix} b_{11} & b_{12} \\ b_{12} & \epsilon \end{vmatrix}}$$

By the same technique show that

$$\left(\frac{\partial F}{\partial P'}\right)_{TL} = \frac{-b_{12}}{\begin{vmatrix} b_{11} & b_{12} \\ b_{12} & \epsilon \end{vmatrix}}$$

$$\left(\frac{\partial F}{\partial \mathcal{E}}\right)_{LT} = -\frac{b_{12}}{b_{11}}$$

$$\left(\frac{\partial P'}{\partial L}\right)_{T\mathcal{E}} = \frac{b_{12}}{b_{11}}$$

13.14 Carry out calculations analogous to those in Problem 13.13 for
(a) a reversible electric cell under pressure and
(b) a hydrostatic system with surface tension.

13.15 Use the results of Sec. 13.3 to sketch the Carnot cycle for a stretched wire and justify the diagram in Fig. 8.12. Draw the corresponding diagram for tensed rubber.

The Physics of Low Temperatures

14.1 Production of Low Temperatures

Interest in and study of the properties of bodies at low temperature began as a result of the attempt to liquefy the so-called permanent gases. Of these, the last to be reduced to the liquid state were hydrogen, which Sir James Dewar liquefied in 1898, and helium, first liquefied by Kamerlingh Onnes in Leiden in 1908.

Before a gas can be liquefied, it must be cooled below its critical temperature. For gases with critical temperatures above room temperature, subjecting the gas to sufficient pressure automatically liquefies it. Once it is in liquid form, rapid evaporation of the liquid produces a refrigerating effect, which can be used to chill yet other gases below their critical points. When a chain of suitable gases is available, we have the essence of the cascade process of the Swiss engineer Pictet. He condensed sulfur dioxide to the liquid state and by forced evaporation of it reached $-65°C$. At this temperature he condensed carbon dioxide to the solid state and on evaporation of this reached $-130°C$. Finally he cooled compressed oxygen to this temperature and allowed it to expand through a pin valve, producing a jet of liquid oxygen. See Table 14.1, where data for gases important in low-temperature work are given.

Once liquid oxygen is available, air, carbon monoxide, and nitrogen can be liquefied. A gap exists between the critical temperature of nitrogen and that of hydrogen, and self-cooling is necessary to reduce hydrogen below its critical temperature. The two methods for accomplishing the self-cooling may be used singly or together. They are as follows:

1. Joule-Kelvin streaming through a porous plug or valve. This had already been used by Pictet and others before Joule and Kelvin studied it systematically. The thermodynamics of the process have been treated in Chap. 12.

2. Claude's process of cooling by adiabatic expansion against an outside pressure.

TABLE **14.1**

Temperature Data for Gases Important in Low-Temperature Work

Gas	T_c	T_{mi}†	Mp	Bp
O_2	154.78	(750)	54.8	90.2
CO	133.0	(630)	74.2	83.2
N_2	126.3	625	63.30	77.3
Ne*	44.5	(230)	24.49	27.3
H_2	33.2	202	13.98	20.36
He^4	5.20	34		4.216
He^3	3.35	?		3.195

* Neon is included for comparison only, since it was not important historically in this connection.
† Values of the maximum inversion temperature in parentheses are estimated from Fig. 12.10.

The Joule-Kelvin method has the advantage of no moving parts, but it does require precooling below the maximum inversion temperature, T_{mi} (see column 3 of Table 14.1). In the original liquefaction of helium, Onnes first prepared large quantities of liquid nitrogen, using a continuously operating Joule-Kelvin apparatus. The liquid nitrogen was used to precool hydrogen below its maximum inversion temperature, after which the hydrogen was liquefied in a smaller Joule-Kelvin apparatus. Finally the liquid hydrogen, with its boiling point of 20.36°K, was used to cool helium below its maximum inversion temperature of 34°K. On Joule-Kelvin expansion the helium was rapidly cooled to its liquefaction point.

When liquid helium is evaporated by having its vapor drawn off by a vacuum pump, still lower temperatures are obtained. In fact, temperatures as low as 0.73°K may be reached in this way, although the smallness of the vapor pressure (see Table 14.3) and the troublesome creeping of the superfluid helium (see Sec. 14.8) make further cooling by this process unfeasible.

14.2   Helium Liquefiers

Since the Onnes cascading process is so expensive of time and apparatus, resort has been had to a combination of the Claude and Joule-Kelvin processes for continuous production of liquid helium.

Kapitza in 1936 first made a continuously operating device for producing liquid helium.[1] In his apparatus the gas, which has been cooled to around 20°K, is allowed to perform work in an adiabatic expansion against a piston. Since no lubricants are usable at such low temperatures, the piston is turned to a loose

---

[1] Kapitza, *Nature*, **133**, 708 (1934).

fit, the escaping helium acting as a very efficient lubricant. This expansion produces a further fall to 10°K. On passage through a Joule-Kelvin valve, liquid helium is produced. One installation in the Mond Laboratory in Cambridge produces 1.8 liters of liquid helium per hour.

Another continuously operating apparatus is the Collins liquefier, which is so designed that it can be used as a constant-temperature bath in which to carry out low-temperature experiments.[2] In this device the helium is first cooled by adiabatic expansion in a reciprocating engine, the cooled gas being used to produce regenerative cooling of the incoming gas. When a low enough temperature has been reached, the gas from the engine goes through a Joule-Kelvin valve and condenses. With helium at room temperature at the start, 2 or 3 hours is required for the production of liquid to begin. After that the rate of production can be as high as 1.3 liters per hour. The Collins apparatus can be used with other gases, such as hydrogen or nitrogen, for which the rate of liquid production is about doubled.

Other methods for the production of liquid helium can yield up to 7 or 8 liters per hour, but they require liquid hydrogen in the precooling stage.

14.3   Measurement of Low Temperatures

The availability of liquid helium in quantity has greatly aided low-temperature research into the properties not only of helium itself but of other substances, including the rare isotope, He^3.

Before considering anything else, however, we must examine the question of extending the temperature scale to this low region. As we saw in Chap. 2, the gas thermometer requires corrections because of the lack of idealness of the gas. These corrections become larger, and the usable pressures become smaller, as the temperature is reduced, until even with helium a limit is reached at around 2°K. The situation requires the extension of the Kelvin scale below this limit, as well as the provision of satisfactory secondary thermometers for the range from room temperature to 0°K. For practical purposes the temperature range below 273°K breaks up into the five subintervals shown in Table 14.2.

TABLE **14.2**

Range, °K	Secondary thermometer	Standardized against
273–80	Platinum resistance	Ice, steam, sulfur points (Table 2.7)
80–14	Lead resistance	Helium (constant-volume) gas thermometer
14–5	Carbon radio resistor	Helium (constant-volume) gas thermometer
5–1	Helium vapor pressure	Thermodynamic formula
1–0	Magnetic	Thermodynamic reduction

---

[2] Collins, *Rev. Sci. Instr.*, **18**, 157 (1947).

In the first three intervals electrical resistance thermometers may be employed, each calibrated either against points already known on the Kelvin scale or directly against the constant-volume helium gas thermometer. For the regions below 5°K special techniques are required. From 5 to around 1°K the vapor pressure of boiling helium makes a very sensitive and satisfactory secondary temperature indicator, since the vessels used are immersed in a liquid helium bath with a readily measured vapor pressure. A rigorous thermodynamic formula is necessary to relate the vapor pressures to the Kelvin scale and is considered in the next section.

For temperatures below 1°K the vapor pressure of helium is too low for accurate measurement. Accordingly, use is made of a so-called magnetic temperature, T^*, which may be defined from the following considerations. A great many paramagnetic materials obey Curie's law, which can be written

$$\chi T = \text{constant} \tag{14.1}$$

where χ is the molar magnetic susceptibility of the substance. This law holds in general, provided the magnetic field is not so large as to produce saturation, down to a temperature known as the Curie point. Below this temperature the Curie law fails, but T^* is defined as though the law still held. Thus if the susceptibility is measured as χ at a temperature, T, above the Curie point and as χ^* at a point below it, we write

$$\chi T = \chi^* T^*$$

and define the magnetic temperature T^* by the relation

$$T^* = \left(\frac{\chi}{\chi^*}\right) T \tag{14.2}$$

We shall see in Sec. 14.13 how magnetic temperatures are reduced to the Kelvin scale.

14.4   The Liquid Helium Vapor Pressure Formula

In Chap. 12 a monatomic vapor pressure formula was obtained by integration of the Clausius-Clapeyron equation on the assumption that the pressures were low enough to justify (1) treating the vapor as strictly ideal and (2) neglecting the variation of the enthalpy of the condensed phase with pressure. This assumption led to the formula (Eq. 12.84) for the vapor pressure,

$$\ln p = -\frac{\Lambda_0}{RT} + \ln T^{5/2} - \frac{1}{R}\int \frac{dT}{T^2}\int_0^T C_p''' \, dT + i_p \tag{14.3}$$

The accurate measurement of p at two values of T in principle permits use of this formula for the calculation of p in terms of T over its range of validity.

FIGURE **14.1**

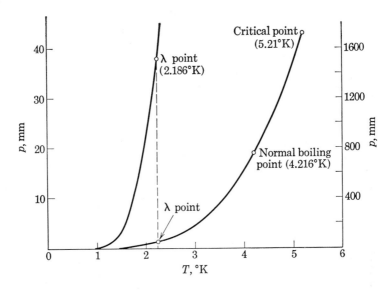

For a vapor pressure thermometer, of course, this application is reversed, and once Λ_0 and i_p are determined, the formula is used to calculate T for any measured value of p.

In the case of liquid helium, as the temperature is lowered below the so-called λ point (at $T = 2.186°$K), a transition occurs to a new and strange superfluid known as helium II. The vapor pressure, however, exhibits a continuous variation through this point, as is shown graphically in Fig. 14.1. Since the pressures fall to very small values at the lower end of the curve, this section has been replotted to a scale forty times as large on the left side of the figure.

The use of vapor pressure as a measure of Kelvin temperature requires careful calculation of the size of the factors neglected in deducing Eq. 14.3. These effects, although small below 1°K, assume increasing importance as the temperature rises. An accurate theoretical formula for the calculation has been devised by Van Dijk.[3] It may be readily obtained from the results already given in Chap. 12. For its derivation we follow the arguments of Sec. 12.6 but use the general relations of Eq. 12.46 for the thermodynamic functions of nonideal gases. We begin as before by equating the Gibbs functions for the liquid and the vapor,

$$G^L = G'$$

where G^L is used to avoid any distinction between the normal and the superfluid liquids.

Since the virial equation is more accurate for the same number of terms

---

[3] Van Dijk, *Physica*, **22**, 760 (1956); and Van Dijk and Durieux, *Physica*, **24**, 1 (1958).

when written in powers of $1/V$, we write for the vapor phase

$$pV = RT + \frac{\mathcal{B}_1}{V} + \frac{\mathcal{B}_2}{V^2}$$

Turning to the set of relations in Eq. 12.46, we next express G' in terms of U' and S' to obtain

$$G' = G° + \frac{2\mathcal{B}_1}{V} + \frac{3\mathcal{B}_2}{2V^2}$$

where $G°$ is the ideal value of Gibbs' function. Use of Eqs. 12.18 and 12.22 then gives

$$G° = RT\left(\frac{5}{2} - \ln T^{3/2} - \ln V - \frac{S_{0TV}}{R}\right)$$

To introduce the pressure, we add to and subtract from this relation $RT \ln p/RT$. Then we replace S_{0TV} by its equivalent from Sec. 9.14, where we found that

$$S_{0Tp} = R \ln R + S_{0TV}$$

Thus we have

$$G° = RT\left(\frac{5}{2} - \ln T^{5/2} + \ln p - \ln \frac{pV}{RT} - \frac{S_{0Tp}}{R}\right)$$

For the liquid, use of Eq. 12.12 for enthalpy (with $V_0 p$ replaced by the original integral) and of Eq. 12.15 for entropy gives

$$G^L = -\Lambda_0 + \int_0^T C_p{}^L dT - TS_0{}^L + \int_0^p V^L dp - T\int \frac{C_p{}^L dT}{T}$$

On equating G' and G^L and solving for $\ln p$, we have finally

$$\boxed{\ln p = -\frac{\Lambda_0}{RT} + \ln T^{5/2} - \frac{1}{RT}\int S^L dT + \frac{1}{RT}\int_0^p V^L dp + \mathcal{E} + i_p} \quad \textbf{(14.4)}$$

where

$$\mathcal{E} = \ln \frac{pV}{RT} - \frac{2\mathcal{B}_1}{RTV} - \frac{3\mathcal{B}_2}{2RTV^2}$$

and is the virial correction. Two of the integrals in the expression for G^L/RT have been replaced by an equivalent, where S^L is the entropy of the liquid. This equation is Van Dijk's vapor pressure formula for helium, where Λ_0 and i_p have the numerical values 59.50 joules/mole and 12.240 cgs units, respectively (the latter calculated from the theoretical expression for i_p to be obtained in Chap. 17).

TABLE **14.3**

The 1958 Helium-4 Vapor Pressure Scale

T, °K	p, mm	T, °K	p, mm
0.01	(2.5×10^{-314})	2.0	23.7674
0.1	(5×10^{-32})	2.5	77.4931
0.5	1.6342×10^{-5}	3.0	182.073
0.7	2.2787×10^{-3}	3.5	355.844
0.9	0.041581	4.0	616.537
1.0	0.120000	4.5	983.066
1.5	3.59897	5.0	1478.535
1.8	12.4661	5.2	1718.817

This formula is used to calculate the theoretical vapor pressure in terms of the Kelvin temperature and is the basis of the Leiden 1955 scale. In 1955 Clement, Logan, and Gaffney[4] developed a scale differing somewhat from the Leiden scale. In June, 1958, the differences were reconciled, and the 1958 scale, with some newer data, was proposed and adopted for international use.[5] A few of the values (with temperatures reliable to a few millidegrees) taken from the 1958 scale are shown in Table 14.3. Since this scale is valid only from 5.2 to 0.5°K, the pressures shown in parentheses were calculated just to show how low the vapor pressures become below 0.5°K.

14.5 Phase Relations of Helium

The phase relations of helium are of great interest since they present a number of new features. The phase diagram for the ordinary isotope of mass 4 is shown in Fig. 14.2. The first thing to note is that the liquid-vapor curve can be followed from the critical point, c, to 0°K without any appearance of the solid. As we have seen, however, at the λ point ($T = 2.186°K$) the normal liquid, HeI, makes a transition to the superfluid form, HeII. Thus the λ point is a triple point at which liquid HeI, liquid HeII, and vapor coexist. Keesom, who first solidified helium, found that the solid did not exist below a pressure of 25 atm. Beginning at a point, say, a, on the melting curve, the solid melts to normal liquid helium, HeI. As the temperature is lowered, a new triple point is reached at b. Here the solid is in equilibrium with the two liquid modifications. The triple points, b and d, are connected by a line that separates the regions of existence of HeII and HeI.

---

[4] Clement, Logan, and Gaffney, *Phys. Rev.*, **100**, 743 (1955).

[5] Brickwedde, Van Dijk, Durieux, Clement, and Logan, *J. Research Natl. Bur. Standards*, **64A**, 1 (1960). See also K. Mendelssohn, *Progress in Cryogenics*, Academic Press, New York, 1960, Vol. II, pp. 121–45.

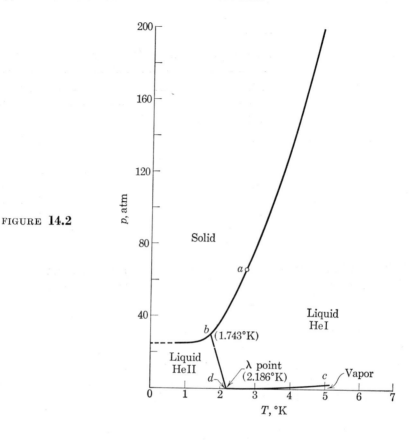

FIGURE **14.2**

The Clausius-Clapeyron equation gives for the slope of the melting curve

$$\frac{dp}{dT} = \frac{\Lambda}{T \, \Delta V}$$

or

$$\Lambda = T \, \Delta V \frac{dp}{dT}$$

where ΔV = change in volume on melting = $V^L - V'''$. Here, as in Sec. 14.4, V^L is used for the liquid phase, and it may refer to either HeII or HeI, depending on whether the liquid is below or above the triple point, b. The size of ΔV as T is lowered through this triple point has been measured very carefully and is shown in Fig. 14.3. The liquid retains a larger volume than the solid down to the limits of measurement. We know therefore that as $T \to 0$, $\Lambda \to 0$ and the melting of the solid to liquid occurs without any latent heat. Since $\Lambda = 0$ for a considerable range, we conclude that no enthalpy change occurs on fusion. Solid helium is not melted by the addition of heat but simply by the release of pressure. Therefore, the passage of the ordered crystalline solid to HeII occurs

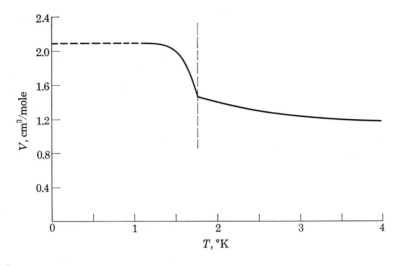

FIGURE **14.3**

with a loss of internal energy in much the same way that a compressed spring loses energy on decompression. Melting is a purely mechanical process.

Let us now return to point a on the fusion curve and move up to higher pressures. Melting to normal liquid occurs until a temperature above T_c is reached. From there on (and the curve has been followed up to some 7000 atm) the solid *melts to a gas*. This peculiar behavior is also found in hydrogen and is consistent with the usual definition of the critical temperature as that temperature above which the liquid may not exist, however great the pressure. In the case of the light isotope He³, the two triple points and the transition line between are all missing. Three phases of this rare substance cannot coexist.

14.6   The Order of a Transition

The ordinary transitions that we have met in the preceding chapters are known as *first-order transitions*.

The order of a transition can be defined in terms of the behavior of Gibbs' function as the temperature is varied. We know that for any phase transition Gibbs' function must vary continuously as the temperature is raised, since Gibbs' function does not change with phase. From CIV for a unit mass, we have

$$dg = -ds\,dT + v\,dp$$

and therefore

$$\left(\frac{\partial g}{\partial T}\right)_p = -s$$

and

$$\left(\frac{\partial g}{\partial p}\right)_T = v$$

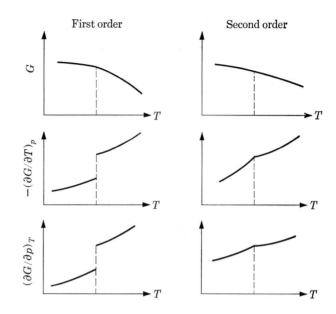

FIGURE **14.4**

For a transition from phase 2 to phase 1 (phase 1 being stable at higher temperatures)

$$g'' - g' = 0 \tag{14.5}$$
$$dg'' - dg' = 0$$

and thus

$$\left(\frac{\partial g''}{\partial T}\right)_p - \left(\frac{\partial g'}{\partial T}\right)_p = s' - s'' = \frac{\lambda_{21}}{T} \tag{14.6}$$

and

$$\left(\frac{\partial g'}{\partial p}\right)_T - \left(\frac{\partial g''}{\partial p}\right)_T = v' - v'' = \Delta v_{21} \tag{14.7}$$

If there is a *finite* change in entropy (that is, a measurable latent heat) and a *finite* change in volume in passage through the transition point, Gibbs' function, although continuous, exhibits a discontinuity in its *first derivatives*. The transition is then called a *first-order transition*. The characteristic behavior of first-order transitions is shown on the left in Fig. 14.4. In contrast to first-order transitions are those in which both G and its first derivative are continuous but which exhibit *discontinuities* in *all of the second-order derivatives*. These are *second-order* transitions, and the right side of Fig. 14.4 refers to them.

To examine second-order transitions, we begin as before with Eq. 14.5. Eqs. 14.6 and 14.7 reduce to zero since now

$$s' = s''$$

and

$$v' = v''$$

The second-order derivatives, however, are not zero and become

$$\left(\frac{\partial^2 g''}{\partial T^2}\right)_p - \left(\frac{\partial^2 g'}{\partial T^2}\right)_p = \frac{c_p'}{T} - \frac{c_p''}{T} \tag{14.8}$$

$$\left(\frac{\partial^2 g'}{\partial p^2}\right)_T - \left(\frac{\partial^2 g''}{\partial p^2}\right)_T = \left(\frac{\partial v'}{\partial p}\right)_T - \left(\frac{\partial v''}{\partial p}\right)_T = -v(\kappa_T' - \kappa_T'') \tag{14.9}$$

$$\frac{\partial^2 g'}{\partial T \, \partial p} - \frac{\partial^2 g''}{\partial T \, \partial p} = \left(\frac{\partial v'}{\partial T}\right)_p - \left(\frac{\partial v''}{\partial T}\right)_p = v(\beta_p' - \beta_p'') \tag{14.10}$$

In other words, a true second-order type of transition should show discontinuities in the specific heats, the compressibilities, and the expansion coefficients.

In the case of a first-order transition, the slope of the equilibrium curve is given by the Clausius-Clapeyron equation as

$$\frac{dp}{dT} = \frac{s' - s''}{v' - v''}$$

In the case of a second- (or higher-) order transition, the right side of this equation becomes $0/0$ and is thus indeterminate. To obtain a determinate value for dp/dT, we return to the first dQ_C expression, which on use of the second law becomes

$$dq_C = T \, ds = c_p \, dT - T\left(\frac{\partial v}{\partial T}\right)_p dp$$

Since

$$T \, ds' = T \, ds''$$

therefore

$$c_p' \, dT - T v' \beta_p' \, dp = c_p'' \, dT - T v'' \beta_p'' \, dp$$

or

$$\boxed{\frac{dp}{dT} = \frac{c_p' - c_p''}{Tv(\beta_p' - \beta_p'')}} \tag{14.11}$$

where $v' = v'' = v$.

This may be expressed in another way if the equality of v' and v'' is utilized. Thus we write

$$dv = \left(\frac{\partial v}{\partial T}\right)_p dT + \left(\frac{\partial v}{\partial p}\right)_T dp$$

or

$$dv = v(\beta_p \, dT - \kappa_T \, dp)$$

and since at the transition point $dv' = dv''$,

$$v(\beta_p' \, dT - \kappa_T' \, dp) = v(\beta_p'' \, dT - \kappa_T'' \, dp)$$

or

$$\boxed{\frac{dp}{dT} = \frac{\beta_p' - \beta_p''}{\kappa_T' - \kappa_T''}} \tag{14.12}$$

These are the two equations deduced by Ehrenfest for second-order transitions. They are the alternate forms taken on by the Clausius-Clapeyron equation when entropy and volume show no discontinuities.

14.7   The λ Transition in Helium

The transition from liquid helium I to liquid helium II at the upper triple point of Fig. 14.2 and along the solid line between points b and d appears to be a normal first-order transition (finite latent heat, etc.). At the lower triple point (the λ point), however, the transition involves most of the characteristics of a second-order transition, as follows:

1. There is no measurable λ, and the volume and entropy show no discontinuities. With single primes for liquid HeI, double primes for liquid HeII, and no primes for the vapor, the Clausius-Clapeyron equation for the slope of the vapor pressure curve becomes

$$\frac{dp}{dt} = \frac{s - s'}{v - v'} \qquad \text{for liquid HeI and vapor}$$

and

$$\frac{dp}{dt} = \frac{s - s''}{v - v''} \qquad \text{for liquid HeII and vapor}$$

Since $s' = s''$ and $v' = v''$, these slopes are identical and therefore no discontinuity in the vapor pressure curve exists at the λ point (see Fig. 14.1).

2. The slope of the volume curve changes sign at the λ point, being positive for HeI and negative for HeII.

3. The specific heat shows the anomalous behavior illustrated in Fig. 14.5. In fact, it was the fancied resemblance of this curve to the Greek letter λ that gave the transition its name. Whether the shape of the curve is to be interpreted as indicating a sudden jump in c_p, a cusp, or an infinite singularity is impossible to establish from the experimental data.

If, for purposes of argument, we regard the change in c_p as a finite jump,

$$c_p' = 1.2 \text{ cal/g at } 2.190°\text{K}$$
and
$$c_p'' = 2.9 \text{ cal/g at } 2.188°\text{K}$$

The corresponding values of the volume coefficients are

$$\beta' = 0.02 \text{ deg}^{-1}$$
and
$$\beta'' = -0.04 \text{ deg}^{-1}$$

With $v = 6.84 \text{ cm}^3/\text{g}$, use of Eq. 14.11 gives for the slope of the equilibrium curve between the two liquids (under their own vapor pressures)

$$\frac{dp}{dt} = -78 \text{ atm/deg}$$

This is in substantial agreement with the observed value of -81 atm/deg.

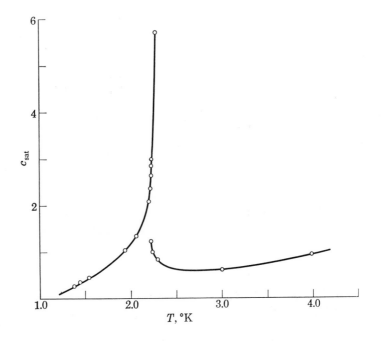

FIGURE **14.5**

If this slope is used in the second Ehrenfest equation, Eq. 14.12, to calculate $\kappa_T{}' - \kappa_T{}''$, the result is -6.2×10^{-10}, which is too small to be measured with any certainty. It thus appears that the transition can, provisionally at least, be classified as a second-order one.

Other examples of higher-order transitions are afforded by superconductors, to which the Ehrenfest equations apply quite satisfactorily. In cases of "order-disorder" transitions in metals (iron and nickel changing from magnetic to paramagnetic substances at the Curie point and the like), β and κ_T show finite jumps whereas c_p exhibits anomalous changes often involving infinite singular points.

14.8   Dynamic Properties of Helium

Although the transition from HeI to HeII is accompanied by very small variations in thermal and static mechanical properties, the new type of liquid possesses many quite surprising dynamic properties.

The Phenomenon of Surface Flow.   Study of the properties of HeII is complicated by the fact that it is difficult to keep the liquid in an open vessel, however uniform the temperature. Daunt and Mendelssohn arranged a small beaker (Fig. 14.6) that could be raised from and lowered into the surface of HeII in a container. When the beaker is lowered into the liquid, HeII collects in it from the bath. When the beaker is raised somewhat, the liquid flows out

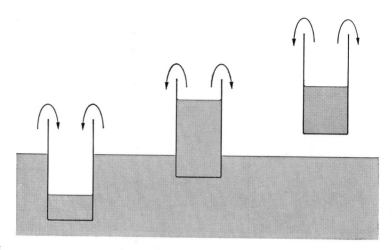

FIGURE **14.6**

into the bath until the surfaces within and without are at the same level. Finally, when the beaker is raised free of the liquid surface, HeII flows out over the sides and drips into the main reservoir until the beaker is emptied. The flow rate in the first two cases is almost constant and independent of the ordinary hydrostatic pressure differences. The flow takes place in a thin film of the order of several hundred atoms in thickness. Although the speed of flow varies with temperature below 1.5°K, it averages around 20 cm/sec.

Abnormal Flow in Capillaries.   A normal liquid flows through a capillary at a rate dependent on the viscosity, η, and the pressure difference, $p_1 - p_2$, between the entrance and the exit ends of the capillary. The mass flow rate is given quantitatively by Poiseuille's formula as

$$\text{mass rate} = \frac{\pi \rho r^4}{8 \eta L} (p_1 - p_2)$$

r and L being the radius and length of the capillary, ρ the fluid density, and η the coefficient of viscosity. In particular, if the capillary radius is reduced by a factor of one half, the flow rate is reduced to only one sixteenth its former value.

In contrast to this behavior, the rate of flow of HeII is independent of the pressure head and varies only slightly with the radius!

At the same time the rate of flow of HeII indicates an abnormally low viscosity, which decreases rapidly as the temperature is lowered from the λ point. This peculiarity is illustrated dramatically in Fig. 14.7, drawn from the data of Osborne and his collaborators[6] for flow through a very small annulus. The results of similar experiments with the rare light isotope He³ are shown as a

---

[6] Osborne, Weinstock, and Abraham, *Phys. Rev.*, **75**, 988 (1949).

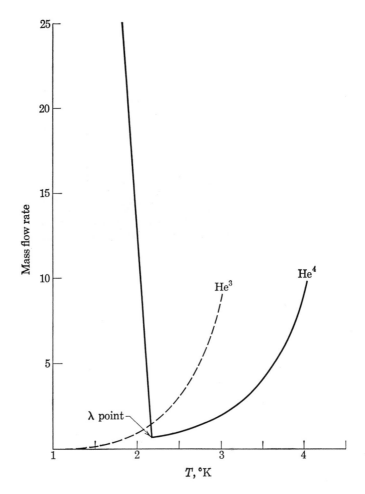

FIGURE **14.7**

dashed line. This isotope gives no evidence of the existence of an abnormal fluid state, the flow rate dropping rapidly to zero at low temperatures.

The Mechanocaloric and Fountain Effects.   If HeII is placed in a container having an opening at the bottom (Fig. 14.8), the container is lowered into the surface of HeII in a larger vessel, and a small amount of heat is supplied by a heating coil, liquid is drawn in until it reaches a steady level higher than the outside level. This is the *mechanocaloric* effect. It also operates in the reverse way, in the sense that when HeII flows out through an opening, it leaves the remaining liquid cooler. In Fig. 14.9 a Dewar flask covered at the top and provided with a small hole at the bottom is filled with HeII. The hole in the bottom is partially obstructed with a layer of fine emery powder. When the flask is raised from the surface of HeII in a bath, liquid flows out, and the liquid remaining shows a rise in temperature of about 0.01°K. When the flask

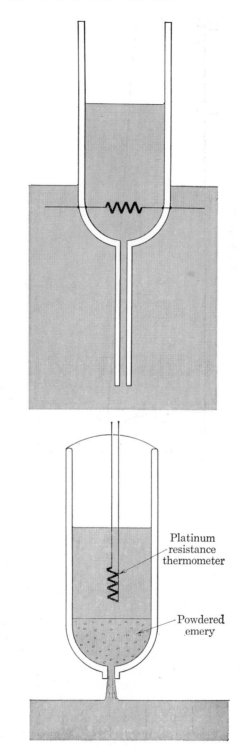

FIGURE **14.8**

FIGURE **14.9**

Platinum
resistance
thermometer

Powdered
emery

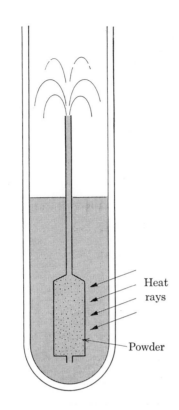

FIGURE **14.10**

Heat
rays

Powder

is lowered into the bath again, flow occurs in the opposite direction, and the liquid is cooled by the same amount.

One of the most striking of the mechanocaloric phenomena is the fountain effect, discovered by Allen and Jones.[7] The apparatus used is shown in Fig. 14.10. A glass tube with a narrow capillary neck and a small hole at the bottom has its lower end filled with fine emery powder. The tube is immersed in a bath of HeII, and the lower end of the tube is warmed by rays from an ordinary flashlight. The liquid rises in the capillary and forms a fountain, which may rise as high as 20 or 30 cm above the end of the tube.

14.9 The Two-Fluid Theory of HeII

Tisza has developed a theory that accounts for the properties and behavior of liquid HeII in terms of the presence of two fluids.[8] According to his model, HeII is a mixture of these two hypothetical fluids: (1) a *normal liquid* composed of normal He atoms showing normal viscosity; and (2) a *hyperfluid* with a definite

[7] Allen and Jones, *Nature*, **141**, 243 (1938); and Allen and Reekie, *Proc. Cambridge Phil. Soc.*, **35**, 114 (1939).

[8] Tisza, *Phys. Rev.*, **72**, 838 (1947).

zero-point energy, no entropy, and the ability to move through the first fluid without viscous effects.

Of course, these two fluids cannot be taken too literally; the Tisza two-fluid theory is simply a picturesque simplification of a more complicated reality. If we suppose the superfluid to be in fact made up of cooperative assemblies of atoms in the lowest quantum state to which the assemblies have access, it has large zero-point energy and yet no heat capacity or entropy. Because of their zero-point energy, these assemblies have momentum and mobility and migrate more freely the less hindered they are by the normal liquid. The normal liquid is then a mixture of all the assemblies in higher quantum states and takes on more and more the properties of ordinary liquid helium as the temperature is raised.

If we designate the density of HeII by ρ, we may write

$$\rho = \rho_s + \rho_n$$

where ρ_s and ρ_n are the densities of the superfluid and normal fluid, respectively. The ratio of the density ρ_n to ρ for HeII has been estimated by several means and is shown graphically in Fig. 14.11, which indicates the predominance of the superfluid over most of the range below the λ point. The abnormal mobility and almost vanishing viscosity of the superfluid are responsible for the surface flow and the abnormal flow in capillaries described in the last section.

The mechanocaloric effects also become qualitatively understandable in terms of the two-fluid theory. If local heating takes place in HeII, local

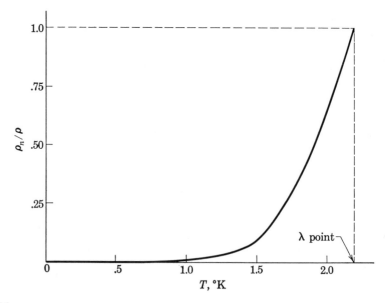

FIGURE **14.11**

depletion of superfluid atoms occurs, owing to the high gradient of the curve in Fig. 14.11 over most of its length. Superfluid atoms then diffuse in rapidly from the outside or flow in through surface films in an attempt to restore balance. The heating observed with the apparatus shown in Fig. 14.9 is due to the upset in the ratio of normal fluid to superfluid as the superfluid molecules flow out at the bottom. Since they take no entropy (only mass) from the vessel, the average level of entropy and hence the temperature of the remainder are raised. The opposite effect occurs when the Dewar flask is immersed in the liquid bath. It is presumably this same effect in an exaggerated form that produces the fountain.[9]

14.10   Superconductivity

It was discovered by Kamerlingh Onnes in 1911 that a thin capillary thread of mercury suddenly ceased to show a measurable electrical resistance when the temperature was lowered below 4.2°K. This phenomenon of superconductivity was later found to exist in many other elements, as well as in many alloys and compounds. That the resistance below the transition temperature is extraordinarily small (and presumably zero) was illustrated by a dramatic experiment. A superconducting lead ring in which a current had been set up in Leiden was flown in its helium bath to a British Association meeting in London, where many hours later the current was still detectable by its effect on a small compass. Clearly superconductivity is another example of cooperative assemblies in which, once a current is set up, electrons continue to circulate in as natural and persistent a manner as, say, an electron circulates in the ground state of a hydrogen atom. The general behavior is illustrated in Fig. 14.12, where r/r_0, the ratio of the resistance at T to its value at some fixed temperature, is shown as a function of T. The transition to immeasurably small values takes place within a range of usually less than 0.01° for pure elements. The transition temperature, T_0, can thus be measured with considerable precision.

Superconductivity is characteristic only of elements near the center of the periodic table; no element with a single valence electron (group I) has thus far exhibited the phenomenon. The twenty-three elements known to show superconductivity are indicated by the circles in Fig. 14.13, where atomic volumes are plotted versus atomic numbers. The superconductors are all of low but not always the lowest atomic volumes.

Although the superconducting isotopes of a single element obey a law of the form

$$T_0 M^{1/2} = \text{constant}$$

where M is the isotope mass, no regularity governs the value of T_0 for different elements. Of the twenty-three elements in Fig. 14.13, about half have

---

[9] For a discussion of liquid helium as a quantum liquid, see C. J. Gorter, ed., *Progress in Low Temperature Physics*, Interscience, New York, 1955, Vol. I, Chap. 2.

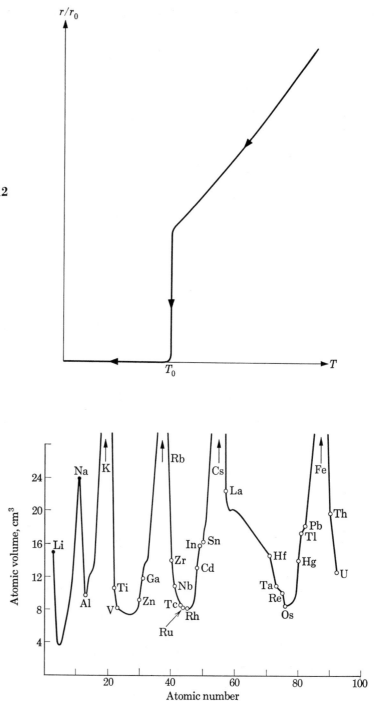

FIGURE **14.12**

FIGURE **14.13**

$T_0 < 2°K$, whereas T_0 for the others ranges as high as $11.2°K$ (technetium, atomic number 43).

14.11   Superconductors in a Magnetic Field

The transition temperature is sensitive to stresses, mechanical as well as magnetic. If a magnetic field is applied to a superconductor *below* its normal transition temperature, it remains superconducting until a critical value of the field, $\mathcal{H}_c$, is reached. For all fields above $\mathcal{H}_c$ it reverts to its normal state. Thus if we plot a curve, Fig. 14.14, of *critical threshold* values of the field versus T, the $\mathcal{H}$-T plane is divided into two areas. To the left and below the threshold curve, the substance is superconducting, and outside this area it is normal. Furthermore, a substance brought to any value of $\mathcal{H}$ and T within the super-conducting region has a state that is strictly fixed by $\mathcal{H}$ and T and independent of how the system got there. Hence the effects concerned are reversible, and thermodynamic arguments may be applied to such systems.

In general, as the temperature is lowered through T_0 at $\mathcal{H} = 0$ (that is, $a \rightarrow b$ in Fig. 14.14), the transition to the superconductor takes place at T_0 without latent heat evolution, although the specific heat shows a discontinuity. In other words, the no-field transition is a *second*-order one. On the other hand, the passage, say, $c \rightarrow d$, involves a finite latent heat at the transition curve, and the transition at a finite field is therefore a first-order one analogous to the ordinary transition of one solid modification of a substance into another.

Inside the threshold curve, $\mathcal{H}$ and T are independent, but along the curve $\mathcal{H} = \mathcal{H}(T)$, and the system is a typical restricted one. To emphasize this relationship, we write critical values of the field as $\mathcal{H}_c$ and have $\mathcal{H} = \mathcal{H}_c(T)$ along the threshold curve.

For all fields with $\mathcal{H} \leq \mathcal{H}_c$, the superconductor is paramagnetic, whereas for larger fields it reverts to the normal metal and is nonmagnetic. Here

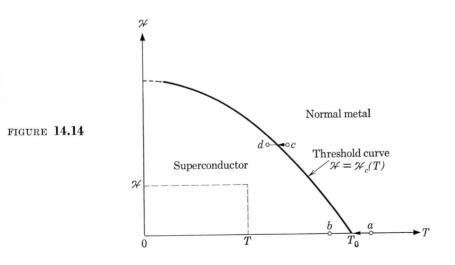

FIGURE **14.14**

B (the magnetic induction) $= \mathscr{H}$, and the field produces no net induction in the metal.

The first law for a paramagnetic substance, Eq. 5.16 from Sec. 5.5, gives

$$dU = dQ_c + \mathscr{H}\,d\mathbf{M} \tag{14.13}$$

Therefore CI becomes

$$dU = T\,dS + \mathscr{H}\,d\mathbf{M} \tag{14.14}$$

within the threshold region. On the critical curve, where the system is made up of superconducting and normal metal in stable equilibrium,

$$dU = \underline{T}\,dS + \mathscr{H}_c\,d\underline{\mathbf{M}} \tag{14.15}$$

Since now T and $\mathscr{H}_c$ are related, we select the underlined variables as independent. Then the modified Jacobian, $J_0{}'$, becomes

$$J_0{}' = \frac{\partial(S, -\mathscr{H}_c)}{\partial(T, \mathbf{M})} = \begin{vmatrix} \left(\dfrac{\partial S}{\partial T}\right)_{\mathbf{M}} & \dfrac{-d\mathscr{H}_c}{dT} \\[2ex] \left(\dfrac{\partial S}{\partial \mathbf{M}}\right)_T & 0 \end{vmatrix} \tag{14.16}$$

the zero arising because $\mathscr{H}_c = \mathscr{H}_c(T)$.

From the symmetry of $J_0{}'$ Maxwell's relation is

$$\frac{d\mathscr{H}_c}{dT} = -\left(\frac{\partial S}{\partial \mathbf{M}}\right)_T \tag{14.17}$$

the latter derivative giving the increase in entropy per unit increase in magnetic moment at fixed T. If we envisage a finite isothermal process in which a mole of superconductor changes to a mole of normal metal, the change in magnetic moment is

$$\mathbf{M}' - \mathbf{M}''$$

the single prime referring to the normal metal, and the entropy change is

$$S' - S'' = \frac{\Lambda}{T}$$

Λ being the heat absorbed in the passage from superconductor to normal metal. Thus Eq. 14.17 can be written

$$\frac{d\mathscr{H}_c}{dT} = \frac{-\Lambda}{T(\mathbf{M}' - \mathbf{M}'')} \tag{14.18}$$

This is the Clausius-Clapeyron equation for the slope of the threshold curve.

In this case the normal metal is nonmagnetic, $B = \mathscr{H}$, and $\mathbf{M}' = 0$. Generally as the threshold curve is approached from below,

$$B = \mathscr{H} + \frac{4\pi\mathbf{M}}{V}$$

If the sample is a long thin rod with the field along its axis so that it produces negligible self-demagnetization, the applied magnetic field can produce *no induction* in the interior of an *infinitely good conductor*. Therefore, within the superconductor $B = 0$, and when $\mathcal{H} = \mathcal{H}_c$,

$$4\pi \frac{\mathbf{M}}{V} = -\mathcal{H}_c$$

or

$$\mathbf{M} = \frac{-V\mathcal{H}_c}{4\pi} = \mathbf{M}''$$

In other words, the magnetic polarization in the interior of a pure unstressed superconductor exactly cancels the applied field. Inserting this value in Eq. 14.18 with $\mathbf{M}' = 0$ and solving for Λ give

$$\Lambda = -\frac{VT\mathcal{H}_c}{4\pi}\frac{d\mathcal{H}_c}{dT} \tag{14.19}$$

For all known superconductors the threshold curve has a strictly finite slope where it intersects the $\mathcal{H} = 0$ axis at T_0, the no-field transition temperature. Since $\mathcal{H}_c = 0$, $\Lambda = 0$ at this point. As the threshold curve approaches the $T = 0$ axis, the *slope* approaches zero, and again Λ vanishes. Everywhere else the slope of the threshold curve is negative, and there is a finite latent heat absorbed on passage from the superconductor to the normal metal. Values of Λ calculated from Eq. 14.19 agree very well with direct calorimetric observations. It is essential to the use of Eq. 14.19 that the metal be as pure as possible and free of all mechanical strain.[10]

14.12 Magnetic Cooling by Adiabatic Demagnetization

We have seen that cooling below about 0.7°K by forced evaporation of liquid helium is difficult owing to the slight vapor pressure (2×10^{-3} mm of mercury). In addition, the rapid creeping of HeII up the sides of a vessel introduces problems that are equivalent to a new source of heat leakage. The HeII moves up Dewar walls to a warmer region, where it evaporates, absorbing heat. It then condenses on the colder liquid and gives off the latent heat again. The result is the transfer of heat to the coldest part of the system.

It was suggested by Debye and independently by Giauque[11] that the properties of certain paramagnetic salts suited them for the production of refrigerating effects in the region below 1°K.

---

[10] For the theory of superconductors, see Casimir and Gorter, *Physik. Z.*, **35**, 963 (1934); *Physica*, **15**, 55 (1949); and F. London, *Superfluids*, Wiley, New York, 1950, Vol. I, particularly Chaps. A and B.

[11] Debye, *Ann. Physik,* **81.** 1154 (1926); and Giauque, *J. Am. Chem. Soc.*, **49**, 1864, 1870 (1927).

Let us return to the general CI expression for a paramagnetic substance in a magnetic field as given in the last section

$$dU = \underline{T}\,dS + \underline{\mathcal{H}}\,d\mathbf{M} \tag{14.14}$$

Since no relation exists between T and $\mathcal{H}$, as in the special case of Eq. 14.15, the system is an *unrestricted* one, and we may choose T and $\mathcal{H}$ as the independent variables, as indicated by the underscoring. Then

$$J_0' = \frac{\partial(S, \mathbf{M})}{\partial(T, \mathcal{H})} = \begin{vmatrix} \left(\dfrac{\partial S}{\partial T}\right)_{\mathcal{H}} & \left(\dfrac{\partial \mathbf{M}}{\partial T}\right)_{\mathcal{H}} \\ \left(\dfrac{\partial S}{\partial \mathcal{H}}\right)_{T} & \left(\dfrac{\partial \mathbf{M}}{\partial \mathcal{H}}\right)_{T} \end{vmatrix} = \begin{vmatrix} a_0 & a_1 \\ a_1 & b_1 \end{vmatrix} \tag{14.20}$$

In this case $a_0 = C_{\mathcal{H}}/T$, where $C_{\mathcal{H}}$ is the heat capacity at constant field and may normally be taken as equal to C_p. The constants a_1 and b_1 are defined in terms of the total magnetic susceptibility for the system. If χ is the molar susceptibility, it is defined by the relation

$$\mathbf{M} = \chi\mathcal{H}$$

Then it follows that

$$b_1 = \left(\frac{\partial \mathbf{M}}{\partial \mathcal{H}}\right)_T = \chi$$

and

$$a_1 = \left(\frac{\partial \mathbf{M}}{\partial T}\right)_{\mathcal{H}} = \mathcal{H}\left(\frac{\partial \chi}{\partial T}\right)_{\mathcal{H}} \tag{14.21}$$

In general, χ decreases with temperature for all materials; as the temperature is raised, the increased temperature agitation reduces the magnetic dipole alignment. For example, if the substance obeys Curie's law as written in Eq. 14.1, and if we avoid too high fields,

$$\chi T = C$$

C being Curie's constant. Then

$$\left(\frac{\partial \chi}{\partial T}\right)_{\mathcal{H}} = -\frac{C}{T^2}$$

and

$$a_1 = -\frac{\mathcal{H}C}{T^2} < 0$$

We now write Maxwell's relation as

$$\left(\frac{\partial S}{\partial \mathcal{H}}\right)_T = \mathcal{H}\left(\frac{\partial \chi}{\partial T}\right)_{\mathcal{H}} = -|a_1| \tag{14.22}$$

where $|a_1|$ is the absolute value of $(\partial \mathbf{M}/\partial_T)_{\mathcal{H}}$. This equation means that as the magnetic field is increased isothermally, the entropy always diminishes; that is, as the magnetic field reduces the *degree* of *disorder* among the randomly directed magnetic dipoles, *entropy always decreases*. We must now apply Eq. 14.22 to two important types of change, isothermal and adiabatic.

Isothermal Magnetization. When the magnetic field applied to the system is increased at constant temperature by $d\mathcal{H}$, the increase in entropy becomes

$$dS = \left(\frac{\partial S}{\partial \mathcal{H}}\right)_T d\mathcal{H} = \mathcal{H}\left(\frac{\partial \chi}{\partial T}\right)_{\mathcal{H}} d\mathcal{H} = -|a_1|\, d\mathcal{H} \qquad (14.23)$$

Therefore, for a finite change from $\mathcal{H} = 0$ to $\mathcal{H}$, we obtain for the total entropy change

$$S(\mathcal{H}, T) - S(0, T) = -\int_0^{\mathcal{H}} |a_1|\, d\mathcal{H} \qquad (14.24)$$

This is always negative and reflects the finite decrease in the disorder of the magnetic dipoles.

Similarly, the heat absorbed, dQ_T, during the change in entropy, dS, is

$$dQ_T = T\, dS = T\mathcal{H}\left(\frac{\partial \chi}{\partial T}\right)_{\mathcal{H}} = -|a_1|T\, d\mathcal{H} < 0$$

For the finite change we have

$$Q_T = -T\int_0^{\mathcal{H}} |a_1|\, d\mathcal{H} < 0 \qquad (14.25)$$

Thus heat is always *rejected* on isothermal magnetization of a paramagnetic material.

Adiabatic Change of Magnetic Field. To find what happens when the magnetic field is changed reversibly and *adiabatically*, we need first the equivalent dQ_C expression for the system. The hydrostatic expression is

$$dQ_C = C_p dT - T\left(\frac{\partial V}{\partial T}\right)_p dp \qquad (14.26)$$

With $p = -\mathcal{H}$ and $V = \mathbf{M}$, this translates to

$$dQ_C = C_{\mathcal{H}} dT + T\left(\frac{\partial \mathbf{M}}{\partial T}\right)_{\mathcal{H}} d\mathcal{H}$$

For an adiabatic change $dQ_C = 0$,

and

$$C_{\mathcal{H}} dT - |a_1|T\, d\mathcal{H} = 0$$

or

$$dT = \frac{|a_1|}{C_{\mathcal{H}}} T\, d\mathcal{H} \qquad (14.27)$$

In other words, increasing the magnetic field adiabatically always raises the temperature.

For the production of cooling the magnetic field must be *reduced adiabatically*. If a sample is at temperature T and field $\mathcal{H}$ and the field is reduced adiabatically to zero, the temperature change is obtained from

$$\int_{T_i}^{T_e} \frac{dT}{T} = \ln \frac{T_e}{T_i} = \int_{\mathcal{H}}^0 \frac{|a_1|}{C_{\mathcal{H}}} d\mathcal{H} = -\int_0^{\mathcal{H}} \frac{|a_1|}{C_p} d\mathcal{H} \qquad (14.28)$$

where $C_{\mathcal{H}}$ is replaced by the ordinary heat capacity.

This result is the thermodynamic basis of magnetic cooling. A paramagnetic salt suspended as in Fig. 14.15 is placed in a bath of liquid helium, which in turn is in a bath of liquid nitrogen. The sample is first cooled to a temperature near 1°K, say, T_i (Fig. 14.16), by vigorous pumping of the liquid helium in the surrounding bath. Thermal contact with the paramagnetic salt is made by filling the inner vessel with helium vapor, which can later be evacuated to isolate the specimen.

With the sample at point i in Fig. 14.16, the Kelvin value of the temperature, T_i, is readily obtained from the helium vapor pressure. When the magnetic field is increased isothermally from 0 to $\mathscr{H}$, heat, Q_T, is evolved and carried off by the helium atmosphere to the helium bath. The system's state changes along the path $i \rightarrow a$. At a the system is isolated, and then the field is reduced to zero ($a \rightarrow e$). The final magnetic temperature, T^*_e, is determined by measurement of the susceptibility in a very weak field by means of the coils surrounding the inner tube (Fig. 14.15).

If two-stage cooling is desired, the paramagnetic system is designed to be separable into two parts: one part acts as the heat reservoir to absorb the heat, Q_T, evolved as the other part is magnetized to b. This process is followed by another adiabatic demagnetization to a still lower temperature, T^*_2. Unfortunately, the reduction achieved in the second operation is only a fraction, say, one half or less, of the first reduction from T_i to T^*_e. As we shall see in Sec. 14.14, this condition of diminishing returns continues to operate as a

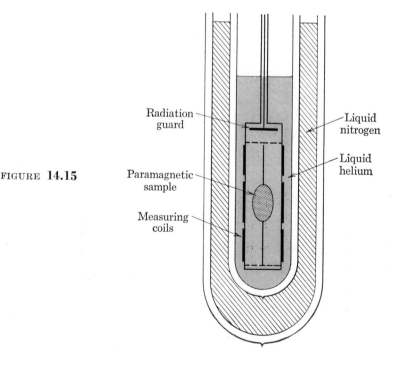

FIGURE **14.15**

Radiation guard

Liquid nitrogen

Liquid helium

Paramagnetic sample

Measuring coils

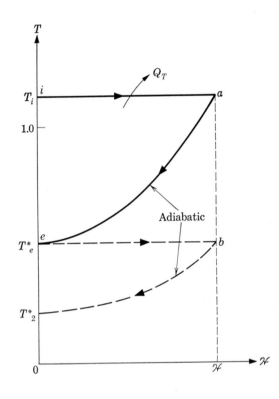

FIGURE **14.16**

consequence of the third law of thermodynamics. This law indicates that 0°K can never be reached by a finite number of repetitions of such a (or any other) cooling process.

Of course, to obtain and maintain these low temperatures requires most scrupulous care, as the flow of energy by conduction or radiation from the outside into the system must be prevented. Energy flows of a few ergs a minute are very troublesome, owing to the extremely low heat capacities of all materials at the low temperatures.

14.13 Magnetic Temperatures

As we saw in Sec. 14.4, the helium vapor pressure scale reaches only to 0.5°K. Below this, temperature must be measured on the magnetic scale, defined in Eq. 14.2. In an adiabatic demagnetization experiment, let T_i and T^*_e be the Kelvin and magnetic temperatures, respectively, corresponding to the points i and e of Fig. 14.16. Then the susceptibilities at these two points must be measured by means of weak fields produced in the auxiliary measuring coils surrounding the inner vessel. If the susceptibilities are χ_i and χ_e, respectively, then, by Eq. 14.2,

$$T^*_e = \left(\frac{\chi_i}{\chi_e}\right) T_i$$

To reduce such magnetic temperatures to the Kelvin scale, it is first necessary to add heat energy to the system in measured amounts, as, for example, by irradiating the paramagnetic sample with weak γ rays. For each irradiation with a known amount of energy, the rise in T^* at $\mathscr{H} = 0$ is determined. Since no external work is involved, the increase in internal energy, ΔU, is entirely due to heat added, which we write as $T \Delta S$. Thus

$$\Delta U = T \Delta S = \Delta Q_{\mathscr{H}}$$

or

$$T = \left| \frac{\Delta U}{\Delta S} \right|_{\mathscr{H}} = \frac{\Delta Q_{\mathscr{H}}}{\Delta S_{\mathscr{H}}}$$

In terms of the magnetic scale,

$$\Delta Q_{\mathscr{H}} = \frac{dQ^*_{\mathscr{H}}}{dT^*} \Delta T^*$$

and

$$\Delta S_{\mathscr{H}} = \left(\frac{\partial S}{\partial T^*} \right)_{\mathscr{H}} \Delta T^*$$

and therefore the Kelvin temperature is fixed by

$$T = \frac{\dfrac{dQ_{\mathscr{H}}}{dT^*}}{\left(\dfrac{\partial S}{dT^*} \right)_{\mathscr{H}}} = \frac{C^*_{\mathscr{H}}}{\left(\dfrac{\partial S}{\partial T^*_e} \right)_{\mathscr{H}}} \qquad (14.29)$$

where $C^*_{\mathscr{H}}$ is the heat capacity measured on the magnetic scale, and all values refer to $\mathscr{H} = 0$. The values of $C^*_{\mathscr{H}}$ are determined from the measured rises in T^*_e caused by the irradiation and can be plotted as functions of T^*_e.

To obtain $(\partial S / \partial T^*_e)_{\mathscr{H}}$, we note, referring to Fig. 14.16, that

$$S_a = S_e$$

since a and e are on the same adiabatic, and therefore

$$S_a - S_i = S_e - S_i$$

This difference is given by Eq. 14.24, and for every value of T_i and $\mathscr{H}$ there is a unique value of T^*_e. When $S_e - S_i$ is plotted versus T^*_e, the slope of the curve gives the desired derivative at $\mathscr{H} = 0$ for use in Eq. 14.29. Thus the magnetic temperature scale is finally reduced to the Kelvin scale.

The lowest temperatures obtainable by adiabatic demagnetization have gradually been reduced as techniques have been improved. Giauque and MacDougall in 1933 worked with gadolinium sulfate, $Gd_2(SO_4)_3 \cdot 8H_2O$, with maximum fields of 8000 oersteds and reached temperatures of about 0.25°K. Later De Haas and Wiersma, using ammonium iron alum, $FeNH_4(SO_4)_2 \cdot 12H_2O$, and fields up to 24,000 oersteds, reached magnetic temperatures of 0.018°K. The lowest temperatures reported from Leiden were reached in 1949 by the use of potassium chrome alum, $Cr_2(SO_4)_3K_2SO_4 \cdot 24H_2O$. A value of $0.0014°K$ was attained.[12]

In all cases it is necessary to work with crystals of complicated form, in which the ion possessing the magnetic dipole is surrounded by a great many nonmagnetic atoms. Thus each dipole is essentially unaffected by the other magnetic dipoles, and the substance is an *ideal* paramagnetic substance. The dipoles are free to be aligned by the field and to revert to disordered orientations as the field is reduced. If the dipoles are close to each other and interact strongly, they "lock" together to form large cooperative assemblies, characteristic of ferromagnetic substances. These substances have magnetic retentivity and are useless for magnetic cooling unless they are widely dispersed, as, for example, impurities in strictly nonmagnetic materials. With *nuclear spins* the interactions are much weaker because the nuclear dipole moments are very small and the dipole interaction even of neighboring atoms is negligible.

At the low temperatures under discussion, the contributions to energy and entropy of a paramagnetic salt are almost entirely of electronic and nuclear spin origin. The contributions of the lattice vibrations are practically nil below $1°K$. The strong crystalline electric fields split the ionic energy levels into two or more closely spaced electronic levels with the population scattered among them at temperatures of a few degrees Kelvin. At the lowest temperatures most of the population is in the single lowest level. Thus at the start of adiabatic demagnetization (the thermodynamic state defined by T_i and $\mathcal{H}$), we have relatively *large* disorder arising from scatter of the population among the electronic sublevels and *small* disorder due to the magnetic dipole orientations in the magnetic field. At the end state (with $\mathcal{H} = 0$ and $T = T^*_e$), the same total amount of disorder exists since entropy is constant. Most of the systems are now in the lowest electronic sublevel, and the dipoles are in disorder. One kind of disorder has simply been traded for another. We shall return to this question of molecular disorder and entropy in detail in the following chapter, on statistical mechanics. In Chap. 19 the Brillouin theory of the ideal paramagnetic substance will be presented as an illustration of the use of statistical methods (see Sec. 19.2).

14.14   The Lowest Temperature in the World

One further possibility for the production of low temperatures involves the use of nuclear magnetic moments rather than the electronic spin moments responsible for paramagnetism. Since nuclear moments are on the order of one thousandth the size of electronic moments, the magnetic field required to produce saturation at ordinary temperatures would be millions of times as large as the fields presently available. Of course, if material could be precooled to suffi-

---

[12] De Klerk, Steenland, and Gorter, *Physica*, **15**, 649, 711 (1949).

ciently low temperatures, say, around 0.01°K, fields of the order of 50,000 to 100,000 oersteds would likely be adequate.

Sir Francis Simon initiated the first nuclear cooling experiments at the Clarendon Laboratory in Oxford in 1956. In these experiments a bundle of fine copper wires was first cooled to about 0.01°K by ordinary adiabatic demagnetization. In the second stage much higher fields were used to orient the nuclear spins, and on demagnetization a temperature of 0.00001°K was attained. Since that time the apparatus and techniques have been considerably improved. Large generators capable of delivering currents of 5000 amp to the energizing coils of the electromagnets have been constructed and installed. Every possible precaution has been taken to ensure complete thermal isolation. Finally, the two-stage process has made possible the truly remarkable temperature of

$$0.000001°K$$

The extreme stringency of the thermal shielding requirements is suggested by the fact that the energy liberated by a small pin falling through $\frac{1}{8}$ in produces enough heat to warm a 100 g specimen from one millionth of a degree to the starting temperature of 0.01°K. For further details of these ingenious and truly heroic experiments, the reader is referred to an article by one of the experimenters, Nicholas Kurti.[13]

14.15   The Third Law of Thermodynamics

What has come to be known as the third law of thermodynamics had its origin in the so-called heat theorem of Nernst. This theorem resulted from the attempt to calculate thermodynamic functions entirely from thermal data—in particular, thermal data on the substances taking part in chemical reactions. As originally given by Nernst (in 1906), it stated simply that the change in entropy involved in an isothermal chemical process between pure crystalline solids tends toward zero as 0°K is reached, that is, that

$$\lim_{T \to 0} \Delta S_T \to 0$$

where ΔS_T is the entropy change for the isothermal reaction. A great deal of experiment and discussion intervened before the heat theorem was recognized, largely owing to the work of Simon, as a special case of a more general truth, which is now called the third law of thermodynamics.

In what we may term the Nernst-Simon form, this states: *"The entropy change involved in a reversible isothermal process in a nongaseous system tends toward zero as $T \to 0°K$."*

---

[13] Kurti, *Physics Today*, **13**, 26 (1960).

Another statement has arisen from the study of the adiabatic cooling process. We saw in Fig. 14.16 that repetition of the cooling cycle resulted in a smaller temperature fall than that obtained in the first stage. This decrease seems to continue indefinitely, each stage producing only a fraction of the temperature fall attained in the previous one. Therefore, the absolute zero can never be reached in any finite series of steps. Fowler and Guggenheim termed this the "unattainability" statement of the third law. It may be phrased as follows: *"It is impossible in principle by any process, however idealized, to attain the absolute zero in a finite number of steps."*

The two statements may be regarded as but two different ways of viewing the same process. Suppose, for example, that we examine two adiabatics in the T-S plane (Fig. 14.17). Let two entropy curves be constructed for a paramagnetic substance, one for $\mathcal{H} = 0$ and the other for an arbitrary value of $\mathcal{H}$.

We suppose not only that the curve for $\mathcal{H} = 0$ lies at higher entropy values, as we know it must, but also that the two curves intersect the $T = 0$ axis at two different values of the entropy, say $S(0, 0°)$ and $S(\mathcal{H}, 0°)$. Clearly such a situation contradicts the third law in the Nernst-Simon form. It also contradicts the second statement, as is seen if repeated magnetic cooling cycles, $a \rightarrow b \rightarrow c$, $c \rightarrow d \rightarrow e$, etc., are carried out, since in a finite number of steps $0°K$ is reached.

If, however, the two curves converge at a common value of the entropy, say, S_0 at $0°K$, the situation is as shown in Fig. 14.18. Then the two statements follow at once, for the series of isothermal magnetizations and adiabatic demagnetizations now produces a series of final temperatures, T_2, T_3, T_4, etc., and the limit of $0°K$ can result only from an indefinite number of stages.

FIGURE **14.17**

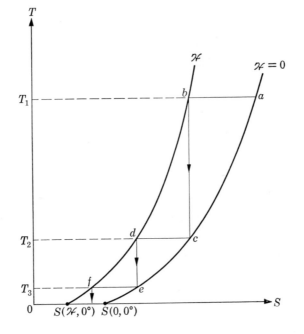

FIGURE **14.18**

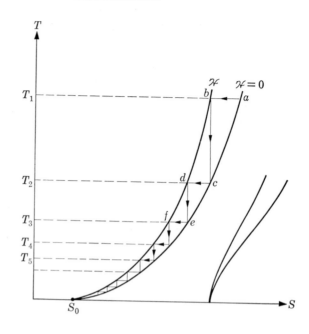

It is not necessary that the shape of the constant-field curves be as drawn on the left of the figure. In fact, at low enough temperatures they probably take on the shape of the pair on the right. The exact shape, however, is not essential to the argument.

The preceding reasoning also shows that in general all stable stressed states of a given sample of matter, whether they are due to impressed electric or magnetic fields, compressions, tensions, shears, etc., have the *same value of the entropy*, S_0, at 0°K. This condition does not tell us the value of S_0 or say that different substances must have the same value of the entropy constant, although Planck actually went so far as to assume the latter possibility and to set $S_0 = 0$ for equilibrium states of condensed phases of pure substances.

We shall see in later chapters, where the molecular interpretation of entropy will be taken up in detail, that adopting $S_0''' = 0$ for all pure substances is reasonable only when *no net nuclear or angular electronic moments* are possessed by the atoms of the material. For a body composed of atoms with nuclei having nonvanishing nuclear spins, even at absolute zero, when the disorder due to temperature is reduced to a minimum, there is still disorder in the orientation of the spin vectors. Thus the zero-point entropy, S_0''', should be greater than when this source of disorder is impossible, owing to the absence of nuclear (or other) spins.

Many general conclusions can be drawn from the third law. Two of these should be mentioned here since they have been discussed as experimental facts in what has gone before and now may be regarded either as proofs of the third law or as deductions from it if it is assumed true on other grounds.

1. The coefficient of thermal expansion, β_p, of any condensed phase must vanish as $T \to 0°K$. Suppose that we regard the entropy of a body as given by

$$S = S(T, p)$$

Then we know that as $T \to 0$, $S \to S_0$, where S_0 is independent of p. Thus we write

$$\lim_{T \to 0} \left(\frac{\partial S}{\partial p}\right)_T = 0$$

since entropy is independent of anything but temperature. By MI

$$\left(\frac{\partial S}{\partial p}\right)_T = -\left(\frac{\partial V}{\partial T}\right)_p$$

and therefore

$$\lim_{T \to 0} \left(\frac{\partial V}{\partial T}\right)_p = 0$$

Since the value of V remains finite, this means that β_p must vanish as $T \to 0$. (See Fig. 3.12, for example.)

2. The slope, dp/dT, of the equilibrium curve between any two condensed phases with a first-order transition must vanish as $T \to 0°K$. Writing the

FIGURE **14.19**

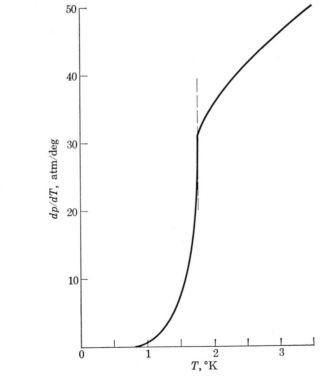

Clausius-Clapeyron equation for such a transition (from phase 3 to 2, say), we have

$$\frac{dp}{dT} = \frac{S'' - S'''}{V'' - V'''}$$

As $T \to 0$, $S'' - S''' \to 0$ also, by the third law. However, since the transition is of the first order, $V'' - V''' \neq 0$, and therefore

$$\lim_{T \to 0} \frac{dp}{dT} = 0$$

The best example of this relation is the melting curve of solid He to liquid HeII, shown in the phase diagram of Fig. 14.2. The slope of this curve has been determined very carefully by Simon and Swenson[14] and has the shape indicated in Fig. 14.19, where dp/dT, in atmospheres per degree, is plotted versus T. The curve changes its shape abruptly at the solid, HeI, and HeII triple point. Below this point it falls very rapidly to zero and is essentially zero for a range of nearly a degree above 0°K.

References

DAUNT and SMITH, *Revs. Modern Phys.*, **26**, 172 (1954).

JACKSON, L. C., *Low Temperature Physics*, Methuen Monographs on Physical Subjects, Wiley, New York, 1959.

MENDELSSOHN, K., *Repts. Progr. in Phys.*, **12** (1948/49), 270; *Progress in Cryogenics*, Academic Press, New York, Vols. I, II, and III, 1959, 1960, 1961.

PARK, *Am. J. Phys.*, **27**, 234 (1959).

SQUIRE, C. F., *Low Temperature Physics*, McGraw-Hill, New York, 1953.

Problems

14.1 Show that two Legendre transformations of

$$dU = T\,dS + \mathscr{H}_c\,d\mathbf{M}$$

give

$$dG = -S\,dT - \mathbf{M}\,d\mathscr{H}_c$$

where G is the Gibbs function for the superconductor at the threshold field and in the absence of external pressure; that is,

$$G = U - TS - \mathbf{M}\mathscr{H}_c$$

Use the expression for dG to obtain the Clausius-Clapeyron equation

$$\frac{d\mathscr{H}_c}{dT} = \frac{-\Lambda}{T(\mathbf{M}' - \mathbf{M}'')} \tag{14.18}$$

14.2 Use the third law to show that the emf of all reversible electric cells must vanish as $T \to 0°K$.

---

[14] Simon and Swenson, *Nature*, **165**, 829 (1950).

14.3 Carry out the same analysis for the case of a surface film. What is the equivalent result when applied to the superconductor on the threshold curve?

14.4 In the case of the superconductor tantalum, the slope of the threshold curve at $T = 3°\text{K}$ (where $\mathcal{H}_c = 450$ oersteds) is found to be

$$\frac{d\mathcal{H}_c}{dT} = -413 \text{ oersteds/deg}$$

If the volume is taken as 10.5 cm³/mole, calculate the latent heat for the transition from the superconductor to the normal metal (calories per mole).

14.5 In the case of potassium chrome alum, the following data are found for $C^*_{\mathcal{H}}$ and $\partial S/\partial T^*$ at $\mathcal{H} = 0$ for the given values of the magnetic temperature, T^*:

T^*	$C^*_{\mathcal{H}}$, cal/g-deg	$\left(\dfrac{\partial S}{\partial T^*}\right)_{\mathcal{H}}$, cal/g-deg
0.050	0.147	10.9
.040	.024	4.07

Find the corresponding Kelvin temperatures. [See De Klerk, *Physica*, **15**, 649, 711 (1949).]

14.6 If the heat capacity of a solid is assumed to obey the Debye cube law,

$$C_p''' = bT^3$$

show that the double integral in the vapor pressure equation, Eq. 14.3, reduces to

$$I(T) = \frac{bT^3}{12R} = \int_0^T S''' \, dT$$

where S''' is the entropy increase of the solid from 0°K to T.

14.7 Using the Jacobian method and the abbreviations of Sec. 14.12, show that C_M, the heat capacity at constant magnetic moment, is

$$C_M = \frac{T(a_0 - a_1^2)}{b_1} \tag{1}$$

It is found experimentally that C_M can be written

$$C_M = \frac{A}{T^2}$$

A being a constant. If, in addition, Curie's law holds, show that Eq. 1 reduces to

$$C_{\mathcal{H}} = \frac{1}{T^2}(A + C\mathcal{H}^2) \tag{2}$$

Combine Eq. 2 with Eq. 14.27 to obtain the differential equation for the temperature fall in adiabatic demagnetization. Show that integration from $T_i, \mathcal{H}$ to $T_e, 0$ gives the result for the ratio of the initial temperature to the final temperature as

$$\frac{T_i}{T_e} = 1 + \frac{C\mathcal{H}^2}{A} \tag{3}$$

CHAPTER FIFTEEN

Entropy and Probability

15.1   Order, Disorder, and the Second Law

With the formal treatment of the laws of thermodynamics and their applications finished in the last chapter, the rest of this book will be devoted to the general subject of statistical mechanics and its applications. Although the subject may be developed from various viewpoints, we shall take as our starting point the molecular interpretation of entropy and its tendency to increase in value as a system proceeds toward a state of final equilibrium.

The tendency for physical processes to proceed in one direction and not another must depend ultimately upon the way in which molecules, taken in great numbers, behave. In general, the tendency for systems to change toward equilibrium conditions is always associated with a progress toward states of ever greater molecular disorder. A high degree of molecular order is seldom observed in any system. We rarely find a large number of molecules in a gas all moving in the same direction with the same speed; we are much more likely to find a highly disorganized condition with speeds and directions showing no pattern. In fact, if we should create such an organized group of molecules and let it flow into an ordinary gas, the original order would soon give way to the normal confusion and disorder present in all gases (Fig. 15.1).

When a hot body and a cold body exist side by side, there is a certain kind of order, which disappears as soon as the two are placed in contact. Originally the molecules with a large average energy were in one volume, and those with a lower average were in another. As equilibrium is reached, this type of order disappears; the over-all disorder increases. In the same way, when gas A mixes with gas B, order is lost. Originally the two types of molecules were sorted out into separate compartments, a kind of ordering lost on mixing. Examination of the spontaneous processes discussed in Chap. 9 shows that they all involve a loss of order or an increase of disorder. If entropy inevitably increases in all these cases, the tendency for entropy to increase may have its origin in the natural tendency for *molecular disorder to increase*. In this event, a system

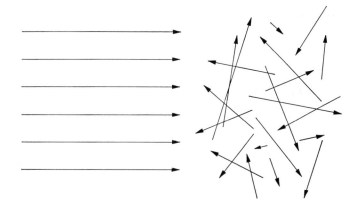

FIGURE **15.1**

reaches stable equilibrium with a maximum entropy simply because it has reached the state of maximum chaos or disorder of which it is capable.

Boltzmann was the first to conceive of this very fruitful idea and to succeed in giving a molecular interpretation of entropy. Although the idea may be extended in principle to systems of all types, we shall in the main be concerned with the specific applications to gases. This theory will provide the basic framework in terms of which extension to more complicated systems is possible.

In dealing with great numbers of particles, it is impossible to follow the motions of individual particles; we must consider rather what on the average is most likely to happen. Individual events are regarded as governed by pure chance, and resort is had to estimates of *probabilities*. This means that we give up *certainties* in favor of *probabilities*.

To understand the second law on a molecular level, we must therefore be able to understand why it is inherently more probable for a system of many particles to increase its entropy than to decrease it.

15.2   Mathematical Probability

It is a matter of common knowledge that if a penny is tossed a great number of times, there is a tendency for heads and tails to turn up roughly an equal number of times. We account for this behavior by saying that the odds or probabilities for heads are the same as for tails, that is, exactly $\frac{1}{2}$.

On the other hand, if we let

$$N_h = \text{number of heads observed}$$
$$N_t = \text{number of tails observed}$$

and $\quad\quad N = \text{total number of tosses}$

where $\quad\quad N = N_h + N_t$

we can define the experimental ratio for heads as

$$r_h = \frac{N_h}{N} \tag{15.1}$$

and for tails as
$$r_t = \frac{N_t}{N} \tag{15.2}$$

where, of course,
$$r_h + r_t = 1$$

In any particular run of N trials, the observed values of the r's might be 0.502 and 0.498, but we should not expect to obtain exactly these values in a second or third run of N trials. In other words, the values of the ratios in Eqs. 15.1 and 15.2 are *experimental numbers*. Although they do tend toward equal values, they do not measure mathematical probabilities; mathematical probabilities are not given as the limit of any series of experiments but rather are calculated directly from the symmetry of the problem or system under discussion.

We assign equal mathematical probabilities to each of two events when it is judged that they have the *same likelihood of happening*. From the physical symmetry of a coin (or, better, a thin disk with only a slight mark on one side to distinguish it from the other), we say that heads and tails have equal likelihoods and assign the value of $\frac{1}{2}$ as the mathematical probability of each. If a die has six sides, the mathematical probability of a given face's turning up is exactly $\frac{1}{6}$. This, of course, presupposes honest dice and neglects the slight natural asymmetry due to the marking dots themselves.

In general, suppose that n events are judged equally likely and that of these n_A are favorable to an event A. Then the mathematical probability, P_A, of event A is defined as

$$P_A = \frac{n_A}{n} \tag{15.3}$$

of event B as
$$P_B = \frac{n_B}{n} \tag{15.4}$$

etc. Thus with $n = 2$ (events A and B only),

$$P_A + P_B = \frac{n_A + n_B}{n} = 1$$

and the sum of all the mathematical probabilities in a given situation is 1. Thus unity corresponds to *certainty* (that is, A or B must occur, since no other events are included in the n events). On the other hand, *certainty against* an event's happening corresponds to a probability of 0. Mathematical probabilities must therefore lie between 0 and 1.

We must not identify the experimental ratios of Eqs. 15.1 and 15.2 with the mathematical probabilities given in Eqs. 15.3 and 15.4, with A representing heads and B tails. However, the tendency of the former ratios to approximate the latter in the case of large numbers is essentially the basis for our faith in probability reckonings. In particular, physical systems made up of huge numbers of particles should furnish us with the very best conditions for the substitution of mathematical probabilities for event ratios that, in the nature of things, we cannot hope to observe.

If two events, A and B, which are independent of one another, have separate probabilities, P_A and P_B, then the probability of their occurring together, P_{AB}, is just the product of the two separate probabilities, that is,

$$P_{AB} = P_A P_B$$

Thus if we shake two coins in a box, the probability of two heads is

$$P_{hh} = \tfrac{1}{2} \times \tfrac{1}{2} = \tfrac{1}{4}$$

The total number of equally likely events is 4: both heads, both tails, the first a head with the second a tail, and vice versa. Clearly then there is only 1 event out of 4 favorable to two heads at once. Since $P_{tt} = \tfrac{1}{4}$, also, and P_h or $P_t = \tfrac{1}{2}$, the sum of the three probabilities is unity, as it should be.

15.3   Distribution of Marked Objects

As a variation of the tossing of coins, suppose that we consider a vessel divided into two equal parts by a plane (dashed line, Fig. 15.2). If a single molecule is turned loose in the box, we inquire as to the probability, if pure chance operates, of its being found at any one instant in, say, the right side or the left

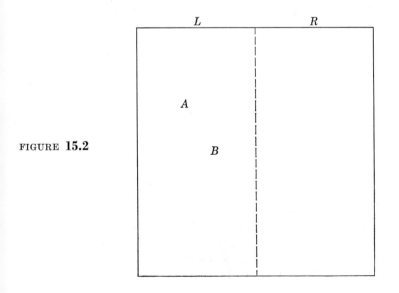

FIGURE **15.2**

side. Here in the absence of unsymmetric gravitational effects, we naturally assign equal probabilities to the two possible events and write

$$P_R = \tfrac{1}{2} = P_L$$

With two molecules, A and B, the probability of their both being on the right, say, $P(A, B)_R$, becomes

$$P(A, B)_R = P(A)_R P(B)_R = \tfrac{1}{2} \times \tfrac{1}{2} = \tfrac{1}{4}$$

Of course, the volume of a single molecule must be *negligible* compared with the entire volume so that its presence in one side does not appreciably reduce the free volume in that half. Further, there must be no forces between the molecules; otherwise, the presence of a molecule in one side will influence the likelihood that the other will also be found in that half. These we recognize as the essential requirements for an ideal gas.

Now place an ideal gas composed of N molecules in the container, and suppose that at any one instant of "observation" N_1 particular molecules are on the right, and the remainder, N_2, are on the left, so that

$$N_1 + N_2 = N$$

With pure chance operating, the probability of finding these N_1 molecules simultaneously in the right half is

$$P(N_1)_R = \tfrac{1}{2} \times \tfrac{1}{2} \times \cdots \times \tfrac{1}{2} = (\tfrac{1}{2})^{N_1}$$

and that of finding the N_2 in the left half is

$$P(N_2)_L = \tfrac{1}{2} \times \tfrac{1}{2} \times \cdots \times \tfrac{1}{2} = (\tfrac{1}{2})^{N_2}$$

Thus the probability of the two arrangements' happening together is just the product of these or

$$P = (\tfrac{1}{2})^{N_1}(\tfrac{1}{2})^{N_2} = (\tfrac{1}{2})^{N}$$

Apart from being a very small number when N is large, this probability is the same *whatever N_1 and N_2 may be*! To grasp the full import of this rather surprising result, we must understand just what we did when we wrote that $P(N_1)_R$ was in fact $(\tfrac{1}{2})^{N_1}$. Suppose that the molecules are identifiable in some way and are marked with numbers or letters, say, A, B, C, D, etc. Then we have assigned N_1 specified molecules to the right and N_2 specified molecules to the left. This detailed assignment we call a *microassignment* (or *complexion*). The result shows that *all microassignments have the same probability*, that is, $(\tfrac{1}{2})^{N}$.

Now consider the question of placing any N_1 molecules in the right (and, of course, the remaining N_2 molecules in the left). Any arrangement in which we merely count the number of particles without specifying which they are we call a *macrodistribution*. Thus we can have a macrodistribution with all on one side or a "uniform" distribution with $N_1 = N/2 = N_2$, etc. Then the important fact emerges that in general the same *macrodistribution* can be reached by any one of a *great many microassignments.*

The number of microassignments corresponding to a certain macrodistribution is simply the number of *different ways* in which the distribution can be arrived at by *permuting* the molecules between the two halves. The number of different permutations of N marked objects between two groups is readily found. We can choose the first molecule on the *right* in N ways. For each of these choices there are $N - 1$ for the second molecule, etc., down to

$$N - (N_1 - 1) = N_2 + 1$$

for the last, or a total of

$$N(N - 1)(N - 2) \cdots (N_2 + 1)$$

ways. Likewise, in filling the left side there are

$$N_2(N_2 - 1) \cdots 1 = N_2!$$

ways. The total number of ways of selecting the N objects is therefore the product of these results or $N!$ This value includes many duplicates since only by interchanging molecules between the two sides do we get different microassignments. Interchanging a pair of molecules within the same side gives us a duplicate. There are $N_1!$ ways of permuting the molecules in the right side among themselves and $N_2!$ possible permutations of those in the left. This makes $N_1!N_2!$ duplicates. If we call W_D the number of actually different microassignments corresponding to the given macrodistribution,

$$W_D = \frac{N!}{N_1!N_2!}$$

We saw that all microassignments must have the same fundamental probability, $(\frac{1}{2})^N$. Thus finally the mathematical probability, P_D, for a given macrodistribution defined by the numbers N_1 and N_2 becomes

$$P_D = \left(\frac{1}{2}\right)^N \frac{N!}{N_1!N_2!} \tag{15.5}$$

This may be expressed in terms of a single variable, n, taken as the amount by which N_1 *exceeds* and N_2 is *less* than $N/2$. Thus if

$$N_1 = \frac{N}{2} + n$$

and

$$N_2 = \frac{N}{2} - n$$

we have

$$P_D = \left(\frac{1}{2}\right)^N \frac{N!}{\left(\frac{N}{2} + n\right)!\left(\frac{N}{2} - n\right)!} \tag{15.6}$$

where, to avoid trouble later, we define 0! as equal to 1.

Now consider a few special cases. Let $n = N/2$ so that all the molecules are in the right half. In this case the result reduces to

$$P_D = (\tfrac{1}{2})^N = \tfrac{1}{2}^N$$

If N is very large (say, of the order of Avogadro's number), this probability is an extremely small number, although finite. This means that if the preceding reasoning is justified, a gas might by chance find itself in one half of the container, thus spontaneously compressing itself. This compression would represent a *spontaneous decrease in entropy*. Since from the macroscopic view of classical thermodynamics, such a decrease is impossible, it is clear that the second law must be reinterpreted in terms of probabilities. The *absolute certainties* of some situations and the *absolute prohibition* of others must be replaced by probabilities, which have values very near unity for the former cases and very close to zero for the latter ones. Entropy may decrease significantly for a short time, to be sure, but the probability of our actually observing it must be taken as extraordinarily minute. (See Problem 15.1.)

For all other distributions the second factor on the right of Eq. 15.6 is greater than unity. Therefore, all other distributions are more probable than the one with $n = N/2$. In particular, consider a distribution with $n = 1$, and compare this with the equal or uniform distribution with $n = 0$. The ratio of the probabilities becomes

$$\frac{P_D\,(n=0)}{P_D\,(n=1)} = \frac{\left(\dfrac{N}{2}+1\right)!\left(\dfrac{N}{2}-1\right)!}{\left(\dfrac{N}{2}\right)!\left(\dfrac{N}{2}\right)!} = \frac{\left(\dfrac{N}{2}+1\right)}{\dfrac{N}{2}} > 1$$

and the equal distribution is more probable. In fact, by comparing, we can see that any distribution with a given value of n has a larger probability than one with $n + 1$. Thus the *equal* distribution is more probable than any of the others. In terms of W_D there are more microscopic ways of attaining the equal distribution. With pure chance operating, it is, therefore, the most probable of all. If the system were under continuous observation, this would be the distribution we should expect to find most of the time.

Let us define $(\tfrac{1}{2})^N$ as the mathematical probability of a microassignment or, better, a *microstate* of the system indicated by P_{ms}. Then W_D is simply the number of molecularly different microstates corresponding to a given macrodistribution. We therefore write

$$P_D = P_{ms}W_D$$

The macrodistribution is something that we can in principle determine from outside by, for example, accurate weighing. We regard it as a *macroscopic property of the system*. In fact, we say that a particular set of distribution numbers (N_1, N_2) fixes a *macrostate of the system.* Thus W (and we may now drop the subscript D) *is the number of microstates in a macrostate,* and therefore

$$P = P_{ms}W \tag{15.7}$$

where P is the mathematical probability of a macrostate having W microstates of probability P_{ms}.

15.4 Microstates and the Disorder Number of a Macrostate

Before attempting to generalize the results of the last section, let us consider a simple example to emphasize the difference between microstates and macrostates. For this purpose take six objects (which later may be taken as molecules), and suppose that they are marked with the letters $A, B, C, D, E,$ and F. Let the volume in which they are to be scattered by pure chance be divided into six equal compartments or *cells.* Number these 1, 2, 3, 4, 5, and 6. Then any microstate of the system requires the assignment of six specified objects to each of six specified cells. On the left of Fig. 15.3 are shown four of the many possible microstates, numbered 1 to 4. In microstate 1, A is in cell 1, B in cell 2, and so on to F in cell 6.   On the right side of the figure are the corresponding macrostates, here numbered I to IV. To define a macrostate, we need give only the total *number* of objects in each cell, *not which ones.* The letters in microstate 1 can be permuted in 6! ways, each of which is a different microstate corresponding to macrostate I. There are therefore $6! = 720$ microstates corresponding to this highly dispersed macrostate, or $W_I = 720$. In contrast, macrostate IV can be achieved in only *one* way; that is, only one microstate exists with all six objects in cell 1. Thus $W_{IV} = 1$. This is the state of the lowest disorder, with the least scattering of the objects, whereas state I has the

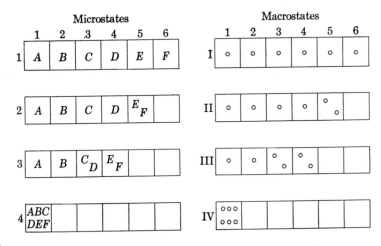

FIGURE **15.3**

highest disorder possible for the system. For macrostate II, since permutation of the objects in cell 5 gives duplicates, the result is only half as large as for state I. $W_{II} = 360$, and, similarly, $W_{III} = 180$. As the volume disorder becomes less marked, W *decreases*, and W may be taken as a measure of disorder, or the *disorder number* of a given macrostate.

It can be shown readily (see Problem 15.2) that for the general macrostate with distribution numbers N_1, N_2, . . . , N_6 for the six cells, the number of microstates or disorder numbers is

$$W = \frac{N!}{N_1!N_2! \cdots N_6!} \tag{15.8}$$

provided that we define $0! = 1$ as before so that the case of empty cells is included in the formula.

Fortunately, for practical purposes, the disorder numbers (the W's) are just as useful as the actual mathematical probabilities (the P's) and are much easier to calculate. Since, from Eq. 15.7, the probabilities are always proportional to the disorder numbers, the ratio of the probabilities for two states of disorder numbers W_1 and W_2 is always given as

$$\frac{P_1}{P_2} = \frac{W_1}{W_2}$$

In other words, the disorder numbers represent the *relative probabilities* of two macrostates, or, what is the same thing, W always measures the probability relative to a macrostate with only *one* microstate. Thus in the example of Fig. 15.3 the relative probabilities of the macrostates I, II, III, and IV are $720:360:180:1$.

Since the W's are easier to calculate than the P's and furnish the information needed in practical applications to physical systems, they may be used exclusively. Their importance in the statistics of physical systems led Boltzmann to term W the *thermodynamic probability* of a macrostate. Macrostates with the highest thermodynamic probabilities occur most frequently in nature, those with small values seldom, if ever, occurring during ordinary intervals of observation. Thus the thermodynamic probability of a macrostate has three aspects: it gives at once the *number of microstates*, the *relative probability*, and the *disorder* number of the macrostate. Strictly speaking, the disorder number can be calculated for any artificial distribution of marked objects; it becomes the thermodynamic probability only when the objects are the identifiable microscopic objects of a physical system. We shall usually refer to the W's as the disorder numbers, both for brevity's sake and for the suggestiveness of the term.

Before going on to consider the detailed application of these ideas to physical systems, let us generalize Eqs. 15.5 and 15.8 to the case of a general macrostate for system of N marked objects distributed among c equal cells.

Let the distribution be characterized as before by the occupancy numbers

$$N_1, N_2, \ldots, N_i, \ldots, N_c$$

N_i being the number in the ith cell. Then, of course,

$$\sum_1^c N_i = N$$

and the disorder number becomes

$$W = \frac{N!}{N_1!N_2! \cdots N_i! \cdots N_c!} = \frac{N!}{\prod_i N_i!} \qquad (15.9)$$

where $\prod$ indicates the product over all the i's from 1 to c.

15.5 The Disorder Number for a Macrostate of a Physical System

Determination of the disorder number or thermodynamic probability, W, for an actual physical system is simplest in the case of an ideal gas. In this case the molecules are considered to have negligible volumes and to exert no forces on one another. These are just the requirements needed to ensure the equal probabilities of microstates, as we saw in Sec. 15.3.[1] If in addition the molecules are monatomic so that they possess no internal coordinates, they may be treated as structureless mass points. In the simple example of the last section, W was determined by scattering the marked objects among a set of equal-sized cells. For any arbitrary macrostate, W thus serves as a measure of scattering among the cells or *dispersion* in *space coordinates* (and hence ultimately of the disorder number of the macrostate). A gas has two types of dispersion in coordinates, dispersion in ordinary space and dispersion in molecular velocities. Thus a gas has two types of disorder, *volume* disorder and *velocity* disorder, and both must be taken into account in the determination of W. We consequently divide the problem into two parts, treating each separately. Let the actual volume, V, of the gas be scattered among a large number of cells, say, $c = r$, of equal volume, v_0, where $v_0 = V/r$. See Fig. 15.4, where this situation is suggested in two dimensions. Suppose that n_1 molecules are in cell 1, n_2 in cell 2, etc., so that the macro-(volume) state is defined by the distribution numbers

$$n_1, n_2, \ldots, n_i, \ldots, n_r$$

---

[1] This equality of likelihood for microstates receives another more general basis in Chap. 16.

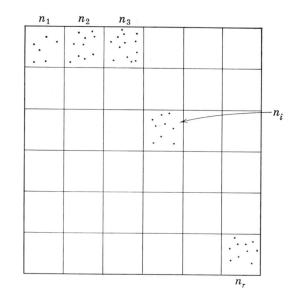

FIGURE **15.4**

Here n_i is the number in the ith volume cell, and, of course,

$$\sum_{i=1}^{r} n_i = N$$

Then, from Eq. 15.9, we write for the disorder number for the volume distribution, W^{vol},

$$W^{\text{vol}} = \frac{N!}{n_1! n_2! \cdots n_i! \cdots n_r!} = \frac{N!}{\prod_i n_i!} \qquad (15.10)$$

The velocity distribution or the *dispersion* in *velocity coordinates* may be treated in much the same way. We construct a *velocity space* in which the three orthogonal axes are the velocity components $\dot{x}$, $\dot{y}$, and $\dot{z}$ (Fig. 15.5). Then a molecule, say, number 1, will have a velocity vector, $\underline{v}_1$, which will reach from the origin to the point $\dot{x}_1, \dot{y}_1, \dot{z}_1$. Thus there will be N image points in velocity space just as in volume space, one for each molecule. In this case the extent of velocity space appropriate to the gas is not so simply fixed as for volume space but clearly must include all of the regions accessible to a molecule (or its image point). If we imagine a sphere drawn about the origin of coordinates and of radius corresponding to the maximum energy a molecule can possibly have, it should do. Actually it is not very important just how large this sphere is, provided it is large enough; as we shall see shortly, no significant difference results if it is allowed to be indefinitely large. If for the present we take the radius of the sphere, v_{max}, so that

$$\tfrac{1}{2} m v_{\text{max}}^2 = \text{total kinetic energy of the gas}$$

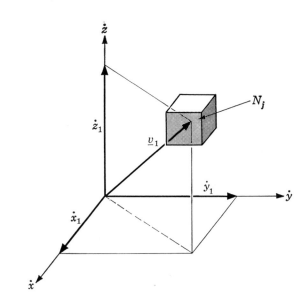

FIGURE **15.5**

its size is certainly adequate. Now let us divide this sphere into a large number, say, s, of equal-sized velocity cells, each of "volume" v_0'. Suppose that a velocity distribution is

$$N_1, N_2, \ldots, N_j, \ldots, N_s$$

where N_j is the number in the jth velocity cell (as n_i was in the ith volume cell).

Here the N's must satisfy two conditions, one for total number, as before, and one for total energy. If we designate the average energy corresponding to points in the jth cell by ϵ_j, then these conditions are

$$\Sigma N_j \epsilon_j = U$$

and

$$\Sigma N_j = N$$

where U is the internal energy of the ideal monatomic gas.

Finally the velocity disorder number, say, W^{vel}, is

$$W^{\text{vel}} = \frac{N!}{N_1! N_2! \cdots N_j! \cdots N_s!} = \frac{N!}{\prod_j N_j!} \qquad (15.11)$$

Since for every microstate in W^{vol} there are W^{vel} possible velocity microstates, W for the entire system is just the product, and

$$W = W^{\text{vol}} W^{\text{vel}} \qquad (15.12)$$

or

$$W = \left(\frac{N!}{\prod_i n_i!} \right) \left(\frac{N!}{\prod_j N_j!} \right) \qquad (15.13)$$

This idea can be extended to include disorder in internal coordinates, disorder in orientation of magnetic spins or electric dipoles, disorder in scattering among electronic states, etc. These situations we postpone for detailed discussion later. In any event, the total thermodynamic probability or disorder number for a system can be envisaged as a product

$$W = W^{(1)}W^{(2)}W^{(3)} \cdots \tag{15.14}$$

where each factor on the right is the disorder number for a particular type of disorder in the system.

15.6   Entropy and the Disorder Number

The thermodynamic probability or disorder number as given in Eq. 15.13 is in general a very large number. If we start with a macrostate of a system that represents a nonequilibrium state, we expect the system to pass to states of ever higher and higher probability and therefore larger and larger values of W. As the original ordering diminishes, the disorder grows, as does its measure, W, until at equilibrium W presumably has attained its largest value, say W_{max}. Thus equilibrium is at once the state of *greatest probability* and *greatest disorder*.

This natural passage toward higher thermodynamic probabilities we associate with the natural increase of entropy. Probability and entropy increase together and reach their maxima together. The increase of entropy in nature, therefore, takes place because, molecularly speaking, it is the most likely thing to occur.

Of course, when we assert that W (and hence S) has reached its maximum value, we do not imply that it attains a certain numerical value and thereafter retains that value indefinitely. In the chaotic motion of the molecules, random variations from the state of greatest W occur, but large variations are extremely rare, and normally only small fluctuations about the state of greatest W are expected. This means that the state of maximum entropy is simply the *most likely state* and that small fluctuations due to molecular changes must be taking place all the time. The truth of the second law depends upon the fact that sizable fluctuations are very rare, so rare in fact that as a practical matter their likelihood may be neglected altogether. The second law becomes, as was suggested earlier, not a statement of absolute certainty but rather one of very great probability.

If, in the light of the foregoing discussion, we take entropy to be essentially determined by the thermodynamic probability or the disorder number, we must write

$$S = f(W) \tag{15.15}$$

In the search for the specific form that the function f must have if such a relation is to hold, there are two general facts to guide us. The function f must be of such a form that with, say, two systems taken together as a single system,

(1) the entropies must be *additive* and (2) the W's must combine by *multiplication*, since they are probabilities (even though relative).

Consider two systems of disorder numbers W_1 and W_2 and entropies S_1 and S_2. From Eq. 15.15 we write

$$S_1 = f(W_1)$$

and

$$S_2 = f(W_2)$$

For the single system made up of the two together,

$$S = S_1 + S_2$$

and

$$W = W_1 W_2$$

Thus finally

$$S = f(W_1 W_2) = f(W_1) + f(W_2)$$

and the function f must be such as to satisfy the general functional equation

$$f(xy) = f(x) + f(y) \tag{15.16}$$

where for convenience W_1 and W_2 have been replaced by x and y.

Since Eq. 15.16 must hold for all values of x, it must hold for $x = 1 + \epsilon$, whatever value ϵ has. In this case the equation becomes

$$f(y + \epsilon y) = f(y) + f(1 + \epsilon)$$

The form of the first and last terms suggests expansion of these terms by Taylor's series. This gives us

$$f(y) + \epsilon y f'(y) + \cdots = f(y) + f(1) + \epsilon f'(1) + \cdots \tag{15.17}$$

where $f'(y) = df/dy$ and $f'(1)$ is the value of f' for the argument unity. Since $f(1)$ is a constant, let us choose it equal to zero when Eq. 15.17 reduces to

$$y \frac{df}{dy} = f'(1) = k$$

where k is a constant. On integration this gives

$$f = k \ln y + \text{constant}$$

This means that

$$S = k \ln W + \text{constant}$$

a result obtained by Boltzmann from a detailed analysis of the dynamic mechanism of intermolecular collisions in a gas. Since the condition $f(1) = 0$ reduces this constant to zero,

$$\boxed{S = k \ln W} \tag{15.18}$$

and the entropy may be defined as *proportional to the logarithm of the disorder number.*

Insertion of the value of W from Eq. 15.13 gives

$$S = k \left(\ln \frac{N!}{\prod_i n_i!} + \ln \frac{N!}{\prod_j N_j!} \right)$$

or

$$S = k \left[\left(\ln N! - \sum_i \ln n_i! \right) + \left(\ln N! - \sum_j \ln N_j! \right) \right] \qquad (15.19)$$

This expresses the entropy as the sum of two terms, the first depending on the distribution in volume space and the second on the distribution in velocity space.

15.7 Conditions for Maximum Entropy

We must now determine the particular values of the n_i's and N_j's in Eq. 15.19 that make S a maximum. These numbers define the (macro)state of equilibrium. They represent the most probable distribution in volume and velocity space expected for a gas left to itself for a sufficient length of time to attain equilibrium.

To find these numbers, imagine the gas kept at constant internal energy and volume. With the equilibrium distribution numbers designated by superscript asterisks (which differentiate them from any arbitrary distribution numbers), this state is described by the two sets of numbers,

$$n_1^*, n_2^*, \ldots, n_i^*, \ldots, n_r^*$$

and

$$N_1^*, N_2^*, \ldots, N_j^*, \ldots, N_s^*$$

The value of the equilibrium entropy, S^*, is regarded as a function of these $(r + s)$ numbers. The numbers are, of course, not all independent, since the n_i^*'s are subject to the condition

$$\sum_i n_i^* = N \qquad (15.20)$$

and the N_j^*'s to the two conditions

$$\Sigma N_j^* = N$$

and

$$\Sigma N_j^* \epsilon_j = U \qquad (15.21)$$

As we saw in Sec. 13.12, for stable equilibrium at constant V and U, any arbitrary (but conceivable) variation must be such that $\delta V = 0$, $\delta U = 0$, and $\delta S = 0$. Imagine variations of the n_i^*'s and N_j^*'s that do not change the total number of particles, N, or the total internal energy, U. These variations have no effect on the sizes or locations of cells, and hence ϵ_j remains constant for each of its values. Molecules (or image points actually) are shifted from one cell to another, subject only to the conditions in Eqs. 15.20 and 15.21. The problem is one of maximizing S with $(r + s)$ variables and three equations of constraint.

A complication arises owing to the analytical unmanageability of factorials. Fortunately, we take care of this trouble when we realize that with an actual gas N is of the order of Avogadro's number. Thus even with large numbers for r and s, there are many of the n_i^*'s and N_j^*'s that are quite large indeed. Terms with these numbers are expected to dominate the terms with small numbers. If an approximation for the factorial is used that is good for large numbers, the total errors involved should not be too serious.

Stirling's approximation to the logarithm of the factorial is of exactly this type (see Appendix 15.1). It becomes of increasing precision as the integers increase in size. It states that

$$\ln x! = x \ln x - x + \cdots \qquad x \gg 1$$

and as long as a few of the distribution numbers are large, rougher approximations in the smaller ones are tolerable. With this relation we write

$$\ln n_i^*! = n_i^* \ln n_i^* - n_i^*$$

or, summing, $\Sigma \ln n_i^*! = \Sigma n_i^* \ln n_i^* - N$

Similarly, for the N_j^*'s,

$$\Sigma \ln N_j^*! = \Sigma N_j^* \ln N_j^* - N$$

and for N itself

$$\ln N! = N \ln N - N$$

Substitution of these results in Eq. 15.19 gives

$$S^* = k(2N \ln N - \Sigma n_i^* \ln n_i^* - \Sigma N_j^* \ln N_j^*) \qquad (15.22)$$

with the restrictions

$$\Sigma n_i^* = N \qquad (15.23)$$

$$\Sigma N_j^* = N \qquad (15.24)$$

$$\Sigma N_j^* \epsilon_j = U \qquad (15.25)$$

To find the distribution that maximizes S^*, we must vary the n_i^*'s and N_j^*'s. Accordingly, we vary the distribution numbers

$$n_1^*, n_2^*, \ldots, n_i^*, \ldots, n_r^*$$

to $n_1^* + \delta n_1^*, n_2^* + \delta n_2^*, \ldots, n_i^* + \delta n_i^*, \ldots, n_r^* + \delta n_r^*$

subject, of course, to the restriction that the number of molecules must not change, that is, that

$$\delta N = \Sigma \delta n_i^* = 0$$

A similar variation is made in the N_j^*'s, subject, of course, to keeping both N and U constant.[2]

15.8   Volume Distribution for Maximum Entropy

Since the volume and velocity distributions are quite independent, we may simplify the problem of maximizing S by taking it in two steps. First we vary the n_i^*'s, keeping all the N_j^*'s constant, and then we reverse the order of the variation process.

Beginning with the volume case, we have, on varying Eq. 15.22,

$$\delta S^* = k\, \delta \Sigma (n_i^* \ln n_i^*) = 0$$

which reduces to $\qquad\qquad \Sigma \ln n_i^*\, \delta n_i^* = 0 \qquad\qquad$ **(15.26)**

subject to $\qquad\qquad\qquad \Sigma \delta n_i^* = 0 \qquad\qquad\qquad$ **(15.27)**

This is a problem in essentially $(r - 1)$ independent variables (or increments). We may take any variation, say, δn_1^*, as the dependent one. Solving Eq. 15.27 for δn_1^* and substituting the result in Eq. 15.26 gives, after the collection of terms,

$$(\ln n_2^* - \ln n_1^*)\, \delta n_2^* + (\ln n_3^* - \ln n_1^*)\, \delta n_3^* + \cdots = 0$$

or simply $\qquad\qquad \displaystyle\sum_{i=2}^{r} (\ln n_i^* - \ln n_1^*)\, \delta n_i^* = 0$

The $(r - 1)$ variations δn_2^* to δn_r^* are independent, and the condition of their independence can be met only if each coefficient of a δn^* vanishes. This situation requires that

$$\ln n_2^* = \ln n_3^* = \cdots = \ln n_r^* = \ln n_1^*$$

This means that the volume condition for S^* requires the *same number of image points in each volume cell* or

$$n_i^* = \frac{N}{r} = \left(\frac{N}{V}\right) v_0 = \hat{n} v_0 \qquad i = 1, 2, \ldots \qquad \textbf{(15.28)}$$

where $\hat{n}$ represents the particle density in volume space. This, of course, shows that *uniform* density is necessary to make entropy a maximum. There are naturally local fluctuations, but uniform molecular density is to be expected most of the time in an equilibrium system.

---

[2] This treatment of the n_i^*'s and N_j^*'s as continuous variables may seem at first unjustified, since the n_i's and N_j's are actual (integral) numbers of molecules. However, the n_i^*'s and N_j^*'s do not represent actual counts per cell at any instant; they are *most probable* values and as such are similar to, say, time averages and are rarely integral. The δn^*'s and δN^*'s are any conceivable small variations from these most probable values. They are *virtual* changes and do not represent *actual* shifts of, say, two or six molecules from one cell to another as might at first be thought.

The preceding result can be obtained more directly by the method of "undetermined multpliers" invented by Lagrange. Since Lagrange's method is quite general and can be used with ease whatever the number of variables or restricting equations, it will be illustrated here for future reference.

Lagrange's method consists of combining the group of simultaneous equations into a *single* equation in which all the variables (rather than only $r - 1$) may be treated as independent. To apply the method in the present case, we multiply Eq. 15.26 by 1 and Eq. 15.27 by λ (where λ is the undetermined multiplier) and add the results. The process is displayed as follows:

$$
\begin{array}{c|c}
1 & \Sigma \ln n_i^* \, \delta n_i^* = 0 \\
\lambda & \Sigma \delta n_i^* = 0 \\
\hline
& \Sigma(\ln n_i^* + \lambda) \, \delta n_i^* = 0
\end{array}
$$

or

This new equation is the single condition replacing the original pair. The vanishing of the sum on the left can always be ensured, whatever the δn_i^*'s may be, by the requirement that the coefficient of each δn_i^* vanish separately. This is tantamount to treating each δn_i^* as independent. Thus the conditions require that

$$\ln n_i^* = -\lambda \qquad i = 1, \ldots, r$$

Since λ is an undetermined quantity, we choose it to be negative when all the n^*'s are positive and must be equal as before.

15.9   Velocity Distribution for Maximum Entropy

Turning to the velocity distribution required to maximize entropy, we set δS^*, δN, and $\delta U = 0$ while varying only the δN_j^*'s. Eqs. 15.19 and 15.21 give the set of simultaneous conditions,

$$
\begin{array}{c|c}
1 & \Sigma \ln N_j^* \, \delta N_j^* = 0 \\
\lambda & \Sigma \delta N_j^* = 0 \\
\beta & \Sigma \epsilon_j \, \delta N_j^* = 0
\end{array}
$$

where it is to be remembered that in the calculation of δU only the N_j^*'s, not the average energies of particles in cells, are varied.

Combining these equations by Lagrange's method requires two undetermined multipliers, say, λ and β, which are indicated. The result of carrying out the process as before is

$$\Sigma(\ln N_j^* + \lambda + \beta \epsilon_j) \, \delta N_j^* = 0$$

The necessary and sufficient condition for the vanishing of this sum is that each coefficient of a δN_j^* vanish. This requires that

$$\ln N_j^* = -(\lambda + \beta \epsilon_j) \qquad j = 1, \ldots, r$$

or

$$N_j^* = e^{-\lambda} e^{-\beta \epsilon_j}$$

Since λ is an unknown constant, so is $e^{-\lambda}$. Writing this as α' gives

$$N_j^* = \alpha' e^{-\beta \epsilon_j} \qquad (15.29)$$

The velocity distribution is therefore far from being uniform as is the volume distribution but rather falls off exponentially as the energy, ϵ_j, associated with a cell increases. Since

$$\epsilon_j = \frac{mv_j^2}{2}$$

where v_j is the speed that gives the average energy for the jth cell, Eq. 15.29 can be written

$$N_j^* = \alpha' \exp -\beta \frac{m}{2} v_j^2$$

This is shown graphically in Fig. 15.6, where a smooth curve is drawn through the succession of increasing values of speed, v_0 ($= 0$), v_1, v_2, ... The curve has its maximum at $v = 0$, and therefore the density of image points is a maximum (and equal to α') at the origin and falls off very rapidly with increasing speed. Since the number of image points in a velocity cell depends on their energy only and is independent of their direction, the density of image points is spherically symmetric about the origin. This situation is suggested by the density of points in the two-dimensional plot in Fig. 15.7. At first sight it seems peculiar to find the maximum density of points at the origin, where the energy is zero, but this condition does not mean that more molecules are at

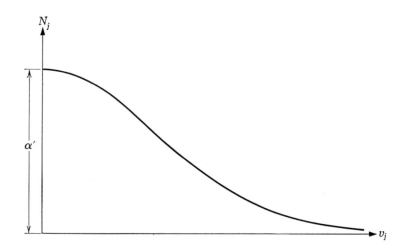

FIGURE **15.6**

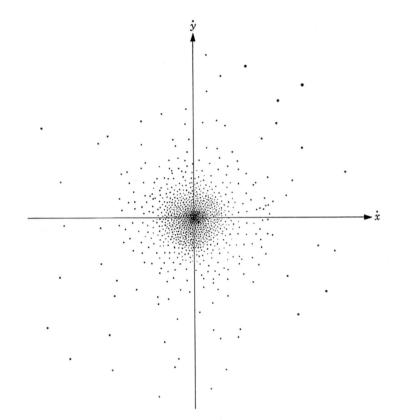

FIGURE **15.7**

rest than at any finite speed. The number of points actually at the origin is vanishingly small.

15.10   Evaluation of the Parameter α'

We must now write the velocity distribution law as given in Eq. 15.29 in more suitable form for calculation. It is clear that although α' is a constant parameter, its value must ultimately depend on how many molecules there are and on how large the velocity cells are. Since doubling N can only increase the density of points everywhere by a factor of 2, we must regard α' as proportional to N itself. Similarly, if the cells are small enough for the local variation in point density to be negligible, doubling the cell size simply doubles the N_j^*'s. We therefore write

$$\alpha' \propto N v_0'$$

or

$$\alpha' = \alpha N v_0'$$

where α is a new parameter independent of the arbitrary cell size or of the number of molecules. The distribution law now becomes

$$N_j^* = N v_0' \alpha e^{-\beta \epsilon_j} \tag{15.30}$$

Dividing through by v_0' gives the average particle density in the jth cell, say, $\overline{\rho'}_j$, so that

$$\overline{\rho'}_j = \frac{N_j^*}{v_0'} = N\alpha e^{-\beta \epsilon_j}$$

To make this result useful for direct calculation, suppose that we endeavor to define a local density at a point in velocity space as a continuous function of the energy. For this discussion we must remember that although N_j is always integral and varies from instant to instant, N_j^*, the most probable number in the jth cell, is essentially equivalent to a long-time average and must be constant for any given cell in velocity space and vary discontinuously from cell to cell. We thus define a local "smoothed-out" density of image points, ρ', as

$$\rho' = \lim_{v_0' \to 0} \frac{N_j^*}{v_0'} = N\alpha e^{-\beta \epsilon} \tag{15.31}$$

where ϵ is now the exact energy of a particle with a velocity vector ending at the point in question.

Now consider the differential number of particles, say, $dN(= d^3N_{\dot{x}\dot{y}\dot{z}})$, with image points lying in an element of volume in velocity space (Fig. 15.8).

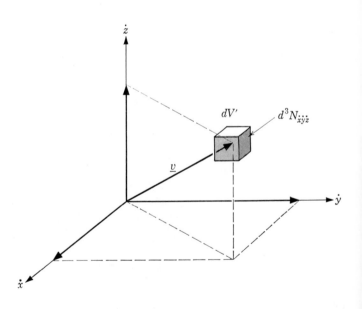

FIGURE **15.8**

Let the element of volume be dV', where

$$dV' = d\dot{x}\, d\dot{y}\, d\dot{z}$$

The vector to the center of this volume has a length, v, equal to the speed of particles with image points lying in dV'. Then we may write

$$dN = \rho'\, dV'$$

which, with Eq. 15.31 for ρ' and $\epsilon = mv^2/2$, becomes

$$dN = N\alpha e^{-\beta mv^2/2}\, dV' \qquad\qquad (15.32)$$

The integration of this result over, say, the jth cell gives N_j^* and over the accessible sphere of velocity space gives N, the total number of molecules. Actually, owing to the rapid decrease of ρ' with speed, the density is essentially negligible for all large values of v outside this sphere, and we may as well integrate, for simplicity's sake, over *all* velocity space. This gives

$$N = N\alpha \int e^{-\beta mv^2/2}\, dV'$$

or

$$\frac{1}{\alpha} = \int e^{-\beta mv^2/2}\, dV'$$

as the condition for determining α.

We can readily throw this integral into a standard form if we notice that the integrand is constant over all spheres of radius v. If, therefore, we first sum the volume within a thin spherical shell of radius v and thickness dv (an octant of which is shown in Fig. 15.9), the result is a product of the constant

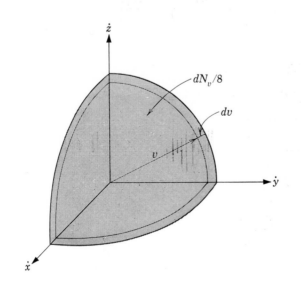

FIGURE **15.9**

exponential and the volume of the shell,

$$4\pi v^2\, dv$$

Indicating the number of molecules with velocity points lying in this shell (that is, with speeds between v and $v + dv$) by dN_v, we obtain from Eq. 15.32

$$dN_v = 4\pi N\alpha e^{-\beta mv^2/2}v^2\, dv \tag{15.33}$$

This is the *Maxwell-Boltzmann speed distribution* law to which we shall return later.

Integration of this equation from $v = 0$ to $v = \infty$ gives the total number of molecules, and after canceling the N's we find

$$\frac{1}{\alpha} = 4\pi \int_0^\infty v^2 e^{-\beta mv^2/2}\, dv \tag{15.34}$$

as the condition that determines α and hence α', since

$$\alpha' = N\alpha v_0'$$

The definite integral occurring here is of the general type

$$I(n) = \int_0^\infty x^n e^{-ax^2}\, dx$$

which occurs so frequently in this sort of discussion that it is often called the "kinetic theory integral." Its values as n varies integrally are given in Table 15.1 and separate into two series according to whether n is odd or even. It can readily be shown that once $I(0)$ and $I(1)$ are known, the rest of the values are calculable from a simple recursion formula (see Problem 15.5).

TABLE **15.1**

Values of the Integral $I(n) = \int_0^\infty x^n e^{-ax^2}\, dx$

n	$I(n)(n\text{ even})$	n	$I(n)(n\text{ odd})$
0	$\dfrac{1}{2}\left(\dfrac{\pi}{a}\right)^{1/2}$	1	$\dfrac{1}{2a}$
2	$\dfrac{1}{4}\left(\dfrac{\pi}{a}\right)^{1/2}\dfrac{1}{a}$	3	$\dfrac{1}{2a^2}$
4	$\dfrac{3}{8}\left(\dfrac{\pi}{a}\right)^{1/2}\dfrac{1}{a^2}$	5	$\dfrac{1}{a^3}$

In the present case $n = 2$, $a = \beta \dfrac{m}{2}$, and

$$\boxed{\alpha = \left(\frac{a}{\pi}\right)^{3/2} = \left(\frac{\beta m}{2\pi}\right)^{3/2}} \tag{15.35}$$

This result enables us to rewrite the distribution law, as obtained originally in the summation form, Eq. 15.30, and as written in the differential form, Eq. 15.32, as

$$\boxed{N_j^* = N \left(\frac{\beta m}{2\pi}\right)^{3/2} e^{-\beta m v_j^2/2} v_0{}'} \tag{15.36}$$

and

$$\boxed{dN = N \left(\frac{\beta m}{2\pi}\right)^{3/2} e^{-\beta m v^2/2} \, dV'} \tag{15.37}$$

15.11   Evaluation of the Parameters k and β

To evaluate the parameters k and β, it is first necessary to incorporate the results of the last three sections in the statistical expression for entropy as originally given in Eq. 15.22. The needed results appear in Eqs. 15.21, 15.28, and 15.36; that is,

$$U = \Sigma N_j^* \epsilon_j$$

$$n_i^* = \left(\frac{N}{V}\right) v_0$$

$$N_j^* = N \left(\frac{\beta m}{2\pi}\right)^{3/2} e^{-\beta m v_j^2/2} v_0{}'$$

Use of these relations in Eq. 15.22 gives, after rearrangement and the removal of N as a factor,

$$S_{\text{stat}} = Nk \left[\ln V - \ln \beta^{3/2} + \beta \frac{U}{N} + \ln \left(\frac{2\pi}{m}\right)^{3/2} \frac{1}{v_0 v_0{}'} \right] \tag{15.38}$$

where the subscript indicates the statistical origin of the entropy value.

We must now rewrite the corresponding extropy expression obtained in Chap. 12 from purely thermodynamic reasoning, that is,

$$S^\circ(T, V) = \int_0^T C_V^\circ \frac{dT}{T} + R \ln V + S_{0TV}^\circ \tag{12.22}$$

so that it applies to ν moles of ideal monatomic gas. For a mole of monatomic gas $C_V^\circ = \frac{3}{2}R$, and on multiplying through by ν, we have for the entropy expression that should parallel Eq. 15.38[3]

$$S_{\text{thermo}} = S^\circ(T, V, \nu) = \nu R \left(\ln V + \ln T^{3/2} + \frac{S^\circ_{0TV}}{R} \right) \qquad \text{(15.39)}$$

Comparison of the two expressions shows that β can have nothing to do with volume and can at most depend on T; that is, $\beta = \beta(T)$. Let us therefore calculate $(\partial S/\partial V)_T$ from the two entropy expressions. We find

$$\left(\frac{\partial S_{\text{stat}}}{\partial V} \right)_T = \frac{Nk}{V}$$

and

$$\left(\frac{\partial S_{\text{thermo}}}{\partial V} \right)_T = \frac{\nu R}{V}$$

For these to agree, we must have

$$\boxed{k = \frac{\nu R}{N} = \frac{R}{N_0}}$$

since $N = \nu N_0$, N_0 being Avogadro's number. Boltzmann's constant, k, is therefore simply the *gas constant per molecule*.[4]

With this identification we may now express U for the ideal monatomic gas as

$$\boxed{U = \tfrac{3}{2}\nu RT = \tfrac{3}{2}NkT} \qquad \text{(15.40)}$$

so that

$$\frac{\beta U}{N} = \frac{3}{2}\beta kT$$

and Eq. 15.38 becomes

$$S_{\text{stat}}^* = Nk \left[\ln V - \ln \beta^{3/2} + \frac{3}{2}\beta kT + \ln \left(\frac{2\pi}{m} \right)^{3/2} \frac{1}{v_0 v_0'} \right] \qquad \text{(15.41)}$$

To determine β, we make use of the derivative $(\partial S/\partial U)_V$, which we know from CI to be the reciprocal of the absolute temperature, that is,

$$\left(\frac{\partial S}{\partial U} \right)_V = \frac{1}{T}$$

---

[3] The constant S°_{0TV}/R must actually depend on ν. See Problem 16.7. This consideration has no effect on the present argument but will lead to Gibbs' paradox in Chap. 16.

[4] This ratio, $\nu R/N$, in Boltzmann's original entropy expression was designated k by Planck and named in Boltzmann's honor.

For the application to the statistical expression for entropy, this is conveniently written as

$$\left(\frac{\partial S}{\partial U}\right)_V = \left(\frac{\partial S}{\partial T}\right)_V \left(\frac{\partial T}{\partial U}\right)_V = \left(\frac{\partial S}{\partial T}\right)_V \frac{2}{3Nk} = \frac{1}{T}$$

so that

$$\left(\frac{\partial S}{\partial T}\right)_V = \frac{3Nk}{2T}$$

We therefore differentiate Eq. 15.41 with respect to T at constant V and set the result equal to $3Nk/2T$. This gives

$$\frac{3Nk}{2T} = Nk\left(-\frac{3}{2}\frac{\beta'}{\beta} + \frac{3}{2}\beta'kT + \frac{3}{2}\beta k\right)$$

where $\beta' = d\beta/dT$. This reduces to

$$\beta'kT - \frac{\beta'}{\beta} + \beta k - \frac{1}{T} = 0$$

which factors to the condition

$$k(\beta'T + \beta)\left(1 - \frac{1}{\beta kT}\right) = 0$$

This will always be satisfied if we set the last factor equal to zero, and therefore

$$\beta = \frac{1}{kT}$$

Inserting this value of β in Eq. 15.41 and collecting all the constant terms together, we find

$$S_{\text{stat}} = Nk\left[\ln V + \ln T^{3/2} + \ln\left(\frac{2\pi k}{m}\right)^{3/2}\frac{1}{v_0 v_0'} + \frac{3}{2}\right] \qquad (15.42)$$

which parallels the thermodynamic result term by term since

$$S_{\text{thermo}} = Nk\left(\ln V + \ln T^{3/2} + \frac{S^\circ_{0TV}}{R}\right)$$

The integration constant, S°_{0TV}/R, from this equation is now identified with the constant in Eq. 15.42; that is,

$$\frac{S^\circ_{0TV}}{R} = \ln\left[\left(\frac{2\pi k}{m}\right)^{3/2}\frac{1}{v_0 v_0'}\right] + \frac{3}{2}$$

The constant S°_{0TV}/R therefore is expressed in terms of the particle mass, m, universal constants, and the product of the arbitrary cell sizes in volume and velocity spaces. In Chap. 17 we shall see how the quantum theory enables us to attach a general size condition to the product $v_0 v_0'$.

15.12   Various Forms of the Velocity Distribution Law

Returning to the distribution law in differential form, Eq. 15.37, with $\beta = 1/kT$, we have

$$dN = N \left(\frac{m}{2\pi kT} \right)^{3/2} \left(\exp - \frac{mv^2}{2kT} \right) dV' \tag{15.43}$$

Since $dV' = d\dot{x}\,d\dot{y}\,d\dot{z}$, the volume of a rectangular parallelopiped $d\dot{x}$, $d\dot{y}$, and $d\dot{z}$ on a side, we may regard dN as essentially a third-order differential. To indicate this condition and also its dependence on differential changes in the three velocity component variables, we write it as $d^3N_{\dot{x}\dot{y}\dot{z}}$, as in Fig. 15.8, when

$$d^3N_{\dot{x}\dot{y}\dot{z}} = N \left(\frac{m}{2\pi kT} \right)^{3/2} \left(\exp - \frac{mv^2}{2kT} \right) d\dot{x}\,d\dot{y}\,d\dot{z} \tag{15.44}$$

This is the *Maxwell-Boltzmann distribution law* in its *velocity form*. It gives the number of molecules with velocity components lying in the range between

$$\dot{x} \text{ and } \dot{x} + d\dot{x}$$
$$\dot{y} \text{ and } \dot{y} + d\dot{y}$$
$$\dot{z} \text{ and } \dot{z} + d\dot{z}$$

In other words, $d^3N_{\dot{x}\dot{y}\dot{z}}$ is the number of image points in the parallelopiped of volume $d\dot{x}\,d\dot{y}\,d\dot{z}$ in velocity space (see Fig. 15.8).

We must remember that in the distribution law

$$v^2 = \dot{x}^2 + \dot{y}^2 + \dot{z}^2$$

when Eq. 15.44 becomes

$$d^3N_{\dot{x}\dot{y}\dot{z}} = N \left(\frac{m}{2\pi kT} \right)^{3/2} \left[\exp - \frac{m(\dot{x}^2 + \dot{y}^2 + \dot{z}^2)}{2kT} \right] d\dot{x}\,d\dot{y}\,d\dot{z} \tag{15.45}$$

If we integrate this over the entire range of $\dot{z}$ values from $\dot{z} = -\infty$ to $\dot{z} = +\infty$, we are essentially summing all the image points in the infinite cylinder of cross section $d\dot{x}\,d\dot{y}$, shown in Fig. 15.10. If the number of molecules in the gas with velocity vectors ending in this cylinder is indicated by $d^2N_{\dot{x}\dot{y}}$, we have

$$d^2N_{\dot{x}\dot{y}} = \int_{-\infty}^{+\infty} d^3N_{\dot{x}\dot{y}\dot{z}}$$

Thus $d^2N_{\dot{x}\dot{y}}$ is the number of molecules having velocities such that their $\dot{x}$ and $\dot{y}$ components are between

$$\dot{x} \text{ and } \dot{x} + d\dot{x}$$

and

$$\dot{y} \text{ and } \dot{y} + d\dot{y}$$

whatever their $\dot{z}$ components may be. To find $d^2N_{\dot{x}\dot{y}\dot{z}}$, therefore, we have, from Eq. 15.45,

$$d^2N_{\dot{x}\dot{y}} = N\left(\frac{m}{2\pi kT}\right)^{3/2}\left[\exp - \frac{m(\dot{x}^2 + \dot{y}^2)}{2kT}\right]d\dot{x}\,d\dot{y}\int_{-\infty}^{+\infty}\left(\exp - \frac{m\dot{z}^2}{2kT}\right)d\dot{z}$$

The integral involved is just $2[I(0)]$ from Table 15.1, where

$$I(0) = \frac{1}{2}\left(\frac{\pi}{a}\right)^{1/2}$$

With

$$a = \frac{\beta m}{2} = \frac{m}{2kT}$$

this becomes

$$2[I(0)] = \left(\frac{2\pi kT}{m}\right)^{1/2}$$

and therefore

$$d^2N_{\dot{x}\dot{y}} = N\left(\frac{m}{2\pi kT}\right)\left[\exp - \frac{m(\dot{x}^2 + \dot{y}^2)}{2kT}\right]d\dot{x}\,d\dot{y} \qquad \textbf{(15.46)}$$

If we integrate this with respect to $\dot{y}$ from $\dot{y} = -\infty$ to $\dot{y} = +\infty$, we are counting all the image points in an infinite slab of thickness $d\dot{x}$. This thin slab is indicated in part in Fig. 15.11, where the axes are rotated to make clear that we are determining how many molecules there are in the gas with velocity

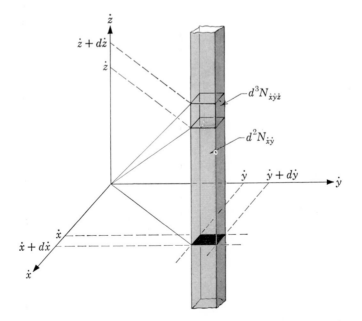

FIGURE **15.10**

vectors ending somewhere in the slab. Calling this number $dN_{\dot{x}}$,

$$dN_{\dot{x}} = \int_{-\infty}^{+\infty} d^2N_{\dot{x}\dot{y}}$$

and integrating Eq. 15.46, we have

$$dN_{\dot{x}} = N\left(\frac{m}{2\pi kT}\right)\left(\exp - \frac{m\dot{x}^2}{2kT}\right)\int_{-\infty}^{+\infty}\left(\exp - \frac{m\dot{y}^2}{2kT}\right)d\dot{y}$$

Evaluating this and writing down the results for the other two possible situations, we obtain

$$dN_{\dot{x}} = N\left(\frac{m}{2\pi kT}\right)^{1/2}\left(\exp - \frac{m\dot{x}^2}{2kT}\right)d\dot{x} \qquad (15.47)$$

$$dN_{\dot{y}} = N\left(\frac{m}{2\pi kT}\right)^{1/2}\left(\exp - \frac{m\dot{y}^2}{2kT}\right)d\dot{y} \qquad (15.48)$$

$$dN_{\dot{z}} = N\left(\frac{m}{2\pi kT}\right)^{1/2}\left(\exp - \frac{m\dot{z}^2}{2kT}\right)d\dot{z} \qquad (15.49)$$

These are the *velocity component* forms of the distribution law.

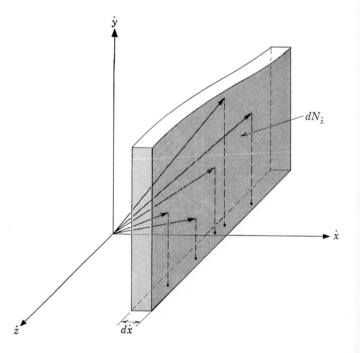

FIGURE **15.11**

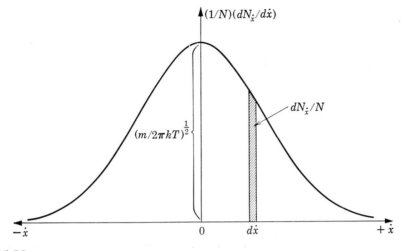

FIGURE **15.12**

Since $dN_{\dot x}/d\dot x$ is a finite ratio, on dividing it by N, we have the fraction of molecules with x velocity components in a unit range at $\dot x$. This fraction has been plotted vertically in Fig. 15.12 over a range of plus and minus values of $\dot x$. The curve is symmetric about the zero-speed axis and represents a Gaussian or "error function" type of distribution. The fraction of the total number of molecules lying in any differential range is given by the area of the differential strip of width $d\dot x$, as shown in the figure. This distribution can readily be converted into a form permitting the use of standard tables of the error function for calculation of the number of molecules lying in any finite range. (See Problem 15.7.)

15.13 The Speed Distribution Law

We return now to the form of the distribution law obtained in evaluating α' in Sec. 15.10, and with $\alpha = (m/2\pi kT)^{3/2}$ and $\beta = 1/kT$, Eq. 15.33 becomes

$$dN_v = 4\pi N \left(\frac{m}{2\pi kT}\right)^{3/2} \left(\exp -\frac{mv^2}{2kT}\right) v^2\, dv \qquad (15.50)$$

This is the *speed distribution* law, and it is quite different from other forms of the distribution law. When we sum up the number of molecules with velocity vectors ending in a spherical shell of radius v and thickness dv, we obtain zero values at $v = 0$ and $v = \infty$. Since

$$dN_v = \rho' 4\pi v^2\, dv$$

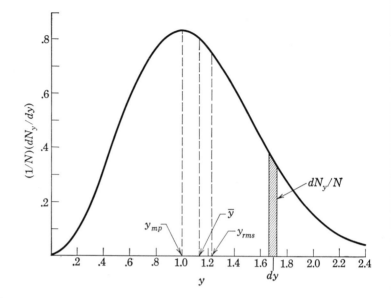

FIGURE **15.13**

although the density is a maximum at the origin, the radius of the shell is zero, and as $v \to \infty$, the spherical volume becomes large, but the density approaches zero. In between these extremes lies a maximum value, as shown in Fig. 15.13. In this figure the results are expressed in a universal form by writing

$$y = \sqrt{a}\, v = \left(\frac{m}{2kT}\right)^{1/2} v$$

when Eq. 15.50 takes the form

$$\frac{1}{N}\frac{dN_y}{dy} = \frac{4}{\sqrt{\pi}}\, e^{-v^2} y^2 \tag{15.51}$$

and all reference to a particular mass or temperature has disappeared. The curve with $(1/N)\, dN_y/dy$ plotted versus y rises from the origin, owing to the y^2 factor. As the negative exponential takes over, a maximum is reached, after which the curve falls exponentially to zero.

The maximum of this curve gives the *most probable speed*, this being the speed possessed by the most molecules. To find this speed, we need only differentiate the right side of Eq. 15.51 with respect to y and set the result equal to zero. This gives for the most probable value of y, say, y_{mp},

$$y_{mp} = 1$$

or, since
$$y = \sqrt{a}\, v$$

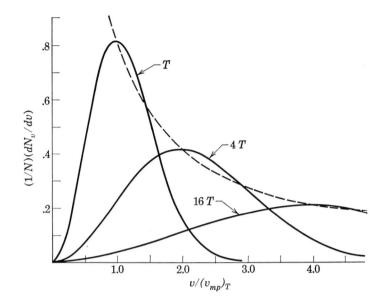

FIGURE **15.14**

the most probable speed, v_{mp}, is

$$v_{mp} = \frac{1}{\sqrt{a}} = \left(\frac{2kT}{m}\right)^{1/2} \qquad (15.52)$$

In the same figure the linear average value, $\bar{y}$, and the root-mean-square value, y_{rms}, are also shown. These will be calculated in the next section.

Since the total area under the curve of Fig. 15.13 must reduce to unity, as the temperature is raised, the curve becomes lower and broader. This behavior is shown in Fig. 15.14, where $(1/N) \, dN_v/dv$ is plotted versus, not the speed, but the ratio of the speed to the most probable speed for the temperature, T, where

$$(v_{mp})_T = \left(\frac{2kT}{m}\right)^{1/2}$$

Thus the unit along the horizontal axis is the most probable speed for the curve at the extreme left, the other two curves being drawn for temperatures of $4T$ and $16T$, respectively. It can readily be shown (see Problem 15.6) that the maxima of these curves lie on an equilateral hyperbola (the dashed line in the figure).

15.14   Mean and Root-Mean-Square Speeds

There are two other important quantities to be obtained from the speed distribution law. These are the average speed, $\bar{v}$, and $\sqrt{\overline{v^2}}$, or the root-mean-square speed, which we write v_{rms}. The first represents the simple average of the speeds of all the molecules in the system, whereas the second is the speed at which all the molecules must travel for the total kinetic energy to be just that of the actual gas. To understand the difference, consider speeds of, say, 2, 4, and 6. Then the linear average speed is

$$\bar{v} = \frac{2 + 4 + 6}{3} = 4$$

whereas the root-mean-square speed is

$$v_{rms} = \sqrt{\bar{v^2}} = \left(\frac{2^2 + 4^2 + 6^2}{3}\right)^{\frac{1}{2}} = 4.32$$

The root-mean-square speed is always somewhat greater than the average speed, since the higher speeds are weighted more heavily in its calculation. Further, it is the more important of the two speeds, since once it is known, the total kinetic energy can be computed.

To find a linear average, we multiply the number of molecules with velocity vectors ending in a given velocity space cell by the speed, add the results for all the cells, and divide by N. Thus

$$\bar{v} = \frac{N_1 v_1 + N_2 v_2 + \cdots}{N} = \frac{\Sigma N_j v_j}{\Sigma N_j} \tag{15.53}$$

v_j being the speed associated with the jth cell. Likewise, to find $\bar{v^2}$, we write

$$\bar{v^2} = \frac{N_1 v_1{}^2 + N_2 v_2{}^2 + \cdots}{N} = \frac{\Sigma N_j v_j{}^2}{\Sigma N_j} \tag{15.54}$$

To evaluate these sums, it is most convenient to replace the discrete sums by integrals as was done in Sec. 15.10. However, since v_j is the same for all cells having a common distance from the origin, we replace N_j not by the dN of the velocity distribution law, Eq. 15.32, but by the dN_v of the speed distribution law just obtained, Eq. 15.50. If we multiply v by dN_v and integrate over all speeds, the result is the numerator of Eq. 15.53, and the denominator is just the integral of Eq. 15.50. Thus

$$\bar{v} = \frac{\int_0^\infty v \, dN_v}{\int_0^\infty dN_v} = \frac{\int_0^\infty v^3 e^{-av^2} \, dv}{\int_0^\infty v^2 e^{-av^2} \, dv} = \frac{I(3)}{I(2)}$$

where $I(3)$ and $I(2)$ are standard forms to be taken from Table 15.1. Thus

$$\bar{v} = \frac{1}{2a^2} 4 \left(\frac{a}{\pi}\right)^{\frac{1}{2}} a = \frac{2}{\sqrt{\pi}} \frac{1}{\sqrt{a}}$$

and with the value of $1/\sqrt{a}$ from Eq. 15.52,

$$\bar{v} = \left(\frac{8kT}{\pi m}\right)^{\frac{1}{2}} = \frac{2}{\sqrt{\pi}}\, v_{mp} = (1.128\ \ldots)v_{mp} \qquad (\textbf{15.55})$$

In a similar manner the average of v^2 becomes

$$\overline{v^2} = \frac{\displaystyle\int_0^\infty v^4 e^{-av^2}\,dv}{\displaystyle\int_0^\infty v^2 e^{-av^2}\,dv} = \frac{I(4)}{I(2)} = \frac{3}{2}\frac{1}{a} = \frac{3}{2}\, v_{mp}^{\ 2} \qquad (\textbf{15.56})$$

and
$$v_{rms} = \sqrt{\overline{v^2}} = \left(\frac{3kT}{m}\right)^{\frac{1}{2}} = \sqrt{\frac{3}{2}}\, v_{mp} = (1.224\ \ldots)v_{mp} \qquad (\textbf{15.57})$$

These two averages are thus about 13% and 22% greater, respectively, than the most probable speed, v_{mp}.

In Fig. 15.13, where the y axis gives speed in units of the most probable speed, v_{mp}, the three speeds, v_{mp}, $\bar{v}$, and v_{rms}, occur at $y = 1.00$, 1.128 . . . , and 1.224, respectively.

15.15 The Equipartition Theorem and the Equation of State of an Ideal Monatomic Gas

Since by definition
$$U = \Sigma N_j \epsilon_j$$

and
$$\epsilon_j = \frac{m}{2}\, v_j^{\ 2}$$

we have, using the definition of $\overline{v^2}$,

$$U = \frac{m}{2}\sum N_j v_j^{\ 2} = N\,\frac{m\overline{v^2}}{2}$$

Use of Eq. 15.57 for $\overline{v^2}$ gives
$$U = \tfrac{3}{2}NkT$$

a result obtained in Sec. 15.11 (Eq. 15.40) by quite another method.

Since
$$\epsilon = \frac{mv^2}{2} = \frac{m\dot{x}^2}{2} + \frac{m\dot{y}^2}{2} + \frac{m\dot{z}^2}{2}$$

we now seek the average values of the energies associated with the three components of velocity. Accordingly, we return to the velocity component distribution laws as given in Eqs. 15.47 to 15.49. Thus for $\overline{\dot{x}^2}$ we need only form the product $\dot{x}^2\,dN_{\dot{x}}$ and sum over all $\dot{x}$ values from 0 to ∞ (since the distribution curve is symmetric, the half range only need be used, and as before the common factors may be omitted). The result is

$$\overline{\dot{x}^2} = \frac{\int_0^\infty \dot{x}^2 e^{-a\dot{x}^2}\,d\dot{x}}{\int_0^\infty e^{-a\dot{x}^2}\,d\dot{x}} = \frac{I(2)}{I(0)} = \frac{\dfrac{1}{4}\left(\dfrac{\pi}{a}\right)^{\frac{1}{2}}\dfrac{1}{a}}{\dfrac{1}{2}\left(\dfrac{\pi}{a}\right)^{\frac{1}{2}}} = \frac{1}{2a}$$

and

$$\overline{\dot{x}^2} = \frac{kT}{m}$$

or

$$\tfrac{1}{2}m\overline{\dot{x}^2} = \tfrac{1}{2}kT$$

Since the treatment of the other components is quite similar, we see at once that

$$\frac{m\overline{\dot{x}^2}}{2} = \frac{m\overline{\dot{y}^2}}{2} = \frac{m\overline{\dot{z}^2}}{2} = \frac{1}{2}kT \tag{15.58}$$

This is a special case of Boltzmann's *equipartition of energy theorem*, which we shall meet in a more general form in the next chapter. According to it, the average energy associated with each component of translation for each molecule in a gas is the same and equal to $\frac{1}{2}kT$. Since there are N molecules and three energy terms for each, the total for the system is $\frac{3}{2}NkT$, as just found.

We are now in a position to obtain the equation of state for the ideal monatomic gas. From CIII,

$$dA = -S\,dT - p\,dV$$

and therefore

$$-\left(\frac{\partial A}{\partial V}\right)_T = p$$

Since we know that $U = \frac{3}{2}NkT$ and since we have a statistical expression for S in Eq. 15.42, we can write down the value of Helmholtz's free energy. Thus with

$$A = U - TS$$

$$A = \frac{3}{2}NkT - NkT\left[\ln V + \ln T^{\frac{3}{2}} + \ln\left(\frac{2\pi k}{m}\right)^{\frac{3}{2}}\frac{1}{v_0 v_0'} + \frac{3}{2}\right]$$

On differentiation this gives

$$-\left(\frac{\partial A}{\partial V}\right)_T = \frac{NkT}{V} = p \tag{15.59}$$

or

$$pV = NkT$$

and the equation of state is obtained almost as an afterthought, as it were. Had we wished to obtain this result at the start, we could of course have arrived at it much more directly by a simple kinetic theory argument. In this chapter, however, we are interested in setting up a general basis for the statistical analysis of physical systems, and the equation of state is only one of the many results to come out of the discussion.

15.16   Mass Flux

An important topic in the kinetic theory of gases is the flow of molecules through small apertures. The usual kinetic theory treatment begins with the cosine law of mass efflux, which leads to other useful relations. Since the truth of these relations is implicit in the results of Sec. 15.14, it is worth digressing from the main statistical argument to obtain them.

For a gas in thermal equilibrium, the mass flux *to* the walls is balanced by the mass flux *away* from the walls with very much the same geometric relations applying as in the case of cavity radiation. In fact, the coefficients *radiancy*, *directional radiancy*, and *parallel beam radiancy* used in Chap. 13 all have direct analogs in the case of mass flux. We can write

$$R = \frac{d\psi}{dA} \qquad F = \frac{d\psi}{dA}$$

$$R_\omega = \frac{d^2\psi}{dA\, d\omega} \qquad F_\omega = \frac{d^2\psi}{dA\, d\omega}$$

$$R_\| = \frac{d^2\psi}{dA'\, d\omega} \qquad F_\| = \frac{d^2\psi}{dA'\, d\omega}$$

etc., where on the right ψ is used to designate mass flux (mass flow per time unit) and F, F_ω, and $F_\|$ are mass flux coefficients that are direct analogs of the radiancies on the left.

For the present purpose F_ω is most important, as it is the mass flux per unit area per unit solid angle (in a direction θ, ϕ either *to* or *from* the wall of a container). It is regarded as the result of summing a quantity, $F_{\omega v}$, over all molecular speeds; that is,

$$F_\omega = \int_0^\infty F_{\omega v}\, dv$$

and therefore

$$\frac{d^3\psi}{dA\, d\omega\, dv} = F_{\omega v}$$

Here $F_{\omega v}$ is the coefficient that measures the mass flux (per unit area of surface per stere per unit speed range) due to molecules moving in a direction, θ, ϕ, say, outward from the surface. Any molecule with a velocity vector lying in the solid angle $d\omega$, with direction angles θ and ϕ, and of speed between v and $v + dv$ we call an ωv molecule. $F_{\omega v}$ thus measures the flux from an area of the surface, dA, at an angle, θ, to the normal to dA, as in Fig. 15.15. If the cylinder shown in the figure is of length $v\, d\tau$ ($d\tau$ being an element of time), then any ωv

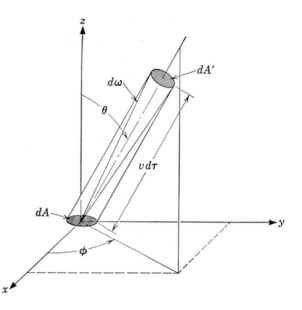

FIGURE **15.15**

molecule in this cylinder passes through dA', the area of the open end, some time during $d\tau$.[5]

The mass flow from dA therefore depends on the product of three factors: (1) the particle mass, m; (2) the particle density of ωv molecules per unit volume in the cylinder (which is the same for all parts of the gas at equilibrium); and (3) the volume of the cylinder itself. Division of the product of these three factors by $d\tau$ and, of course, by $dA\,d\omega\,dv$ gives the coefficient $F_{\omega v}$. Thus

$$F_{\omega v} = m \left(\begin{array}{c}\text{number of } \omega v \text{ molecules in} \\ \text{a unit volume of gas}\end{array}\right) \left(\begin{array}{c}\text{volume of} \\ \text{cylinder}\end{array}\right) \frac{1}{d\tau\,dA\,d\omega\,dv} \quad \textbf{(15.60)}$$

We now need to find the number of ωv molecules per unit volume in the cylinder. To do this, we make use of the exact spherical symmetry of the velocity distribution in the gas. Imagine a unit sphere inscribed about an origin in ordinary space as in Fig. 15.16, and let the velocity vector of every molecule be drawn from the origin to intersect this sphere at a point (those of speed less than unity are projected to intersection). Then the spherical surface contains N points, which, owing to the symmetry of the velocity distribution, everywhere have the same surface density. Consequently, any small solid angle, $d\omega$, cuts off an area on the unit sphere that contains the same number of points no matter what the direction (θ, ϕ) may be. This number, say, dN_ω,

---

[5] Of course, some ωv molecules in this small cylinder fail to pass through dA', owing to scattering from collisions. But on the average as many are *added* to the ωv class as are *lost* from it because of collision with other molecules.

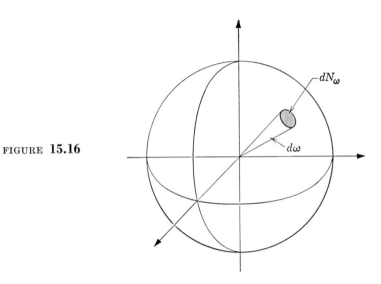

FIGURE **15.16**

bears the same ratio to the total number N as $d\omega$ bears to the total solid angle, 4π, subtended at the origin by the sphere; that is,

$$\frac{dN_\omega}{N} = \frac{d\omega}{4\pi}$$

or

$$dN_\omega = \frac{N}{4\pi} d\omega$$

Now consider all the molecules of speeds between v and $v + dv$, say, dN_v. These we also regard for statistical purposes as spread uniformly over the unit sphere so that the number of ωv molecules, $dN_{\omega v}$, bears the same ratio to dN_v as dN_ω bears to N. Then

$$\frac{dN_{\omega v}}{dN_v} = \frac{d\omega}{4\pi}$$

or

$$dN_{\omega v} = \frac{dN_v}{4\pi} d\omega$$

To obtain the volume density of ωv molecules, we now divide both sides of this result by the total volume of the gas and have

$$\frac{dN_{\omega v}}{V} = \frac{dN_v \, d\omega}{4\pi V} \tag{15.61}$$

As the volume of the differential cylinder is simply $v \, d\tau \, dA'$ or $v \cos \theta \, dA \, d\tau$, we find for $F_{\omega v}$, from Eq. 15.60,

$$F_{\omega v} = \frac{m \, dN_v}{4\pi V} v \cos \theta \frac{1}{dv}$$

and thus finally

$$F_{\omega v}\, dv = \frac{d^3\psi}{dA\, d\omega} = \frac{mv \cos \theta}{4\pi V}\, dN_v$$

To find F_ω, which is the *directional* mass flux coefficient (mass flux per unit area per stere), we must of course integrate this result from $v = 0$ to $v = \infty$. This gives

$$F_\omega = \int_0^\infty F_{\omega v}\, dv = \frac{m \cos \theta}{4\pi V} \int_0^\infty v\, dN_v = \frac{m\bar{v}N \cos \theta}{4\pi V}$$

with the definition of the average speed, $\bar{v}$. From Eq. 15.55 $\bar{v} = (8kT/\pi m)^{\frac{1}{2}}$, and with the gas density, $\rho = mN/V$, this becomes

$$F_\omega = \frac{d^2\psi}{dA\, d\omega} = \frac{\rho}{\pi}\left(\frac{kT}{2\pi m}\right)^{\frac{1}{2}} \cos \theta \tag{15.62}$$

At equilibrium the mass flux *from* an area of the walls equals that *to* the area. Imagine, therefore, that the area dA is the area of a *hole* in the (supposedly) thin wall of the container. Then $d^2\psi$ is the mass flux *through* the area dA in the solid angle of size $d\omega$ in the direction, θ, to the *outer* normal. We thus write Eq. 15.62 as

$$d^2\psi = \frac{\rho}{\pi}\left(\frac{kT}{2\pi m}\right)^{\frac{1}{2}} \cos \theta\, dA\, d\omega \tag{15.63}$$

which becomes the *cosine law for mass efflux into a vacuum*. For the particular case of normal efflux, $\theta = 0°$, $\cos \theta = 1$, and F_ω is replaced by $F_\parallel$, the parallel beam coefficient. In this case, with ψ_n indicating normal flux,

$$d^2\psi_n = F_\parallel\, dA\, d\omega \tag{15.64}$$

and

$$F_\parallel = \frac{\rho}{\pi}\left(\frac{kT}{2\pi m}\right)^{\frac{1}{2}} \tag{15.65}$$

This result is of particular value in atomic and molecular beam experiments. Suppose, for example, that a metal is kept molten at some high temperature in a furnace (Fig. 15.17), the region outside being highly evacuated. If a slit in the furnace and a slit above it have small areas, ΔA_1 and ΔA_2, respectively, we can write, from Eqs. 15.64 and 15.65, for the (essentially) parallel beam mass flux through the second slit the approximate relation

$$\Delta^2\psi_n = F_\parallel \Delta A_1 \Delta\omega = \frac{\rho}{\pi}\left(\frac{kT}{2\pi m}\right)^{\frac{1}{2}} \frac{\Delta A_1 \Delta A_2}{r^2}$$

Since $\rho = \dfrac{Nm}{V}$ and $p = \dfrac{N}{V}kT$, this can also be written

$$\Delta^2\psi_n = \left(\begin{matrix}\text{mass flux in beam}\\ \text{beyond slit 2}\end{matrix}\right) = \frac{p}{\pi}\left(\frac{m}{2\pi kT}\right)^{\frac{1}{2}} \frac{\Delta A_1 \Delta A_2}{r^2} = \text{constant } \frac{p}{\sqrt{T}} \tag{15.66}$$

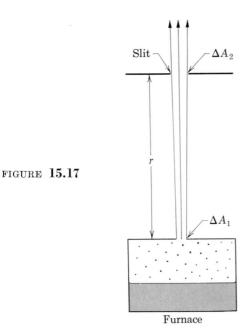

FIGURE **15.17**

Furnace

where all the natural and apparatus constants have been lumped together. Since the pressure, p, is the vapor pressure of the molten metal, it increases much faster with T than does the square root, and the mass flux in the beam therefore increases rapidly with T. Returning to Eq. 12.64, we have

$$\ln p = A - \frac{B}{T} \qquad (12.64)$$

The vapor pressure, p, can be calculated once the constants A and B are known. This together with Eq. 15.66 then determines the mass flux in the beam for any temperature.[6]

Problems

15.1   Consider the probability, obtained in Sec. 15.3, that a gas composed of N ideal gas molecules might compress itself to half its original volume. Take $N = N_0$, and calculate the number of years you would have to wait to observe this state for as much as 1 sec.

---

[6] For interesting applications of these results to a test of the Maxwell-Boltzmann distribution law, see, for example, Eldridge, *Phys. Rev.*, **30**, 931 (1927); Coster, Smyth, and Compton, *Phys. Rev.*, **30**, 349 (1927); and Estermann, Frisch, and Stern, *Z. Physik*, **73**, 348 (1931). For other aspects of the subject of the kinetic theory of gases, see, in particular, M. Knudsen, *The Kinetic Theory of Gases*, Methuen Monographs on Physical Subjects, Wiley, New York, 1950; and F. L. Arnot, *Collision Processes in Gases*, Methuen Monographs on Physical Subjects, Wiley, New York, 1950.

15.2 Show that beginning with macrostate I of Fig. 15.3 W is reduced by a factor of 2! on passage from state I to state II and by another factor of 2! on passage to state III. (*Hint:* Consider state I, and for purposes of counting permutations, remove the partition between cells 5 and 6, cells 4 and 5, etc.) Then show that with N_1 in cell 1 and one atom or none in the other cells, W becomes $N!/N_1!$, and hence by generalization arrive at Eqs. 15.8 and 15.9.

15.3 Calculate the probabilities given by Eq. 15.6,

$$P_D(n) = \left(\frac{1}{2}\right)^N \frac{N!}{\left(\dfrac{N}{2} + n\right)! \left(\dfrac{N}{2} - n\right)!} \tag{15.6}$$

for the case of $N = 10$. Plot the results versus n, and draw a smooth curve through these points. Now toss 10 pennies 10 at a time for 100 trials, counting in each case the excess of heads over tails (that is, $2n$). Plot these results on your graph for comparison.

15.4 In the proofs in Secs. 15.8 and 15.9, only the first variation of the entropy, δS, is set equal to zero. The results obtained are therefore the conditions for a *stationary* value of S. Show by calculating $\delta^2 S$ that the conditions of Eqs. 15.28 and 15.29 make $\delta^2 S < 0$ and thus in fact correspond to a maximum of entropy.

15.5 In the case of the definite integral of Sec. 15.10,

$$I(n) = \int_0^\infty x^n e^{-ax^2}\, dx$$

show that

$$I(n + 2) = -\frac{\partial I(n)}{\partial a}$$

so that once the integral has been evaluated for $n = 0$ and $n = 1$, this recursion formula permits all the other integrals to be found.

15.6 Taking the speed distribution law,

$$dN_v = 4\pi N \left(\frac{m}{2\pi kT}\right)^{3/2} \left(\exp - \frac{mv^2}{2kT}\right) v^2\, dv \tag{15.50}$$

and setting $y = dN_v/dv$, show that the maxima of the curves for different temperatures fall on an equilateral hyperbola given by

$$yv_{mp} = \frac{4N}{e\sqrt{\pi}}$$

15.7 With the velocity component distribution law in the form

$$dN_{\dot{x}} = N \left(\frac{m}{2\pi kT}\right)^{1/2} \left(\exp - \frac{m\dot{x}^2}{2kT}\right) d\dot{x} \tag{15.47}$$

the number of molecules with speeds between 0 and $\dot{x}$ is

$$\int_0^{\dot{x}} dN_{\dot{x}} = N \left(\frac{m}{2\pi kT}\right)^{1/2} \int_0^{\dot{x}} \left(\exp - \frac{m\dot{x}^2}{2kT}\right) d\dot{x}$$

$$= \frac{N}{\sqrt{\pi}} \int_0^x (\exp - x^2)\, dx$$

where $x = (m/2kT)^{\frac{1}{2}}\dot{x}$. The error function of x, written $erf(x)$, is defined as

$$erf(x) = \frac{2}{\sqrt{\pi}} \int_0^x (\exp - x^2)\, dx$$

and values are tabulated in many places, including Pierce's *Short Tables of Integrals*. Using such tables, calculate the fraction of the molecules in gaseous He at 0°C with x components lying between 100 and 125 meters/sec.

15.8   Return to Secs. 13.5 to 13.8, and translate all the radiation equations into their equivalents for mass flux in an ideal gas. In particular, obtain the mass rate of evaporation from a unit area of a liquid surface into a vacuum, say, F, as

$$F = \frac{mN\bar{v}}{4V}$$

and the pressure analog of Eq. 13.31 as

$$p = \frac{1}{3}\frac{N}{V}\overline{mv^2} = \frac{2}{3}u$$

where u is the energy per unit volume of the gas. How do you reconcile this with the fact that for radiation

$$p = \frac{1}{3}u?$$

15.9   Apply Eq. 15.66 to obtain the total mass flux in grams per second for the case of a furnace at 1700°C containing molten silver. Take the slits to be alike and of area equal to 0.002 cm², and let $r = 20$ cm.

CHAPTER SIXTEEN

Classical Statistical Mechanics

16.1 Introduction

In the last chapter we saw the fruitfulness of the statistical interpretation of entropy. In the present chapter this approach will be generalized in a systematic manner. This generalization will require a sketch of the background of what has come to be known as *statistical mechanics*.

Statistical mechanics seeks to deduce the large-scale or bulk properties of matter from a study of the behavior of atoms and molecules as they respond to the laws of mechanics, which are considered to govern their behavior. If the mechanics is that of Newton, Lagrange, and Hamilton, we have *classical* statistical mechanics; if quantum mechanics furnishes the basic laws of motion, then *quantum* statistics results. In this chapter Newtonian behavior will be assumed throughout; atoms will be assumed to behave like the masses of classical mechanics and to have velocities, momenta, energies, etc., that take on continuous ranges of values. In the next chapter the results will be modified to provide for the discreteness of certain energies as given by the quantum theory. Finally in Chap. 18 the elements of quantum mechanics as embodied in the wave equation will be developed, and the statistical results formulated to fit the new point of view.

The discussion in this chapter is intended to indicate the full generality of the methods to be presented. Certain predictions, notably those regarding the heat capacities of polyatomic gases, will be found to be definitely at variance with experiment. In fact, these discrepancies constitute the "black cloud" that Lord Kelvin, toward the end of the nineteenth century, saw overlying the whole subject of the kinetic theory of matter.

In the historical development of statistical mechanics, every effort has been made to express the methods and principles in sufficiently general form to include the widest possible range of systems. This practice has entailed the introduction of the following devices:

1. Curvilinear coordinates for use as generalized configuration and velocity coordinates (indicated by q's and $\dot{q}$'s).

2. Transformation to the general configuration and momentum coordinates of Hamilton (indicated by q's and p's).

3. The invention and use of hyperspaces or manifolds called *phase spaces*, in which the status of a molecule or other system with f degrees of freedom can be described by a single point. Although such phase spaces can be used for independent systems of any degree of complexity, so that f may be as large as is necessary, the systems envisaged in the present case will usually be molecules. Such phase spaces will therefore be called μ spaces to suggest *molecular spaces*.

4. The defining and use of a hyperphase space in which a large number of subsystems taken together as a *single hypersystem* have their status fixed by a single point. In the present instance, if the hypersystem is a collection of poly-atomic molecules (that is, a gas), this hyperphase space is *gas* space. It will be called Γ space for short to suggest this application.

5. Study of the behavior of systems in these phase spaces as determined by Hamilton's equations of motion. This will perforce be rather condensed and will not involve detailed knowledge of the origin and use of Hamilton's equations as such.

16.2   Configuration-Velocity Space

In Chap. 15 the status of a monatomic molecule indealized as a structureless mass point was described by the location of its position in one three-dimensional space and of its velocity in another. Great economy of method is brought about if we invent a space of more than three dimensions, in which the position coordinates and the velocity components $(x, y, z, \dot{x}, \dot{y}, \dot{z})$ are used to locate a *single* point, the image point for the particle. This possibility, of course, requires a six-dimensional space, and naturally such a space cannot be visualized or sketched since the space of our experience is strictly three-dimensional. We must regard it as a mathematical space invented for the purpose of study and calculation and accept the fact that we can never hope to do more than picture cross sections of it. We imagine this so-called six-space built up by the addition one after another of orthogonal coordinates, each perpendicular to the others. This building-up process can be illustrated by the case of a circle (or sphere). In one dimension the sphere is defined by

$$x^2 = C$$

and is a locus of two points equally spaced on either side of the origin on the x axis. If we add a y axis and a z axis, each perpendicular to the original x axis and to one another, the sphere becomes in turn

$$x^2 + y^2 = C$$

and
$$x^2 + y^2 + z^2 = C$$

If now a fourth, fifth, and sixth square term is added, the result is

$$x^2 + y^2 + z^2 + \dot{x}^2 + \dot{y}^2 + \dot{z}^2 = C$$

a six-dimensional "sphere." This has much more complicated properties than a three-dimensional one, which it includes as a special case.

In the same way a mass point with x coordinates lying in the interval between x and $x + dx$ has its image point in the (one-dimensional) interval dx between x and $x + dx$. If its coordinates are bounded by

and

$$x \text{ and } x + dx$$
$$y \text{ and } y + dy$$
$$z \text{ and } z + dz$$

we say that its image point lies in the volume element

$$dx\, dy\, dz$$

Finally if six coordinates are such as to lie between

x and $x + dx$	$\dot{x}$ and $\dot{x} + d\dot{x}$
y and $y + dy$	$\dot{y}$ and $\dot{y} + d\dot{y}$
z and $z + dz$	$\dot{z}$ and $\dot{z} + d\dot{z}$

we say that the image point lies in the six-dimensional element or parallelopiped of volume

$$dx\, dy\, dz\, d\dot{x}\, d\dot{y}\, d\dot{z}$$

If every molecule in the gas has its instantaneous state fixed by its image point, the gas is completely described by the N image points in this six-dimensional space, which we shall refer to as *configuration-velocity* space. By the device used in Chap. 15 we can define a local point density, ρ, such that $\rho\, dx\, dy\, dz\, d\dot{x}\, d\dot{y}\, d\dot{z}$ gives us the differential number of image points to be expected in this element of volume. Since this number vanishes as a sixth-order differential product, we regard it as a sixth order differential and write

$$d^6N_{xyz\dot{x}\dot{y}\dot{z}} = \rho\, dx\, dy\, dz\, d\dot{x}\, d\dot{y}\, d\dot{z} \tag{16.1}$$

Integration of this over the total range of the velocity components from $-\infty$ to $+\infty$ gives all the molecules (whatever their velocities) in the element of ordinary volume, $dx\, dy\, dz$. If we write this number as d^3N_{xyz},

$$d^3N_{xyz} = \hat{n}\, dx\, dy\, dz$$

where $\hat{n}$ is the ordinary particle density in this region of the gas. Integration of this over the ranges of x, y, and z gives N, the total number of molecules. In the same way integration of Eq. 16.1 with respect to x, y, and z gives $d^3N_{\dot{x}\dot{y}\dot{z}}$

as

$$d^3N_{\dot{x}\dot{y}\dot{z}} = \rho'\, d\dot{x}\, d\dot{y}\, d\dot{z}$$

where ρ' is the image point density in this region of velocity space.

It is to be noted that $d^6N_{xyz\dot{x}\dot{y}\dot{z}}$ counts only the molecules with positions fixed in the element $dx\,dy\,dz$ of ordinary space *and* with velocities simultaneously in the element $d\dot{x}\,d\dot{y}\,d\dot{z}$ of velocity space. Of course, this number is much smaller than d^3N_{xyz} (which counts molecules of all velocities) or $d^3N_{\dot{x}\dot{y}\dot{z}}$ (which numbers molecules from all parts of the gas). The relations are illustrated in Fig. 16.1(a) for the two separate physical and velocity elements. In Fig. 16.1(b) are three cross sections of configuration-velocity space. These contain the image points referred to in $d^6N_{xyz\dot{x}\dot{y}\dot{z}}$ (here shown as five points), which are simply projected in turn onto the three planes.

The extension of this type of description to more general systems, including the molecules of polyatomic gases, requires the introduction of more general coordinates. Suppose, for example, that we have a set of curves such as those in Fig. 16.2, which are defined by two parameters, say, q_1 and q_2, that have taken on sets of constant values. The grid work obtained when q_1 takes on the constant values a_1, a_2, a_3, etc., and q_2 the values b_1, b_2, b_3, etc., constitutes a general *curvilinear coordinate system*. Any point in this plane is located from the values of q_1 and q_2 that cause two members of the set to intersect at the point. We say that q_1 and q_2 are the curvilinear coordinates of the point in question. If, as in this case, the curves always intersect at right angles, they constitute an *orthogonal system*, and there is no particular advantage in the use of other systems. If the a's represent the fixed radii of circles concentric around the origin, and the b's give the angles of radial lines from the origin, we have

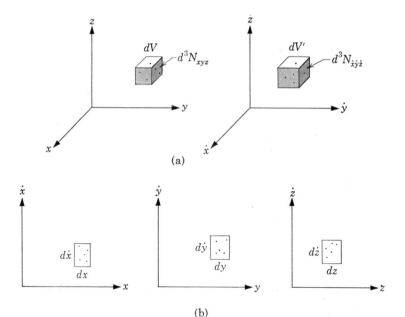

FIGURE **16.1**

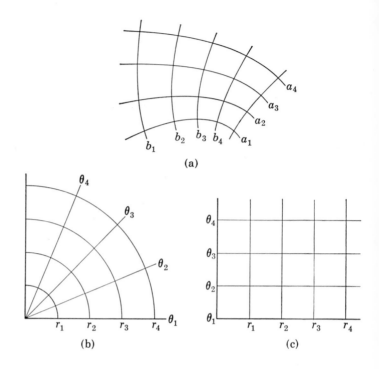

FIGURE 16.2

ordinary plane polar coordinates, Fig. 16.2(b). Note that we can perfectly well measure the r's and θ's along Cartesian axes in Fig. 16.2(c).

Now consider a system with, say, f degrees of freedom. We need f curvilinear coordinates, say, q_1, q_2, . . . , q_f, to describe the system's configuration. If in addition we know how fast each coordinate is changing with time, we have the f generalized velocities, $\dot{q}_1$, $\dot{q}_2$, . . . , $\dot{q}_f$. All told, then, a general configuration-velocity space of $2f$ dimensions is required. In this space a single image point describes the state of the system uniquely. If we are able to write down Newton's equations of motion, giving the accelerations (the $\ddot{q}$'s), integration gives the q's as functions of time and the initial conditions, and the subsequent history of the motion is determined. Unfortunately, however, this procedure is difficult, and each case presents a special problem, depending upon the particular nature of the curvilinear coordinates.

16.3   Hamiltonian Coordinates and Phase Space

There are great advantages in substituting for the velocity coordinates, $\dot{q}_1$, . . . , $\dot{q}_f$, what are known as generalized *momentum* coordinates, usually designated by p_1, . . . , p_f.

When Cartesian coordinates are used for the q's, as, for example with a single particle,

$$q_1 = x$$
$$q_2 = y$$
$$q_3 = z$$

the proper momentum coordinates for use with this particular choice of q's turn out to be the ordinary components of linear momentum, and

$$p_1 = m\dot{x}$$
$$p_2 = m\dot{y}$$
$$p_3 = m\dot{z}$$

We say that these are the momentum coordinates *conjugate* to x, y, and z.

In general, each particular choice of q's has its own conjugate p's. The general rules for finding the proper p's are very simple.

1. Express the kinetic energy in terms of the $\dot{q}$'s. This gives

$$\epsilon^{\text{kin}} = \epsilon^{\text{kin}}(\dot{q}_1, \ldots, \dot{q}_f)$$

2. By definition the p's are given as

$$p_i = \frac{\partial \epsilon^{\text{kin}}}{\partial \dot{q}_i} \qquad i = 1, \ldots, f$$

That is, we differentiate the kinetic energy partially with respect to the $\dot{q}$'s to obtain the conjugate p's.

Now consider a few examples.

Free Point Mass in Space. Let a point mass be located by the Cartesian coordinates x, y, and z. Then

$$\epsilon^{\text{kin}} = \epsilon^{\text{kin}}(\dot{q}_1, \dot{q}_2, \dot{q}_3) = \tfrac{1}{2}m(\dot{x}^2 + \dot{y}^2 + \dot{z}^2)$$

and therefore

$$p_1 = \frac{\partial \epsilon^{\text{kin}}}{\partial \dot{q}_1} = m\dot{x}$$

$$p_2 = \frac{\partial \epsilon^{\text{kin}}}{\partial \dot{q}_2} = m\dot{y}$$

$$p_3 = \frac{\partial \epsilon^{\text{kin}}}{\partial \dot{q}_3} = m\dot{z}$$

in agreement with the previous statement. Solving these for the $\dot{q}$'s and expressing the kinetic energy in terms of the p's give

$$\epsilon^{\text{kin}} = \frac{1}{2m} (p_1^2 + p_2^2 + p_3^2) \tag{16.2}$$

In the absence of any potential energy term, this is the total energy of the particle, which we now write

$$\mathbf{H} = \mathbf{H}(q, p) = \frac{1}{2m} (p_1^2 + p_2^2 + p_3^2) \tag{16.3}$$

where **H** is the *Hamiltonian function* for the system and represents the energy of the system in terms of the p's (and the q's, when needed).

In general, the Hamiltonian function is defined as the sum of the kinetic energy and the potential energy expressed entirely in terms of the p's and q's. In the important case in which the potential energy expression does *not* contain the *time* explicitly, that is, when $\epsilon^{pot} = \epsilon^{pot}(q_1, \ldots, q_f)$, the Hamiltonian represents an integral of the equations of motion that gives the total energy. Thus we regard the Hamiltonian as the total energy written in terms of the q's and p's,

$$\mathbf{H} = \epsilon^{kin}(q_1, \ldots, q_f, p_1, \ldots, p_f) + \epsilon^{pot}(q_1, \ldots, q_f)$$

or
$$\mathbf{H} = \mathbf{H}(q_i, p_i)$$

To represent the instantaneous state of the point mass, we construct a six-dimensional manifold using not the q's and $\dot{q}$'s but the q's and p's, that is, with the orthogonal axes x, y, z, p_1, p_2, and p_3. Plotting the values of these six coordinates for the particle gives an image point that moves as time goes on and traces out a trajectory that gives the detailed history of the motion. Such a configuration-momentum space is called a *phase* space, and the path traced by the image point is the *phase trajectory*.

In the case of a monatomic gas this six-dimensional phase space replaces the earlier configuration-velocity space. Each molecule has its image point, and the N image points determine the state of the gas. More complicated molecules (and subsystems in general) require phase spaces of higher dimensionality, although it is convenient to call them all *molecular spaces* or μ *spaces* for brevity.

Symmetric Rotor with a Fixed Axis.   In this case the q and $\dot{q}$ coordinates are naturally taken as θ and $\dot{\theta}$. In terms of $\dot{\theta}$ the kinetic energy expression is

$$\epsilon^{kin} = \tfrac{1}{2} I \dot{\theta}^2 \tag{16.4}$$

where I is the moment of inertia about the given axis. We then define p_θ as

$$p_\theta = \frac{\partial \epsilon^{kin}(\dot{\theta})}{\partial \dot{\theta}} = I \dot{\theta} \tag{16.5}$$

and p_θ is the ordinary angular momentum of the system. The status of the system is plotted in a two-dimensional phase space with orthogonal axes for θ and p_θ. The Hamiltonian function for the system is found by taking the sum

$$\epsilon^{kin}(\dot{\theta}) + \epsilon^{pot}(\theta)$$

and eliminating $\dot{\theta}$ in favor of p_θ. The resulting sum is the Hamiltonian function

$$\mathbf{H} = \mathbf{H}(p, q) = \frac{1}{2I} p_\theta^2 + \epsilon^{pot}(\theta) \tag{16.6}$$

If there is no force acting, $\epsilon^{pot} = 0$, and **H** reduces to a single squared term.

Mass Point Moving in Space about the Origin.   Let the Cartesian coordinates of the mass point be replaced by the spherical coordinates, r, θ, and ϕ. These then constitute the q's. We have

$$x = r \sin \theta \cos \phi$$
$$y = r \sin \theta \sin \phi \qquad \text{(16.7)}$$
and
$$z = r \cos \theta$$

The kinetic energy can always be written directly in terms of the Cartesian velocities, $\dot{x}$, $\dot{y}$, and $\dot{z}$, as

$$\epsilon^{\text{kin}} = \tfrac{1}{2}m(\dot{x}^2 + \dot{y}^2 + \dot{z}^2)$$

On differentiating Eq. 16.7 by the time and substituting in the result, we obtain after considerable reduction

$$\epsilon^{\text{kin}} = \epsilon^{\text{kin}}(\dot{q}_1, \dot{q}_2, \dot{q}_3) = \frac{m}{2}(\dot{r}^2 + r^2\dot{\theta}^2 + r^2 \sin^2 \theta \dot{\phi}^2) \qquad \text{(16.8)}$$

The moments conjugate to r, θ, and ϕ are then found by differentiation of this expression to give

$$p_r = m\dot{r}$$
$$p_\theta = mr^2\dot{\theta} \qquad \text{(16.9)}$$
$$p_\phi = mr^2 \sin^2 \theta \dot{\phi}$$

The coordinates r, θ, ϕ, p_r, p_θ, and p_ϕ are thus a proper set of dynamic or Hamiltonian coordinates for this problem.

To find the Hamiltonian function, we solve Eq. 16.9 for $\dot{r}$, $\dot{\theta}$, and $\dot{\phi}$ and express ϵ^{kin} in terms of the momenta. On adding to this the potential function $\epsilon^{\text{pot}}(r, \theta, \phi)$, we have the result

$$\mathbf{H} = \mathbf{H}(p_i, q_i) = \frac{1}{2m}p_r{}^2 + \frac{1}{2mr^2}p_\theta{}^2 + \frac{1}{2mr^2 \sin^2 \theta}p_\phi{}^2 + \epsilon^{\text{pot}}(r, \theta, \phi] \qquad \text{(16.10)}$$

The Rotating Vibrator. Suppose that the mass point just discussed is bound to an equilibrium value of r, say, r_0, by a restoring force that varies linearly with the separation $(r - r_0)$ from this position. In this case the potential energy is independent of θ and ϕ and depends only on $r - r_0$. Now define a new variable, ξ, where

$$\xi = r - r_0 \qquad \text{(16.11)}$$
Then
$$\epsilon^{\text{pot}} = \tfrac{1}{2}K\xi^2 \qquad \text{(16.12)}$$

where K is the restoring force constant. If we differentiatate Eq. 16.11 with respect to time,

$$\dot{\xi} = \dot{r}$$

and therefore $\dot{\xi}$ can be introduced into the original energy expression (Eq. 16.8) in place of $\dot{r}$. The proper momentum coordinate, p_ξ, conjugate to ξ is thus $m\dot{\xi}$, and p_ξ simply replaces p_r in the Hamiltonian (Eq. 16.10). The moment of inertia, I, of the mass, m, a distance r from the origin is $I = mr^2$, and with these alterations Eq. 16.10 becomes

$$H = \frac{1}{2m} p_\xi^2 + \frac{1}{2} K\xi^2 + \frac{1}{2I} p_\theta^2 + \frac{1}{2I \sin^2 \theta} p_\phi^2$$

Now, of course, I depends on r, and $r = r_0 + \xi$, so that $I = I(\xi)$. In fact,

$$I = m(r_0 + \xi)^2 = mr_0^2 + 2mr_0\xi + m\xi^2$$

We can neglect the terms in ξ and ξ^2 if ξ is small enough. Thus we have finally as the Hamiltonian for the *idealized rotating vibrator*

$$H = \frac{1}{2m} p_\xi^2 + \frac{1}{2} K\xi^2 + \frac{1}{2I_0} p_\theta^2 + \frac{1}{2I_0 \sin^2 \theta} p_\phi^2 \qquad (16.13)$$

where the idealization assumes (1) a simple harmonic vibration and (2) a constant moment of inertia (that is, the effects of vibration and centrifugal force on I are neglected).

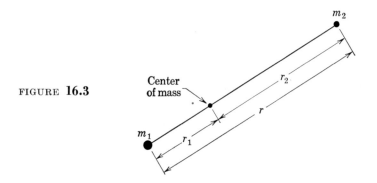

FIGURE **16.3**

The idealized rotating vibrator requires the coordinates ξ, θ, ϕ, p_ξ, p_θ, and p_ϕ, or a phase space of six dimensions. If, in addition, we regard its center of mass as being in motion, this condition requires the six extra coordinates needed for the point mass, or twelve all told. In a phase space of twelve dimensions, each rotating vibrator has its image point fixed by the coordinates x, y, z, ξ, θ, ϕ, p_1, p_2, p_3, p_ξ, p_θ, and p_ϕ. This idealized rotating vibrator is a very good approximation to a diatomic molecule, and this phase space is a satisfactory μ space for an ideal diatomic gas.

For this discussion we regard a diatomic molecule as made up of two point masses a distance, r, apart (Fig. 16.3). Let the two atoms have masses m_1 and m_2; then the center of mass of the molecule divides r into two lengths, r_1 and r_2, such that

$$r = r_1 + r_2$$

and

$$m_1 r_1 = m_2 r_2 = m'r \qquad (16.14)$$

where m' is the so-called *reduced* mass of the molecule, previously defined in Sec. 6.14 as

$$m' = \frac{m_1 m_2}{m_1 + m_2}$$

If we differentiate Eq. 16.14 with respect to time,

$$m_1 \dot{r}_1 = m_2 \dot{r}_2 = m' \dot{r}$$

and the kinetic energy becomes

$$\epsilon^{kin} = \tfrac{1}{2} m_1 \dot{r}_1{}^2 + \tfrac{1}{2} m_2 \dot{r}_2{}^2 = \tfrac{1}{2} m' \dot{r}^2$$

or, with the new coordinate ξ from Eq. 16.11, since $\dot{\xi} = \dot{r}$,

$$\epsilon^{kin} = \tfrac{1}{2} m' \dot{\xi}^2$$

To find the potential energy associated with the displacement from the equilibrium position, we need the curve

$$\epsilon^{pot} = \epsilon^{pot}(r)$$

A typical curve for a diatomic molecule is shown in Fig. 16.4(a). Since the restoring force, F, which permits oscillations, is given as

$$F = - \frac{\partial \epsilon^{pot}}{\partial r}$$

it is plotted in Fig. 16.4(b). The force vanishes at $r = r_0$, where the potential curve has a minimum. Along the linear portion of the force curve,

$$F = -K(r - r_0) = -K\xi$$

where K is the force constant. The potential curve corresponding to this portion of the curve is of the form

$$\epsilon^{pot} = \frac{K}{2} (r - r_0)^2 = \frac{K}{2} \xi^2$$

and is shown as a dashed line in Fig. 16.4(a).

If we agree to represent the actual diatomic molecule by this idealized simple harmonic approximation,

$$\epsilon^{vib} = \tfrac{1}{2} m' \dot{\xi}^2 + \tfrac{1}{2} K \xi^2$$

or in the Hamiltonian coordinates p_ξ and ξ,

$$\epsilon^{vib} = \mathbf{H}^{vib} = \frac{1}{2m'} p_\xi{}^2 + \frac{1}{2} K \xi^2$$

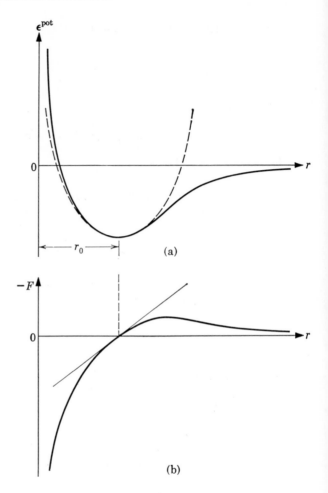

FIGURE **16.4**

The remaining two terms in Eq. 16.13 give the rotational contribution. If I is the moment of inertia of the diatomic molecule about an axis through the center of mass and normal to the figure axis,

$$I = m_1 r_1{}^2 + m_2 r_2{}^2 = m'r^2 = m'(r_0 + \xi)^2$$

or, with the changes in r neglected as before,

$$I = I_0 = m'r_0{}^2$$

and m' simply replaces the m of the earlier expression. Since the complete Hamiltonian for the molecule in space must include the translatory energy of the center of mass, we have

$$\mathbf{H} = \mathbf{H}^{\text{trn}} + \mathbf{H}^{\text{vib}} + \mathbf{H}^{\text{rot}} = \frac{1}{2m}\,(p_1{}^2 + p_2{}^2 + p_3{}^2) + \mathbf{H}^{\text{vib}} + \mathbf{H}^{\text{rot}}$$

where $m = (m_1 + m_2)$ is the total mass of the molecule.

More complicated subsystems (such as polyatomic molecules) with f degrees of freedom require μ spaces of $2f$ dimensionality. In general, however, all proper phase spaces have *two important properties:* (1) their volumes are invariant to mere change of scale; and (2) their volumes have the universal dimension of

$$(\text{energy} \times \text{time})^f = (\text{action})^f$$

Thus take a two-space with $q = x$ and $p = m\dot{x}$. An element of volume is

$$dq\,dp = m\,dx\,d\dot{x}$$

Now change to a new coordinate, q', where

$$q' = ax$$

a being a scale factor. Then, since $\epsilon^{\text{kin}} = \frac{1}{2}m\dot{x}^2$ and $\dot{q}' = a\dot{x}$,

$$\epsilon^{\text{kin}} = \frac{1}{2}\frac{m}{a^2}\,(\dot{q}')^2$$

and

$$p' = \frac{m\dot{q}'}{a^2}$$

when

$$dq'\,dp' = \frac{m\,d\dot{q}'\,dq'}{a^2} = m\,dx\,d\dot{x} = dp\,dq$$

the same as before.

Now consider the dimensions of a product of a p by a q.

$$pq = \frac{\partial\epsilon^{\text{kin}}}{\partial\dot{q}}\,q = \frac{\text{energy}}{\dfrac{q}{\text{time}}} \times q = \text{energy} \times \text{time}$$

Energy times *time* has the units of *action*, and for an elementary volume, therefore,

$$dq\,dp = \text{action}$$

In a general μ space of $2f$ dimensions, the element of volume, which we write $d\mu$, is

$$d\mu = dq_1 \cdots dq_f\,dp \cdots dp_f$$

or

$$d\mu = \prod_i dq_i\,dp_i$$

so that

$$d\mu = (dp\,dp)^f = (\text{action})^f$$

and all phase space elements have dimensions that are powers of the unit of action. This fact will be of great significance in the next chapter.

16.4 µ Space and Γ Space

Suppose now that we wish to generalize the method used in Chap. 15 for calculating equilibrium conditions and seek to maximize the entropy of a system made up of N subsystems of f degrees of freedom. We may proceed as follows. First we imagine a general μ space of $2f$ dimensions and divide the accessible part of this into $2f$-dimensional μ cells of *equal* size. We call this size $\Delta\mu$ and let

$$\Delta\mu = \Delta q_1 \cdots \Delta p_f = \prod_i^f \Delta q_i \Delta p_i \qquad (16.15)$$

Next we consider an arbitrary distribution of the N image points that describe the state of the system in μ space, say,

$$N_1, N_2, \ldots, N_j, \ldots, N_s$$

s being the number of cells in accessible μ space. According to Boltzmann's combinatory analysis, we then calculate the number of ways of permuting the subsystems (or polyatomic molecules) among these cells to give W, the number of microstates in the distribution, as

$$W = \frac{N!}{\Pi N_j!}$$

where j covers all the cells from 1 to s. The significance of W rests on the crucial assumption that all the microstates *have equal probability*. In Chap. 15 this equality of probability was made to rest on the equal likelihood of N independent assignments of N specific molecules, whatever the microstate happened to be. Equality of probability may well exist, but it is desirable to establish it as a consequence of physical laws rather than as a plausible assumption.

A great deal of the most brilliant work on the foundations of classical statistics has gone into the attempt to solve this difficult problem, but only a brief indication of the line of argument can be given here. For the purpose of this presentation, it is necessary for us to invent an even more involved space than μ space.

Thus we imagine a phase space in which each of the $2f$ coordinates of the N subsystems has its own axis, that is, a phase space of $2Nf = 2F$ dimensions. Since N is of the order of Avogadro's number, this is a *hyperphase space* in which the number of coordinates is so huge that we can never hope to enumerate, much less follow, their detailed changes. In this new system space or Γ space, the status of the entire system is fixed by a *single image point*. As time progresses, the various coordinates of each particle change, and the $2F$ coor-

dinates of the system alter. However, the coordinates are Hamiltonian ones
and proper for expressing the laws of mechanics in general Hamiltonian form.[1]
    Hamilton's equations are

$$\frac{\partial q_i}{\partial t} = \dot{q}_i = \frac{\partial H}{\partial p_i}$$

$$\frac{\partial p_i}{\partial t} = \dot{p}_i = -\frac{\partial H}{\partial q_i} \qquad i = 1, \ldots, Nf = F \qquad (16.16)$$

where H is the Hamiltonian function for the entire system (of subsystems)
expressed as a function of the $2Nf = 2F$ coordinates. The equations are of the
first order and on integration give each coordinate as a function of the time, t,
and, say, an initial value at an initial time, t_0. Thus the system's image point
starts at a given point at t_0, changes with time, owing to the laws of mechanics,
and traces out a trajectory in Γ space. Even in the case of the ideal monatomic
gas, $2F = 6N$, and the system trajectory must suffer a change in direction for
every collision of every pair of molecules in the gas. Since collisions take place
at a very high rate all through the gas, this curve is extraordinarily complicated,
with numerous twists and bends and kinks in any small length. It wanders
through Γ space with the passage of time and in theory eventually reaches essentially all parts of Γ space accessible to the system. If we regard the system's
internal energy, U, as being fixed between differential limits such that

$$U_0 \leq U \leq U_0 + dU_0$$

the image point traces this trajectory in a thin *energy shell*. We may imagine
the differential energy shell shown in cross section in Fig. 16.5(a), with a
trajectory being traced out as in Fig. 16.5(b).

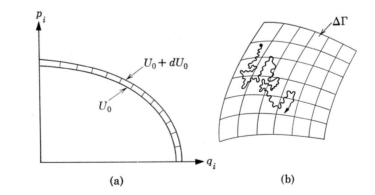

FIGURE **16.5**

(a)   (b)

[1] See, for example, J. W. Leech, *Classical Mechanics*, Wiley, New York, 1958, Chap. 5.

Now suppose that the energy shell is divided into hypercells of equal volume, say, $\Delta\Gamma$, where

$$\Delta\Gamma = \Delta q_1 \cdot \cdot \cdot \Delta p_F$$

If we imagine coordinates numbered from 1 to f for the first molecule, f to $2f$ for the second molecule, etc., this may be written

$$\Delta\Gamma = \prod_{i=1}^{N} \Delta\mu_i$$

where $\Delta\mu_i$ is the volume of a μ cell in the subspace appropriate to the ith molecule.

We say that the system point is in a given Γ cell when its coordinates lie in the range given by

$$q_1 \text{ and } q_1 + \Delta q_1 \qquad p_1 \text{ and } p_1 + \Delta p_1$$

$$\cdot \quad \cdot \quad \cdot \quad \cdot \quad \cdot \qquad \cdot \quad \cdot \quad \cdot \quad \cdot \quad \cdot$$

$$\cdot \quad \cdot \quad \cdot \quad \cdot \quad \cdot \qquad \cdot \quad \cdot \quad \cdot \quad \cdot \quad \cdot$$

$$q_F \text{ and } q_F + \Delta q_F \qquad p_F \text{ and } p_F + \Delta p_F$$

This is just the requirement that the gas be in a given microstate; every single molecule is in a specified cell in μ space. If a single molecule moves out of its proper cell of size $\Delta\mu$ in μ space, the system point moves out of the Γ cell of size $\Delta\Gamma$ in Γ space. This means that every cell in Γ space defines a *microstate of the system*. These microstates are indicated in Fig. 16.5(b). As the system point

FIGURE **16.6**

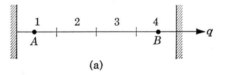

(a)

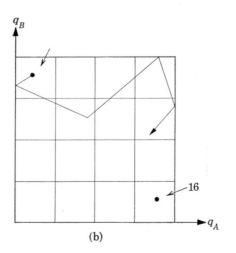

(b)

moves along its trajectory, it changes from one Γ cell to another and thus passes from one microstate to another. It is therefore easier to conceive of a microstate in Γ space than in the much simpler μ space.

For aid in understanding the relation of these two spaces, take the following very simple example. Consider two particles, A and B, confined to a segment of the q axis. Thus μ space has but one dimension, the q axis, shown in Fig. 16.6(a). The accessible part of this is divided into four equal μ cells numbered 1 to 4. Let microstate #1 be defined as having A in μ cell #1 and B in μ cell #4.

In this case Γ space is two-dimensional, with the axes q_A and q_B, one for each particle. The cells fixing the sixteen possible microstates (equal to 4^2) are shown in Fig. 16.6(b). The microstate in question corresponds to the Γ cell in the upper left corner. Now interchange A and B in μ space. The system point moves to the Γ cell in the lower right corner marked 16. Thus every microstate corresponds to a particular Γ cell, and every Γ cell in turn fixes a microstate.

If the particles A and B are in motion, colliding with the boundaries and with one another, the system point moves along a path, the trajectory of the system, from one Γ cell to another.

16.5 Liouville's Theorem and Equal a Priori Probabilities in Γ Space

Unfortunately, in the case of an actual physical system, the stupendous number of variables and the utter lack of knowledge of the instantaneous values of the $2Nf$ coordinates mean that we cannot hope to follow the system trajectory in time. We rely on statistical mechanics, therefore, to obtain useful results when we do not know the initial conditions for even the simplest physical system and could not determine the trajectory if we did! In such a situation we must resort to a calculation of probabilities. Given a certain fixed volume with energy confined in a certain narrow range, where are we most likely to find the system point? The general answer to this question has not been found, but the results suggest that *no part of accessible Γ space is preferred* and that the image point on the average spends *equal time in every Γ cell*. In other words, we have *equal a priori probability* for every Γ cell; the system at any instant is just as likely to be in one Γ cell as in another. This of course means that *all possible microstates of the system have equal a priori probabilities.*

This conclusion we now interpret in terms of a famous theorem due to the French mathematician Liouville. Suppose that instead of having one system only, with its single image point, we imagine a huge assembly or *ensemble* of systems, all of the same volume, energy, and number, N, of subsystems (or molecules, in this particular case).[2] These systems will in general be in all sorts

---

[2] This type of ensemble was termed by Gibbs a *microcanonical* ensemble. Two other ensembles are of great value, the *macrocanonical* ensemble and the *grand canonical* ensemble. In the first of these two, the systems are in thermal contact so that energies fluctuate, whereas in the last they are allowed to interchange heat *energy* and *particles* so that both N and U fluctuate. See Sec. 19.5 *et seq.*

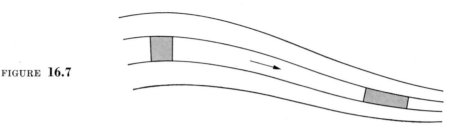

FIGURE **16.7**

of microstates, and their image points will be scattered throughout accessible Γ space. At any one point in this region we may define a density of system points, D, where in general

$$D = D(q_i, p_i, t)$$

Liouville's theorem (see Appendix 16.1) is equivalent to the statement that along any trajectory D *remains constant.* If, in addition, all the systems of the assembly are in equilibrium, D is independent of time and is the same everywhere. This means that the system image points flow through Γ space like a uniform incompressible fluid in hydrodynamics. (See Fig. 16.7.) We now make the assumption, known as the *ergodic hypothesis,* that the trajectory for each system in the ensemble will eventually pass through every other region of phase space of the same energy. Thus, for the constancy of D to be preserved, each image point must spend "equal times in equal volumes." This being true, if a system is picked at random from the assembly, it is just as likely to be in one Γ cell as in any other. From this argument we are able to understand the dynamic reason for the *principle of equal a priori probabilities in Γ space.*

16.6   The Equilibrium Distribution in μ Space

We are now ready to return to the problem raised in the first part of Sec. 16.4, that of finding the equilibrium distribution function for N subsystems distributed among the s cells of a general μ space of $2f$ dimensionality. With the arbitrary distribution numbers

$$N_1, N_2, \ldots, N_j, \ldots, N_s$$

we have

$$W = \frac{N!}{\prod_j N_j!}$$

and therefore the Boltzmann entropy expression becomes

$$S = k \ln \frac{N!}{\prod_j N_j!} \tag{16.17}$$

The steps required to maximize S parallel those used in Chap. 15 and will be given with a minimum of repetition. Using Stirling's formula on Eq. 16.17, we have

$$S = k(N \ln N - N - \Sigma N_j \ln N_j + \Sigma N_j)$$

or, since

$$N = \Sigma N_j$$

$$S = k(N \ln N - \Sigma N_j \ln N_j) \tag{16.18}$$

Combining this with

$$N = \Sigma N_j \tag{16.19}$$

and

$$U = \Sigma N_j \epsilon_j \tag{16.20}$$

forms the set needed for maximizing S at constant U and N. Writing down the variation of these three equations (omitting for simplicity the asterisks used previously) and setting them equal to zero gives the three conditions that we combine by the Lagrangian method as follows:

$$
\begin{array}{r|c}
1 & \Sigma \ln N_j \, \delta N_j = 0 \\
\lambda & \Sigma \delta N_j = 0 \\
\beta & \Sigma \epsilon_j \, \delta N_j = 0
\end{array}
$$

to give

$$\Sigma(\ln N_j + \lambda + \beta\epsilon_j) \, \delta N_j = 0$$

The sufficient condition for the vanishing of this single equation is that each coefficient of a δN_j shall vanish. The result is

$$\ln N_j = -(\lambda + \beta\epsilon_j)$$

or

$$N_j = e^{-\lambda}e^{-\beta\epsilon_j}$$

which we write as

$$N_j = \alpha' e^{-\beta\epsilon_j}$$

or

$$\boxed{N_j = \alpha N \, \Delta\mu e^{-\beta\epsilon_j}} \tag{16.21}$$

where α' is replaced by $\alpha N \Delta\mu$ and α is independent of cell size or molecule number. Here α and α' are different from the constants appearing in Eqs. 15.29 and 15.30.

This is the new distribution law, and although it is of the same form as the earlier one obtained for velocity space, it is in fact much more general. It gives the number of image points in a $2f$-dimensional μ cell of volume $\Delta\mu$.

We now proceed to evaluate α. Imagine the image points smeared out to give a continuously varying phase density, ρ, where

$$\rho = \lim_{\Delta\mu \to 0} \frac{N_j}{\Delta\mu} = \frac{d^{2f}N_{q_1 \cdots q_f p_1 \cdots p_f}}{dq_1 \cdots dq_f dp_1 \cdots dp_f}$$

From Eq. 16.21 we see that ρ is given as

$$\rho = \alpha N e^{-\beta\epsilon}$$

or

$$\rho = \alpha N e^{-\beta H(p_i, q_i)}$$

since we suppose that the energy at the $2f$-dimensional point where ρ is measured is expressed entirely in terms of the p's and q's. Thus for the differential number in a $2f$-dimensional element of volume

$$d\mu = dq_1 \cdots dq_f dp_1 \cdots dp_f$$

we have

$$d^{2f}N_{q_1 \ldots p_f} = \alpha N e^{-\beta H(p,q)} \, d\mu \qquad (16.22)$$

On integration with respect to the $2f$ coordinates, each over its proper range, the left side of this expression gives N, and therefore the value of α is fixed by

$$\frac{1}{\alpha} = \int \cdots \int e^{-\beta H(p,q)} \, d\mu \qquad (16.23)$$

The $2f$-fold integral on the right is the general *partition integral* and fixes the value of the parameter α. Once it has been evaluated, both Eqs. 16.21 and 16.22, the *discrete* and the *differential* forms of the μ space distribution laws, are ready for use.

16.7   The General Partition Function in μ Space

Before attempting to evaluate the partition integral in special cases, let us express it in terms of the so-called *partition function*. Indicating this by Z, we define it formally as

$$Z \equiv \sum_j e^{-\beta \epsilon_j} \qquad (16.24)$$

that is, the sum of $e^{-\beta \epsilon_j}$ over all the accessible cells in μ space. This is, of course, a $2f$-dimensional sum and will at this point be expressed in terms of the $2f$-fold partition integral. Thus if we sum both sides of Eq. 16.21 over all μ cells, we have

$$N = \Sigma N_j = \alpha N \, \Delta\mu \Sigma e^{-\beta \epsilon_j}$$

or

$$Z = \frac{1}{\alpha \, \Delta\mu} \qquad (16.25)$$

Since $1/\alpha$ is the partition integral,

$$Z = \frac{1}{\Delta\mu} \int e^{-\beta H(p,q)} \, d\mu \qquad (16.26)$$

In a major share of the practical applications, the Hamiltonian function splits into independent terms. Since we may rearrange and regroup $\Delta\mu$ and $d\mu$ in any order we like, the integral, and hence Z, breaks up into a number of factors. Each of these factors or *subpartition functions* is of the form of Eq. 16.26, but now evaluated over an appropriate subportion of phase space.

If the N independent subsystems of f degrees of freedom are the polyatomic molecules of an ideal gas, the Hamiltonian can always be split into two terms, the first a function of the momenta of the center of mass of the molecule and the other a function of the coordinates describing the internal motions; that is,

$$\mathbf{H}(p, q) = \mathbf{H}^{\text{trn}} + \mathbf{H}^{\text{int}} \tag{16.27}$$

The first term gives the translatory kinetic energy of the moving molecule and is of the form of Eq. 16.2; that is,

$$\mathbf{H}^{\text{trn}} = \frac{1}{2m} (p_1{}^2 + p_2{}^2 + p_3{}^2)$$

where m is the mass of the entire molecule. The Hamiltonian of the internal coordinates can be further separated into rotational and vibrational terms in the case of the idealized diatomic molecule, etc. In such cases

$$\mathbf{H}^{\text{int}} = \mathbf{H}^{\text{vib}} + \mathbf{H}^{\text{rot}} \tag{16.28}$$

and these individual terms may often be even further separated.

If for purposes of argument we assume the separation indicated in Eqs. 16.27 and 16.28, Z can be written

$$Z = \left(\frac{1}{\Delta\mu^{\text{trn}}} \int e^{-\beta \mathbf{H}^{\text{trn}}} d\mu^{\text{trn}} \right) \left(\frac{1}{\Delta\mu^{\text{vib}}} \int e^{-\beta \mathbf{H}^{\text{vib}}} d\mu^{\text{vib}} \right) \left(\frac{1}{\Delta\mu^{\text{rot}}} \int e^{-\beta \mathbf{H}^{\text{rot}}} d\mu^{\text{rot}} \right)$$

or

$$Z = Z^{\text{trn}} Z^{\text{vib}} Z^{\text{rot}}$$

where each factor is a separate subpartition function evaluated over its own subregion of the general μ space. Thus

$$Z^{\text{trn}} = \frac{1}{\Delta\mu^{\text{trn}}} \int\!\!\int\!\!\int\!\!\int\!\!\int\!\!\int e^{-\beta \mathbf{H}^{\text{trn}}} dx\, dy\, dz\, dp_1\, dp_2\, dp_3 \tag{16.29}$$

and is to be evaluated over the six-dimensional translational subspace of the general μ space.

Each of the other factors is to be evaluated by carrying out the appropriate number of integrations over the accessible parts of the vibrational and rotational subspaces, respectively. The details of these integrations must, of course, depend upon the form of $\mathbf{H}^{\text{vib}}$ and $\mathbf{H}^{\text{rot}}$ and the actual number of variables used. Whatever the nature of the ideal *polyatomic* gas, however, the translatory partition function always has the form given in Eq. 16.29, and the complete partition function can always be written

$$Z = Z^{\text{trn}} Z^{\text{int}}$$

In the case of the ideal *monatomic* gas the first factor is the *entire partition function*, and we have

$$Z^{\text{mono}} = Z^{\text{trn}}$$

16.8   The Ideal Monatomic Gas

Let us now evaluate the partition function for the ideal monatomic gas. For convenience we consider the gas to be in a cubic container, say, L on an edge, and place this cube with one corner at the origin and the three edges along the x, y, and z axes. Then the limits of integration are 0 to L for x, y, and z and for mathematical simplicity from $-\infty$ to $+\infty$ for the three momentum variables. Actually, of course, the accessible part of translational μ space is finite in extent, but the contributions to the integrals in the outer reaches is negligibly small owing to the extreme paucity of image points. Thus we have

$$Z^{\text{trn}} = \frac{1}{\Delta\mu^{\text{trn}}} \int_{-\infty}^{+\infty} \int_{-\infty}^{+\infty} \int_{-\infty}^{+\infty} \int_0^L \int_0^L \int_0^L \left[\exp - \frac{\beta}{2m}(p_1{}^2 + p_2{}^2 + p_3{}^2) \right] dx\, dy\, dz\, dp_1\, dp_2\, dp_3$$

where $\Delta\mu^{\text{trn}} = \Delta x\, \Delta y\, \Delta z\, \Delta p_1\, \Delta p_2\, \Delta p_3$ and in terms of the separate volume and velocity cells used in Chap. 15 is given by

$$\Delta\mu^{\text{trn}} = \Delta V m^3 \Delta V' = v_0 m^3 v_0'$$

This integral can be rewritten

$$Z^{\text{trn}} = \left[\frac{1}{\Delta x\, \Delta p_1} \int_{-\infty}^{+\infty} \int_0^L \left(\exp - \frac{\beta p_1{}^2}{2m} \right) dx\, dp_1 \right]$$
$$\left[\frac{1}{\Delta y\, \Delta p_2} \int_{-\infty}^{+\infty} \int_0^L \left(\exp - \frac{\beta p_2{}^2}{2m} \right) dy\, dp_2 \right]$$
$$\left[\frac{1}{\Delta z\, \Delta p_3} \int_{-\infty}^{+\infty} \int_0^L \left(\exp - \frac{\beta p_3{}^2}{2m} \right) dz\, dp_3 \right] \quad (16.30)$$

The integration of each of the independent factors can be carried out over the geometric coordinate (to give L), and the rest of the equation is just twice the standard integral $I(0)$ of Table 15.1, where

$$I(0) = \int_0^\infty e^{-ax^2}\, dx = \frac{1}{2}\left(\frac{\pi}{a}\right)^{\frac{1}{2}}$$

Since $a = \beta/2m$, we obtain

$$Z^{\text{trn}} = \frac{L}{\Delta x\, \Delta p_1}\left(\frac{2\pi m}{\beta}\right)^{\frac{1}{2}} \frac{L}{\Delta y\, \Delta p_2}\left(\frac{2\pi m}{\beta}\right)^{\frac{1}{2}} \frac{L}{\Delta z\, \Delta p_3}\left(\frac{2\pi m}{\beta}\right)^{\frac{1}{2}} \quad (16.31)$$

or, since $V = L^3$, the separate so-called "one-dimensional" partition functions combine to give

$$Z^{trn} = \frac{V}{\Delta\mu^{trn}} \left(\frac{2\pi m}{\beta}\right)^{3/2}$$

(16.32)

In the general case, Z is always given by Eq. 16.25 as

$$Z = \frac{1}{\alpha \Delta\mu}$$

and therefore the distribution law, and hence the internal energy, entropy, etc., can all be expressed formally in terms of Z. The general distribution law in Eq. 16.21 now becomes

$$N_j = \frac{N}{Z} e^{-\beta\epsilon_j}$$

(16.33)

By definition

$$Z = \Sigma e^{-\beta\epsilon_j}$$

and differentiation with respect to β gives

$$\frac{\partial Z}{\partial \beta} = - \sum e^{-\beta\epsilon_j}\epsilon_j$$

(16.34)

On use of Eqs. 16.33 and 16.34, the definition of internal energy becomes

$$U = \sum N_j\epsilon_j = \frac{N}{Z} \sum e^{-\beta\epsilon_j}\epsilon_j = - \frac{N}{Z} \frac{\partial Z}{\partial \beta}$$

(16.35)

Since $(1/Z)\partial Z/\partial\beta$ is the logarithmic derivative, this may be written

$$U = -N \frac{\partial \ln Z}{\partial \beta}$$

(16.36)

Use of Eq. 16.32 for Z^{trn} in this relation gives

$$U^{trn} = -N \frac{\partial \ln Z^{trn}}{\partial \beta} = N \frac{3}{2\beta} = N \frac{3}{2} kT$$

or

$$\frac{U^{trn}}{N} = \overline{\epsilon^{trn}} = \frac{3}{2} kT$$

that is, the average translational energy per monatomic molecule is just $\frac{3}{2}kT$. Since there are three degrees of freedom and three squared terms in the expression for the translational energy, *the average energy per squared term is exactly $\frac{1}{2}kT$*. This is the Boltzmann equipartition theorem for this special case.

Returning to the general entropy expression given in Eq. 16.18, we find that it too can be expressed in terms of Z and its derivatives. Use of Eq. 16.33, in fact, gives

$$S = K\left[N \ln N - \sum N_j\left(\ln \frac{N}{Z}\right) + \beta \sum N_j\epsilon_j\right]$$

Since $\Sigma N_j = N$ and the last sum in the bracket is U, we have finally

$$S = Nk\left[\ln Z - \beta \frac{\partial \ln Z}{\partial \beta}\right] \tag{16.37}$$

The results in Eqs. 16.33 to 16.37 are quite general and may be specialized for for the case of the ideal monatomic gas by the insertion of Z^{mono} for the general value of Z. With

$$Z^{\text{mono}} = \frac{V}{\Delta\mu^{\text{trn}}}\left(\frac{2\pi m}{\beta}\right)^{3/2}$$

the partial derivative with respect to β can be calculated. The result gives for the term in the logarithmic derivative in Eq. 16.37

$$-\beta \frac{\partial \ln Z^{\text{mono}}}{\partial \beta} = \frac{3}{2}$$

and thus

$$S^{\text{mono}} = Nk\left[\ln V - \ln \beta^{3/2} + \ln \frac{(2\pi m)^{3/2}}{\Delta\mu^{\text{trn}}} + \frac{3}{2}\right] \tag{16.38}$$

From the foregoing calculations, β can only be a function of the absolute temperature and in fact is readily shown to be $1/kT$ as before. This proof is left as an exercise (see Problem 16.1).[3] With $\beta = 1/kT$, the expression for entropy becomes

$$S^{\text{mono}} = Nk\left[\ln V + \ln T^{3/2} + \ln \frac{(2\pi mk)^{3/2}}{\Delta\mu^{\text{trn}}} + \frac{3}{2}\right] \tag{16.39}$$

which is seen to be equivalent to the value obtained by the more cumbersome arguments of Sec. 15.11 and given in Eq. 15.42, since $\Delta\mu^{\text{trn}} = m^3 v_0 v_0'$.

16.9   The Ideal Gas in a Uniform Gravitational Field

Let us now consider an interesting application of the present methods to the case of a gas in an external field of force. As long as the potential energy of a particle is due entirely to an external force field, the translational part of the

---

[3] The identification of β with $1/kT$ has, strictly speaking, been made only for an isochoric process. It can be shown to apply, however, for the general thermodynamic process. In this case the volume alters, and the number of cells in accessible μ space over which we must sum changes also. See, for example, A. Sommerfeld, *Thermodynamics and Statistical Mechanics*, Academic Press, New York, 1956, pp. 221 ff.

Hamiltonian contains no terms involving the position coordinates of other molecules, and

$$H^{trn} = \frac{1}{2m}(p_1{}^2 + p_2{}^2 + p_3{}^2) + H^{pot}(x,y,z) + H^{int}$$

or

$$H = H^{trn} + H'$$

where H' is the rest of the Hamiltonian, which is independent of the translational coordinates.

For a perfect gas the energy of a particle depends solely upon its cell in μ space and not upon the density of image points in that or neighboring cells (that is, there is no mutual potential energy between any two gas molecules). In this case Boltzmann's method of computing W is legitimate, and all the arguments of Sec. 16.6 proceed as before. In particular, only a single β multiplier is used in the Lagrangian method. Thus the general distribution law as given in Eqs. 16.21 and 16.22 applies. The latter equation may be written

$$d^{2f}N_{xyzp_1p_2p_3(q_i,p_i)} = \alpha N e^{-\beta H^{trn}} d\mu^{trn} e^{-\beta H'} d\mu'$$

where the symbol (q_i, p_i) indicates the $(2f - 6)$ coordinates involved in $d\mu'$. Now suppose that this relation is integrated over these $(2f - 6)$ variables. On the left we have $d^6N_{xyzp_1p_2p_3}$, and therefore

$$d^6N_{xyzp_1p_2p_3} = \alpha N e^{-\beta H^{trn}} d\mu^{trn} \int e^{-\beta H'} d\mu'$$

On integration over the remaining six translational coordinates, we obtain N on the left when α is given as

$$\alpha = \frac{1}{\int e^{-\beta H^{trn}} d\mu^{trn} \int e^{-\beta H'} d\mu'}$$

where the integrals are independent, each over its own subregion of μ space. If we combine these two results to eliminate α, the integrals over $d\mu'$ cancel, and

$$d^6N_{xyzp_1p_2p_3} = \frac{N e^{-\beta H^{trn}} d\mu^{trn}}{\int e^{-\beta H^{trn}} d\mu^{trn}}$$

If we now integrate over the momentum coordinates only, the left-hand term of the result is d^3N_{xyz}, the differential number of image points in the volume $dx\,dy\,dz$. Dividing through by $dx\,dy\,dz$ gives the *local particle density* in ordinary space. Since this is $\hat{n}$,

$$\hat{n} = \frac{d^3N_{xyz}}{dx\,dy\,dz} = \frac{e^{-\beta \epsilon^{pot}} N \int\int\int e^{-\beta \epsilon^{kin}} dp_1\,dp_2\,dp_3}{(PI)^{trn}} \tag{16.40}$$

where $(PI)^{trn}$ is an abbreviation for the partition integral over translational space. The ratio of these two integrals times N is just some parameter, say, A, and accordingly we have

$$\hat{n} = Ae^{-\beta\epsilon^{pot}} \tag{16.41}$$

In other words, the particle density, $\hat{n}$, is a function of x, y, and z, since ϵ^{pot} depends on these variables only.

Now consider the equilibrium of the ideal gas in a uniform gravitational field. Let the z axis be along the direction of increasing gravitational potential so that

$$\epsilon^{pot} = mgh(z - z_0) \tag{16.42}$$

where z_0 is the reference level from which potential energy is measured. Then the particle density at any value of z, say, $\hat{n}_z$, is given by

$$\hat{n}_z = Ae^{-\beta mgh(z-z_0)}$$

If we let $z = z_0$, the exponential reduces to unity, and

$$\hat{n}_0 = A$$

$\hat{n}_0$ being the particle density at the reference level. Thus

$$\hat{n}_z = \hat{n}_0 e^{-\beta mgh(z-z_0)} \tag{16.43}$$

Since the gas remains ideal at all elevations

$$p = \frac{N}{V}kT = \hat{n}kT$$

so that

$$p_z = \hat{n}_z kT$$

$$p_0 = \hat{n}_0 kT$$

and

$$p_z = p_0 e^{-\beta mgh(z-z_0)} \tag{16.44}$$

where p_z and p_0 are the pressures at z and z_0, respectively, and $\beta = 1/kT$ as usual.

These very compact results are the two forms of the so-called *aerostatic equation*, which gives the particle density or pressure as a function of elevation in an isothermal ideal gas in a gravitational field. Both particle density and pressure fall off exponentially. The form of these results indicates that even in the presence of an external gravitational field, once equilibrium has been reached, *a single uniform temperature exists throughout the system.* It had previously been argued by many that this situation was impossible, since as particles travel in the direction of the field they acquire more kinetic energy and thus have more than their new neighbors in the new location (the reverse is true, of course, for motion in the opposite direction).

Equilibrium is, in fact, impossible unless the particle density of the gas increases in the direction of the field. Imagine a surface normal to the field, as shown in cross section in Fig. 16.8(a). If we begin with a uniform density, on the average fewer particles will be able to cross this surface *against* the field than with it; that is, only the faster particles diffuse against the field, while some slow molecules moving upward *above* the surface may reverse their directions and move below the surface. This activity sets up a density gradient, which grows until equilibrium is reached and is thereafter maintained at a constant value.

The classical example of the use of these results was J. B. Perrin's direct determination of Avogadro's number. He made a study of the variation of particle density in a colloidal suspension of the gum gamboge. Although here the results are deduced for ideal gas molecules, they also apply to any dilute constituent of a mixture of particles, including microscopically visible colloidal particles in thermal equilibrium with the liquid in which they are suspended. Thus Perrin, by measuring as accurately as possible the variation of the particle density with z, could calculate from the average mass of his particles the value of β and hence of Boltzmann's constant, k. Since $N_0 = R/k$, the value of N_0 was immediately obtainable. The best results of this method give

FIGURE **16.8**

(a)   (b)

$N_0 = 6.09 \times 10^{23}$, in remarkably good agreement with the results of less direct methods.[4]

16.10   The Boltzmann Equipartition Theorem

One of the most general results of classical statistics is the equipartition theorem, which we may establish for much more general systems than the monatomic gas considered in Sec. 16.8.

Suppose that we have a system made up of N independent subsystems, each with f degrees of freedom. These subsystems need not be specified in general but here may be taken to be the polyatomic molecules of an ideal gas. In this case, as we saw in Sec. 6.16, the total number of degrees of freedom (for nonlinear molecules) is determined by the number of atoms per molecule; that is,

$$f = 3n_a$$

If six degrees are used to fix the center of mass of the molecule and its orientation in space, there are $f - 6 = 3n_a - 6$ left to describe internal vibrations. If the number of vibrations is indicated by f^{vib},

$$f^{\text{vib}} = 3n_a - 6 = 3(n_a - 2) \qquad n_a > 2$$

For small oscillations it is always possible by a proper choice of coordinates to have the total Hamiltonian function for the molecule reduce to r squared terms, where

$$r = f + f^{\text{vib}} = 6(n_a - 1) \qquad n_a > 2$$

This means that each vibration adds *two* squared terms, one a kinetic energy term and one a potential energy term. Thus the total Hamiltonian can conveniently be written in the general form

$$\mathbf{H}(p, q) = \sum_{j=1}^{r} \frac{1}{2} \lambda_i \zeta_j^2 \tag{16.45}$$

Here the λ's are parameters that may depend on the q's (but not the p's) and ζ_j is a general running coordinate that may be a p or a q. Thus ζ_j runs through all the p's and such of the q's as refer to the vibratory motions.[5]

---

[4] Since mg in Eq. 16.43 is the actual weight of a gas molecule in free space, we must replace it by the net or effective weight of a particle buoyed up by the liquid in which it is suspended. This is $mg(\rho_2 - \rho_1)/\rho_2$, where ρ_1 is the mass density of the fluid and ρ_2 that of the particle. See J. B. Perrin, *The Atom*, Constable, London, 1923. The same method was used by Svedberg and later by Westgren; see *Arkiv. Mat.*, **13**, No. 14 (1918).

[5] In the case of a linear molecule (that is, one with all the nuclei on a line), only five coordinates are needed to describe the molecule's position and orientation, and so

$$f^{\text{vib}} = 3n_a - 5$$

Accordingly, such molecules have *one* more squared term in $\mathbf{H}$ than nonlinear molecules with the same number of atoms per molecule. See Secs. 6.14 and 6.15.

For such a molecule a $2f$-dimensional μ space is required. The partition integral is therefore a $2f$-fold one, and Z is of the form

$$Z = \frac{1}{\Delta\mu} \int \cdots \int e^{-\beta H(p,q)} \, dq_1 \cdots dp_f \qquad (16.46)$$

Let the q's and p's now be replaced by the running variable ζ_j, where j goes from 1 to $2f$. The variables may be rearranged in order such that the first r are the variables occurring in the Hamiltonian, Eq. 16.45. These have the limits of $-\infty$ to $+\infty$ and include all the p's and certain of the q's. Now suppose that the $2f$ variables are divided in three groups such that *group 1* contains ζ_1, $\zeta_2, \ldots, \zeta_{r-t}$, all of which have coefficients in Eq. 16.45 that are *constants*, whereas the t variables of *group 2*, $\zeta_{r-t+1}, \ldots, \zeta_r$, have λ's depending in some way on one or more of the remaining variables, which we indicate as *group 3*, $\zeta_{r+1}, \zeta_{r+2}, \ldots, \zeta_{2f}$. This last group contains all the variables not in the Hamiltonian *and* those on which the nonconstant λ's depend. These are all q's and vary over finite limits, fixed by the geometry of the system.

Now integrate Eq. 16.46 with respect to the first group of $(r - t)$ variables. Each integration gives a result of the form

$$\left(\frac{\pi}{a}\right)^{\frac{1}{2}} = \left(\frac{2\pi kT}{\lambda}\right)^{\frac{1}{2}}$$

and thus produces a factor in Z of the form

$$\frac{(2\pi kT)^{(r-t)/2}}{(\lambda_1\lambda_2 \cdots \lambda_{r-t})^{\frac{1}{2}}}$$

Integration over the t variables in group 2 likewise gives

$$\frac{(2\pi kT)^{t/2}}{(\lambda_{r-t+1} \cdots \lambda_r)^{\frac{1}{2}}}$$

where, however, the denominator, depending on certain variables in group 3, must remain inside the integral signs. Thus we have

$$Z = \frac{(2\pi kT)^{(r-t)/2}(2\pi kT)^{t/2}}{(\lambda_1\lambda_2 \cdots \lambda_{r-t})^{\frac{1}{2}}} \int \cdots \int \frac{d\zeta_{r+1} \cdots d\zeta_{2f}}{(\lambda_{r-t+1} \cdots \lambda_r)^{\frac{1}{2}}}$$

The $(2f - r)$-fold integral remaining can only produce a result independent of T, and we may write finally

$$\boxed{Z = A T^{r/2}}$$

where A is a quantity involving the volume and various dynamic and geometric parameters but *not the temperature*.

The energy of the system is now found directly as

$$U = NkT\frac{\partial \ln Z}{\partial T} = rN\frac{kT}{2}$$

or

$$\boxed{\bar{\epsilon} = \frac{U}{N} = r\frac{kT}{2}} \tag{16.47}$$

and the *average energy of each of the squared terms in H is again* $kT/2$. This is a general form of the equipartition of energy theorem, of which we have had a special example in the case of the monatomic gas.[6]

From Eq. 16.47 the molar heat capacity of a polyatomic ideal gas must be constant and have the value given by

$$C_V = r\frac{N_0 k}{2} = r\frac{R}{2}$$

Comparison with experiment reveals the nonconstancy of C_V. Actually, nonlinear polyatomic molecules have molar heat capacities that begin at $3N_0 k$ at the lowest temperatures, rise rapidly, owing to the full excitation of the two or three permitted degrees of rotational freedom, and then rise more slowly as more and more vibration is acquired. See Table 6.2 again, where all the molecules with $n_a = 2$ have $C_V = \frac{5}{2}R$ or higher and those with $n_a \geq 3$ have C_V values definitely above $3R = 5.96$ cal/mole at 15°C. In practice, as the temperature rises, the classical predictions of the equipartition theorem given in Table 6.3, column 6, are seldom reached, owing to the onset of dissociation of one type or another.

This failure of classical statistics save for the monomolecular case constituted Lord Kelvin's "black cloud" and indicated the need for a radically new starting point.

16.11   Fluctuations in Entropy

Since W is literally the number of microstates corresponding to a given macrostate, consider two macrostates for which there are W_1 and W_2 microstates, respectively. The first corresponds to a volume $W_1 \Delta \Gamma$ of Γ space, and the second to a volume $W_2 \Delta \Gamma$, and the relative times that a system may be expected in the two macrostates is given by the ratio of the two volumes, which is simply

$$\frac{W_1}{W_2}$$

---

[6] When the Hamiltonian contains terms that are *not quadratic*, as with the gas in a gravitational field, the results are, of course, quite different. An interesting example is given by Peterlin, *Am. J. Phys.*, **28**, 716 (1960). Note also that in the discussion of the subject in Secs. 6.14 to 6.16 the coordinates used were actually q's and $\dot{q}$'s, since Hamiltonian coordinates had not then been introduced.

The interpretation of the W's as relative probabilities is thus correct, since the system spends a time in each macrostate that is proportional to W.

Now let $W_2 = W^*$, where W^* refers to an *equilibrium* state, and let $W_1 = W$, corresponding to any nonequilibrium state where $W < W^*$. We have

$$S^* = k \ln \frac{W^*}{N!}$$

$$S = k \ln \frac{W}{N!}$$

and

$$- |\Delta S| = S - S^* = k \ln \frac{W}{W^*}$$

or

$$\exp \frac{S - S^*}{k} = \frac{W}{W^*} = \exp - \frac{|\Delta S|}{k} \qquad (16.48)$$

From Eq. 9.49, the entropy of ν moles of ideal monatomic gas, since $\nu R = Nk$, becomes

$$S^* = S^\circ = Nk \left(\ln VT^{3/2} + \frac{S_{0TV}}{R} \right) = NkF^*$$

where F^* is simply an abbreviation for the quantity in brackets. Let us suppose that $|\Delta S|$ is written

$$|\Delta S| = NkF^*x$$

where x is the *fractional decrease* of the entropy of the gas from its equilibrium value due to a fluctuation of absolute size, $|\Delta S|$. Then Eq. 16.48 gives

$$\frac{W}{W^*} = e^{-NF^*x} \qquad (16.49)$$

where, owing to the presence of N in the exponent, even very small values of x cause W to be very much smaller than W^*. This means simply that the portion of accessible Γ space *corresponding to equilibrium microstates is vast* compared with that portion belonging to the microstates of any nonequilibrium state with entropy that differs significantly from S^*. In Problems 16.7 and 16.8 it is left to the reader to show that the data so far given permit us to evaluate S^* for helium gas and to write for the case of the gas at 0°C and 1 atm

$$F^* \approx 15$$

so that

$$\frac{W}{W^*} \approx e^{-15Nx} \qquad (16.50)$$

which, of course, represents an extremely small ratio indeed.

If we set $N = N_0$ and assign to x the value of 10^{-6} (that is, take an entropy decrease of 1 part in a million),

$$\frac{W}{W^*} \approx e^{-10^{19}} \approx (2.7)^{-10^{19}}$$

a ratio of the order of ten raised to the -10^{19}th power! Clearly the odds against spontaneous decreases in entropy of even this modest size are overwhelmingly great. Therefore, when the second law states that spontaneous decreases in entropy do *not* occur, it means that the probability of sizable decreases is so nearly zero as to be unobservable experimentally.

Although sizable fluctuations in entropy are very rare, small fluctuations are taking place all the time, and the smaller the size of the system, the larger these become. In local regions within a large system, fluctuations are more characteristic than constancy. The general theory of fluctuations has been developed at length by von Smoluchowski[7] and Einstein,[8] who emphasized the connection between fluctuations in entropy and other important parameters of a system. Thus suppose that l is some property of a system that fluctuates. Let l^* be the normal value of this parameter corresponding to the maximum entropy of the system, S^*. When S^* decreases to S because of a fluctuation, what is the probability that l will assume a value between $l^* + \Delta l$ and $l^* + \Delta l + dl$? This probability, say, dP_l, obviously must depend upon the probability of the *state* of entropy S and the size of the interval dl. By Eq. 16.48, the *relative* probability of this state is

$$W = W^* \exp \frac{-|\Delta S|}{k}$$

and hence the mathematical probability of this state is proportional to $\exp -|\Delta S|/k$. Setting dP_l proportional to the product of this term and the size of the interval dl gives

$$dP_l = C \left(\exp \frac{-|\Delta S|}{k} \right) dl \qquad (16.51)$$

Here the proportionality parameter, C, is determined by the normalization condition

$$\int dP_l = 1$$

since the value of l must lie in *some* interval dl.

As an example of the use of this relation, suppose that we consider a Brownian particle of density greater than that of the liquid in which it is placed. By the laws of hydrostatics it should sink to the bottom and stay there, this condition corresponding to the maximum entropy of the liquid. To raise the particle to a vertical height, say, $z - z_0$ above the bottom of the vessel, would require mechanical energy $m'g(z - z_0)$ to be supplied by the liquid. (Here, of course, m' is the apparent mass of the particle, as explained in footnote 4.) If the whole system is thermally insulated from its surroundings,

---

[7] Von Smoluchowski, *Ann. Physik*, **21**, 756 (1906); **25**, 205 (1908).

[8] A. E. Einstein, *The Brownian Movement*, Methuen, London, 1926; *Ann. Physik*, **19**, 37 (1906).

this energy can be supplied only by a decrease in its internal energy, and in general $\Delta S = \Delta U / T$ since no volume change occurs and therefore no work is done against external pressures. Thus

$$|\Delta S| = \frac{m'g(z - z_0)}{T}$$

With $l \equiv z$, the probability, dP_z, of finding the Brownian particle at a height between $z - z_0$ and $z + dz - z_0$ becomes, from Eq. 16.51,

$$dP_z = C \left[\exp \frac{-m'g(z - z_0)}{kT} \right] dz \qquad (16.52)$$

and decreases rapidly with m' and z. This can readily be shown to be consistent with the results obtained in Sec. 16.9 by a different line of argument. Similar considerations apply to fluctuations in velocity, angular orientation, etc.

Since all movable objects are subject to thermal fluctuations, this theory has been profitably applied to the thermal oscillations of torsion balances, radiometers, delicate galvanometer suspensions, etc. In liquids and gases these same local fluctuations produce local variations in density and hence in refractive index. These effects are the basic cause of light scattering by fluids and lead in the case of gases to the Rayleigh scattering formula, in which the scattering varies inversely as the fourth power of the wave length of the light involved. These same fluctuations in the flow of electrons cause the thermal noise (Johnson noise) in electrical resistances and the "shot effect" in vacuum tube amplifiers. The agreement between the predictions of the theory of fluctuations and observations in such diverse fields constitutes one of the most satisfactory verifications of the general soundness of the statistical approach. For further details, the reader is referred to an article by Epstein[9] and a comprehensive review article by Barnes and Silverman.[10]

16.12   Entropy and Gibbs' Mixing Paradox

The Boltzmann expression for entropy as given in Eq. 16.39 was later examined by Gibbs, who showed that unless it was modified slightly, it must lead to his now famous mixing paradox.

We have already considered the mixing of two ideal (mutually inert) gases and found that if they are allowed to interdiffuse reversibly while doing work against suitable semipermeable membranes, a calculable increase in entropy results (Sec. 9.7). If the two samples of gas are identical, the membranes are

---

[9] P. S. Epstein, "Limitations of Thermodynamics," in F. G. Donnan and A. Haas, eds., *Commentary on the Scientific Writings of J. Willard Gibbs*, Yale Univ. Press, New Haven, Conn., 1936, Vol. II, pp. 105–12.

[10] Barnes and Silverman, *Revs. Modern Phys.*, **6**, 162 (1934).

permeable in both directions, no work can be extracted from the process, and no entropy change can occur. However, entropy expressions of the Boltzmann type predict an entropy increase in *both* cases. This is the paradox which Gibbs discovered and showed could be avoided only by a modification of Boltzmann's entropy equation.

Gibbs went on to show that the paradox arose from the fact that in Boltzmann's result,

$$S = Nk\left[\ln V + \ln T^{3/2} + \ln \frac{(2\pi mk)^{3/2}}{\Delta\mu^{\text{trn}}} + \frac{3}{2}\right] \tag{16.39}$$

the quantity in the brackets is independent of N. Entropy, however, depends not so much on V as on V/N, *the volume available per molecule*. If we add $-Nk \ln N$ to the right side of Eq. 16.39, the paradox disappears. The results of Gibbs' argument (see Problems 16.3 and 16.4) can be reached somewhat more readily as follows.

Returning to the entropy expressions obtained for a mole of an ideal monatomic gas in Sec. 9.14,

$$S°(T, V) = R\left[\ln T^{3/2} + \ln V^{3/2} + \frac{S_{0TV}}{R}\right] \tag{9.49}$$

and

$$S°(T, p) = R\left[\ln T^{5/2} - \ln p + \frac{S_{0Tp}}{R}\right] \tag{9.50}$$

we rewrite them to emphasize the dependence on the number, N_0, of molecules of gas. Since $R = N_0 k$, we have

$$S(T, V, N_0) = N_0 k \left[\ln T^{3/2} + \ln V + \ln C_{0TV}\right] \tag{16.53}$$

and

$$S(T, p, N_0) = N_0 k \left[\ln T^{5/2} - \ln p + \ln C_{0Tp}\right] \tag{16.54}$$

where $\ln C_{0TV}$ and $\ln C_{0Tp}$ are simply alternate ways of writing the respective constant terms. Beginning with the equation in terms of T and p, let a system be made up of ν subsystems, each of N_0 molecules at a common T and p. The entropy of this system must be exactly ν times the right side of Eq. 16.54. For this condition to apply, $\ln C_{0Tp}$ must be independent of N_0. Thus we write for ν moles, or better, N molecules, where $\nu N_0 = N$,

$$S(T, p, N) = Nk \left[\ln T^{5/2} - \ln p + \ln C_{0Tp}\right]$$

Now change to the variables T and V by setting

$$p = \frac{\nu RT}{V} = \frac{NkT}{V}$$

when

$$S(T, V, N) = Nk\left[\ln T^{3/2} + \ln \frac{V}{N} + \ln \frac{C_{0Tp}}{k}\right]$$

or

$$S(T, V, N) = Nk\left[\ln T^{3/2} + \ln V + \ln \frac{C_{0Tp}}{Nk}\right] \tag{16.55}$$

Comparison with Eqs. 9.49 and 16.53 (where N_0 is replaced by N) shows that

$$\frac{S_{0TV}}{R} = \ln C_{0TV} = \ln \frac{C_{0Tp}}{Nk}$$

Comparison of Eq. 16.55 with Boltzmann's result in Eq. 16.39 shows that the N in the denominator of the last logarithmic term is absent from the Boltzmann equation. Thus we should add, as Gibbs concluded, $- Nk \ln N$ to the right side of Eq. 16.39 to obtain a result of the correct functional form. Of course, we can hardly do this without inquiring as to where such a term could have arisen in the first place. Clearly such a term could arise only from $k \ln N!$, and we may either add $- k \ln N!$ to Boltzmann's original starting point,

$$S = k \ln W$$

to give

$$S = k \ln \frac{W}{N!} \tag{16.56}$$

or add the equivalent, $- Nk \ln N + Nk$, to Eq. 16.39. The result is the (empirically) modified Gibbs-Boltzmann entropy expression,

$$S(T, V, N) = Nk \left[\ln T^{3/2} + \ln V + \ln \frac{(2\pi mk)^{3/2}}{N \, \Delta\mu^{\text{trn}}} + \frac{5}{2} \right] \tag{16.57}$$

This is not only of the proper form to avoid the mixing paradox but also, owing to the replacement of the $3/2$ of Eq. 16.39 by $5/2$, of the exact size required to account for the absolute vapor pressure measurements on monatomic solids (see Sec. 17.2). It must be remembered, however, that this modification confuses the logic of the original Boltzmann argument.

16.13   Thermodynamic Functions in Terms of the Partition Function

The mixing paradox could have been discussed with ideal polyatomic gases, since only the translational partition function, which is the same for all ideal gases, depends on V. As a result, the general entropy expression given in Eq. 16.37 for the polyatomic case must hold, provided that we add $- Nk(\ln N - 1)$ and, of course, replace β by $1/kT$. Since we can always write

$$\frac{\partial}{\partial \beta} = \left(\frac{\partial}{\partial T} \right) \left(\frac{\partial T}{\partial \beta} \right) = -kT^2 \frac{\partial}{\partial T}$$

we have

$$S = Nk \left[\ln \frac{Z}{N} + T \left(\frac{\partial \ln Z}{\partial T} \right)_V + 1 \right] \tag{16.58}$$

where V has been written outside the partial derivative to indicate its constancy during the differentation. Replacing β by $1/kT$ in Eq. 16.36, we obtain

$$U = NkT^2 \left(\frac{\partial \ln Z}{\partial T} \right)_V$$

(16.59)

and this gives for the average energy, $\bar{\epsilon}$, of a particle in the system

$$\bar{\epsilon} = \frac{U}{N} = kT^2 \left(\frac{\partial \ln Z}{\partial T} \right)_V$$

(16.60)

With U and S given, the other potentials can be written down at once. Since $A = U - TS$,

$$A = - NkT \left(\ln \frac{Z}{N} + 1 \right)$$

(16.61)

Helmholtz's free energy is thus the quantity most closely related to the partition function and usually the one first determined in any statistical investigation of a new system. With A known, CIII gives

$$dA = - S\,dT - p\,dV$$

whence

$$- \left(\frac{\partial A}{\partial T} \right)_V = S$$

and

$$- \left(\frac{\partial A}{\partial V} \right)_T = p$$

The first of these relations leads to the expression in Eq. 16.58, and the second gives

$$p = NkT \left(\frac{\partial \ln Z}{\partial V} \right)_T$$

(16.62)

which determines the equation of state for the system. The corresponding expression for the enthalpy, $H = U + pV$, is

$$H = NkT \left[T \left(\frac{\partial \ln Z}{\partial T} \right)_V + V \left(\frac{\partial \ln Z}{\partial V} \right)_T \right]$$

(16.63)

Finally for Gibbs' potential, with $G = A + pV$, we obtain

$$G = -NkT\left[\ln\frac{Z}{N} - V\left(\frac{\partial \ln Z}{\partial V}\right)_T + 1\right] \qquad (16.64)$$

From these considerations it is apparent that the partition function is a most important statistical quantity. Once it is determined, *all the thermodynamic properties of the system may be computed from it.*

To understand a little more clearly just what the nature of this partition function is, we write it out as a sum.

$$Z = e^{-\beta\epsilon_1} + e^{-\beta\epsilon_2} + e^{-\beta\epsilon_3} + \cdots + e^{-\beta\epsilon_j} + \cdots + e^{-\beta\epsilon_s}$$

It is the sum of a large but strictly finite number of terms equal to the total number, s, of cells in accessible μ space. Since the exponents are all of the form $-\beta\epsilon_j = -\epsilon_j/kT$, these terms must diminish rapidly as the ratio of energy to kT becomes large. Since there is a term for each cell, we can regard Z as a *weighted counting* of all the cells in μ space that are accessible to the system. Cells with small energy are counted heavily, and those with large energy are counted lightly. Of course, the cells with *small* energy have the *largest* number of image points, and vice versa. In the weighted cell count that Z represents, therefore, densely occupied cells receive large weighting, and thinly populated ones receive hardly any weighting at all.

16.14   Summary of Useful General Formulas

The failures of classical statistics can be attributed primarily to the method of evaluating the partition function, Z, as a continuous integral. Once we obtain the proper discrete energies from quantum theory and evaluate the partition function by summing over these discrete values, the general methods developed here carry over directly to quantum statistics. In particular, the general formulas obtained in Sec. 16.13 expressing thermodynamic functions in terms of Z are in their general and correct form, although their theoretical basis remains to be re-examined. These formulas are collected here for future reference. They express in a concise and useful way some of the most general statistical results for systems of independent particles.

$$Z = \Sigma e^{-\beta\epsilon_j}$$

$$N_j = \frac{N}{Z}e^{-\beta\epsilon_j}$$

$$U = NkT^2\left(\frac{\partial \ln Z}{\partial T}\right)_V$$

$$S = Nk\left[\ln\frac{Z}{N} + T\left(\frac{\partial \ln Z}{\partial T}\right)_V + 1\right]$$

$$A = -NkT\left(\ln\frac{Z}{N} + 1\right)$$

$$p = NkT\left(\frac{\partial \ln Z}{V}\right)_T$$

$$H = NkT\left[T\left(\frac{\partial \ln Z}{\partial T}\right)_V + V\left(\frac{\partial \ln Z}{\partial V}\right)_T\right]$$

$$G = -NkT\left[\ln\frac{Z}{N} - V\left(\frac{\partial \ln Z}{\partial V}\right) + 1\right]$$

where for the ideal gas

$$Z = Z^{\text{trn}}Z^{\text{int}}$$

and

$$Z^{\text{mono}} = Z^{\text{trn}} = \frac{V}{\Delta\mu^{\text{trn}}}(2\pi mkT)^{3/2} \tag{16.65}$$

Problems

16.1   Show that in the entropy expression for an ideal monatomic gas,

$$S^{\text{mono}} = Nk\left[\ln V - \ln \beta^{3/2} + \ln\frac{(2\pi m)^{3/2}}{\Delta\mu^{\text{trn}}} + \frac{3}{2}\right] \tag{16.38}$$

we must have $\beta = 1/kT$. [*Hint:* Use as a starting point CI, which gives $(\partial U/\partial S)_V = T$].

16.2   Integrate Eq. 16.1 with $\rho = N\alpha e^{-\beta\epsilon}$ over the range of the momentum coordinates to obtain the ordinary particle density of the gas in the form

$$\frac{d^3 N_{xyz}}{dx\,dy\,dz} = \frac{N}{V} = \hat{n}$$

16.3   Show that if W_A and W_B are the thermodynamic probabilities for any macro-distribution of two gases, A and B, each alone in the volume V_{AB},

$$W_{AB} = W_A W_B$$

where W_{AB} is the thermodynamic probability (or disorder number) for the *mixture* in the same total volume. Then, setting

$$S_{AB} = k \ln W_{AB}$$

carry out an argument analogous to that used in Sec. 16.6 to show that for the equilibrium mixture

$$S_{AB} = N_A k\left[\ln V_{AB} + \ln\frac{(2\pi m_A kTe)^{3/2}}{\Delta\mu}\right] + N_B k\left[\ln V_{AB} + \ln\frac{(2\pi m_B kTe)^{3/2}}{\Delta\mu}\right]$$

where N_A, N_B, m_A, and m_B are the respective particle numbers and masses for the two gases.

16.4 Show that the expression for the increase of entropy on the mixing of two ideal monatomic gases becomes

$$\Delta S = N_A k \ln \frac{V_{AB}}{V_A} + N_B k \ln \frac{V_{AB}}{V_B}$$

and is consistent with the result obtained by direct thermodynamic reasoning in Sec. 9.7. What happens to this when $A \equiv B$? How do you resolve the paradox?

16.5 Show that

$$p = NkT \left(\frac{\partial \ln Z}{\partial V} \right)_T$$

leads directly to the equation of state for the ideal monatomic gas if we take

$$Z = Z^{\text{mono}} = \frac{V(2\pi m k T)^{3/2}}{\Delta \mu^{\text{trn}}} \qquad (\mathbf{16.32})$$

16.6 Show that the other quantities given in terms of Z in the summary in Sec. 16.14 reduce to their proper values for the ideal monatomic gas.

16.7 The thermodynamic expression for the entropy of ν moles of an ideal monatomic gas may be obtained from Eq. 9.49 as

$$S = \nu R \left(\ln V + \ln T^{3/2} + \frac{S'_{0TV}}{R} \right)$$

where the constant now written S'_{0TV} refers to ν moles. Show that this may be written in the form

$$S = \nu N_0 k \left(\ln \frac{V}{\nu} + \ln T^{3/2} + i_p + \frac{5}{2} - \ln R \right)$$

i_p being the absolute vapor pressure constant (cgs units and natural logarithms). Taking i_p' for helium from Table 12.5, show that $i_p = 12.24$ and that therefore

$$S = \nu N_0 k \left(\ln \frac{V}{\nu} + \ln T^{3/2} - 3.48 \right)$$

Using this as S^*, show that for $0°C$ and 1 atm

$$S^* = \nu N_0 k (14.96)$$

16.8 As we see from Eq. 16.49,

$$\frac{W}{W^*} = e^{-NF^*x} \qquad (\mathbf{16.49})$$

and the likelihood of a given fluctuation from the equilibrium value of entropy depends on the number of molecules in a system. Determine the ratio W/W^* for samples of helium at $0°C$ and 1 atm that occupy, respectively, volumes of

(a) 10^{-6}mm^3 and
(b) 10^{-9}mm^3.

Take $x = 10^{-8}$ in each case.

16.9   Starting with the fact that

$$A = -NkT \left(\ln \frac{Z}{N} + 1 \right)$$

calculate the pressure for systems of ideal monatomic, diatomic, and polyatomic gases. What is your conclusion?

16.10   Starting with the partition function for an ideal diatomic gas in Sec. 16.7, show that

$$Z = \frac{V}{\Delta \mu^{\text{trn}}} (2\pi m k T)^{\frac{3}{2}} \frac{8\pi^2 I_0 k T}{\Delta \mu^{\text{rot}}} \frac{2\pi k T}{\Delta \mu^{\text{vib}}} \left(\frac{m'}{\sqrt{K}} \right)^{\frac{1}{2}}$$

and hence that C_V is predicted to be

$$C_V = (3 + 2 + 2) \frac{R}{2} = 7 \frac{R}{2}$$

CHAPTER SEVENTEEN

Advent of the Quantum Theory

17.1 Cell Size and Planck's Constant

Boltzmann emphasized that the cells in μ space could not be taken as infinitesimal, since then the entropy would be infinite. Moreover, they had to be large enough so that some at least would contain a great many particles. Since the cell size appeared in the entropy equation only as a constant term, Boltzmann actually set $\Delta\mu$ equal to m^3 times unity.[1] It was Sommerfeld[2] who first proposed that since Planck's constants, h, was a universal unit of action in the atomic and molecular world, it should be used to fix the cell size in a general way. As we saw in Sec. 16.3, the dimensions of any elementary phase area, $\Delta p_i \Delta q_i$, are, whatever the specific coordinates employed, those of *action*. Thus if we set

$$\Delta p_i \Delta q_i = h$$

we have at once

$$\Delta\mu = h^f$$

and

$$\Delta\Gamma = h^{Nf}$$

as *universal results for all physical systems.*

The validity of this identification was demonstrated within a year by the brilliant discussion of the vapor pressure of ideal monatomic vapors by Sackur and independently by Tetrode. We shall return to their results in more detail.

Further evidence for the necessity of some such quantum limitation on cell size came later from de Broglie's hypothesis of the wavelike nature of all particles (1923) and from the uncertainty principle of Heisenberg (1927). According to this principle, it is impossible to fix both the position and the coordinates of a particle with infinite precision. The product of the uncer-

---

[1] L. Boltzmann, *Vorlesungen uber Gas Theorie*, 3rd Ger. ed., Barth, Leipzig, 1923, Vol. I, pp. 54 ff.

[2] Sommerfeld, *Physik. Z.*, **12**, 1057 (1911).

tainties, Δp and Δq, in a given pair of coordinates must always be limited by a universal condition,

$$\Delta p \, \Delta q > h$$

or, in a more rigorous form,

$$\Delta p \, \Delta q > \frac{h}{4\pi}$$

This means, of course, that a particle's image point cannot be located exactly in phase space. We can assign it to a cell, but we can never say exactly where it is in the cell. For statistical purposes this uncertainty is all right, since we need know only the total number of particles in a cell, not where they are. It does, however, at once call into question the classical method of defining continuous point densities in phase space and substituting continuous integrations for actual summation over discrete cells.

Furthermore, h itself is a very small quantity. Therefore, since $\Delta \mu = h^f$, even for a monatomic gas $\Delta \mu$ is *exceedingly* small. This condition renders questionable the assumption of many particles per cell, the use of Stirling's formula, etc. We shall return to these important problems after examining the effect of Sommerfeld's postulate on the entropy expression for a monatomic gas.

17.2   The Sackur-Tetrode Vapor Pressure Formula

In the case of a monatomic gas, $f = 3$, $\Delta \mu = \Delta \mu^{\text{trn}} = h^3$, and the Gibbs-Boltzmann entropy expression, Eq. 16.57, becomes

$$S = Nk \left[\ln V + \ln T^{3/2} + \ln \frac{(2\pi mk)^{3/2} e^{5/2}}{Nh^3} \right]$$

If pressure is introduced instead of volume,

$$V = \frac{NkT}{p}$$

and

$$S = Nk \left[\ln T^{5/2} - \ln p + \ln \frac{(2\pi m)^{3/2} (ke)^{5/2}}{h^3} \right] \tag{17.1}$$

This is the entropy formula obtained almost simultaneously by Sackur and Tetrode.[3] We now return to the molar entropy expression obtained in Chap. 12, Eq. 12.23, which with $C_p^\circ = \tfrac{3}{2} R$ becomes

$$S^\circ = S^\circ(T, p, N_0) = R \left(\ln T^{5/2} - \ln p + \frac{S_{0Tp}^\circ}{R} \right)$$

[3] Sackur, *Ann. Physik*, **40**, 67 (1913); and Tetrode, *Ann. Physik*, **38**, 434 (1912); **39**, 255 (1912).

where the constant S_{0Tp}°/R is independent of the number of molecules present. For a system of N molecules, this gives

$$S^\circ(T, p, N) = Nk\left(\ln T^{5/2} - \ln p + \frac{S_{0Tp}^\circ}{R}\right) \qquad (17.2)$$

and comparison with Eq. 17.1 shows that

$$\frac{S_{0Tp}^\circ}{R} = \ln \frac{(2\pi m)^{3/2}(ke)^{5/2}}{h^3}$$

or

$$\frac{S_{0Tp}^\circ}{R} = \ln \left(\frac{2\pi}{N_0}\right)^{3/2} \frac{(ke)^{5/2}}{h^3} + \ln M^{3/2} \qquad (17.3)$$

where M is the molecular weight of the gas.

This value we now substitute in the (thermodynamic) vapor pressure formula given in Eq. 12.88,

$$\ln p = -\frac{\Lambda_0}{RT} + \ln T^{5/2} - \int \frac{dT}{RT^2} \int_0^T C_p'''\, dT + \frac{S_{0Tp}^\circ - S_0'''}{R} - \frac{5}{2} \qquad (12.88)$$

Since $\ln e^{5/2} = 5/2$, the last term in Eq. 12.88 cancels on substitution from Eq. 17.3, to give

$$\ln p = -\frac{\Lambda_0}{Rt} + \ln T^{5/2} - I(T) + \ln \left(\frac{2\pi}{N_0}\right)^{3/2} \frac{k^{5/2}}{h^3} + \ln M^{3/2} - \frac{S_0'''}{R} \qquad (17.4)$$

where $I(T)$ represents the double integral and the constant terms constitute the theoretical vapor pressure constant. On converting to common logarithms and pressure in atmospheres, we have for $(i_p')_{\text{theor}}$, the theoretical value of the *practical* vapor pressure constant,

$$(i_p')_{\text{theor}} = \log \left(\frac{2\pi}{N_0}\right)^{3/2} \frac{k^{5/2}}{h^3 p_0} + \log M^{3/2} - \frac{S_0'''}{2.30R}$$

In Chap. 12 the thermodynamic analog of Eq. 17.4 was Eq. 12.86, which now becomes

$$\log P_{\text{atm}} = -\frac{\Lambda_0}{2.30RT} + \ln T^{5/2} - I(T) + (i_p')_{\text{obs}}$$

The data of Table 12.5 reappear in Table 17.1 in a different form for more direct comparison of the theoretical predictions with the empirical observations. Column 3 gives the values $(i_p')_{\text{obs}} - \log M^{3/2}$, which are seen to be fairly constant and to have an average value of -1.577 with an average departure of $\pm.04$. In the last column the value of the universal constant,

$$\log \left(\frac{2\pi}{N_0}\right)^{3/2} \frac{k^{5/2}}{h^3 p_0} = (i_p')_{\text{theor}} - \log M^{3/2} + \frac{S_0'''}{R}$$

is entered. This constant has the value -1.592 and is very close to the average of the results in column 3.

TABLE **17.1**

Theoretical and Empirical Vapor Pressure Constants for Monatomic Vapors with ${}^1S$ Ground States

Gas	M	$(i_p')_{obs} - \log M^{3/2}$	$\log \left(\dfrac{2\pi}{N_0}\right)^{3/2} \dfrac{k^{5/2}}{h^3 p_0}$
(H$_2$)	2.016	-1.57	
He	4.003	-1.58	
Ne	20.18	-1.57	
Ar	39.9	-1.59	
Kr	83.7	-1.59	
Xe	131.03	-1.58	-1.592
Mg	24.32	-1.61	
Zn	65.38	-1.51	
Cd	112.4	-1.63	
		-1.51	
Hg	200.6	-1.60	
Pb	207.2	-1.68	
	Av	$-1.585(\pm.03)$	

The behavior of monatomic gases may thus be adequately accounted for by (1) the hypothesis of Sommerfeld that $\Delta\mu^{\text{trn}} = h^3$ and (2) Planck's assumption that the entropy of all pure condensed states may be taken as zero at $T = 0$. This makes $S_0''' = 0$, and therefore

$$(i_p')_{\text{theor}} = \log \left(\frac{2\pi}{N_0}\right)^{3/2} \frac{k^{5/2}}{h^3 p_0} + \log M^{3/2} \qquad (17.5)$$

Since all the molecules in Table 17.1 are without spin or orbital momentum in their ground states, this conclusion applies only to ${}^1S$ atomic (or ${}^1\Sigma$ molecular) states. This chapter will deal with atoms and molecules of these types only.

17.3   Basic Weaknesses of the Classical Argument

Although the identification of $\Delta\mu^{\text{trn}}$ with h^3 gives an entropy expression in gratifying agreement with experiment, this agreement is rather fortuitous since two logically troublesome points have been left in the classical argument. These are (1) Gibbs' paradox and (2) the assumption that the number of cells in phase space is sufficiently *small* that the number of image points in a cell can be taken as usually quite large.

Although Gibbs' empirical correction to Boltzmann's entropy expression led to a result of the proper form, it did violence to the Boltzmann statistical argument. For it gave

$$S_{\text{Gibbs}} = k \ln \frac{W}{N!} = -k\Sigma \ln N_j! \tag{16.18}$$

and for S to be positive the $N_j!$'s must be *fractions*. This requirement disrupts the statistics as well as invalidating the use of Stirling's formula.

The introduction of the new quantum cell size offers further evidence of the improper use of Stirling's formula. Even in the case of a monatomic gas, for which $\Delta\mu = h^3 \approx 10^{-79}$ (erg-sec)^3, the cell size is so small that there are vastly more cells in accessible phase space than particles. Hence on the average only a few cells have any population at all.

According to the phase space distribution law,

$$N_j = \frac{Ne^{-\beta\epsilon_j}}{Z} \tag{16.33}$$

the greatest value of N_j occurs for cells for which $\epsilon_j = 0$ when

$$(N_j)_{\text{max}} = \frac{N}{Z}$$

For the monatomic gas with $\Delta\mu = h^3$,

$$Z = V \frac{(2\pi mkT)^{3/2}}{h^3}$$

and

$$(N_j)_{\text{max}} = \frac{Nh^3}{V(2\pi mkT)^{3/2}}$$

For a mole of the lightest monatomic gas, helium, at normal temperature and pressure, this gives

$$(N_j)_{\text{max}} \approx \frac{1}{300,000}$$

This means that even in the *most densely occupied region of phase space there is at most one particle to 300,000 cells* and an even sparser population for larger energies and heavier particles! Thus the number of cells in accessible phase space is prodigiously larger than N, and most of the cells are empty all the time. This assumption is basic and can be remedied only by a fundamental revision of the statistical argument.

17.4   Indistinguishability of Identical Particles

The crux of the difficulty lies in the implicit assumption that two particles of the same kind and in the same energy cell can be identified or distinguished from one another by means of a number or mark of some kind. According to quantum statistics, *identical particles cannot be distinguished from one another in any way; they can only be counted.* The classical impasse arises from a semantic confusion of *symbols* with *real atoms* and *molecules*. If we have a set of identical particles represented by the letters $a, a, a, a, \ldots$, we can, to be sure, attach subscripts and write $a_1, a_2, a_3, a_4, \ldots$, but any results so obtained refer only to *manipulated letters*, not to real particles. The only way we can differentiate identical particles is by giving them different amounts of energy, and then they are no longer in the same cell! It is impossible to attach dots, numbers, or colored tags to the ultimate particles of matter. Hence the calculation of thermodynamic probability from the formula of Boltzmann

$$W_{\text{Boltz}} = \frac{N!}{\Pi N_j!}$$

is not legitimate. This fact was first recognized by Bose in a study of the statistics of light corpuscles (or photons) in which *identity* and *indistinguishability* of light quanta of the *same energy appeared evident from the start*.[4] The same considerations were shortly thereafter extended to assemblies of material particles by Einstein,[5] and the general statistics resulting is consequently called the *Bose-Einstein* statistics.

Before obtaining the general formulas for the new approach, let us consider a simple example. It will show clearly the significance of removing the postulate of distinguishability.

Suppose that we take *two* particles and *three* cells of equivalent energies (or three equal energy levels). From the classical point of view, the two particles are alike but distinguishable, and so we designate them a_1 and a_2. Indicating the three energy states by horizontal lines, we find the microassignments shown in Fig. 17.1.

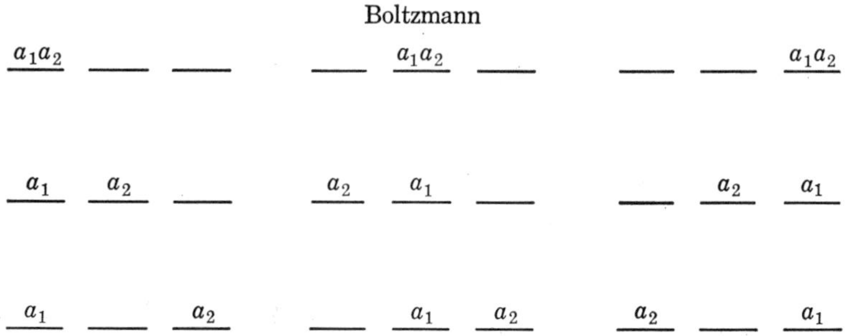

Boltzmann

FIGURE **17.1**

There are thus nine distinct and different assignments, and $W_{\text{Boltz}} = 9$. However, it is to be noted that these nine microassignments are not obtained by permuting the particles among the cells of a single (macro)distribution.

---

[4] Bose, *Z. Physik*, **26**, 178 (1924).

[5] Einstein, *Sitzber. deut. Akad. Wiss. Berlin, Math.-naturw. Kl.*, **22**, 261 (1924).

Actually there are six macrodistribution number sets (N_1, N_2, N_3) in the figure; they are underlined in the following array.

$$
\begin{array}{ccc}
200 & 020 & 002 \\
\underline{110} & \underline{110} & 011 \\
\underline{101} & \underline{011} & 101
\end{array}
$$

Here $W = 1$ for all distributions with all the particles in a single cell (top row) just as it was for the distribution marked IV in Fig. 15.3 (in that case there were five others of the same probability). Distributions of the type 110, 101, and 011 have $W = 2$ each, and no single formula of the Boltzmann type can give the result $W = 9$. In Boltzmann statistics a *single specific macrodistribution is assumed*, and W is calculated for it by the expression

$$
W = \frac{N!}{\prod_j N_j!} \tag{17.6}
$$

No grouping into cells of equal energies is involved. Particles are distributed subject only to the fixed conditions on total number of particles and on total energy.

When the Bose-Einstein approach is adopted, all the subscripts of the a's must be removed. On elimination of the duplicates, the scheme in Fig. 17.2 remains, and $W_{\text{B-E}} = 6$.

To determine the proper W for a whole system by the Bose-Einstein method, we must assume a set of distribution numbers,

$$
N_1, N_2, \ldots, N_j, \ldots
$$

for a *set of energy shells* (or levels) of different energies,

$$
\epsilon_1, \epsilon_2, \ldots, \epsilon_j, \ldots
$$

Then we calculate W for each energy shell separately, obtaining

$$
W_1, W_2, \ldots, W_j, \ldots
$$

For each of the legitimate permutations W_1, there are W_2 independent ones for the second shell, W_3 for the third, etc., so that W for the entire distribution is given as a product,

$$
W_{\text{B-E}} = \prod_j W_j \tag{17.7}
$$

The W_j in this expression has no simple connection with the W in Eq. 17.6.

In general, the values of W calculated from the Bose-Einstein approach are quite different from those of classical statistics. As we shall see shortly, however,

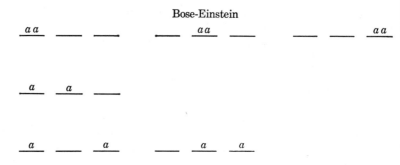

FIGURE **17.2**

the Bose-Einstein method leads to the same distribution law as the Boltzmann method for a large and important class of problems.

17.5   The Combinatory Formula for Identical Objects

To obtain the proper formula for the new type of combinatory analysis, we begin by considering the problem of distributing N (marked) objects among g boxes. Let the N objects be indicated as

$$a_1, a_2, a_3, \ldots, a_N$$

and the g boxes as

$$B_1, B_2, B_3, \ldots, B_g$$

First find the number of ways of combining the $(g + N)$ symbols in an array such as

$$B_6 \; a_1 \; a_2 \; B_1 \; a_4 \; a_6 \; a_7 \; B_3 \; B_5 \; a_3 \; \ldots$$

where we adopt the conventions that (1) the array always *begins* with a B, (2) the a's to the *right* of a B are in that box, and (3) when no a occurs after a B, that box is *empty*. Thus, in the example, objects a_1 and a_2 are in box B_6, objects a_4, a_6, and a_7 are in box B_1, box B_3 is empty, etc.

The number of ways of combining the $(g + N)$ symbols in such an array is simply

$$g(g + N - 1)!$$

since we may choose the first symbol (always a B) in g ways, the second in $(g + N - 1)$ ways, etc., down to the last place, for which there is only one choice.

This reckoning gives us essentially $g!$ duplicates, since if we put brackets around each B *and its contents* and rearrange the brackets, we have in fact only changed the order of writing, not increased the number of distinct arrangements of N objects among g boxes. There result, then,

$$\frac{g(g + N - 1)!}{g!} = \frac{(g + N - 1)!}{(g - 1)!}$$

meaningful arrangements.

Now drop the subscripts, thus rendering the N objects identical and indistinguishable. This requires dividing the last result by $N!$, the number of ways of permuting the N objects among themselves, which $N!$ permutations now give identical arrangements. Finally the number of ways of scattering N identical physical particles among g equal boxes (or cells or energy states) becomes

$$W_{\text{B-E}} = \frac{(g + N - 1)!}{(g - 1)!N!} \tag{17.8}$$

17.6   The Bose-Einstein Distribution Law

To apply Eq. 17.8 to an ideal gas, envisage a general μ space of $2f$ dimensions, and imagine it divided into energy shells arranged in order of increasing energy. Let the jth such cell contain N_j image points of N_j *identical particles*, and suppose the shell to correspond to an energy ϵ_j. Further, let the energy shell be of such "volume" as to contain g_j quantum cells, all of equal size. In view of the success of Sommerfeld's hypothesis in the monatomic case, we take these cells to have the general quantum size, h^f. Then the number of ways of distributing these N_j identical particles among the g_j equal cells of the jth energy shell, say, W_j, is, from Eq. 17.8,

$$W_j = \frac{(g_j + N_j - 1)!}{(g_j - 1)!N_j!} \tag{17.9}$$

Since each W_j is calculated separately and independently for each N_j of a general distribution defined by

$$N_1 N_2, \; \ldots \; , N_j, \; \ldots$$

the value of W for the whole distribution becomes simply the product

$$W_1 W_2 \; \cdot \; \cdot \; \cdot$$

or
$$W = \prod_j W_j = \prod_j \frac{(g_j + N_j - 1)!}{(g_j - 1)!N_j!} \tag{17.10}$$

In any actual case unity may be safely ignored compared with g_j or $g_j + N_j$, although we need make no restriction at this point about the relative sizes of g_j and N_j. With this slight simplification, the new expression for entropy becomes.

$$S = k \ln W = k \sum \ln \frac{(g_j + N_j)!}{g_j!N_j!} \tag{17.11}$$

Since an energy shell may be made large enough to contain a great many cells of the very small size of h^f, the number of molecules, N_j, in the shell may be taken to be large enough to permit the use of Stirling's formula (even though the number in a single cell is a minute fraction).[6] This reduces Eq. 17.11 to the form,

$$S = k \left[\sum g_j \ln \left(1 + \frac{N_j}{g_j} \right) + \sum N_j \ln \left(\frac{g_j}{N_j} + 1 \right) \right] \qquad (17.12)$$

We now proceed just as before. Starting with an equilibrium distribution of the N_j's giving a maximum value to S, we vary the distribution and set $\delta S = 0$.

To save future duplication, we carry out the maximization of S under *two* separate sets of conditions, as follows: (1) the total energy and the total number of particles are held constant (material particles—no chemical reactions); and (2) the total energy only is held constant (a photon gas, for example, made up of photons of all possible frequencies). The volume is implicitly assumed constant in both instances.

In the first case, in addition to the entropy expression, there are the usual conditions on the internal energy, U, and on N,

$$U = \Sigma N_j \epsilon_j = \text{constant}$$
$$N = \Sigma N_j = \text{constant}$$

Setting $\delta S = \delta U = \delta N = 0$ as before (note that both g_j and ϵ_j are constant for this variation) gives the three conditions

$$
\begin{array}{c|c}
-1 & \Sigma \ln \left(\dfrac{g_j}{N_j} + 1 \right) \delta N_j = 0 \\
\beta & \Sigma \epsilon_j \, \delta N_j = 0 \\
\lambda & \Sigma \delta N_j = 0
\end{array} \qquad (17.13)
$$

Using the Lagrangian multipliers -1, β, and λ gives[7]

$$\sum \left[-\ln \left(\frac{g_j}{N_j} + 1 \right) + \beta \epsilon_j + \lambda \right] \delta N_j = 0$$

and thus for the general condition for a maximum of S

$$\frac{g_j}{N_j} + 1 = e^{\beta \epsilon_j} e^{\lambda} = B e^{\beta \epsilon_j}$$

---

[6] The exact size of an energy shell cannot be specified any more than could the size of one of Boltzmann's cells. All we need is to have the shells large enough for some N_j's to be large; the actual volume of an energy shell is $g_j h^f$, and in the calculation of any thermodynamic property such as entropy all the g_j's drop out, leaving only h^f in the constant term. See Problems 17.2 and 17.3.

[7] The reason for using -1 as the first multiplier is simply to retain the same meaning for β as before.

where $B = e^{\lambda}$ is an unknown parameter. Finally

$$N_j = \frac{g_j}{Be^{\beta\epsilon_j} - 1} \qquad g_j \gg 1 \qquad\qquad \textbf{(17.14)}$$

This is the general Bose-Einstein distribution law for material particles and is seen to differ from the Boltzmann law by having -1 in the denominator. Here B is a normalization constant, and β turns out to be $1/kT$ as before.

In the second case, with only the total energy held constant, we merely omit the last of the three conditions in Eq. 17.13 and have

$$
\left.
\begin{array}{r}
-1 \\[1.5em]
\beta
\end{array}
\right|
\begin{array}{l}
\displaystyle\sum \ln\left(\frac{g_j}{N_j} + 1\right)\delta N_j = 0 \\[1.5em]
\displaystyle\sum \epsilon_j\,\delta N_j = 0
\end{array}
$$

$$\sum\left[-\ln\left(\frac{g_j}{N_j} + 1\right) + \beta\epsilon_j\right]\delta N_j = 0$$

Therefore, the distribution law when particle number is *not conserved* is

$$N_j = \frac{g_j}{e^{\beta\epsilon_j} - 1} \qquad\qquad \textbf{(17.15)}$$

which is seen to be a special case of the general Bose-Einstein distribution law for material particles with $B = 1$. We shall return to this in Chap. 19 in connection with the statistics of radiation.

17.7   The Boltzmann Approximation

The rigorous Bose-Einstein distribution law given in Eq. 17.14 is very difficult to use. The difficulty arises because the normalization constant, B, must be found from

$$N = \sum N_j = \sum \frac{g_j}{Be^{\beta\epsilon_j} - 1}$$

and cannot be factored out as before.

Fortunately, however, for all systems made up of ordinary gaseous molecules at temperatures higher than a few degrees Kelvin, the parameter B satisfies the condition

$$B \gg 1$$

and the term -1 in the denominator can be neglected, so that Eq. 17.14 becomes

$$\boxed{N_j = g_j A e^{-\beta \epsilon_j}} \qquad A = \frac{1}{B} \qquad (17.16)$$

This is of the Boltzmann form and is called the *Boltzmann approximation* to the Bose-Einstein distribution law. Since B is large, A is small, and therefore

$$N_j \ll g_j$$

The Boltzmann approximation can be introduced in the original formula for the Bose-Einstein expression for W_j,

$$W_j = \frac{(g_j + N_j - 1)!}{(g_j - 1)! N_j!}$$

With $g_j \gg N_j \gg 1$, the factorial in the numerator may now be approximated as

$$g_j g_j \ \cdot \ \cdot \ \cdot \ g_j (g_j - 1)! = (g_j)^{N_j}(g_j - 1)!$$

and therefore

$$W_j = \frac{(g_j)^{N_j}}{N_j!}$$

so that

$$\boxed{W = \prod_j \frac{(g_j)^{N_j}}{N_j!}} \qquad (17.17)$$

With this approximation for W, a new entropy expression results, with $S = k \ln W$ as

$$S_{\text{Boltz approx}} = k(\Sigma N_j \ln g_j - \Sigma \ln N_j!)$$

Since we have already taken $N_j \gg 1$ (which means that each energy shell is large compared to h^f), we may use Stirling's formula for $N_j!$ to give

$$\boxed{S_{\text{Boltz approx}} = k\left(\sum N_j \ln \frac{g_j}{N_j} + N\right)} \qquad (17.18)$$

If N_j from Eq. 17.16 is summed over all energy shells to give N,

$$N = A \sum_j g_j e^{-\beta \epsilon_j} \qquad (17.19)$$

where now g_j appears as a number, a *weighting factor* for the exponentials in the sum. Since it also gives the number of cells of size h^f that have the same energy ϵ_j, it is really a *degeneracy* factor. Energy states with $g = 1$ are *nondegenerate*, and each value of the energy corresponds to a single μ cell. When $g > 1$, the state is *multiply degenerate*, and the corresponding exponential is counted g

times in the sum in Eq. 17.19. This means that instead of summing $e^{-\beta\epsilon_j}$ over all the μ cells as formerly, we sum $g_j e^{-\beta\epsilon_j}$, which counts all the μ cells of the same energy, over all the energy shells (or energy states). Thus the sum in Eq. 17.19 is just the partition function, Z, for the gas, and we have

$$Z = \sum_j g_j e^{-\beta\epsilon_j} = \frac{N}{A} = {\sum}' e^{-\beta\epsilon_j} \qquad (17.20)$$

where the first summation is over *energy shells* and Σ' is over μ cells of size h^f. From Eq. 17.20, $A = N/Z$ when Eq. 17.16 gives

$$\boxed{\frac{g_j}{N_j} = \frac{Z}{N} e^{\beta\epsilon_j}} \qquad (17.21)$$

This is the most important quantity in the new entropy expression, Eq. 17.18, which now, on replacement of $\Sigma N_j \epsilon_j$ by U, reduces to

$$S_{\text{Boltz approx}} = Nk \left(\ln \frac{Z}{N} + \beta \frac{U}{N} + 1 \right)$$

·Since just as before

$$U = NkT^2 \left(\frac{\partial \ln Z}{\partial T} \right)_V$$

and

$$\beta = \frac{1}{kT}$$

this becomes

$$\boxed{S_{\text{Boltz approx}} = Nk \left[\ln \frac{Z}{N} + T \left(\frac{\partial \ln Z}{\partial T} \right)_V + 1 \right]} \qquad (17.22)$$

in complete agreement with Gibbs' modification of Boltzmann's original entropy expression given in Eq. 16.58. The result now, however, rests on a firm statistical foundation based on the indistinguishability of identical particles and the appropriate combinatory analysis. Consequently, the general equations for thermodynamic properties in terms of log Z and its derivatives assembled in Eq. 16.65 are now validated for applications for which use of the Boltzmann approximation to the Bose-Einstein statistics is justified.

On comparison of the two distribution laws,

Bose-Einstein

$$N_j = \frac{g_j}{Be^{\beta\epsilon_j} - 1}$$

Boltzmann approximation

$$N_j = \frac{g_j}{Be^{\beta\epsilon_j}} = g_j A e^{-\beta\epsilon_j}$$

it is clear that when $Be^{\beta\epsilon_j}$ becomes comparable with 1, we should expect

$$(N_j)_{\text{B-E}} > (N_j)_{\text{Boltz approx}}$$

In other words, denser crowding of image points in any given energy shell in phase space is predicted by the Bose-Einstein statistics. This Bose-Einstein "condensation" is not significant at high temperatures but becomes so as the temperature is lowered and the particle mass becomes smaller. In particular, H_2 and He gas below 1°K should both exhibit this condensing effect, which, although having no effect on ordinary space density, should alter the heat capacity. Unfortunately, no way is known whereby an alteration in heat capacity due solely to the statistics of an ideal gas can be distinguished experimentally from the effect of intermolecular attractions due to departures from ideality of the gas.

Comparison of Eqs. 17.20 and 16.25 gives

$$Z = \frac{N}{A} = \frac{1}{\alpha \, \Delta\mu}$$

and thus $A = N\alpha \, \Delta\mu$. The parameter α, however, is simply the reciprocal of the partition integral. Therefore, with $\Delta\mu = h^f$, we have (compare, say, with Eq. 16.26)

$$Z = \frac{1}{h^f} \int e^{-\beta H(p,q)} \, d\mu \qquad (17.23)$$

for all cases in which continuous integration may be substituted for discrete summation over energy shells.

In the special case of the monatomic gas with $f = 3$, this leads to the result

$$Z^{\text{mono}} = \frac{V(2\pi mkT)^{3/2}}{h^3} \qquad (17.24)$$

which in turn gives the proper values of entropy and the other thermodynamic quantities.

17.8   Diatomic Molecule in a $^1\Sigma$ State

For a general diatomic molecule, the total energy may always be separated into translatory energy and internal energy. The translatory energy leads to the same partition function for translations as that given for the monatomic molecule in Eq. 17.24.

The internal energy can conveniently be taken as the sum of five separate parts, as follows:

$$\epsilon^{\text{int}} = \epsilon^{\text{nu}} + \epsilon^{\text{el}} + \epsilon^{\text{vib}} + \epsilon^{\text{rot}} + \epsilon^{\text{interaction}}$$

The first four terms are the nuclear energy, the energy due to the configuration and motion of the external electrons, the vibrational energy, and the rotational energy, respectively. Each of these is given by the quantum theory in terms of one or more suitable quantum numbers. The last term, the interaction energy, involves in principle all the quantum numbers occurring in the other terms. It is the energy due to the coupling of all the types of motion present in the molecule. Although theoretically it includes all possible types of interaction, there is actually little coupling between the nuclei and the rest of the molecule. Great simplification results if we further restrict ourselves to the simplest possible nuclear and electronic configurations. For the present purpose, therefore, we choose molecules with no *nuclear spins* and with ground states involving no orbital *angular momentum* or *net spin* of the external electrons. There remains then only the interaction between vibration and rotation, and as in the classical treatment in Chap. 16, this can usually be neglected to a very satisfactory degree of approximation. We therefore assume the idealized diatomic molecule of Sec. 16.3, in which vibrations are strictly harmonic, the moment of inertia constant, and all interactions are neglected.

A final point arises concerning molecules made up of two identical atoms, such as H_2 and O_2, so-called *homonuclear* molecules. A molecule made up of two dissimilar atoms, a *heteronuclear* molecule, is in reality simpler to treat statistically. When such a molecule rotates, it must turn through 360° before it is again in a configuration identical with its initial one. In obtaining the classical partition function for rotation, Z^{rot} (see Sec. 16.7 and Problem 16.10), we therefore integrate quite properly from $\phi = 0$ to $\phi = 2\pi$. The homonuclear molecule, however, returns to a configuration indistinguishable from its initial one at 180° and again at 360°, since the atoms and hence the nuclei are now identical. Consequently, integration from 0 to 180° is required.

Since integration over half the range reduces the rotational partition function by half, we may write for the classical case of the *homonuclear* molecule

$$Z^{\text{rot}}_{\text{homo}} = \tfrac{1}{2} Z^{\text{rot}}_{\text{cl}}$$

where $Z^{\text{rot}}_{\text{cl}}$ is the ordinary classical rotational partition function for the heteronuclear molecule. In fact, if a symmetry number, σ', is introduced, the two types can be included in a single formula,

$$Z^{\text{rot}} = \frac{1}{\sigma'} Z^{\text{rot}}_{\text{cl}} = \frac{8\pi^2 I k T}{\sigma' h^2} \tag{17.25}$$

where $\sigma' = 1$ for a heteronuclear molecule and 2 for a homonuclear molecule.

In quantum theory the situation is considerably complicated by certain symmetry requirements, a complication that we have avoided heretofore by considering only high temperatures and in what follows by restricting the discussion of rotation to the heteronuclear case.

With the suggested rather drastic simplifications, the energy expression reduces to the one considered classically in Chap. 16, that is,

$$\epsilon^{\text{int}} = \epsilon^{\text{vib}} + \epsilon^{\text{rot}}$$

these energies being relative to the normal electronic ground state of the molecule, which is without spin or orbital angular momentum. Such an electronic state is a so-called *singlet sigma state* (written $^1\Sigma$), and it is the ground state of a vast majority of the some 300 stable diatomic molecules the spectra of which have been studied. It is analogous to a ^1S state for an atom. (See Table 17.2.)

17.9 Quantization of Vibration and Rotation

In the older quantum theory, vibration and rotation were treated on the basis of Bohr's quantum postulate. According to this, only those states were stable quantum states for which an appropriate phase space integral was an integral multiple of h. Thus

$$\oint p\, dg = nh \qquad n = 0, 1, 2, \ldots$$

where the phase integral was evaluated over one complete cycle of the motion. Application of this to vibration gave for the linear oscillator

$$\epsilon^{\text{vib}} = h\nu v \qquad v = 0, 1, 2, \ldots \qquad (17.26)$$

v, now replacing n, being the *vibrational quantum* number and ν the frequency of the vibration. The wave mechanical treatment of the same problem (see Sec. 18.5) gives

$$\epsilon^{\text{vib}} = h\nu(v + \tfrac{1}{2}) \qquad v = 0, 1, 2, \ldots \qquad (17.27)$$

Thus in each case the vibrator has a set of accessible states of constant separation, $n\nu$. However, Eq. 17.27, which is in accord with experiment, predicts a *zero-point* energy, $\epsilon_0 = h\nu/2$, which corresponds to the lowest accessible state. See Fig. 17.3, where a few of the lower vibratory states have been plotted.

For the rotational motion of a rigid rotor, both the older and the later forms of the quantum theory predict that angular momentum must be a multiple of $\hbar$, where $\hbar = h/2\pi$. The older theory gives this as $J\hbar$, whereas wave mechanics predicts that it must be $[J(J+1)]^{1/2}\hbar$, J being an integer in each case. The latter result leads to an expression for the energy, again in agreement with experiment, of the form

$$\epsilon^{\text{rot}} = \frac{h^2}{8\pi^2 I} J(J+1) \qquad J = 0, 1, 2, \ldots \qquad (17.28)$$

where I is the moment of inertia of the rigid rotor. The resulting accessible states for the rigid rotor constitute a set of closely spaced levels, the spacing increasing rapidly with increasing J (Fig. 17.4). Owing to the smallness of the rotational factor, $h^2/8\pi^2 I$, compared with the vibrational constant, $h\nu$, the rotational levels are on a much finer scale than the vibrational ones. See Fig. 17.5, where rotational and vibrational levels are plotted together for a typical case. Since spectroscopic data are usually expressed in centimeters^{-1} instead of actual frequencies, we convert energy to this unit by dividing by hc.

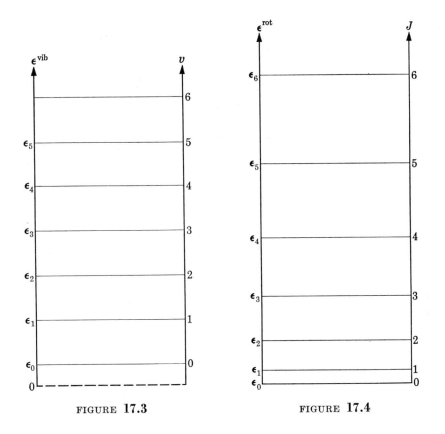

FIGURE **17.3**   FIGURE **17.4**

Thus we reduce Eqs. 17.27 and 17.28 to the spectroscopic *term values* for vibration and rotation, say, $G(v)$ and $F(J)$,

$$G(v) = \frac{\epsilon^{\text{vib}}}{hc} = \omega\left(v + \frac{1}{2}\right) \qquad (17.29)$$

$$F(J) = \frac{\epsilon^{\text{rot}}}{hc} = BJ(J + 1) \qquad (17.30)$$

where $\omega = \nu/hc$ and $B = h/8\pi^2 Ic$ are the spectroscopic vibrational and rotational constants for the molecule in centimeters^{-1}. In general, ω/B is a ratio having values of the order of a hundred to several thousand. The sum of the vibrational and rotational terms gives the vibration-rotation term value,

$$G(v) + F(J) = \omega(v + \tfrac{1}{2}) + BJ(J + 1) \qquad (17.31)$$

This is plotted vertically in Fig. 17.5 for a few values of v and J for the case of $\omega/B = 100$, a ratio roughly that for the ordinary hydrogen molecule, H_2.

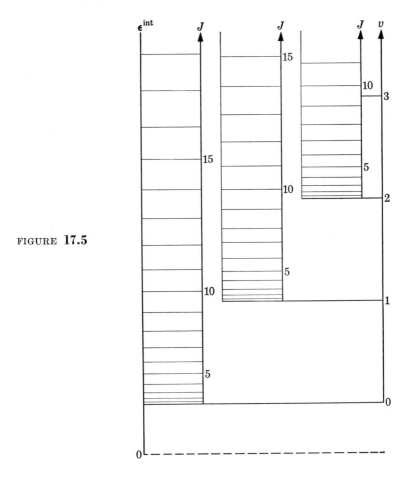

FIGURE **17.5**

17.10 Rotation and Rotation-Vibration Bands

For a diatomic molecule to absorb (or radiate) energy with a change in its rotational or vibrational state (or in both), it must possess an electric moment. If this is taken to be a dipole moment, then, for it to exist, there must be some electric asymmetry along the nuclear axis, and this requires that the molecule be *heteronuclear*. Examples are the hydrides of the halogens, such as HCl, HBr, and HI, with strong dipole moments, and CO, NO, etc., with much smaller ones. The frequency of the absorbed (or radiated) energy is governed by the Planck frequency condition. Using *single* primes to indicate quantities belonging to the *upper* energy state and *double* primes for the *lower* one, we have

$$\epsilon' - \epsilon'' = h\nu$$

or in wave numbers

$$\tilde{\nu} = \frac{\epsilon'}{hc} - \frac{\epsilon''}{hc} = G(v') + F(J') - G(v'') - F(J'')$$

where $\tilde{\nu}$ is the frequency in centimeters^{-1} of the radiant energy involved and v' and J' and v'' and J'' are the quantum numbers of the upper and lower states, respectively. Use of Eq. 17.31 gives

$$\tilde{\nu} = \omega(v' - v'') + B[J'(J' + 1) - J''(J'' + 1)] \qquad (17.32)$$

where ω and B are assumed not to vary with v and J. With the values of ω and B found in practice, the frequencies predicted by Eq. 17.32 lie entirely in the near and far infrared and must be observed in absorption. Since $\omega \gg B$, these frequencies are chiefly governed by the first term, the second adding only finer detail. With the absorbing gas at room temperature, by far the most molecules are in the ground vibrational state with $v = 0$, and v can therefore only increase; that is,

$$v' - v'' = \Delta v = 0, +1, +2, +3, \ldots$$

When $\Delta v = 0$, any absorption must be due to a rotational transition only. Fortunately the spectrum is much simplified by the operation of a rigid selection rule that forbids changes other than unity in J. Since here J can only *increase*,

$$J' - J'' = \Delta J = 1$$

The possible rotational transitions are indicated in Fig. 17.6 and give rise to a

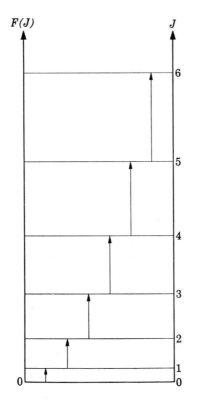

FIGURE 17.6

pure rotation spectrum. Inserting the selection condition into Eq. 17.32 gives

$$\tilde{\nu} = 2B(J'' + 1) = 2BJ' \qquad (17.33)$$

resulting in a series of absorption lines of constant separation $2B$ (see Fig. 17.7, where increasing frequency is toward the left and the lines are identified by the values of J'').

FIGURE **17.7**

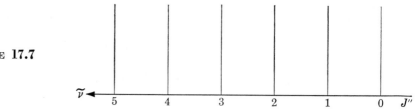

Such a pure rotation spectrum was first observed and analyzed by Czerny[8] for the hydrogen halides in the far infrared. These spectra consisted of a succession of absorption maxima with a nearly constant separation. Actually the maxima drew together somewhat with increasing rotation, owing to centrifugal stretching of the molecule. This of course increases the moment of inertia and reduces B as J increases.

When both v and J change, *vibration-rotation* spectra are produced. They usually lie in the near infrared. For each value of Δv, there is a separate group of closely spaced lines forming a *band*. Since J is free to increase or decrease, $\Delta J = \pm 1$, and two groups of lines result, symmetrically arranged about the frequency, $\omega\,\Delta v$. These groups of lines are called *branches*, the group with $\Delta J = +1$ being the R branch and the other, with $\Delta J = -1$, the P branch. Inserting $J' = J'' + 1$ and $J' = J'' - 1$ in Eq. 17.32 gives

$$\tilde{\nu} = \omega\,\Delta v + 2B(J'' + 1) \qquad R \text{ branch}$$

and

$$\tilde{\nu} = \omega\,\Delta v - 2BJ'' \qquad P \text{ branch}$$

FIGURE **17.8**

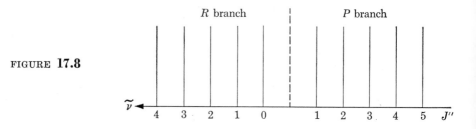

[8] Czerny, *Z. Physik*, **34**, 227 (1925).
[9] Imes, *Astrophys. J.*, **50**, 251 (1919).

The expected lines are shown in Fig. 17.8, where the dashed line or *origin* of the band lies at the frequency, $\omega \Delta v$, given by the hypothetical transition $J'' = 0 \to J' = 0$. The actually observed rotation-vibration bands exhibit a gradual variation in the line separation just as the pure rotation bands do and for a similar reason. This type of spectrum was first observed by Imes[9] for the case $v'' = 0 \to v' = 1$, the so-called 0,1 band of HCl, subsequently studied by many others. In every instance the intensity of absorption in each branch first rises to a maximum and then falls gradually to low values.

This phenomenon offers a direct and simple method of verifying the theoretical statistical weights for rotational energy states and the effect of the Boltzmann factor in fixing absorption intensities. In general, we expect the amount of energy absorbed from a beam of radiation by molecules in a given state to depend upon the number of molecules in this particular state that the beam encounters in passing through the gas. This number, of course, depends upon the size and shape of the absorption tube, the density of the gas, and, assuming the Boltzmann distribution, the factor $\exp -\epsilon''/kT$ (ϵ'' being the energy of the state *from* which absorption occurs). We therefore expect to write theoretically for, say, a case where $v'' = 0$ and thus the energy, ϵ'', is entirely rotational

$$\text{intensity of absorption} = C \exp \frac{-BhcJ''(J'' + 1)}{kT} \qquad \textbf{(17.34)}$$

C being an over-all apparatus constant.

Here the absorption lines should diminish in intensity exponentially with J''. Experimentally, as we noted before, they do not; the intensity rises to a maximum in each branch and falls off exponentially to zero. Typical behavior is shown in Fig. 17.9, which gives the curves of Spence and Holley[10] for absorption in the 0,1 band of HCl. The upper curve was taken at 200°K, and the lower one at 291°K. Frequency rises to the left, and the R and P branches are at the

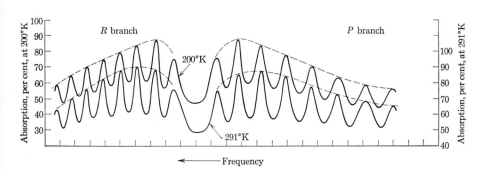

FIGURE **17.9**

left and right, respectively, of the depression marking the band origin. (The percentage absorption scale on the left applies to the upper curve, and that on the right to the lower one.) The intensity of absorption is seen to increase to a maximum and then fall as we move outward along either branch. These results are typical and can be accounted for quantitatively only by the relation

$$\text{intensity of absorption} = C(2J'' + 1) \exp \frac{-BhcJ''(J'' + 1)}{kT} \quad (17.35)$$

This means that for some reason (see Sec. 18.8) the number of molecules in the gas with a given value of J'' is just $(2J'' + 1)$ times as large as was implied in Eq. 17.34. In other words, each rotational energy state *exhibits a $(2J + 1)$-fold degeneracy*, and in any statistical calculation this must be taken into account. In particular, in the determination of the rotational partition function, each exponential term in the sum must be counted $(2J + 1)$ times or, what is the same thing, each exponential must be multiplied by the proper rotational statistical weight, g^{rot}, where

$$g^{rot} = (2J + 1)$$

To find the value of J'' in a band branch at which the maximum absorption for any temperature occurs, we differentiate Eq. 17.35 with respect to J'' and set the result equal to zero. This gives

$$T = \frac{1}{2} (2J''_{max} + 1)^2 \frac{Bhc}{k}$$

With rising temperature, therefore, the maximum of the absorption curve should shift *away* from the band origin to higher J'' values, behavior that the curves of Fig. 17.9 plainly show.

17.11   The Partition Function for a Diatomic Gas

Starting with the total energy expression for a molecule discussed in Sec. 17.8 and neglecting all interaction energy, we have

$$\epsilon = \epsilon^{nu} + \epsilon^{el} + \epsilon^{trn} + \epsilon^{vib} + \epsilon^{rot} \quad (17.36)$$

The complete partition function now becomes

$$Z = \sum_i e^{-\beta \epsilon_i}$$

where the summation is over all the possible energies of the system arranged in order of increasing values. Since the energy terms in Eq. 17.36 are all inde-

---

[10] Spence and Holley, *J. Opt. Soc. Am.*, **7**, 169 (1923).

pendent, this summation can be converted to a fivefold sum, which can then be written as the factored partition function,

$$Z = Z^{\mathrm{nu}} Z^{\mathrm{el}} Z^{\mathrm{trn}} Z^{\mathrm{vib}} Z^{\mathrm{rot}}$$

Each of these factors is a sum of the general form

$$1 + e^{-\theta_1/T} + e^{-\theta_2/T} + \cdots$$

where $\qquad \theta_1/T = \epsilon_1/kT, \qquad \theta_2/T = \epsilon_2/kT, \text{ etc.}, \cdots$

and the θ's are characteristic temperatures for the particular energies involved.

In the case of nuclear levels, the excited states of the nucleus have such high energies that θ^{nu} is of the order of millions of degrees and is of significance only in thermonuclear systems. If the nuclear ground state is degenerate, the ground state occurs g^{nu} times in the sum, and we must write

$$Z^{\mathrm{nu}} = g^{\mathrm{nu}} \times 1$$

where of course g^{nu} reduces to unity for singlet nuclear states.

In the case of electronic levels, θ^{el} is much lower (see the last column of Table 17.2) but still so large that Z^{el} usually reduces to the g value of the lowest or ground electronic state. If this is taken as g^{el}, then

$$Z^{\mathrm{el}} = g^{\mathrm{el}} \times 1$$

where g^{el} is unity for all $^1\Sigma$ states.

The translational partition function, whether evaluated as a sum over energy shells or over quantum cells of volume h^3, has the classical value given in Eq. 17.24,

$$Z^{\mathrm{trn}} = \frac{V(2\pi mkT)^{3/2}}{h^3} \qquad (17.24)$$

With the simple energy expressions given in Eqs. 17.27 and 17.28 for vibration and rotation, that is,

$$\epsilon^{\mathrm{vib}} = \frac{h\nu}{2} + h\nu v$$

and $\qquad \epsilon^{\mathrm{rot}} = \dfrac{h^2}{8\pi^2 I} J(J+1)$

the vibrational and rotational partition functions take the form

$$Z^{\mathrm{vib}} = \sum_{v=0}^{\infty} \exp - \beta h\nu \left(v + \frac{1}{2} \right) \qquad (17.37)$$

and $\qquad Z^{\mathrm{rot}} = \displaystyle\sum_{J=0}^{\infty} (2J+1) \exp - \dfrac{\beta h^2 J(J+1)}{8\pi^2 I} \qquad (17.38)$

These are the quantum partition functions for the idealized vibrating rotor and will be examined in turn.

17.12   The Partition Function and Internal Energy for Vibration

Since each vibrational state in the general vibrational energy expression given in Eq. 17.27,

$$\epsilon^{\text{vib}} = h\nu(v + \tfrac{1}{2}) \tag{17.27}$$

is strictly nondegenerate, the vibrational partition function may be summed in closed form. One complication, however, arises from the fact that when $v = 0$, the vibratory energy goes not to zero but to a *zero-point* value, ϵ_0^{vib}, where

$$\epsilon_0^{\text{vib}} = \epsilon_0 = \frac{h\nu}{2}$$

Thus from each term in Eq. 17.37 we may remove a factor

$$e^{-\beta h\nu/2} = e^{-\beta\epsilon_0}$$

when

$$Z^{\text{vib}} = e^{-\beta\epsilon_0} \sum_v e^{-\beta h\nu v} = e^{-\beta\epsilon_0} Z'$$

Here Z' is the partition function calculated with the *relative* energies, ϵ', where

$$\epsilon' = \epsilon^{\text{vib}} - \epsilon_0 = h\nu v$$

used in the exponential in place of ϵ^{vib} itself.

Taking the logarithm of Z^{vib} gives

$$\ln Z^{\text{vib}} = -\frac{\epsilon_0}{kT} + \ln Z'$$

If we calculate the term $T(\partial \ln Z/\partial T)$ occurring in the general formulas of Eq. 16.65, we have

$$\frac{T \partial \ln Z^{\text{vib}}}{\partial T} = \frac{\epsilon_0}{kT} + \frac{T \partial \ln Z'}{\partial T}$$

The general formula for entropy is

$$S = Nk\left(\ln\frac{Z}{N} + T\frac{\partial \ln Z}{\partial T} + 1\right)$$

Leaving the $+1$ and $\ln 1/N$ with the translatory terms, we obtain for the vibratory contribution to entropy

$$S^{\text{vib}} = Nk\left(\ln Z' + T\frac{\partial \ln Z'}{\partial T}\right)$$

the entropy term due to vibration being evaluated directly from Z' since the constant terms ϵ_0/RT and $-\epsilon_0/RT$ cancel.

In the case of U (and hence of the other thermodynamic functions), use of Z' in place of Z^{vib} requires the addition of a constant term. Thus

$$U^{vib} = NkT^2 \left(\frac{\partial \ln Z^{vib}}{\partial T} \right) = NkT^2 \left(\frac{\epsilon_0}{kT^2} + \frac{\partial \ln Z'}{\partial T} \right)$$

or

$$U^{vib} = N\epsilon_0 + U'$$

where $N\epsilon_0$ is just the difference between the vibrational energy of the whole system measured from the state with $v = 0$ and that measured from the vibrationless state. Since

$$C_v{}^{vib} = \frac{\partial U^{vib}}{\partial T} = \frac{\partial U'}{\partial T}$$

either vibratory partition function may be used for heat capacities.

Let us now determine Z'. We write

$$Z' = \sum_{v=0}^{\infty} e^{-\beta \epsilon'(v)} = \sum_{v=0}^{\infty} e^{-\beta h \nu v} = \sum_{v=0}^{\infty} e^{-uv} \tag{17.39}$$

where the convenient vibrational parameter, u, is used as before. Here

$$u = \beta h \nu = \frac{hc\omega}{kT} = \frac{\Theta^{vib}}{T}$$

Θ^{vib} being the characteristic temperature for vibration. In terms of Θ^{vib}, we have

$$Z' = 1 + e^{-\Theta^{vib}/T} + e^{-2\Theta^{vib}/T} + \cdots \tag{17.40}$$

When $T \ll \Theta^{vib}$, the exponentials become negligible, and $Z' \to 1$. Then $U' = 0$, and

$$U^{vib} = \frac{Nh\nu}{2} = N\epsilon_0 \qquad C_V{}^{vib} = 0$$

The assembly of diatomic molecules thus behaves as though *vibration were frozen*. When T is comparable with Θ^{vib} or larger, the entire series is needed. Fortunately this series can be written in closed form.

$$Z' = (1 + e^{-u} + e^{-2u} + e^{-3u} + \cdots) = (1 - e^{-u})^{-1} \tag{17.41}$$

Since in general

$$N_j = \frac{Ne^{-\beta \epsilon_j}}{Z}$$

on substitution of v for j, uv for $\beta \epsilon_j$, and Z' for Z, we obtain the vibrational distribution function from Eq. 17.41 as

$$N_v = [N(1 - e^{-u})]e^{-uv} \tag{17.42}$$

Here N_v is the number of vibrators with a particular value of v, and the coefficient in the bracket is the maximum value of N_v, the number in the ground state of vibration for which $v = 0$. This number is a temperature function.

Designating it by N_0' (to differentiate it from N_0, Avogadro's constant), we have

$$N_0' = N(1 - e^{-u}) = N(1 - e^{-\Theta vib/T})$$

As $T \to 0$, $N_0' \to N$, and all the oscillations pass to the ground state.

As the temperature rises from $T = 0$, more and more molecules acquire one or more units of vibration, and N_0' gradually decreases as N_2, N_3, etc., increase. This behavior is shown graphically in Fig. 17.10, where N_v is indicated by the lengths of the horizontal lines for three typical temperatures, $T = \frac{1}{4}\Theta^{vib}$, Θ^{vib}, and $4\Theta^{vib}$, respectively (that is, $u = 4$, 1, and $\frac{1}{4}$).

From Eq. 17.41,

$$U' = NkT^2 \frac{\partial \ln Z'}{\partial T} = NkT \frac{u}{e^u - 1} \tag{17.43}$$

and thus for the average relative energy, $\bar{\epsilon}'$, we have

$$\bar{\epsilon}' = kT \frac{u}{e^u - 1} = \frac{h\nu}{e^u - 1}$$

Since $\bar{\epsilon}' = h\nu\bar{v}$ in general, dividing $\bar{\epsilon}'$ by $h\nu$ gives the average value, $\bar{v}$, of the vibrational quantum number; that is,

$$\bar{v} = \frac{\bar{\epsilon}'}{h\nu} = \frac{1}{e^u - 1} \tag{17.44}$$

This average has been calculated for the three cases of Fig. 17.10 to give $\bar{v} = 0.0186$, 0.582, and 3.52 (indicated in the figures by the horizontal dashed lines). Thus at the lowest temperature, $T = \frac{1}{4}\Theta^{vib}$, less than 2 molecules in 100

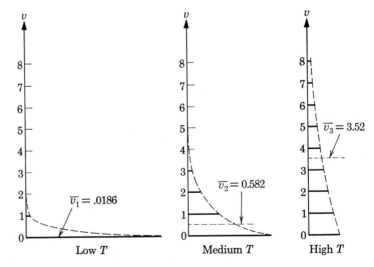

FIGURE **17.10**

have a unit of vibration, whereas at $T = 4\Theta^{\text{vib}}$ the average has increased to 3.52 units per molecule.

Using Eq. 17.43 with $N = N_0$, we have for a mole of oscillators

$$\frac{U^{\text{vib}}}{R} = \frac{h\nu}{k}\left(\frac{1}{e^u - 1} + \frac{1}{2}\right) \tag{17.45}$$

or, since $h\nu/k = \Theta^{\text{vib}}$,

$$\frac{U^{\text{vib}}}{R\Theta^{\text{vib}}} = \frac{1}{e^u - 1} + \frac{1}{2} \tag{17.46}$$

and the ratio $U^{\text{vib}}/R\Theta^{\text{vib}}$ is a universal function of the variable $u = \Theta^{\text{vib}}/T$. This dimensionless ratio is plotted as the solid curve in Fig. 17.11 versus $1/u = T/\Theta^{\text{vib}}$. It is seen to rise from $\frac{1}{2}$ and to approach asymptotically the broken line drawn in at 45°. This line, in the present dimensionless terms, is a plot of the classical energy of the oscillator, say, $U_{\text{cl}}^{\text{vib}}$, which from the results

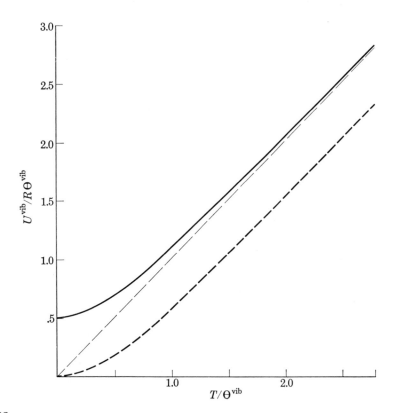

FIGURE 17.11

of Sec. 16.10 is seen to be

$$U_{cl}^{vib} = RT$$

or

$$\frac{U_{cl}^{vib}}{R\Theta^{vib}} = \frac{T}{\Theta^{vib}}$$

The dashed line starting from the origin is drawn for U' and is, of course, $\frac{1}{2}$ unit lower than the solid quantum curve. It is clear that the quantum prediction approaches the classical result as the temperature increases.

17.13   Vibratory Heat Capacity

The vibratory contribution to the molar heat capacity results on differentiation of Eq. 17.43, as

$$C_V{}^{vib} = R\frac{u^2 e^u}{(e^u - 1)^2} = RE(u)$$

$$(17.47)$$

where

$$E(u) = \frac{u^2 e^u}{(e^u - 1)^2}$$

is the *Einstein* vibratory function discussed earlier in Sec. 7.7. This new expression for $C_V{}^{vib}$ has the following limits:

at low temperatures $\lim\limits_{T\to 0} C_V{}^{vib} = R \lim\limits_{u\to\infty} E(u) = 0$

at high temperatures $\lim\limits_{T\to\infty} C_V{}^{vib} = R \lim\limits_{u\to 0} E(u) = R$

Thus at low enough temperatures vibration ceases to contribute to the heat capacity, whereas at high enough temperatures the classical limit of R is reached.

In Fig. 17.12 the dimensionless ratio

$$\frac{C_V{}^{vib}}{R} = E(u)$$

is plotted versus $1/u = T/\Theta^{vib}$. The curve rises from zero in an S shape, most of the rise taking place before $T = 2\Theta^{vib}$; the ordinate is less than 0.005 at $T = \Theta^{vib}/10$ and has reached 97.9% of the limit at $T = 2\Theta^{vib}$. A further slow rise to 99.5% at $T = 10\Theta^{vib}$ follows. For $T < \Theta^{vib}/10$, we can neglect $C_V{}^{vib}$, and for $T > 10\Theta^{vib}$, we can call it R. Each approximation is accurate to within $\frac{1}{2}\%$.

In Table 17.2 pertinent data are given for a few important diatomic molecules. Column 2 gives the spectroscopic designation of the ground electronic state (to be considered in more detail in the next chapter). Most of the molecules are seen to be in $^1\Sigma$ states and to possess no electronic orbital or spin momenta. The vibrational frequencies of molecules in general diminish with increasing vibration, and we write for the general vibrational term, $G(v)$ (in centimeters^{-1}),

$$G(v) = \omega_e(v + \tfrac{1}{2})[1 - x_e(v + \tfrac{1}{2}) + y_e(v + \tfrac{1}{2})^2] \qquad (17.48)$$

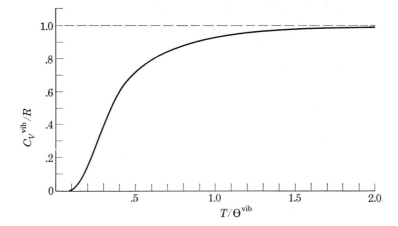

FIGURE **17.12**

TABLE **17.2**

**Vibrational and Electronic Data
for Diatomic Molecules***

Molecule	Ground state	ω_e, cm^{-1}	$x_e\omega_e$, cm^{-1}	Θ^{vib}, °K	u at 300°K	C_V^{vib} at 300°K	θ^{el} for first excited state, °K
H$_2$	$^1\Sigma_g^+$	4395.24	117.99	6320	21.1	≈ 0	129,000
HD	$^1\Sigma_g^+$	3817.1	94.958	5500	18.3	≈ 0	129,000
D$_2$	$^1\Sigma_g^+$	3118.5	64.10	4490	15.0	≈ 0	129,000
HCl	$^1\Sigma^+$	2989.74	52.05	4330	14.0	≈ 0	
HBr	$^1\Sigma^+$	2649.67	45.21	3820	12.7	≈ 0	
N$_2$	$^1\Sigma_g^+$	2359.61	14.456	3390	11.3	0.002	71,500
CO	$^1\Sigma^+$	2170.21	13.461	3120	10.4	.003	55,900
NO	$^2\Sigma_{1/2}$	1904.03	13.97	2745	9.16	.009	178
O$_2$	$^3\Sigma_g^-$	1580.36	12.073	2278	7.60	.029	11,300
Cl$_2$	$^1\Sigma_g^+$	564.9	4.0	814	2.71	.561	22,500
Br$_2$	$^1\Sigma_g^+$	323.2	1.07	465	1.55	.822	21,200
I$_2$	$^1\Sigma_g^+$	214.57	0.6127	309	1.03	.917	17,000
He$_2$	$^1\Sigma_u^+$	1811.2	39.2	2610	8.70	.013	

* The data in columns 2, 3, and 4 are largely from W. Jevons, *Report on Band Spectra of Diatomic Molecules*, Physical Society, London, 1932, and G. Herzberg, *Molecular Spectra and Molecular Structure*, 2nd ed., Van Nostrand, New York, Vol. I, 1950.

Thus ω_e is the natural frequency in the vibrationless state (equivalent to $v = -\frac{1}{2}$), and x_e, y_e, etc., are anharmonicity constants. (See Problem 17.6.) The values of ω_e and $x_e\omega_e$ are given in columns 3 and 4. In column 5 are the values of $\Theta^{\mathrm{vib}} = hc\omega_e/k = 1.4389\omega_e$ in degrees, and in column 6 the equivalent values of $u = \Theta^{\mathrm{vib}}/T$ for $T = 300°$K. Column 7 gives the values of C_V^{vib}/R for the same temperature, as calculated from Eq. 17.47. Only for the halogen molecules, with their low values of ω_e, does $C_V^{\mathrm{vib}}/R = E(u)$ depart significantly from zero.

In Fig. 17.13 a few experimental values for C_V/R are plotted versus T/Θ^{vib}. The vertical scale begins at 2.5, and the rise above this therefore represents

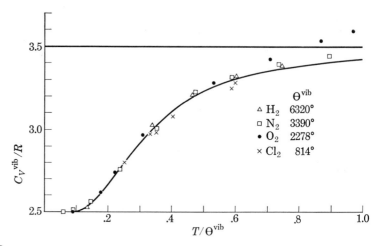

FIGURE **17.13**

C_V^{vib}/R, the solid curve being $E(u) + \frac{5}{2}$. The molecules chosen have ω_e values varying from 4395 cm^{-1} for H_2 to 565 cm^{-1} for Cl_2. The experimental results scatter well along the theoretical curve, especially below T/Θ^{vib} equal to about 0.6. Above this point the increasing anharmonicity of the vibration and the interaction between rotation and vibration begin to be significant. In the case of O_2 (as we see from the last column of Table 17.2), $\Theta^{\mathrm{el}} = 11{,}300°$K, and electronic excitation to the first excited electronic level makes a notable further increase in the heat capacity at the high temperature end of the curve. (See Sec. 18.11.)

17.14   The Partition Function and Internal Energy for Rotation

We now return to the quantum form of the rotational partition function,

$$Z^{\mathrm{rot}} = \sum_{j=0}^{\infty} (2J + 1) \exp - \frac{\beta h^2 J(J+1)}{8\pi^2 I} \qquad (\mathbf{17.38})$$

As in the vibrational case, it is convenient to define a dimensionless quantity, the *rotational parameter*, σ, where

$$\sigma = \frac{\beta h^2}{8\pi^2 I} = \frac{Bhc}{kT} = \frac{\Theta^{\text{rot}}}{T} \tag{17.49}$$

Here B is the rotational spectroscopic constant defined earlier as

$$B = \frac{h}{8\pi^2 Ic}$$

and

$$\Theta^{\text{rot}} = \frac{Bhc}{k} = \frac{h^2}{8\pi^2 Ik}$$

is the characteristic temperature for rotation described in Chap. 6. In terms of σ, Z^{rot} becomes

$$Z^{\text{rot}} = 1 + 3e^{-2\sigma} + 5e^{-6\sigma} + 7e^{-12\sigma} + \cdots \tag{17.50}$$

which unfortunately cannot be summed in closed form.

As before, with $T \ll \Theta^{\text{rot}}$, $\sigma \gg 1$, Z^{rot} reduces to 1, and rotation makes no contribution to the internal energy or heat capacity. Rotation at these low temperatures is frozen. For purposes of comparison, data for the molecules of Table 17.2 are given in Table 17.3. Column 2 gives the values of B (called B_e, since it is calculated, as was ω_e, for the vibrationless molecule). Column 3 gives the values of the rotational temperatures, Θ^{rot}. These temperatures fall with increasing mass of the molecule from 87.5°K for H_2 to 0.054°K for the heavy molecule I_2. The ratio $\Theta^{\text{vib}}/\Theta^{\text{rot}}$ (or ω_e/B_e) is given for comparison in the last column. It is clear that, except for the H_2 molecule and its isotopic variants

TABLE **17.3**

Rotational Constants for Diatomic Molecules

Molecule	$B_e = \dfrac{h}{8\pi^2 I_e c}$, cm^{-1}	$\Theta^{\text{rot}} = \dfrac{h^2}{8\pi^2 I_e k}$, °K	$\dfrac{\Theta^{\text{vib}}}{\Theta^{\text{rot}}} = \dfrac{\omega_e}{B_e}$
H_2	60.809	87.5	72
HD	45.655	65.8	84
D_2	30.429	43.8	103
HCl	10.591	15.2	290
HBr	8.473	12.2	313
N_2	2.010	2.89	1170
CO	1.9314	2.78	1120
NO	1.7046	2.45	1120
O_2	1.4457	2.08	1100
Cl_2	0.2438	0.351	2320
Br_2	.0809	.116	4000
I_2	.0374	.0537	5750

HD and D_2, the question of observations with $T \ll \Theta^{rot}$ is purely academic. All the other gases condense to the solid state long before their characteristic temperatures have been reached. For all ordinary gases, therefore, we can take σ to be so small that Z^{rot} may be approximated by a convenient asymptotic form suitable for high temperatures. For this we use a special case of the general Euler-Maclaurin summation formula.[11] This formula enables us to replace a convergent series of the form

$$\sum_{n=a}^{\infty} f(n)$$

where n is an integer, by an integral over the range a to ∞ plus a series of correction terms that usually diminish rapidly in size. The formula becomes

$$\sum_{n=a}^{\infty} f(n) = \int_a^{\infty} f(x)\,dx + \frac{1}{2}f(a) - \frac{1}{12}f'(a) + \frac{1}{720}f'''(a)$$
$$- \frac{1}{30,240}f'''''(a) + \cdots$$

where $f(a)$, $f'(a)$, $f'''(a)$, etc., are the values of the function of x and its odd derivatives at the lower limit of the integral. Here, of course, the series on the right must converge for the formula to be valid.

In the present case

$$f(n) = f(J) = (2J + 1)e^{-\sigma J(J+1)}$$

and with $a = 0$, the integral is

$$\int_0^{\infty} f(x)\,dx = \int_0^{\infty} (2x + 1)e^{-\sigma x(x+1)}\,dx = \int_0^{\infty} e^{-\sigma y}\,dy = \frac{1}{\sigma}$$

On calculating the odd derivatives of $f(x)$ at $x = 0$, we find after some labor that the series reduces finally to

$$Z^{rot} = \frac{1}{\sigma}\left(1 + \frac{\sigma}{3} + \frac{\sigma^2}{15} + \frac{4\sigma^3}{315} + \cdots\right) \tag{17.51}$$

This is good to about 1% if $\sigma \leq 1$. For larger values of σ, it is necessary to use the original series given in Eq. 17.50, fewer terms being required as σ becomes larger.

For the highest temperature ranges, the series in Eq. 17.51 can be broken off after the first term, and the high-temperature rotational partition function reduces to the classical value,

$$Z^{rot} = \frac{1}{\sigma} = \frac{8\pi^2 IkT}{h^2} \qquad \sigma \ll 1 \tag{17.52}$$

---

[11] See J. E. Mayer and M. G. Mayer, *Statistical Mechanics*, Wiley, New York, 1940, p. 152.

To include homonuclear as well as heteronuclear molecules, we divide this result by the symmetry number, σ', obtaining

$$Z^{\text{rot}} = \frac{8\pi^2 I k T}{\sigma' h^2} \qquad \sigma \ll 1 \qquad (17.53)$$

Since σ' is a constant, it has no effect on rotational internal energies and heat capacities but, of course, appears as a constant in the rotational entropy term. For this high-temperature range,

$$U^{\text{rot}} = NkT^2 \left(\frac{\partial \ln Z^{\text{rot}}}{\partial T} \right) = NkT$$

and

$$C_V^{\text{rot}} = Nk \qquad (17.54)$$

These are the results obtained in Chap. 16, Problem 16.10, and once again the classical formulas are the limiting values of the quantum predictions as temperatures rise indefinitely.

It is now clear why most diatomic gases have $C_V = \frac{5}{2}R$; room temperatures are small compared with Θ^{vib}, and $u \gg 1$. Thus no appreciable vibration is excited, and rotation is essentially classical. The notable exception in Table 6.1 is Cl_2, for which at 15°C $C_V = 5.93$ cal/mole. For Cl_2, $\Theta^{\text{vib}} = 814°K$, and the ratio $T/\Theta^{\text{vib}} = 288/814 = 0.354$. From the curve in Fig. 17.13 we find $C_V \approx 3.04R = 6.04$ calories in much better agreement.[12]

For intermediate and just higher temperatures, we must use the series given in Eqs. 17.50 and 17.51, which now apply only to the case of heteropolar molecules. The calculated curve for C_V^{rot}/R is shown in Fig. 17.14 and unlike

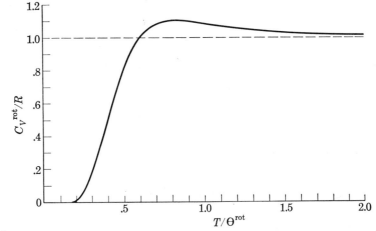

FIGURE **17.14**

---

[12] Strictly speaking, Cl_2 gas is a mixture of isotopic molecules, of which $Cl^{35}Cl^{35}$ constitutes 60% and $Cl^{35}Cl^{37}$ most of the rest. The data of Table 17.3 refer to the lighter molecule. The effect is to make C_V^{rot} for the natural mixture only about 0.1% higher than for a pure sample of the lighter isotope.

that for $C_V{}^{\text{vib}}/R$ rises steeply to a maximum at about $T = 0.8\Theta^{\text{vib}}$. This lies about 10% above the final asymptotic limit of 1, to which it sinks slowly as T rises. For $T < \Theta^{\text{vib}}/5$, $C_V{}^{\text{rot}}$ can be neglected to within about 1%, whereas for $T > 5\Theta^{\text{vib}}/3$, it can be taken as R to the same precision. The experimental results of Clusius and Bartholomé for the gas HD verify the theoretical expectations in a very satisfactory way, rising to a maximum at about $T = 0.8\Theta^{\text{rot}}$ and thereafter falling toward the classical value.[13]

The rotational heat capacities of the heavier diatomic molecules are beyond direct observation, and the behavior of homonuclear molecules requires more quantum theory for its discussion. (See Chap. 18.)

17.15   The Vapor Pressure Constant for a Diatomic Gas

The treatment of the vapor pressures of solids with monatomic vapors can be paralleled for those with diatomic vapors. The rotational heat capacities of the heavier diatomic gases attain the classical values at such very low temperatures that we may approximate their over-all behavior quite satisfactorily by taking $C_p^{\circ} = \frac{7}{2}R$ from 0°K to the temperature involved (provided, of course, that this is low enough for no significant vibration to be excited). Then the vapor pressure formula becomes

$$\ln p = -\frac{\Lambda_0}{RT} + \ln T^{7/2} - I(T) + i_p$$

where
$$i_p = \frac{S_{0Tp}^{\circ} - S_0'''}{R} - \frac{7}{2} \qquad (17.55)$$

To find S_{0Tp}°, we need the complete partition function,

$$Z = Z^{\text{nu}} Z^{\text{el}} Z^{\text{trn}} Z^{\text{rot}} Z^{\text{vib}}$$

With temperatures low enough for us to set $Z^{\text{vib}} = Z' = 1$ and yet use the classical value of Z^{rot}, Eq. 17.53, we have

$$Z = g^{\text{nu}} g^{\text{el}} \frac{V(2\pi mkT)^{3/2}}{h^3} \frac{(8\pi^2 IkT)}{\sigma' h^2} = \frac{T^{7/2} N(2\pi m)^{3/2} k^{5/2}}{p} \frac{(8\pi^2 Ik)}{h^3} \frac{(8\pi^2 Ik)}{\sigma' h^2} g^{\text{nu}} g^{\text{el}} \quad (17.56)$$

on introduction of $pv = NkT$. The general entropy expression from Eq. 16.65 being

$$S = Nk \left(\ln \frac{Z}{N} + T \frac{\partial \ln Z}{\partial T} + 1 \right) \qquad (16.65)$$

we obtain from Eq. 17.56

$$S = Nk \left[\ln \frac{T^{7/2}}{p} + \ln \frac{(2\pi m)^{3/2} k^{5/2}}{h^3} + \ln \frac{8\pi^2 Ik}{\sigma' h^2} + \ln g^{\text{nu}} g^{\text{el}} + \frac{7}{2} \right] \quad (17.57)$$

---

[13] Clusius and Bartholomé, *Z. Elektrochem.*, **40**, 526 (1934).

The constant terms inside the brackets now give us the theoretical value of S_{0Tp}°/R. Conversion of Eq. 17.57 to common logarithms and pressure in atmospheres gives for i_p', the *conventional* vapor pressure constant,

$$i_p' = \log\left(\frac{2\pi}{N_0}\right)^{3/2}\frac{k^{5/2}}{h^3 p_0} + \log\frac{8\pi^2 k}{10^{40}h^2} + \log\frac{M^{3/2}I \times 10^{40}}{\sigma'} + \log g^{nu}g^{el} - \frac{S_0'''}{R}$$

$$(17.58)$$

The first constant on the right is the translational constant obtained in Sec. 17.3 for the monatomic gas, where

$$\log\left(\frac{2\pi}{N_0}\right)^{3/2}\frac{k^{5/2}}{h^3 p_0} = -1.592$$

The second is the analogous universal constant for rotation,

$$\log\frac{8\pi^2 k}{10^{40}h^2} = -1.607$$

and the total is -3.199. (Here $\log 10^{40}$ is introduced into Eq. 17.58 because of the small values of I_0.)

To determine S_0'''/R, theoretically we need a similar treatment of the solid crystal from which the vapor comes. As we shall see in Chap. 19, the general partition function, Z^K, for a crystal can be written in a form that takes into account the lattice vibrations, the internal vibrations of groups at the lattice points, and finally the electronic energy and the nuclear energy of such groups. However, as we saw in the discussion of paramagnetic salts in Chap. 14, as the temperature is lowered below $1°K$, the lattice vibration ceases to be of importance, and this factor in the partition function reduces to unity. As the temperature falls still lower, the system tends toward the lowest possible energy state. Thus the factor due to internal vibrations reduces to unity also, and we are left with only $Z^{nu}Z^{el} = (g^{nu}g^{el})^{(K)}$, where K indicates the crystal. A further factor must be considered in this case, the so-called partition function for orientation, Z^{orn}, which is different from unity when the lattice-point groups in the crystal have more than one possible orientation (of essentially equal energy). If a molecule such as CO has two orientations in the crystal, CO and OC, which are essentially identical in energy, there is an *orientation* degeneracy, and we have to write $Z^{orn} = g^{orn} = 2$. The disorder arising from these two orientations produces an extra factor of 2 in the total partition function, adds the term $Nk \ln 2$ to the entropy, etc. We therefore write finally

$$Z^K = (g^{nu}g^{el})^{(K)}g^{orn}$$

and obtain for the solid's entropy constant

$$\frac{S_0'''}{R} = \ln (g^{nu}g^{el})^{(K)}g^{orn}$$

TABLE **17.4**

Vapor Pressure Constants for Diatomic Molecules in $^1\Sigma$ States

Gas	M	$I \times 10^{40}$, cgs	Symmetry number, σ'	$(i_p')_{obs}$	$(i_p')_{obs} -$ $\log M^{3/2}I \times 10^{40}$ $\overline{\sigma'}$	Eq. 17.59
N_2	28.02	13.9	2	$-0.16 \pm .03$	-3.17	
HCl	36.47	2.66	1	$-0.40 \pm .03$	-3.17	
HBr	80.92	3.30	1	$+0.24 \pm .04$	-3.14	
HI	127.93	4.26	1	$+0.65 \pm .05$	-3.14	
Cl_2	70.9	114.5	2	$+1.66 \pm .08$	-2.87	
Br_2	159.8	345	2	$+2.59 \pm .10$	-2.95	
I_2	253.8	746	2	$+3.08 \pm .05$	-3.10	
					Av $\overline{-3.07 \pm .1}$	-3.199
CO	28.01	14.3	1	$-0.07 \pm .05$	$-3.40 \quad .1$	-3.500

Inserting these results in Eq. 17.58 gives us for the general diatomic case

$$(i_p')_{theor} - \log \frac{M^{3/2}I \times 10^{40}}{\sigma'} - \log \frac{(g^{nu}g^{el})^{(g)}}{(g^{nu}g^{el})^{(K)}} \frac{1}{g^{orn}} = -3.199 \quad (17.59)$$

For comparison with experiment, the values of i_p' as reported by Eucken[14] for $^1\Sigma$ diatomic molecules are given in column 5 of Table 17.4. Columns 2, 3, and 4 give, respectively the molecular weight, M, the moment of inertia, I (as obtained from band spectra), multiplied by the convenient factor 10^{40}, and the symmetry factor, σ'. In column 6 are values of $(i_p')_{obs} - \log M^{3/2}I \times 10^{40}/\sigma'$. These, with the exception of the value for CO, are averaged to give $-3.07(\pm.1)$. The last column contains the value on the right of Eq. 17.59, that is, -3.199. Although the results are not as clear-cut as those for the monatomic gases, they strongly suggest that the term in Eq. 17.59 containing the statistical weights is to be taken as zero for all but CO. Since these molecules are all in $^1\Sigma$ states, g^{el} is zero for the gas and presumably zero for the molecules in the solid as well. Since evaporation should have no effect on nuclear states, g^{nu} likewise should be identical for both phases and therefore cancel. The conclusion is that only possibly for CO is g^{orn} different from unity. If in this case we take $g^{orn} = 2$, $\log g^{orn} = 0.301$, and Eq. 17.59 gives

$$(i_p')_{theor} - \log \frac{M^{3/2}I \times 10^{40}}{\sigma'} = -3.199 - 0.301 = -3.500$$

Then the value in column 6 is -3.40, again in reasonably good agreement with observations.

---

[14] Eucken, *Phys. Z.*, **30**, 818 (1929); **31**, 361 (1930).

Problems

17.1 Find the number of ways of distributing four objects among three equal energy levels (as was done in Sec. 17.4) according to the Boltzmann and the Bose-Einstein methods of counting.

17.2 The volume of a thin spherical shell in the momentum space of a monatomic molecule is

$$4\pi p^2 \Delta p$$

where Δp is the thickness of the shell in momentum units. The corresponding energy shell in six-dimensional phase space must be V times as great (since molecules from all over the gas may have momenta lying in this shell). The number of quantum cells of volume h^3 in such an energy shell, say, g_i, is thus

$$g_i = \frac{V 4\pi m^3 v_i{}^2 \Delta v_i}{h^3} \tag{1}$$

Find g_i for a mole of He gas at normal temperature and pressure if $v_i = 200$ meters/sec and $\Delta v_i = 10^{-4}$ meters/sec.

17.3 Combining Eqs. 17.16, 17.20, and 17.24 gives the distribution law for the ideal gas as

$$N_j = \frac{N}{V} \frac{h^3 g_j e^{-\beta \epsilon_j}}{(2\pi m k T)^{3/2}}$$

From this and Eq. 1 determine the number of molecules in the energy shell used in Problem 17.3.

17.4 Calculate the contribution to the molar heat capacity made by vibration in the cases of N_2 and O_2 at 500°K.

17.5 Using the tables given by Mayer and Mayer, p. 450 (see footnote 11), calculate the error introduced when C_V for a diatomic gas such as CO is taken to be constant and equal to $\frac{5}{2}R$. (In their notation $Q_{jmt} \equiv Z^{rot}$, $E_{jmt} \equiv U^{rot}$, and $C_{jmt} \equiv C_V{}^{rot}$.)

17.6 The effective vibrational frequency, ω, may be defined as

$$\omega = \frac{\partial G(v)}{\partial v}$$

Use this definition to interpret the significance of ω_e in Eq. 17.48.

CHAPTER EIGHTEEN

Quantum Statistics

18.1 Photons and Matter Waves

The use of quantum theory as a means of modifying classical statistics has led to a rational basis for the Sackur-Tetrode entropy formula and accord between theory and experiment. It must, however, be obvious that the theory remains a compromise. We started with Newtonian mechanics and introduced such empirical changes as were needed to remove serious fallacies in reasoning and to justify a result in agreement with experiment. We must now examine the general problem of building a quantum statistics with the classical statistics as a guide and with the asymptotic limit to which the quantum statistics proceeds as temperatures rise without limit.

Although the macroscopic world as we know it is governed by Newton's equations (at least for nonrelativistic speeds), the world of atoms and molecules is most accurately described by Schrödinger's wave equation. Although the intricacies of this equation form a whole subject in itself, some of the significant points can be brought out with only a brief examination of the nature of the new approach.

For this discussion we are concerned with the wave-particle duality in nature. In the case of electromagnetic radiation interacting with objects large compared with the wave length, wave properties are predominant. When the objects concerned become individual atoms and molecules, the wave length ceases to be important; frequency is the significant parameter, and the corpuscular properties of the photon of energy are now predominant.

In much the same way, Newtonian mechanics and the corpuscular or particle view of matter is adequate for large-scale objects. As soon, however, as we descend to atomic dimensions, the corpuscular view becomes inadequate, and wave properties begin to dominate the phenomena observed. We wish to see what the results of this duality are when it is carried to its logical conclusion.

Consider an electromagnetic wave of frequency ν and wave length λ for which we write by definition

$$\lambda = \frac{c}{\nu} = \frac{hc}{h\nu} \tag{18.1}$$

$h\nu$ being the energy of photons of frequency ν. With the relativity relation, energy $= mc^2 = h\nu$, this becomes

$$\lambda = \frac{h}{mc} \tag{18.2}$$

and the wave length is inversely proportional to the *momentum* of the *associated photons*. If such a relation is assumed to hold for material particles of mass m and speed v, the associated *matter* wave has a wave length given by

$$\lambda = \frac{h}{mv} = \frac{h}{p} \tag{18.3}$$

which is the famous de Broglie relation and the starting point for the wave intepretation of matter. In this case λ is the wave length of the particle waves, and v is the velocity of the particle itself. A wave in general must be characterized by a wave length λ, a frequency ν, and a wave velocity or *phase* velocity, v_{ph}.

In the case of light waves in vacuo,

$$v_{\mathrm{ph}} = c$$

but in the case of *matter* waves, we must not assume that the *phase* velocity and the *particle* velocity are necessarily the same thing, for in general

$$v \neq v_{\mathrm{ph}}$$

The reason for this lies in the fact of *dispersion*, the dependence of v_{ph} on λ. In fact, we take the phase velocity to be given *by definition* as

$$\lambda = \frac{v_{\mathrm{ph}}}{\nu} \tag{18.4}$$

Now consider a third velocity, the so-called *group* velocity, v_{gr}, which is defined as

$$v_{\mathrm{gr}} = \frac{\partial \nu}{\partial \left(\dfrac{1}{\lambda} \right)} = -\lambda^2 \frac{\partial \nu}{\partial \lambda} \tag{18.5}$$

or literally the rate of change of ν with wave number. From Eq. 18.4

$$\frac{\partial \nu}{\partial \lambda} = \frac{-v_{\mathrm{ph}}}{\lambda^2} + \frac{1}{\lambda} \left(\frac{\partial v_{\mathrm{ph}}}{\partial \lambda} \right)$$

and only when v_{ph} is *independent* of λ (that is, when there is *no* dispersion), do we have

$$v_{gr} = v_{ph}$$

The phase velocity is the velocity of propagation of a strictly monochromatic wave train that is essentially infinitely long and has therefore been established an infinitely long time. On the other hand, any finite wave train or pulse consists of a disturbance localized in space and having a large range of wave lengths from small to large. In Fig. 18.1 such a wave train is shown, with the dominant or *group* wave length, λ_{gr}, given as the distance from crest to crest at the center of the disturbance. The wave group or wave packet travels with the group velocity, which in general is quite different from the phase velocity (which in turn is different for each wave length in the group).

In the case of matter waves, it is the *group* velocity that must be identified with the particle velocity, that is,

$$v_{gr} \equiv v = v_{particle}$$

From Eqs. 18.5 and 18.3

$$v = v_{gr} = \frac{\partial \nu}{\partial \left(\dfrac{1}{\lambda}\right)} = \frac{\partial \nu}{\partial \left(\dfrac{mv}{h}\right)} = \frac{h}{m}\frac{d\nu}{dv}$$

where v and λ are the *particle* velocity and associated wave length. This equation we now write

$$mv\,dv = h\,d\nu$$

Integrating both sides gives

$$\boxed{\tfrac{1}{2}mv^2 = h\nu} \tag{18.6}$$

or the *kinetic energy of the particle is h times the frequency of the matter wave.* This produces a consistent picture in which $h\nu$ represents a quantum of energy whether associated with a particle or with a photon of radiant energy.

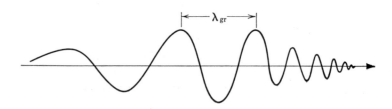

FIGURE **18.1**

18.2   Wave Amplitudes and Probability

To obtain a further insight into this all-pervading duality of corpuscles versus waves, we now inquire into the question of wave amplitudes. In the case of ordinary waves, the intensity of the wave is determined by the square of the wave amplitude. If we designate the amplitude of a wave at any time and position by Ψ, then Ψ^2 is a measure of the instantaneous intensity at that position. Thus Ψ^2 becomes a natural measure of intensity for waves of all types, including matter waves. For a beam of particles the strength of the beam in space can be given as the product of the volume density of particles and their velocity. We thus associate Ψ^2 with a *particle density*.

When we carry out a diffraction experiment, for example, by allowing a beam of electrons to pass through a powdered crystal sample, we calculate the expected wave amplitude, Ψ, at every point on the photographic film and square this value to obtain the intensity of the radiant waves at the point. This is interpreted in turn as the particle flux (that is, particle density times velocity) at the film. Of course, such a procedure cannot say anything about where a particular electron goes; Ψ^2 is a measure of the *expected* flux density, or relative *probability* of an electron's arriving.

In the case of standing waves, Ψ becomes the amplitude of the standing wave at a point, and its square leads to an expected particle density at the point. We cannot observe particle density for a single particle, but only as a result of averaging. The quantity Ψ^2 thus assumes the properties of a *statistical probability density*. The amplitudes themselves remain unobservable despite the fact that the laws governing atomic and molecular systems could hardly be formulated so simply without them.

18.3   The Wave Equation

Consider a monochromatic wave traveling along the x axis. Its amplitude will now depend on both x and t and therefore

$$\Psi = \Psi(x, t)$$

where Ψ indicates the general space- and time-dependent wave function. If the wave length is λ and the frequency ν, the amplitude of a wave proceeding toward increasing x can be written

$$\Psi = A \begin{Bmatrix} \sin \\ \cos \end{Bmatrix} 2\pi \left(\frac{x}{\lambda} - \nu t \right)$$

In contrast to this situation, a *standing* wave is characterized by loops and nodes that are stationary in space. The amplitude of such a wave can be written as a product of a space function and a time function,

$$\Psi = A \begin{Bmatrix} \sin \\ \cos \end{Bmatrix} \left(\frac{2\pi x}{\lambda} \right) e^{-2\pi i \nu t}$$

where, as before, either the sine or cosine may be selected (or any combination of the two).

Since it is desirable to be as general as possible, we now go a step further and assume the very general form

$$\Psi = A \exp 2\pi i \left(\frac{x}{\lambda} - \nu t \right) \tag{18.7}$$

where A may be a complex quantity and in general is taken to be so in what follows. Since we can only compare the square of an amplitude, that is, Ψ^2, with experiment, this is always real.

To find the general differential equation that Ψ must satisfy, we proceed as follows. First we insert into Eq. 18.7 the basic de Broglie condition (Eq. 18.3) and the quantum energy condition, that is,

$$\lambda = \frac{h}{p} = \frac{2\pi\hbar}{p}$$

and

$$\epsilon = h\nu = 2\hbar\pi\nu$$

where ϵ is the total energy of the particle. We obtain as a result

$$\Psi = A \exp \frac{i}{\hbar} (px - \epsilon t) \tag{18.8}$$

Now we calculate the two partial derivatives of Ψ with respect to x :

$$\frac{\partial \Psi}{\partial x} = A \left(\frac{ip}{\hbar} \right) \exp \frac{i}{\hbar} (px - \epsilon t) = \left(\frac{ip}{\hbar} \right) \Psi$$

and

$$\frac{\partial^2 \Psi}{\partial x^2} = - \frac{p^2}{\hbar^2} \Psi \tag{18.9}$$

Similarly, for the time derivative

$$\frac{\partial \Psi}{\partial t} = - \frac{i}{\hbar} \epsilon \Psi \tag{18.10}$$

With $\epsilon^{\text{kin}} = \frac{p^2}{2m}$, Eq. 18.9 may be written

$$- \frac{\hbar^2}{2m} \frac{\partial^2 \Psi}{\partial x^2} = \epsilon^{\text{kin}} \Psi$$

whereas Eq. 18.10 becomes

$$\frac{\hbar}{i} \frac{\partial \Psi}{\partial t} = - \epsilon \Psi$$

Adding these last two results gives

$$- \frac{\hbar^2}{2m} \frac{\partial^2 \Psi}{\partial x^2} + \frac{\hbar}{i} \frac{\partial \Psi}{\partial t} = - (\epsilon - \epsilon^{\text{kin}}) \Psi$$

or finally, since $\epsilon = \epsilon^{\mathrm{kin}} + \epsilon^{\mathrm{pot}}$,

$$-\frac{\hbar^2}{2m}\frac{\partial^2\Psi}{\partial x^2} + \epsilon^{\mathrm{pot}}\Psi = -\frac{\hbar}{i}\frac{\partial\Psi}{\partial t} \qquad (18.11)$$

This is the complete Schrödinger wave equation for a single particle.

As long as we confine ourselves to problems in which the potential energy, ϵ^{pot}, does not contain the time explicitly, Eq. 18.11 may be separated into two ordinary differential equations, one in terms of t and the other in terms of x. Thus let Ψ be written as the product of two separate functions,

$$\Psi(x, t) = \psi(x)\phi(t)$$

Then substitution in Eq. 18.11 gives

$$\frac{1}{\psi(x)}\left[-\frac{\hbar^2}{2m}\frac{d^2\psi(x)}{dx^2} + \epsilon^{\mathrm{pot}}\psi(x)\right] = -\frac{\hbar}{i\phi(t)}\frac{d\phi(t)}{dt}$$

However, if (and only if) the potential energy is time-independent,

$$\epsilon^{\mathrm{pot}} = \epsilon^{\mathrm{pot}}(x)$$

and the left side is a function of x alone, and the right side of t alone. Since x and t are independent variables, this can mean only that the two sides have a value independent of either x or t and are thus constant. Calling this constant w gives two separate equations, one for $\phi(t)$ and the other for $\psi(x)$:

$$\frac{d\phi(t)}{dt} = -\frac{iw\phi(t)}{\hbar} \qquad (18.12)$$

and

$$\frac{\hbar^2}{2m}\frac{d^2\psi(x)}{dx^2} + (w - \epsilon^{\mathrm{pot}})\psi(x) = 0 \qquad (18.13)$$

The first relation gives $\phi(t)$ as a periodic time function, whereas the second fixes the amplitude. The complete solution therefore represents a *standing wave*. Since the amplitude through its square fixes the probability of finding the particle at any particular value of x, the amplitude equation is the important one. Hereafter, it will usually be referred to as the *wave equation*, and its solutions as *wave functions*.

The solution of the amplitude equation must be subject to certain general, as well as specific, requirements. For ψ to have physical meaning, it must remain *finite* at *all* x's including very large values (that is, as $x \to \infty$). It must be zero in any ranges of x from which, by the conditions of the problem, the particle is completely excluded. Since ψ^2 represents the probability of finding a particle between x and $x + dx$, we must further require that

$$\int_{-\infty}^{+\infty} \psi^2(x)\, dx = 1$$

the so-called normalization condition.

Although w is by its definition an arbitrary constant, $\epsilon^{\text{pot}} = \epsilon^{\text{pot}}(x)$, and therefore the coefficient of ψ is a variable. The amplitude equation is therefore a second-order linear differential equation with a *variable* coefficient. Well-behaved solutions of this equation (in contrast to those with constant coefficients) do not exist for any arbitrary value of w but only for certain discrete or *characteristic* values (*eigen* values, in German) w_0, w_1, w_2, w_3, ... Since these turn out to represent fixed values of the total energy of the system, they will be designated as

$$\epsilon_0, \ \epsilon_1, \ \epsilon_2, \ \epsilon_3, \ \cdot \ \cdot \ \cdot$$

Corresponding to this set of characteristic values is the set of *characteristic* wave functions,

$$\psi, \ \psi_1, \ \psi_2, \ \psi_3, \ \cdot \ \cdot \ \cdot$$

which satisfy the wave equation and are everywhere finite, etc. The nature of these wave functions naturally depends on the form assigned to the potential energy function, $\epsilon^{\text{pot}} = \epsilon^{\text{pot}}(x)$, which fixes the force field in which the particle moves.

When the particle is free to move in space, the single second derivative with respect to x in Eq. 18.13 is replaced by the Laplacian, and

$$\frac{\partial^2 \psi}{\partial x^2} + \frac{\partial^2 \psi}{\partial y^2} + \frac{\partial^2 \psi}{\partial z^2} + \frac{2m}{\hbar^2} \, (w - \epsilon^{\text{pot}})\psi = 0 \qquad (18.14)$$

is the amplitude equation in space, where, of course, $\epsilon^{\text{pot}} = \epsilon^{\text{pot}}(x, y, z)$. For more than one particle, ψ depends on all the variables of all the particles, and the differential equation is accordingly more complicated, although capable of being written down formally in a very direct manner.[1]

18.4   Particle in a Box

As a special case of considerable interest, let us take a particle free to move along the x axis but limited to a definite range of x by hard reflecting walls a distance, L, apart. Since the walls are to be taken as impenetrable, no matter what speed and energy the particle may have, we must imagine them as exerting indefinitely large forces at the boundaries of the motion. In other words, we have a particle subject to a potential function, $\epsilon^{\text{pot}}(x)$, such that

$$\epsilon^{\text{pot}}(x) = 0 \ \text{ when } 0 < x < L$$
$$\epsilon^{\text{pot}}(x) = \infty \ \text{ when } 0 \geq x \geq L$$

A solution, $\psi(x)$, of the wave equation is therefore required that is finite in the range between 0 and L and that must vanish at the boundaries and beyond in both directions, since the particle can never get outside the box.

---

[1] See, for example, C. W. Sherwin, *Introduction to Quantum Mechanics*, Holt, Rinehart & Winston, New York, 1959, Chap. 5.

In this case the wave equation, Eq. 18.13, reduces to

$$\frac{d^2\psi}{dx^2} = -\frac{2mw}{\hbar^2}\psi \tag{18.15}$$

This is of the simple harmonic type, with x replacing time and a spring constant, K, given by

$$K = \frac{2mw}{\hbar^2}$$

Its solution is therefore expressible as

$$A \sin \sqrt{K}x$$

or
$$B \cos \sqrt{K}x$$

or a combination of these. Since ψ must vanish at both $x = 0$ and $x = L$, the cosine solution is ruled out, and we must require that

$$\sqrt{K} = \frac{n\pi}{L} \qquad n = 1, 2, 3, \ldots$$

so that the proper wave functions for the problem are

$$\psi_n = A_n \sin \frac{n\pi x}{L} \tag{18.16}$$

For each wave function with its value of n,

$$K = \frac{2mw}{\hbar^2} = \frac{n^2\pi^2}{L^2} \tag{18.17}$$

and therefore a *characteristic* value of w, say, w_n, is determined. From the original amplitude equation (Eq. 18.13), it is clear that w must have the dimensions of energy, and the results are understandable only if w_n is identified as the *total energy* of the system for the given n. We thus[2] replace w_n by ϵ_n and have, from Eq. 18.17,

$$w_n = \epsilon_n = n^2 \frac{h^2}{8mL^2} \qquad n = 1, 2, 3, \ldots \tag{18.18}$$

The solution to the problem of the free particle in a one-dimensional box is therefore a set of wave functions having an *even* or *odd* number of maxima and minima according to whether n is even or odd. Shifting the origin of x to the mid-point of the interval between the two boundaries, we write Eq. 18.16 in two forms (in which factors that merely alter signs have been omitted):

$$\psi_n = A_n \sin \frac{n\pi}{L}x \qquad n \text{ even}$$

$$\psi_n = A_n \cos \frac{n\pi}{L}x \qquad n \text{ odd}$$

---

[2] The original wave equation will still be written in terms of w to emphasize that this is a *constant* and not a function of the coordinates, as, for example, ϵ^{pot}.

These correspond to simple standing waves with even and odd numbers of half-waves in the length L and are shown in Fig. 18.2 for a few values of n. The values of $|\psi|^2$ are given in Fig. 18.3 and indicate where the particle is most likely to be found.

Returning to the energies, we note that there is a set of permitted energies having values that increase with n^2. The lowest occurs at

$$\epsilon_1 = \frac{h^2}{8mL^2}$$

and corresponds from the particle view to a back and forth motion with a finite speed. Each wave function, in fact, fixes a possible speed and possible

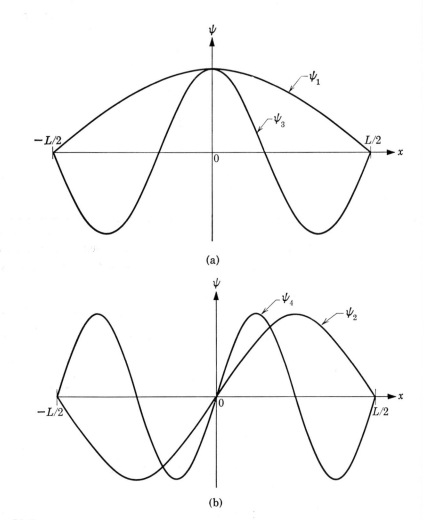

(a)

(b)

FIGURE **18.2**

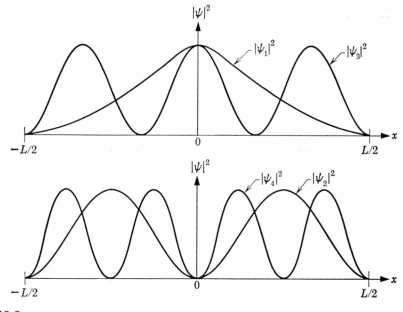

FIGURE **18.3**

energy; translational energy is therefore quantized and not continuously variable as in classical mechanics.

Of course, for ordinary objects of large-scale nature, $h^2/8mL^2$ is extremely minute, and the spacing of the discrete levels is so fine that no significant error is introduced by the treatment of kinetic energy as a continuously variable quantity. In the atomic realm, however, with mass so much smaller, the levels are more openly spaced, and the effects of this spacing must be examined more closely.

The case of a mass particle in a three-dimensional box is not much more complicated than that of a particle in a one-dimensional box. Starting with the amplitude equation in the form

$$\frac{\partial^2 \psi}{\partial x^2} + \frac{\partial^2 \psi}{\partial y^2} + \frac{\partial^2 \psi}{\partial z^2} + \frac{2m}{\hbar^2}(w - \epsilon^{\text{pot}})\psi = 0$$

we seek a solution in the form

$$\psi(x, y, z) = \psi^{(1)}(x)\psi^{(2)}(y)\psi^{(3)}(z)$$

when the original equation breaks up into three of the simple one-dimensional type, one for each of the separate functions. The final solutions may be written

$$\psi = \psi_{n_1}(x)\psi_{n_2}(y)\psi_{n_3}(z) = \psi_{n_1 n_2 n_3}$$

where n_1, n_2, and n_3 are integers as before. The energies for the case of a cubic box with $V = L^3$ are specified in terms of the kinetic energies associated with the three components of motion and are of the form of Eq. 18.18,

$$\epsilon^x = n_1{}^2 \frac{h^2}{8mL^2} \qquad n_1 = 1, 2, 3, \ldots$$

$$\epsilon^y = n_2{}^2 \frac{h^2}{8mL^2} \qquad n_2 = 1, 2, 3, \ldots$$

$$\epsilon^z = n_3{}^2 \frac{h^2}{8mL^2} \qquad n_3 = 1, 2, 3, \ldots \qquad \text{(18.19)}$$

where n_1, n_2, and n_3 are independent integers. Thus the energy of translation becomes

$$\epsilon^{\text{trn}} = \epsilon^{\text{trn}}(n_1, n_2, n_3) = (n_1{}^2 + n_2{}^2 + n_3{}^2)\frac{h^2}{8mL^2} \qquad \text{(18.20)}$$

and the permitted values of energy are determined by the assignment of all the possible sets of integers to the n's. The lowest energy results for the set $1, 1, 1$, for which

$$\epsilon_{111} = 3\frac{h^2}{8mL^2} = 3\frac{h^2}{8mV^{2/3}}$$

If we define a characteristic temperature, for translation, Θ^{trn}, as

$$\Theta^{\text{trn}} = \frac{\epsilon_{111}}{3k} = \frac{h^2}{8mV^{2/3}k} \qquad \text{(18.21)}$$

then the ratios ϵ^{trn}/k can all be written as multiples of Θ^{trn},

$$\frac{\epsilon^{\text{trn}}}{k} = (n_1{}^2 + n_2{}^2 + n_3{}^2)\Theta^{\text{trn}}$$

A few of these ratios are given in Table 18.1, column 4; the last column gives the associated wave function. We see at once that permuting the indexes in the wave function, $\psi_{n_1 n_2 n_3}$, gives new wave functions of identical energy. Thus ψ_{211}, ψ_{121}, and ψ_{112} are states of the same energy. However, since in quantum mechanics each wave function fixes a state of the system and all states of the same energy have the same a priori probability, the *number* of wave functions corresponding to a given energy level fixes the degeneracy of the level and thus

TABLE **18.1**

n_1	n_2	n_3	ϵ^{trn}/k	$\psi_{n_1 n_2 n_3}$
1	1	1	$3\Theta^{\text{trn}}$	ψ_{111}
2	1	1	$6\Theta^{\text{trn}}$	ψ_{211}
2	2	1	$9\Theta^{\text{trn}}$	ψ_{221}
1	2	2	$9\Theta^{\text{trn}}$	ψ_{122}
3	1	1	$11\Theta^{\text{trn}}$	ψ_{311}
2	2	2	$12\Theta^{\text{trn}}$	ψ_{222}

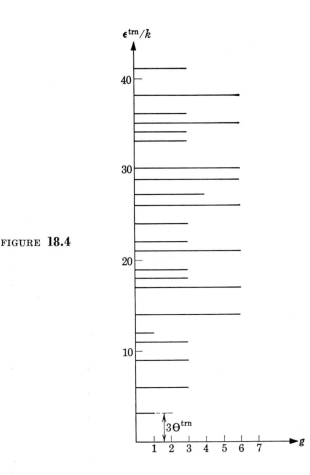

FIGURE 18.4

the statistical weight, g. The energies of a few of the earlier states are plotted in Fig. 18.4, the length of the horizontal line at each level being proportional to g according to the scale at the bottom of the figure. The weights are seen to vary in a rather irregular manner.

18.5   The Linear Vibrator

In the case of the linear vibrator of mass m, the potential energy is

$$\epsilon^{pot} = \tfrac{1}{2} K x^2$$

and the amplitude equation becomes

$$\frac{d^2\psi}{dx^2} + \frac{2m}{\hbar^2}\left(w - \frac{1}{2}Kx^2\right)\psi = 0$$

If we define the parameters a and b as

$$a = \frac{2mw}{\hbar^2}$$

and

$$b^2 = \frac{mK}{\hbar^2} = \left(\frac{K}{h\nu}\right)^2$$

where $\nu = \frac{1}{2\pi}\left(\frac{K}{m}\right)^{1/2}$, this takes the form

$$\frac{d^2\psi}{dx^2} + (a - b^2x^2)\psi = 0 \tag{18.22}$$

We now seek a solution of this equation over the range $-\infty \leq x \leq +\infty$, subject to the general requirements outlined earlier. Owing to the presence of the term x^2, this differential equation has a singular point at the two limits of x, and the solution must accordingly be arranged so as to be well behaved there.

For large x, $a \ll b^2x^2$, and the equation reduces to its asymptotic form,

$$\frac{d^2\psi}{dx^2} = b^2x^2\psi \tag{18.23}$$

An asymptotic solution of this is $\psi = e^{\pm bx^2/2}$. Since only the minus sign gives a solution well behaved at $\pm\infty$, we select this and write

$$\psi_{asmp} = e^{-bx^2/2}$$

Calculation of $d^2\psi/dx^2$ gives $b^2(x^2 - 1/b)e^{-bx^2/2}$, which is seen to approach the right side of Eq. 18.23 at large x.

Now seek a solution that satisfies the original equation (Eq. 18.22) for small x and approaches ψ_{asmp} as $x \to \infty$. To find this, we set

$$\psi = f(x)e^{-bx^2/2}$$

On substitution in Eq. 18.22, the exponential cancels, and the equation for $f(x)$ is

$$f'' - 2bxf' + (a - b)f = 0 \tag{18.24}$$

This is reduced to its standard Hermitian form by the substitution

$$\xi = \sqrt{b}\, x$$

Then $f(x) = f(\xi/\sqrt{b}) = H(\xi)$, where $H(\xi)$ is a new function that must satisfy the equation

$$H'' - 2\xi H' + \left(\frac{a}{b} - 1\right)H = 0 \tag{18.25}$$

It can be shown that a solution of this in the form of a power series,

$$H(\xi) = a_0 + a_1\xi + a_2\xi^2 + \cdots \tag{18.26}$$

at large ξ (and hence x) behaves as $e^{\xi^2/2}$. Since such a solution is not finite at infinity, the general series solution must be terminated to give a polynomial solution. In that event the final solution has the form

$$\psi(x) = Ae^{-bx^2/2}H(\sqrt{b}\,x) = Ae^{-\xi^2/2}H_n(\xi) \qquad \xi = \sqrt{b}\,x \qquad (18.27)$$

The details of the evaluation of the constants and the termination of the series are given in Appendix 18.1. The result is a set of polynomials, $H_n(\xi)$, the so-called *Hermitian polynomials*, where

$$H_0(\xi) = 1$$
$$H_1(\xi) = 2\xi$$
$$H_2(\xi) = 4\xi^2 - 2$$
$$H_3(\xi) = 8\xi^3 - 12\xi, \text{ etc.}$$

In general, $H_n(\xi)$ is an *even* function when n is *even* and an *odd* one when n is *odd*. Thus the general wave function becomes

$$\psi_n(x) = A_n e^{-bx^2/2}H_n(\sqrt{b}\,x) = A_n e^{-\xi^2/2}H_n(\xi) \qquad \xi = \sqrt{b}\,x$$

and is a *symmetric* function for *even* n values and an *antisymmetric* one for *odd* n values. Here the constant A_n is usually determined as a normalization factor such that

$$\int_{-\infty}^{+\infty} |\psi_n|^2\,dx = 1$$

This gives

$$A_n = \left[\left(\frac{b}{\pi}\right)^{\frac{1}{2}}\frac{1}{2^n n!}\right]^{\frac{1}{2}}$$

The first few of these wave functions are plotted in Fig. 18.5. They illustrate the symmetry [Fig. 18.5(a)] and antisymmetry [Fig. 18.5(b)] of the solutions. Here, of course, ψ_0 is simply the Gaussian error function, $e^{-bx^2/2}$.

Turning now to the characteristic values of a and hence to the permitted energies, we recall that in order to terminate the power series (Eq. 18.26), we had to set

$$\frac{a}{b} - (2n + 1) = 0 \qquad n = 0, 1, 2, 3, \ldots$$

or

$$a = (2n + 1)b \qquad (18.28)$$

For a given value of $b = K/h\nu$, the characteristic values w_0, w_1, w_2, etc., are fixed by the values of n. With

$$a = \frac{2mw}{\hbar^2} = \frac{8\pi^2 mw}{h^2} = \frac{8\pi^2 mw_n}{h^2}$$

and

$$b = \frac{K}{h\nu} = \left(\frac{4\pi^2 mK}{h^2}\right)^{\frac{1}{2}}$$

the permitted energies, then, are

$$w_n = \epsilon_n = \frac{h\nu}{2}(2n + 1) = \frac{h\nu}{2} + nh\nu$$

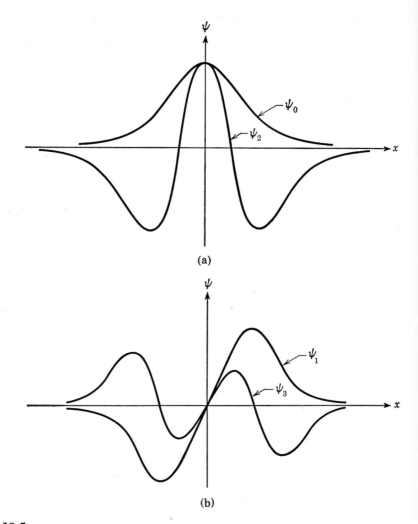

FIGURE **18.5**

Since n is recognized as the vibrational quantum number, we replace it by v to conform to the previous usage, in the last chapter, where

$$\epsilon_v = \frac{h\nu}{2} + vh\nu \qquad v = 0, 1, 2, 3, \ldots \qquad (17.27)$$

We thus have discrete energies and a set of wave functions that are *symmetric* for $v = 0, 2, 4, \ldots$ and *antisymmetric* for $v = 1, 3, 5, \ldots$.

If the wave functions plotted in Fig. 18.5 are squared, the results are as shown in Fig. 18.6. In each case the probability of finding the particle at a given

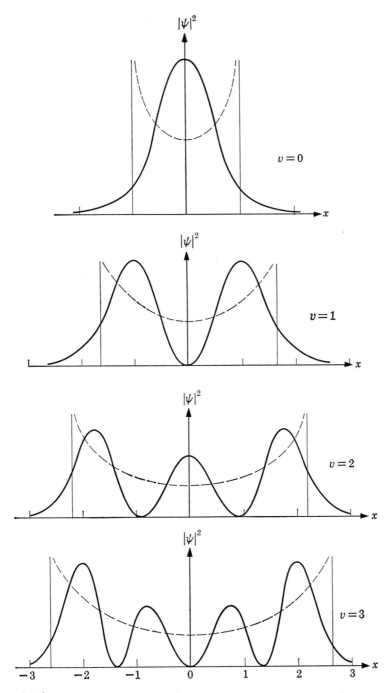

FIGURE **18.6**

x for the equivalent harmonic oscillator of classical mechanics is shown by the dotted curves. These rise to a maximum at the limits of the classical oscillation and for small values of n differ markedly from the quantum predictions. However, as n increases there is a closer correspondence, the dotted curves representing more nearly an average of the oscillatory predictions of quantum mechanics. This is an example of Bohr's correspondence principle, according to which the behavior of quantum systems approaches the predictions of classical mechanics as the value of the quantum numbers involved becomes larger and larger. In statistical terms, this means, of course, in the limit of high temperatures, and this phenomenon we have already observed with vibratory and rotational heat capacities.

18.6   The Rigid Rotor in Space

For this discussion the simplest model of the rigid rotor is that used in Chap. 16, a mass, m', constrained to move on the surface of a sphere of constant radius about a fixed center so that the moment of inertia of the mass is $I = m'r^2$, m' being the reduced mass of the molecule. Since here the potential energy term is zero, the wave equation in space, Eq. 18.14, becomes

$$\frac{\partial^2 \psi}{\partial x^2} + \frac{\partial^2 \psi}{\partial y^2} + \frac{\partial^2 \psi}{\partial z^2} + \frac{2m'w}{\hbar^2}\psi = 0 \qquad (18.29)$$

Cartesian coordinates are not suited to this case, and so we must convert to spherical polar coordinates. Because of the constancy of r, the equation reduces to one in θ and ϕ only and takes the form

$$\frac{1}{\sin \theta}\frac{\partial}{\partial \theta}\left(\sin \theta \frac{\partial \psi}{\partial \theta}\right) + \frac{1}{\sin^2 \theta}\frac{\partial^2 \psi}{\partial \phi^2} + \frac{2Iw}{\hbar^2}\psi = 0 \qquad (18.30)$$

This may best be solved as the product of two functions, $\Phi(\phi)$ and $\Theta(\theta)$. If we set

$$\psi = \Phi(\phi)\Theta(\theta)$$

the equation becomes separable into two independent equations (by the same argument employed on the complete wave equation), which we set equal to a constant. Calling this constant m^2, we have

$$\frac{d^2\Phi}{d\phi^2} = -m^2\Phi \qquad (18.31)$$

and
$$\frac{1}{\sin \theta}\frac{d}{d\theta}\left(\sin \theta \frac{d\Theta}{d\theta}\right) + \left(\frac{2Iw}{\hbar^2} - \frac{m^2}{\sin^2 \theta}\right)\Theta = 0 \qquad (18.32)$$

The first of these equations integrates to

$$\Phi(\phi) = e^{\pm im\phi} \qquad m = 0, 1, 2, 3, \ldots$$

where, to preserve the continuity at $\phi = 0$, m must be integral. The second, on substitution of $\cos \theta = x$, becomes

$$(1 - x^2)\frac{d^2\Theta}{dx^2} - 2x\frac{d\Theta}{dx} + \left[n(n + 1) - \frac{m^2}{1 - x^2}\right]\Theta = 0 \qquad \textbf{(18.33)}$$

where the unknown constant term in w has been replaced by $n(n + 1)$, that is,

$$n(n + 1) = \frac{2Iw}{\hbar^2} \qquad \textbf{(18.34)}$$

This is the standard form of the associated Legendre equation or the equation for the *associated spherical harmonics*. It can be solved in terms of polynomials of degree n, which are closely related to the Legendre polynomials. In fact, it can be shown (see Appendix 18.2) that if the Legendre polynomial of degree n is indicated by $P_n(x)$, the solutions of Eq. 18.33 may be written in the form

$$\Theta = (1 - x^2)^{m/2}\frac{d^m P_n(x)}{dx^m} = \Theta_n{}^m(x) \qquad \textbf{(18.35)}$$

where d^m/dx^m indicates the mth-order derivative of the Legendre polynomial and $\Theta_n{}^m(x)$ is a convenient designation of the nth-degree associated spherical harmonic of order m. In this case m takes on all the values from 0 to n itself.

This means formally that, since $x = \cos \theta$, the solution of the original wave equation (Eq. 18.30) may be written

$$\psi(\theta, \phi) = \Theta_n{}^m(\cos \theta)e^{\pm im\phi} \qquad \textbf{(18.36)}$$

Owing to the $\pm$ sign in the exponent of the exponential, there are two solutions for each nonvanishing value of m, and another for $m = 0$. Since m takes on the values 0, 1, 2, 3, . . . , n, a total of $(2n + 1)$ such solutions exists for each value of n.

From Eq. 18.34 the condition on the energy parameter, w, is that

$$w = w_n = n(n + 1)\frac{\hbar^2}{2I}$$

In other words, the rotational energy of the rotor, $\epsilon^{\text{rot}}\ (= w_n)$, becomes

$$\epsilon^{\text{rot}} = J(J + 1)\frac{h^2}{8\pi^2 I} \qquad J = 0, 1, 2, . . . \qquad \textbf{(18.37)}$$

where n has been replaced by J, the usual designation of the rotational quantum number. This is the expression quoted and used in Chap. 17; it now takes on added significance since we can see why each rotational state is degenerate. The energy is fixed by $J\ (= n)$ but is quite independent of m. Since for each J there are $(2J + 1)$ wave functions of the form of Eq. 18.36, there are $(2J + 1)$ states of the system of *identical energy*. Each rotational energy level, therefore, has a degeneracy of $2J + 1$, and in calculating the rotational partition function, as we have seen, we must assign each exponential the statistical weight of

$2J + 1$. This situation is the theoretical reason for the intensity variation observed in the absorption spectra discussed in Sec. 17.10.

Since the associated spherical harmonics, which we now write $\Theta_J{}^m (\cos \theta)$, are all polynomials of degree J, they are *odd* or *even* depending on whether J is *odd* or *even*. Thus the wave functions for the rigid rotor are *symmetric* when $J = 0, 2, 4, \ldots$ and *antisymmetric* when $J = 1, 3, 5, \ldots$.

18.7   The Quantum Partition Function for Translation

In Sec. 18.4 the translational energy of a particle in a cubic box of volume $V = L^3$ was obtained as

$$\epsilon^{\text{trn}} = (n_1{}^2 + n_2{}^2 + n_3{}^2) \frac{h^2}{8mV^{2/3}} = (n_1{}^2 + n_2{}^2 + n_3{}^2)\Theta^{\text{trn}}k$$

where $\Theta^{\text{trn}} = h^2/8mV^{2/3}k$, and in terms of this the translational partition function may be written as a triple sum,

$$Z^{\text{trn}} = \sum_{n_1=1} \sum_{n_2=1} \sum_{n_3=1} \exp - \frac{\Theta^{\text{trn}}}{T} (n_1{}^2 + n_2{}^2 + n_3{}^2)$$

As we saw in Fig. 18.4, the energies increase in an irregular fashion, so that direct summation of the series is difficult.[3] If the temperature is very low and energies are measured relative to the lowest state, $\epsilon_{111} = 3\Theta^{\text{rot}}k$, then we should have a relative transitional partition function, Z', given by

$$Z' = 1 + \exp \frac{-3\Theta^{\text{trn}}}{T} + 3 \exp \frac{-6\Theta^{\text{trn}}}{T} + \cdots$$

using the data from Fig. 18.4 or Table 18.1. If $T \ll 3\Theta^{\text{trn}}$, Z' reduces to 1, and translation is frozen. For such temperatures U^{trn} would have the constant value

$$U^{\text{trn}} = NkT^2 \frac{\partial \ln Z^{\text{trn}}}{\partial T} = 3N\Theta^{\text{trn}}k$$

Thus $C_V{}^{\text{trn}}$ would vanish, and the gas would have no heat capacity at all.

Of course, Θ^{trn} depends upon the mass of the molecules in the gas as well as the size of the containing vessel. For a cube of volume 22.4 liters and a strictly ideal gas of the mass of helium,

$$\Theta^{\text{trn}} = \frac{h^2}{8mV^{2/3}k} = \frac{N_0 h^2}{8 \times 4(22.4)^{2/3}k} \approx 10^{-15}{}^\circ\text{K}$$

---

[3] See Rosenstock, *Am. J. Phys.*, **30**, 38 (1962), where expressions for Z^{trn} and $C_V{}^{\text{trn}}$ suitable for low temperatures are obtained.

Thus, in general, T is always *very* large compared with Θ^{trn}, and the translational analog of the type of degeneration exhibited by vibration and rotation becomes a purely academic matter. In practice, therefore, we may safely assume that the temperature is vastly greater than the characteristic temperature for translation and that the spacing of translational levels is always very small compared to kT.

To find how many levels we may expect in a given range of energy, $\Delta \epsilon^{\text{trn}}$, we proceed as follows. Suppose that a vector, $\underline{n}$, is defined with orthogonal components having the values n_1, n_2, and n_3, so that

$$|\underline{n}|^2 = n^2 = n_1{}^2 + n_2{}^2 + n_3{}^2$$

First construct an "n space" of such form that any permissible set of values of n_1, n_2, and n_3 fixes the tip of the **vector** $\underline{n}$ (see Fig. 18.7, where this situation is suggested in two dimensions). Each of these points determines an energy state for the system, and there is one point for each unit of "volume" in the positive portion of this n space. Then construct a thin shell of radius n and thickness Δn. For small values of n the number of points in this shell changes rather erratically with n, but as n becomes larger, we can begin to treat it as continuously variable. Accordingly, the number, say, Δg_n, of permitted energy states in the range between $\epsilon_n{}^{\text{trn}}$ and $\epsilon_n{}^{\text{trn}} + \Delta \epsilon_n{}^{\text{trn}}$ becomes the volume of an octant of the

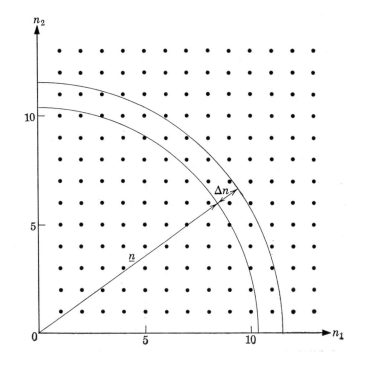

FIGURE **18.7**

shell; that is,

$$\Delta g_n = \frac{\pi}{2} n^2 \Delta n \tag{18.38}$$

This measures the degeneracy, Δg_n, of the shell of energy $\epsilon_n{}^{\text{trn}}$, where

$$\epsilon_n{}^{\text{trn}} = \Theta^{\text{trn}} k n^2 \tag{18.39}$$

The triple sum in the partition function may now be replaced by a single sum over all energy shells, and

$$Z^{\text{trn}} = \sum_n \Delta g_n \exp - \frac{\epsilon_n{}^{\text{trn}}}{kT} = \frac{\pi}{2} \sum_n n^2 \left(\exp - \frac{\Theta^{\text{trn}} n^2}{T} \right) \Delta n$$

To find how closely the energy levels for translation are spaced, we calculate $\Delta g_n / \Delta \epsilon_n{}^{\text{trn}}$, which gives the number of energy states per unit range of energy. From Eq. 18.39

$$\Delta \epsilon_n{}^{\text{trn}} = 2 \Theta^{\text{trn}} k n \, \Delta n$$

Division of Eq. 18.38 by this and elimination of n by Eq. 18.39 give

$$\frac{\Delta g_n}{\Delta \epsilon_n{}^{\text{trn}}} = \frac{\pi}{4} \frac{(\epsilon^{\text{trn}})^{1/2}}{(\Theta^{\text{trn}} k)^{3/2}} \propto (\epsilon^{\text{trn}})^{1/2} \tag{18.40}$$

This means that the number of levels per unit range of energy increases with $(\epsilon^{\text{trn}})^{1/2}$. These levels were *very* close for the lowest energies and may be taken as extremely closely packed at high energies. If we assume an essentially continuous spread of levels, the discrete sum for Z^{trn} becomes an integral, and

$$Z^{\text{trn}} = \frac{\pi}{2} \int_0^\infty n^2 \exp - \frac{\Theta^{\text{trn}} n^2}{T} \, dn = \frac{\pi}{2} I(2)$$

or

$$Z^{\text{trn}} = \frac{V(2\pi m k T)^{3/2}}{h^3}$$

with $\Theta^{\text{trn}} = h^2 / 8m V^{2/3} k$. Since this is exactly the result obtained from the partition integral with $\Delta \mu^{\text{trn}} = h^3$, we conclude that for all practical purposes kinetic energy of translation may be treated as a continuously variable quantity and the classical results used without question.

18.8 Angular Momentum and Statistical Weights

In the case of the rigid rotor, the demand for a well-behaved solution of the associated Legendre equation required that the energy, which is, of course, kinetic energy of rotation, be given as

$$\epsilon^{\text{rot}} = J(J + 1) \frac{\hbar^2}{2I}$$

with J integral. In general, angular momentum, $I\dot\phi$, is related to the energy by

$$\epsilon^{rot} = \frac{1}{2I}(I\dot\phi)^2$$

whence $\qquad (I\dot\phi) = [J(J+1)]^{\frac{1}{2}}\hbar \qquad J = 0, 1, 2, \ldots$

Angular momentum is therefore a quantity that is always of size $[J(J+1)]^{\frac{1}{2}}$ when measured in units of $\hbar$. This turns out to be a general result in quantum mechanics. If we define a vector, $\underline{\mathcal{J}}$, which represents the angular momentum, the size of $\underline{\mathcal{J}}$ is always given by

$$|\underline{\mathcal{J}}| = \mathcal{J} = [J(J+1)]^{\frac{1}{2}}\hbar$$

The general angular momentum quantum number, J, is limited, according to circumstances, to *integral* or *half-integral* values (for the diatomic molecule with the present restriction to $^1\Sigma$ states and nuclei with zero spin, the values are integral, and J is the rotational quantum number used earlier).

In a molecule some magnetic moment is always associated with the mechanical rotation giving rise to $\underline{\mathcal{J}}$ in the first place. In the presence of an external magnetic field, the vector $\underline{\mathcal{J}}$ accordingly experiences a torque and undergoes a Larmor precession around the direction of the magnetic field, $\mathcal{H}$. By the principle of *space* or *oriental* quantization, only those angles between $\underline{\mathcal{J}}$ and $\mathcal{H}$ are permitted for which the projection of $\underline{\mathcal{J}}$ on $\mathcal{H}$, say, $\mathcal{J}_{\mathcal{H}}$, satisfies the relation

$$\mathcal{J}_{\mathcal{H}} = M_{\mathcal{H}}\hbar \qquad M_{\mathcal{H}} = 0, \pm 1, \pm 2, \ldots, \pm J$$

Here $M_{\mathcal{H}}$ is the so-called *magnetic* quantum number and can be positive or negative, depending on whether $\mathcal{J}_{\mathcal{H}}$ is along or opposite $\mathcal{H}$. Thus $M_{\mathcal{H}}$ takes on a set of values, $2J+1$ in number,

$$+J, +(J-1), +(J-2), \ldots, -(J-1), -J$$

each with its own orientation and energy.

Possible orientations are shown in Fig. 18.8(a) for $\mathcal{J} = 0$, $\sqrt{2}\hbar$, and $\sqrt{6}\,\hbar$, the corresponding values of J being 0, 1, and 2, The projections, $\mathcal{J}_{\mathcal{H}}$, along the direction of the field are shown by the vertical vectors, and the values of $M_{\mathcal{H}}$ are indicated on the left. In Fig. 18.8(b) the corresponding energy levels are shown also, with the values of $M_{\mathcal{H}}$ on the left. In general, with J integral an *odd* number of levels is symmetrically spaced about the original no-field position. (The number of sublevels is always even when J is half-integral.) As the field goes to zero, these levels collapse on the no-field energy value to produce $(2J+1)$ levels of identical energy for the field-free system. These are the $(2J+1)$ independent solutions of the wave equation obtained in Sec. 18.6 for each value of J and therefore for each energy level. Since this result is typical of the general case, we find a $(2J+1)$-fold degeneracy for any atomic or molecular system with a total angular momentum

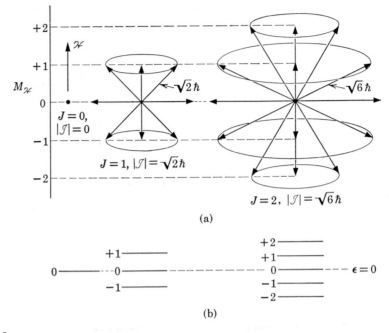

(a)

(b)

FIGURE **18.8**

quantum number of J and thus assign to the energy state involved a statistical weight, $g = 2J + 1$.

In atoms angular momentum is due to *nuclear* spins as well as to *orbital momentum* and *spin* of the external electrons, and all these factors must be examined in detail. In molecules in $^1\Sigma$ electronic states and with no nuclear spins, the J vector represents solely the mechanical momentum of the rotating masses; that is, it is of purely mechanical origin. In more complicated molecular states, this condition is, of course, not true.

In all cases we may write the general partition function as

$$Z = \Sigma e^{-\epsilon_i/kT} = \Sigma g_j e^{-\epsilon_j/kT}$$

where the first summation is over all the *accessible states*, one for each proper wave function, and the second is over all the permitted *energy states*, each with its proper statistical weight. The factoring of Z then carries through as in the earlier examples, as soon as ϵ_j is separated into independent terms.

18.9   Statistical Weights for Atoms

The interaction between the combined spins of the neutrons and protons in the nucleus and the electronic angular momentum vectors of the external electrons is so slight that the corresponding energies may be treated quite separately.

Since neutrons and protons each have the same spin vector, we assign to each nucleon a spin momentum vector, $\underline{s}$, where

$$\underline{s} = [s^{nu}(s^{nu} + 1)]^{\frac{1}{2}}\hbar \qquad s^{nu} = \frac{1}{2}$$

and s^{nu} is the *spin quantum number* of a single nucleon. These individual spin vectors then compound to give the total angular momentum vector, $\underline{\mathscr{I}}$, for the nucleus, where

$$\underline{\mathscr{I}} = [i(i + 1)]^{\frac{1}{2}}\hbar \qquad \begin{array}{l} i = 0, 1, 2, \ldots \\ \text{or } \frac{1}{2}, \frac{3}{2}, \frac{5}{2}, \ldots \end{array}$$

Here i is the *total nuclear quantum number* and is restricted to *integral* values for atoms of *even* mass number and *half*-integral values for atoms of *odd* mass number. The particular value of i for a given nucleus must be determined by experiment, although there is a tendency in most cases for the spins to cancel pairwise to produce low values of i. Values obtained from the study of hyperfine structure are given in Table 18.2, column 3. The corresponding nuclear statistical weights for the ground state of the nucleus, $g_0{}^{nu}$, as given by

$$g_0{}^{nu} = 2i + 1$$

are shown in column 4 and naturally vary from isotope to isotope of the same element.

In general, any partition function takes the form

$$g_0 + g_1 e^{-\theta_1/kT} + \cdots$$

In the case of nuclear states, as was pointed out earlier, the characteristic temperature of even the first excited nuclear states is usually of the order of millions of degrees. Thus for ordinary purposes the series breaks off after the first term, and

$$g^{nu} = g_0{}^{nu}$$

The behavior of the external electrons is described in terms of an orbital momentum vector, $\underline{\mathscr{L}}$, and an electronic spin vector, $\underline{\mathscr{I}}$, each measured in terms of $\hbar$, as before. In this case

$$\mathscr{L} = [L(L + 1)]^{\frac{1}{2}}\hbar \qquad L = 0, 1, 2, 3, \ldots$$
$$\text{and} \qquad \mathscr{I} = [S(S + 1)]^{\frac{1}{2}}\hbar \qquad S = 0, 1, 2, 3, \ldots \text{ or } \frac{1}{2}, \frac{3}{2}, \frac{5}{2}, \ldots$$

L and S being the *orbital* and *spin* quantum numbers for the atom. Of course, $\mathscr{I}$ and S may be written $\mathscr{I}^{el}$ and S^{el} to avoid confusion, but the superscripts are omitted here for simplicity. The electronic states of atoms are classified according to the L values, which largely determine the system's energy. In the electronic transitions giving rise to optical spectra, the lines produced by transitions from a succession of states of the *same* L value constitute an optical series. Thus the *sharp* series originates in states with $L = 0$, the *principal*

TABLE **18.2**

Nuclear and Electronic Data for a Few Atomic Species

Element	Isotope	Nuclear quantum number, i	Nuclear stat wt, g_0^{nu}	Ground electronic state	Electronic stat wt, g_0^{el}	Θ^{el} for excited multiplet level, °K
Hydrogen	H^1	$\frac{1}{2}$	2	^2S	2	
	H^2 (D)	1	3	^2S	2	
	H^3 (T)	$\frac{1}{2}$	2	^2S	2	
Helium	He^3	$\frac{1}{2}$	2	^1S	1	
	He^4	0	1	^1S	1	
Lithium	Li^6	1	3	^2S	2	
	Li^7	$\frac{3}{2}$	4	^2S	2	
Carbon	C^{12}	0	1	$^3P_0$	1	
				$^3P_1$	3	236
				$^3P_2$	5	627
Nitrogen	N^{14}	1	3	^4S	4	
Oxygen	O^{16}	0	1	$^3P_2$	5	
				$^3P_1$	3	228
				$^3P_0$	1	326
Chlorine	Cl^{35}	$\frac{3}{2}$	4	$^2P_{3/2}$	4	
				$^2P_{1/2}$	2	1299
Mercury	Hg^{199}	$\frac{1}{2}$	2	^1S	1	
	Hg^{201}	$\frac{3}{2}$	4	^1S	1	
	Hg^{198}	0	1	^1S	1	
	Hg^{200}	0	1	^1S	1	
	Hg^{202}	0	1	^1S	1	
	Hg^{204}	0	1	^1S	1	

series in states with $L = 1$, the *diffuse* series in states with $L = 2$, etc. Historically these states were designated by the initial letters of their names, and we accordingly have the following spectroscopic designations:

$$L \text{ value} \qquad 0\ 1\ 2\ 3\ 4\ \dots$$
$$\text{Electronic state} \qquad S\ P\ D\ F\ G\ \dots$$

If no electronic spin is present,

$$\mathcal{L} = \mathcal{J}$$
and
$$L = j$$

j being the total quantum number for the state (the lower-case letter being used for atoms and the capital for molecules). In this case the electronic states are so-called *singlet* states, written ^1S, ^1P, ^1D, etc., according to the value of L. Since for singlet states $j = L$, the electronic statistical weights are given by the odd integers

$$g^{el} = 2j + 1 = 2L + 1$$

When spin is not zero, the vectors $\mathcal{L}$ and $\mathcal{S}$ combine to form the total angular momentum vector, $\mathcal{J}$, around which the two precess. In Fig. 18.9 the magnitudes of these three vectors are indicated in terms of the orbital quantum number, L, the spin quantum number, S, and the total angular momentum vector, j.

The angles that $\mathcal{L}$ and $\mathcal{S}$ bear to $\mathcal{J}$ must be chosen so that with L and S integral, j is also integral (or when S is half-integral, j is also half-integral). See Problem 18.3. Thus with $S = \frac{1}{2}$, j can take on only two values, $j_1 = \frac{3}{2}$ and $j_2 = \frac{1}{2}$. This situation produces a *doublet* state, and according to the value of L, we have ^2S, ^2P, ^2D, etc., states.

The ^2S state is doubly degenerate, and for all such states $g_0 = 2$. With ^2P states the two spin orientations are energetically close but distinct, and the members of the doublet are indicated as $^2P_{3/2}$ and $^2P_{1/2}$, the subscripts indicating the value of j and hence fixing the statistical weights of these states as 4 and 2, respectively.

In a similar way the behavior of more complicated states may be predicted. In general, the spectroscopic multiplicity of a level of given L and S is fixed by the number of different j values that can be produced, that is,

$$|j| + |S|, \ |j| + (|S| - 1), \ \ldots, \ |j| - |S|$$

a total of $2S + 1$. This fixes the upper left prefix before the letter symbol S, P, etc. Each of these $(2S + 1)$ states has its own statistical weight of $2j + 1$. The results for singlet, doublet, and triplet electronic states are collected in Table 18.3 and given in the next to last column of Table 18.2 for the ground states of the elements of that table. It is to be noted that whereas g^{nu} varies from isotope to isotope of the same element, g^{el} does not.

The electronic partition function for a gas now becomes

$$Z^{el} = g_0{}^{el} + g_1{}^{el}e^{-\theta_1{}^{el}/T} + \cdots$$

In general, the first excited electronic states of atoms have such large values of θ^{el} that the second and higher terms are quite negligible except in hot plasmas and the like, where temperatures of 50,000 to 100,000°K or so may be expected. The notable exception occurs when the ground electronic state is a narrow

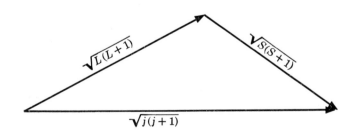

FIGURE **18.9**

TABLE **18.3**

Statistical Weights for Electronic States of Atoms

Multi-plicity, $2S+1$	L = 0			L = 1			L = 2			L = 3		
	Symbol	j	g^{el}	Symbol	j	g^{el}	Symbol	j	g^{el}	Symbol	j	g^{el}
Singlet $S=0$	^1S	0	1	^1P	1	3	^1D	2	5	^1F	3	7
Doublet $S=\frac{1}{2}$	^2S	$\frac{1}{2}$	2	^2P	$\frac{3}{2}$	4		$\frac{5}{2}$	6		$\frac{7}{2}$	8
					$\frac{1}{2}$	2	^2D	$\frac{3}{2}$	4	^2F	$\frac{5}{2}$	6
Triplet $S=1$	^3S	1	3	^3P	2	5		3	7		4	9
					1	3	^3D	2	5	^3F	3	7
					0	1		1	3		2	5

multiplet, and then Θ^{el} may be relatively small. (See the last column of Table 18.2.) In such cases the excited electronic levels should make sizable contributions to Z^{el} and hence to the free energy and entropy of the atomic gas. Unfortunately no thermal data are available for the atomic gases carbon, oxygen, and chlorine. The first element is refractory, and the other two exist normally as stable diatomic molecules.

For the monatomic gases, for which only the ground electronic states need be considered, the nuclear and electronic partition functions take the form

$$Z^{nu}Z^{el} = g_0{}^{nu}g_0{}^{el}$$

All the functions involving $\ln Z$ accordingly acquire an extra term containing

$$\ln g_0{}^{nu}g_0{}^{el}$$

whereas U and C_V are unaffected.

The vapor pressure constant for monatomic vapors is of the form

$$i_p = \frac{S_{0Tp}^G - S_0{}'''}{R} - \frac{5}{2}$$

From the argument of Sec. 17.15, the *nuclear* weight appears in both S_{0Tp}^G and $S_0{}'''$ and therefore cancels. As long as the electronic state is the same for the vapor and the solid, the same condition holds for the *electronic* weight. This seems to be true for ^1S states of atoms, thus accounting for the agreement of observations with the simpler treatment of Sec. 17.2, where these effects were assumed absent. It also holds for diatomic molecules in $^1\Sigma$ states, as the results of Table 17.4 indicate.

A similar argument applies to the presence in a substance of the natural mixture of isotopes. Thus suppose that a monatomic material consists of x

parts of isotope 1 with nuclear weight $g_1{}^{nu}$ and $(1 - x)$ parts of isotope 2 with nuclear weight $g_2{}^{nu}$. For comparison with a pure isotopic sample of no nuclear degeneracy (and therefore $g^{nu} = 1$), we have to add to the molar extropy an extra term of the form

$$x N_0 k \ln g_1{}^{nu} + (1 - x) N_0 k \ln g_2{}^{nu} = k \ln (g_1{}^{nu})^x (g_2{}^{nu})^{1-x}$$

The addition of a term of exactly the same form to the entropy expression of the solid is required, and no net change in i_p is expected. For this reason entropy contributions due to the presence of more than one isotope are omitted in the general formulas.

18.10   Statistical Weights of Diatomic Molecular States

In an atom, a valence electron moves in an electric field due to the core of the atom, a field in general with *spherical* symmetry. In the case of a diatomic molecule, the situation is similar except that now the core is the *molecular core* with a pronounced *axial* symmetry around the internuclear axis. Let $\mathcal{L}$, as in the atomic case, represent the orbital angular momentum of the valence electrons of the molecule of magnitude $[L(L + 1)]^{1/2} \hbar$. This vector precesses rapidly about the nuclear axis, and its projection on this axis, the vector $\underline{\Lambda}$ (see Fig. 18.10), is quantized and, in units of $\hbar$, Λ can assume only integral values. Thus

$$\underline{\Lambda} = \Lambda \hbar \qquad \Lambda = 0, 1, 2, 3, \ldots$$

where Λ is the *electronic quantum* number for the molecule and is the nearest equivalent to L in the atom. Molecular states are classified by their Λ values

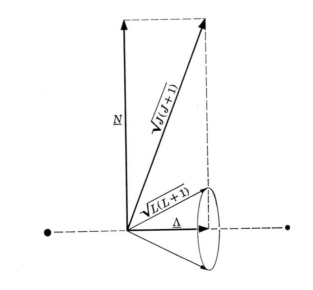

FIGURE **18.10**

according to the scheme

Λ value   0 1 2 3 · · ·

Molecular state   Σ Π Δ Φ · · ·

the Greek letters Σ, Π, Δ, Φ, etc., being employed where the Latin letters S, P, D, and F were used for the atomic case.

The vector $\underline{\Lambda}$ combines with a vector $\underline{N}$ (non-quantized in general), representing the mechanical momentum of the rotating nuclei, to give the total angular momentum, $\underline{\mathcal{J}}$, where

$$\underline{\mathcal{J}} = [J(J + 1)]^{\frac{1}{2}}\hbar \qquad J = 0, 1, 2, 3, \ldots$$

For Σ states, since $\Lambda = 0$, J is equal to N, and the result is the simple case of Chap. 17, in which the total angular momentum arises from the mechanical rotation of the nuclei.

In the absence of spins the molecular electronic states are single and are designated, as were the singlet atomic states, by $^1\Sigma$, $^1\Pi$, $^1\Delta$, etc. The $^1\Sigma$ state is the simplest type, with no electronic spin and no electronic angular momentum, and this is the state of the simple rotor discussed in Chaps. 16 and 17.

Once mechanical rotation of the molecule sets in, all electronic states with $\Lambda = 1$ or higher undergo a doubling known as Λ-*type doubling*. Since this doubling is very small on an energy scale, it is tantamount to rendering all such states doubly degenerate and producing therefore an electronic statistical weight of two. Thus $g^{\text{el}} = 1$ for $^1\Sigma$ states and 2 for $^1\Pi$, $^1\Delta$, $^1\Phi$, etc., states.[4]

When electronic spin is present, the spins of the individual extracore electrons couple together as in the atoms to give an $\underline{\mathcal{S}}$ vector, which in turn produces multiple electronic levels. Although discussion of the many varieties of possible coupling is beyond the present scope, we shall consider an important and common one. The magnetic moment associated with $\underline{\Lambda}$ causes the $\underline{\mathcal{S}}$ vector to precess around the nuclear axis also to give a projection Σ (the multiple uses of this symbol are unfortunate), as in Fig. 18.11. $\underline{\Lambda}$ and $\underline{\Sigma}$ then add to give a total electronic vector, $\underline{\Omega}$, which combines with the vector $\underline{N}$ to give $\underline{\mathcal{J}}$ as before. Thus when $S = \frac{1}{2}$, we may have $\Sigma = +\frac{1}{2}$ or $-\frac{1}{2}$, depending on whether $\underline{\Sigma}$ is along or antiparallel to $\underline{\Lambda}$. The result is an electronic doublet, with $S = 1$ a triple state, etc. When $\Lambda = 0$, the $(2S + 1)$ spin multiplet levels are degenerate (at least for ordinary temperatures), and $g^{\text{el}} = 2S + 1$, just as in the atomic case. When $\Lambda \neq 0$, the corresponding multiplet levels are significantly different in energy, and each must be assigned a g^{el} value of 2, owing to Λ-type doubling.

As an example, consider a case with $L = 1$, $\underline{\mathcal{L}} = [1(1 + 1)]^{\frac{1}{2}}\hbar = \sqrt{2}\,\hbar$, and the quantized projection of $\underline{\mathcal{L}}$ on the axis giving $\Lambda = 1$. With $S = \frac{1}{2}$, we have $^2\Pi$ states with $\Lambda + |\Sigma| = \Omega_1 = \frac{3}{2}$ and $\Lambda - |\Sigma| = \Omega_2 = \frac{1}{2}$. The two

---

[4] This doubling is a strictly nonclassical effect although for heteronuclear molecules it is associated with the two possible orientations of $\underline{\Lambda}$ with respect to the electric field along the axis.

FIGURE **18.11**

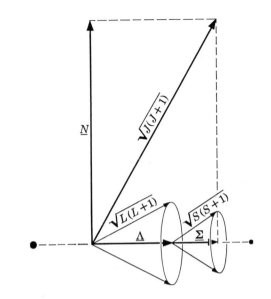

doublet levels are written $^2\Pi_{3/2}$ and $^2\Pi_{1/2}$ in close analogy with the atomic case. Each rotational state of each of these electronic levels then has $g^{el} = 2$, owing to Λ-type doubling.

The rotational term value, $F(J)$, for a molecule with Λ or Σ (or both) different from zero is of the form

$$F(J) = BN^2 + \cdots = B[J(J+1) + S(S+1) - \Sigma^2 - \Omega^2] + \cdots$$
$$= BJ(J+1) + B[S(S+1) - \Sigma^2 - \Omega^2] + \cdots$$

where the difference $S(S+1) - \Sigma^2$ measures the components of $[S(S+1)]^{1/2}$ along the axis of N. The total term value for the molecule may then be written

$$T_e + A\Lambda\Sigma + B[S(S-1) - \Sigma^2 - \Omega^2] + G(v) + BJ(J+1) + \cdots \quad \textbf{(18.41)}$$

where T_e is the electronic term value, the same for all substates of an electronic multiplet, and $A\Lambda\Sigma$ arises from the coupling between $\underline{\Lambda}$ and $\underline{\Sigma}$. Thus, for a given electronic substate, the first three terms in Eq. 18.41 represent a *constant* to which are added the ordinary vibrational and rotational terms used for the $^1\Sigma$ states (for which $\Lambda = \Sigma = 0$) discussed in Chap. 17.

18.11   Electronic Heat Capacities

When a molecule has a low-lying excited electronic state, it is no longer legitimate to regard Z^{el} as a constant. We must write

$$Z^{el} = g_0{}^{el} + g_1{}^{el}e^{-\theta_1{}^{el}/T} + g_2{}^{el}e^{-\theta_2{}^{el}/T} + \cdots \quad \textbf{(18.42)}$$

or, for the case of a single such level,

$$Z^{el} = g_0{}^{el} + g_1{}^{el}e^{-\theta_1{}^{el}/T} \quad \textbf{(18.43)}$$

Thus, for temperatures where $T \approx \Theta^{\text{el}}$ and rotation is classical, we have

$$Z = \frac{V}{h^3} (2\pi m'kT)^{3/2} \frac{8\pi^2 IkT}{h^2} (g_0 + g_1 e^{-\Theta_1^{\text{el}}/T})$$

or

$$Z = \text{constant } VT^{5/2} Z^{\text{el}}$$

Since

$$C_V = \left(\frac{\partial U}{\partial T}\right)_V = Nk \left[\frac{\partial}{\partial T} \left(T^2 \frac{\partial \ln Z}{\partial T}\right)\right]_V$$

for a mole

$$C_V = \frac{5}{2}R + C_V{}^{\text{el}}$$

where

$$C_V{}^{\text{el}} = R \left[\frac{\partial}{\partial T} \left(T^2 \frac{\partial \ln Z^{\text{el}}}{\partial T}\right)\right]_V \tag{18.44}$$

or

$$C_V{}^{\text{el}} = \frac{Nkg_0 g_1 \left(\dfrac{\Theta^{\text{el}}}{T}\right)^2}{(g_0 e^{\Theta^{\text{el}}/2T} + g_1 e^{-\Theta^{\text{el}}/2T})^2} \tag{18.45}$$

The only two gases in Table 17.2 with which observable contributions to C_V are to be expected are NO and O_2.

In the case of NO, the ground state is a $^2\Pi_{1/2}$ state with the $^2\Pi_{3/2}$ member of the doublet at a height that gives $\Theta^{\text{el}} = 178°K$. Since each member of the doublet state must show Λ-type doubling, $g_0 = g_1 = 2$, and with $\Theta^{\text{el}} = \Theta$, we have for a mole

$$\frac{C_V}{R} = \frac{5}{2} + \frac{\left(\dfrac{\Theta}{T}\right)^2}{(e^{\Theta/2T} + e^{-\Theta/2T})^2} = \frac{5}{2} + \frac{\left(\dfrac{\Theta}{2T}\right)^2}{\cosh^2 \dfrac{\Theta}{2T}} \tag{18.46}$$

This has been plotted as the solid curve in Fig. 18.12, along with the experimental data of Eucken and d'Or,[5] over the temperature range 120 to 180°K. Without this effect the dashed line at $C_V/R = 2.5$ would represent the total heat capacity.

In the case of the O_2 molecule, the ground state is a $^3\Sigma$ state ($g_0 = 3$), and the next excited state is a $^1\Delta$ state ($g_1 = 2$). Since for this state $\Theta^{\text{el}} = 11,300°K$, high temperatures are involved, and the vibrational partition function,

$$Z^{\text{vib}} = (1 - e^{-u})^{-1}$$

must be included. Thus for this molecule

$$Z = \frac{V(2\pi mkT)^{3/2}}{h^3} \frac{8\pi^2 I_0 kT}{h^2} \frac{1}{1 - e^{-u}} (3 + 2e^{-\Theta/T}) \tag{18.47}$$

where $u = hc\omega/kT$.

---

[5] Eucken and d'Or, *Nachr. Ges. Wiss. Göttingen, Math.-physik. Kl.*, **1932**, 107.

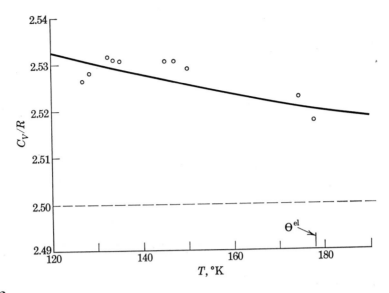

FIGURE **18.12**

High-temperature data on the heat capacity of O_2 have been obtained by exploding ozone in a bomb calorimeter (see Sec. 6.4), and hence the results give not C_V but $\overline{C_V}$ averaged between 300°K and T. To find this average, we must obtain the internal energy. Since

$$U_T - U_{T_0} = \int_{T_0}^{T} C_V \, dT = \overline{C_V}(T - T_0)$$

therefore
$$\overline{C_V} = \frac{U_T - U_{T_0}}{T - T_0} = \frac{R}{T - T_0}\left(T^2 \frac{\partial \ln Z}{\partial T}\right)_{T_0}^{T}$$

The dotted curve in Fig. 18.13 is calculated in this way from the partition function given in Eq. 18.47, the electronic contributions being *omitted*. The next higher curve (dashed) includes the effect of stretching and anharmonicity of the vibration. To obtain this correction, it is necessary to sum the partition function with a more exact expression for the energies of vibration and rotation including the interaction between the two. For this case Mayer and Mayer have shown that we can write the combined partition function,

$$Z^{\text{vib}} Z^{\text{rot}} Z^{\text{corr}}$$

where the first two factors are the vibrational and rotational partition functions as obtained before and Z^{corr} is a correction factor that includes the effect of stretching and anharmonicity (see Problem 18.4). The combined partition function has been calculated, and the correction added to the dotted curve to give the dashed curve. Finally the electronic factor has been added to give the solid line. The observed values of Lewis and Von Elbe are plotted and are seen

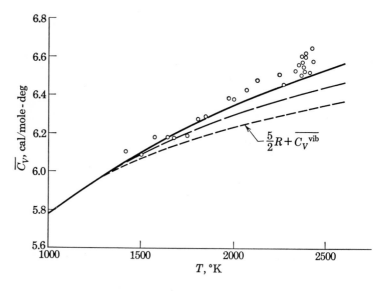

FIGURE **18.13**

to lie somewhat above the theoretical curve at the high-temperature end, indicating that there may well be some other factors that have been neglected.[6]

The over-all effect of a single electronic level is shown in Fig. 18.14, where C_V^{el}/R is plotted versus T/Θ^{el} for the two cases $g_1/g_0 = 1\,(NO)$ and $g_1/g_0 = \frac{2}{3}\,(O_2)$. The maximum contribution to C_V^{el} is made in each case around $T = 0.4\Theta^{el}$ and falls to 1% of R by the time $T = 5\Theta^{el}$ has been reached. Thus at high enough temperatures the effect of a single electronic level on C_V is

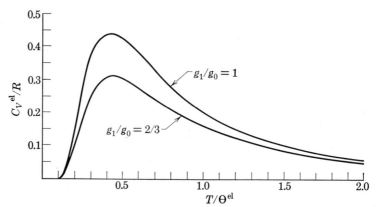

FIGURE **18.14**

[6] Lewis and Von Elbe, *J. Am. Chem. Soc.,* **55,** 511 (1933). See also Johnson and Walker, *J. Am. Chem. Soc.,* **57,** 682 (1935).

negligible. The high-temperature ends of the C_V^{el} curves drop off rather slowly with rising temperature. Returning to Eq. 18.45, we see that as the temperature rises, the exponentials in the denominator eventually reduce to unity, where the asymptotic expression results.

$$C_V^{el} = R \frac{g_0 g_1}{(g_0 + g_1)^2} \left(\frac{\Theta^{el}}{T}\right)^2 = \frac{\text{constant}}{T^2} \qquad (18.48)$$

This is precisely the way in which the total heat capacities of many paramagnetic salts behave at temperatures low enough for the lattice contribution to be negligible. Fig. 18.15 shows C_V^*/R versus $(1/T^*)^2$ for chromium methylamine alum between 4 and 1°K (where the differences between T^* and T are essentially negligible). The values are those given by Gardiner and Kurti.[7] Theoretically an isolated Cr^{+++} ion should be in a $^4F_{9/2}$ state, but the symmetry of the internal crystalline electric field suppresses orbital L values different from zero to produce a ^4S state in the crystal. This state is further split into a narrow Stark effect doublet with $g_0 = g_1 = 2$ and an equivalent temperature, $\Theta^{el} = 0.27°K$.[8] The data for C_V/R are plotted in Fig. 18.16 for temperatures below 0.4°K. The dashed curve has been drawn in from Eq. 18.45 and follows

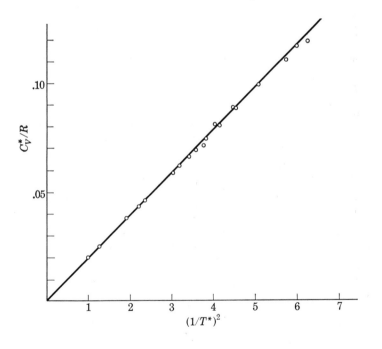

FIGURE **18.15**

[7] Gardiner and Kurti, *Proc. Roy. Soc. (London)*, **A223**, 543 (1954).

[8] In the normal Zeeman effect the levels are symmetric about the no-field position and with $S = \frac{3}{2}$ should have four substates with $M_{\mathcal{H}} = +\frac{3}{2}, +\frac{1}{2}, -\frac{1}{2}$, and $-\frac{3}{2}$. [See Fig. 18.8(b), where, since j is integral, the number of these states is odd.] In the Stark effect, however, states of $\pm M_{\mathcal{E}}$ have the *same* energy, and there are thus only two states, $\pm\frac{1}{2}$ and $\pm\frac{3}{2}$, each of statistical weight 2.

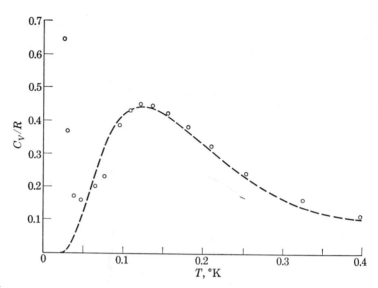

FIGURE **18.16**

the observations quite closely. The rapid rise in the heat capacity below 0.08°K indicates the effect of the interaction of the spins of neighboring ions on one another. This presumably attains a maximum value and then descends to zero at very much lower temperatures.[9]

In any event, when more than two Stark levels are produced and even in the presence of other complications, the linear variation of C_V/R with $1/T^2$ seems to be generally observed (see Problem 18.5).

18.12   Formation of a Molecule from Atoms

Before examining the total wave function for a diatomic molecule, let us look at the formation of the molecule out of two separate atoms. For convenience take the simplest example, the formation of the hydrogen molecule, H_2, from two separate hydrogen atoms. In this case the two valence electrons of the individual atoms become the valence electrons of the united molecule. Although the two nuclei remain distinct, we might expect similarities between the hydrogen molecule and the so-called "united atom" with which H_2 is isoelectronic, that is, helium. Each in fact has a set of singlet electronic states (with the electron spins opposed) and a set of triplet states (with the spins parallel). Furthermore, each exhibits a pattern of levels similar to that of the other, although the actual spacings are quite different. In Fig. 18.17 a few of the lowest singlet levels for each are shown. For He the ground state is a ^1S followed by another ^1S and a somewhat higher ^1P level. Similarly, the H_2

[9] Van Vleck, *J. Chem. Phys.*, **5**, 320 (1937) (development of theory); and Hebb and Purcell *J. Chem. Phys.*, **5**, 338 (1937) (detailed applications of theory).

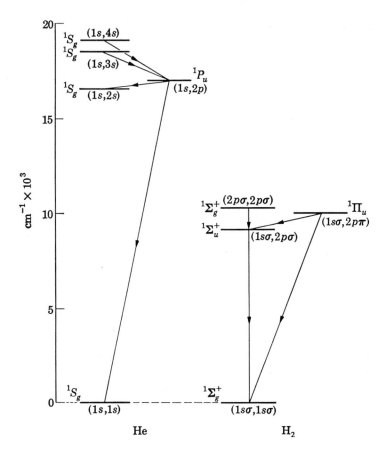

FIGURE **18.17**

molecule has a $^1\Sigma$ ground state followed by another $^1\Sigma$ and a slightly higher $^1\Pi$ level.

Now imagine two isolated H atoms, each in its normal ground state. This is a ^2S state with the total quantum number, $n, = 1$ (first Bohr orbit). Each atom then has an electron in the lowest possible orbit with, owing to the peculiar requirements of quantum mechanics, *no* angular momentum. Such an electron with $n = 1$ and $l = 0$ is described as a "$1s$ electron" (with lower-case letters to describe the electronic state of the individual electron; $L = l = 0$, thus producing an S state). Since $l = 0$ for each electron, as the atoms unite to form H_2, the projection on the molecular axis must be zero for each electron. Such electrons with $\Lambda = \lambda = 0$ are sigma-state electrons, designated as $1s\sigma$.[10]

---

[10] The assignment of such definite "orbital" properties to the extracore electrons in molecules is not really justified except in the case of small nuclear separations. It does, however, aid in a qualitative understanding of the way in which molecular states arise. For a general treatment see G. Herzberg, *Molecular Spectra and Molecular Structure*, 2nd ed., Van Nostrand, New York, Vol. I, 1950, Chap. VI.

For the molecule as a whole $\Lambda = 0$, and a Σ state results. If the electronic spins are opposed, the total spin is zero, and the state is a $^1\Sigma$ one. The case of the electronic spins being parallel is ruled out by the Pauli exclusion principle, which requires that *no two electrons may have the same values for all of the four quantum numbers:* n (the total quantum number), l (the angular momentum quantum number), λ (the projection of l on the nuclear axis), and m_S (the projection of the electronic spin on the axis, this being $\pm\frac{1}{2}$ for a single electron).

All electronic states of atoms and of homonuclear molecules are classified spectroscopically according to whether the sum of the l values of the valence electrons is an *even* or an *odd* number. Since even and odd are used in so many different senses, it has been agreed to give these states their German names, *gerade* and *ungerade*, and to indicate them by the subscripts g and u. Thus the ^1S states of He, with $l = 0$ for each electron, are *gerade*, and the ^1P state with $l = 0$ and $l = 1$ (that is, a $1s$ and a $2p$ electron) becomes *ungerade*. These atomic states are accordingly shown as ^1S_g and ^1P_u in Fig. 18.17, with the designation of the electronic configurations in parentheses. Spectroscopically no transitions in atoms may occur except between *gerade* and *ungerade* states.

A further spectroscopic subdivision of all molecular states into so-called *positive* (or $+$) and *negative* (or $-$) states must be considered. This has no analog in the case of single atoms since it is concerned with rotation. Every rotational state (or substate) of a molecule is *positive* or *negative*, and no transitions (in the absence of external fields) are observed between states of the same sign. In the case of a Σ state, the symbol Σ^+ indicates that the rotational states with $J = 0, 2$, and 4 are $+$ and those with $J = 1, 3$, and 5 are $-$. (The $+$ and $-$ signs are reversed for Σ^- states.)

In Fig. 18.18 these relations are illustrated for a $^1\Sigma^+$, a $^1\Sigma^-$, and a $^1\Pi$ state. In Fig. 18.18(a), drawn for a $^1\Sigma^+ \to {}^1\Sigma^+$ electronic transition, the possible transitions are indicated by the lines connecting the upper levels (J') with the proper lower levels (J'') according to the selection rules

$$\Delta J = \pm 1, 0$$
$$+ \rightleftharpoons -$$

In Fig. 18.18(b) similar relations are shown for a $^1\Pi \to {}^1\Sigma^-$ electronic transition,

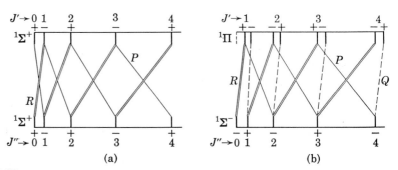

FIGURE **18.18**

and now the upper levels are doubled owing to Λ-type doubling. The solid lines indicate P branches ($\Delta J = J' - J'' = -1$), the double lines R branches ($\Delta J = J' - J'' = +1$), and the dotted lines the so-called Q branches ($\Delta J = 0$). Q branches are allowed for the $^1\Pi \rightarrow {}^1\Sigma^-$ transition but not for the $^1\Sigma^+ \rightarrow {}^1\Sigma^+$ change.

Theoretically $+$ and $-$ states are distinguished by the behavior of the total wave function on the changing of the signs of all the coordinates (*electronic* and *nuclear*). This transformation, whereby x_i, y_i, and z_i are replaced by $-x_i$, $-y_i$, and $-z_i$ for each particle in the molecule, is known as *central inversion* and corresponds to the reflection of each particle once in each of three mutually perpendicular mirrors. These mirrors include one passing through the two nuclei and two passing through the center of mass of the molecule. When central inversion leaves the wave function unchanged in sign, the state is $+$, and when it reverses the sign, the state is $-$. The detailed wave function analysis is in agreement with the empirical designations from spectroscopy.

In the case of H_2 the two lower $^1\Sigma$ states in Fig. 18.17 are $^1\Sigma_g^+$ and $^1\Sigma_u^+$ (positive ground states being much more common in nature than negative ones; see Table 17.2). Whereas the $+$ and $-$ designation is important for both homonuclear and heteronuclear molecules, the gerade and ungerade classification applies only to the *former* group.

With these considerations in mind, we may now represent the formation of a H_2 molecule from two atoms as follows. The lowest state involves the combination of two atoms in ^2S states with $n = 1$ and $l = 0$. Thus

$$H[1s(^2S)] + H[1s(^2S)] \rightarrow H_2[(1s\sigma, 1s\sigma)^1\Sigma_u^+] \tag{18.49}$$

If one of the hydrogen atoms is excited to a ^2P state, there are three possibilities:

$$H[1s(^2S)] + H[2p(^2P)] \rightarrow \begin{cases} H_2[1s\sigma, 2p\pi(^1\Pi_u)] \\ \{H_2[1s\sigma, 2p\sigma(^3\Sigma_u^+)]\} \\ H_2[1s\sigma, 2p\sigma(^1\Sigma_u^+)] \end{cases}$$

In the lowest possibility the electron spins are *opposed* and cancel, producing a $^1\Sigma$ state. Since the sum of the l's is odd, the state is ungerade and turns out to have the combining properties of a $+$ state. It is therefore written as $^1\Sigma_u^+$. In the middle possibility the spins are parallel, and the state is a $^3\Sigma_u^+$, but since it is unstable, it is written in braces. In the upper possibility the $2p$ electron has a projection giving $\lambda = 1 = \Lambda$, and the state is a $^1\Pi_u$. (This lies very close to the upper $^1\Sigma_g^+$ state, the separation in Fig. 18.17 being exaggerated for clarity.) Thus the $^1\Sigma_u^+$ and $^1\Pi_u$ molecular states are really variations of the ^1P_u state for the united atom. If each of the electrons is excited to the $2p$ level, another $^1\Sigma_g^+$ state is produced with a $2p\sigma, 2p\sigma$ electronic configuration, etc.

18.13   Nuclear Symmetry and Nuclear Weights

The total wave functions for a homonuclear molecule must satisfy certain over-all symmetry requirements not met with in the case of a heteronuclear molecule.

Consider first a heteronuclear molecule of the type AB. Suppose that the nucleus of atom A has a nuclear spin quantum number $S_A{}^{nu}$, whereas for atom B this is $S_B{}^{nu}$. Then, as we have come to expect, there is degeneracy in each nuclear energy level. The nuclear ground state of A has $g_A{}^{nu}$ oriental wave functions corresponding to a single energy, where

$$g_A{}^{nu} = g_A = 2S_A{}^{nu} + 1$$

and likewise for atom B,

$$g_B{}^{nu} = g_B = 2S_B{}^{nu} + 1$$

Once the molecule is formed, the nuclear axis provides a unique direction with respect to which the nuclear spin vectors orient themselves. For each of the g_A orientations of the spins of atom A, there is a wave function of the form $\psi(A)$ that depends on the coordinates of nucleus A. Thus we have a set

$$\psi_1(A), \psi_2(A), \ldots, \psi_{g_A}(A)$$

and likewise another set

$$\psi'_1(B), \psi'_2(B), \ldots, \psi'_{g_B}(B)$$

each depending on the coordinates of the other nucleus.

The possible nuclear states of the molecule are now described in terms of product functions of the type

$$\psi_i(A)\psi'_j(B)$$

We can form exactly $g_A g_B$ different combinations of this type. Since these wave functions all correspond to the same energy, that of the ground state, this energy state is degenerate with a degeneracy

$$g_{AB}{}^{nu} = g_A g_B$$

Thus for a *heteronuclear* molecule the nuclear partition function becomes simply

$$\boxed{Z^{nu}_{\text{hetero}} = g_A g_B}$$

For *homonuclear* molecules (of type AA)

$$g_A = g_B = g$$

and there are g^2 wave functions. These g^2 functions must be divided into two classes, those *symmetric* in the coordinates of the nuclei and those *antisymmetric* in these coordinates. If we consider a product function of the type used previously,

$$\psi_i(A)\psi_j(B)$$

interchange of the nuclei cannot alter the sign of the product since A and B are identical. This therefore constitutes a *symmetric* function in the nuclei. Since order is immaterial, there can be only g functions of this type,

$$\psi_1(A)\psi_2(B), \ \psi_1(A)\psi_3(B), \ . \ . \ .$$

To obtain the others required, we resort to combinations of the type

$$\psi_i(A)\psi_j(B) + \psi_j(A)\psi_i(B)$$

which must likewise be *symmetric* in the nuclei. There are $\frac{1}{2}g(g-1)$ of this type or, all told,

$$\frac{1}{2}g(g-1) + g = \frac{1}{2}g(g+1)$$

wave functions of *symmetric* type. The remaining ones must be *antisymmetric* and may be written

$$\psi_i(A)\psi_j(B) - \psi_j(A)\psi_i(B)$$

There are $\frac{1}{2}g(g-1)$ of this group, making up the total of g^2 required.

If the nucleus has no spin, $g = 1$, there is only *one* wave function, and this one must be *symmetric* in the nuclei. Nuclear states antisymmetric in the nuclei would have a statistical weight of zero and be *altogether forbidden*.

18.14 $^1\Sigma$ States of Homonuclear Molecules

Let us now examine the properties of the total wave function of a homonuclear molecule. For simplicity the discussion is confined to $^1\Sigma$ states. The general results of quantum mechanics show that for homonuclear molecules of *odd* mass the total wave function is *antisymmetric* and for those of *even* mass the total wave function is *symmetric*.

In general, the total wave function may be written as a product of transla- tory, vibration, rotational, electronic, and nuclear wave functions; that is,

$$\psi = \psi^{\text{trn}}\psi^{\text{vib}}\psi^{\text{rot}}\psi^{\text{el}}\psi^{\text{nu}}$$

Of these the translatory wave function is independent of the relative nuclear positions and must therefore be *symmetric*. We saw in Sec. 18.5 that the vibra- tional wave functions were symmetric for $v = 0, 2, 4$ and antisymmetric for $v = 1, 3, 5$. Since we are interested in temperatures at which little vibration is excited, we may take $v = 0$ and therefore ψ^{vib} as symmetric. Since H_2 and D_2 are the only homonuclear molecules for which rotation has not become classical at or below room temperature, we are chiefly concerned with $^1\Sigma_g^+$ states.

Consider for a moment the general electronic wave function. One of the facts to emerge from the study of molecular wave functions is that gerade states (that is, all states in which the sum of the l's of the valence electrons is 0, 2, 4, . . .) have wave functions *symmetric* in the coordinates of the electrons. Thus ψ^{el} is symmetric in the electronic coordinates for all Σ_g states. Now suppose that central inversion of all particle coordinates leaves ψ^{el} unaltered in sign. Then the state is a *positive* one and becomes a $^1\Sigma_g^+$. If we invert the electrons through the origin and follow this inversion with central inversion for *all* particles, the electrons are returned to their original positions, and *only the nuclei have been interchanged*. Since neither process produces a sign change, the Σ_g^+ state is *symmetric in the coordinates of the nuclei*. In the same way a Σ_u^- state must also be *symmetric* in the nuclear coordinates, since these two inversions restore the wave function to its original sign with only the nuclei interchanged. By the same reasoning Σ_g^- and Σ_u^+ states must be *antisymmetric* in the nuclear coordinates.

We now write the total nuclear wave function as a product,

$$\psi^{\mathrm{nu}} = \psi^{\mathrm{nc}}\beta$$

where ψ^{nc} depends only on the nuclear coordinates and β is the nuclear spin wave function. The β function determines the nuclear weight, which is $\frac{1}{2}g(g+1)$ when β is *symmetric* and $\frac{1}{2}g(g-1)$ when β is *antisymmetric* (here $g_A = g$ and is the nuclear weight of a single atom). We can assemble these results in tabular form, as follows:

Electronic state	ψ^{el}	ψ^{nc}	β	Nuclear weight
Σ_g^+	s	s		
Σ_g^-	s	a	s	$\frac{1}{2}g(g+1)$
			or	
Σ_u^+	a	a	a	$\frac{1}{2}g(g-1)$
Σ_u^-	a	s		

With the vibratory and translatory factors eliminated, the total wave function symmetry is now fixed by the product

$$\psi^{\mathrm{el}}\psi^{\mathrm{nc}}\beta\psi^{\mathrm{rot}}$$

This product must be symmetric for nuclei of *even* mass and antisymmetric for those of *odd* mass.

As an example, consider the case of the molecule H_z, for which $S^{\mathrm{nu}} = \frac{1}{2}$ and $g = 2$. Since the mass of each atom is odd, the product must be *antisymmetric*. The ground state of H_z is a $^1\Sigma_g^+$ state (see Table 17.2). Thus ψ^{el} and ψ^{nc} are both symmetric. We therefore have two possibilities for ψ^{total}, which must be antisymmetric.

$$\underset{s\ \ \ s\ \ \ s\ \ \ a}{\psi^{\mathrm{el}}\psi^{\mathrm{nc}}\beta\psi^{\mathrm{rot}}} \quad \text{or} \quad \underset{s\ \ \ s\ \ \ a\ \ \ s}{\psi^{\mathrm{el}}\psi^{\mathrm{nc}}\beta\psi^{\mathrm{rot}}}$$

The first, with the antisymmetric rotation function, is required (with $J = 1$, 3, 5, . . .) when β is symmetric with a nuclear weight of $\frac{1}{2}g(g + 1) = 3$. The second applies to $J = 0, 2, 4, \ldots$, for which the weight must be $\frac{1}{2}g(g - 1) = 1$. Thus the rotational levels must *alternate* in intensity, the odd rotational levels having three times the intensity of the even ones.

Since most of the homonuclear molecules for which data are available have nuclei of even mass, Table 18.4 has been prepared for this case.

To see the bearing of this argument on the rotational and nuclear partition functions, we first adopt the abbreviations

$$Z_{\mathrm{odd}}^{\mathrm{rot}} = \sum_{J=1,\ldots} (2J + 1)e^{-\sigma J(J+1)}$$

and

$$Z_{\mathrm{even}}^{\mathrm{rot}} = \sum_{J=0,\ldots} (2J + 1)e^{-\sigma J(J+1)}$$

Then by definition the sum over all J values is just the sum of these two terms, that is, the ordinary rotational partition function,

$$Z^{\mathrm{rot}} = \sum_{J=0,1,\ldots} (2J + 1)e^{-\sigma J(J+1)} = Z_{\mathrm{odd}}^{\mathrm{rot}} + Z_{\mathrm{even}}^{\mathrm{rot}}$$

The results for the three important cases—*heteronuclear* molecules of type AB; *homonuclear* molecules of type AA, A odd; and *homonuclear* molecules of type AA, A even—may now be written down.

TABLE **18.4**

Symmetry Requirements for Σ State Homonuclear Molecules of Even Mass*

Total wave function, ψ^{total}	Electronic state	Electronic function, ψ^{el}	Nuclear function		Rotational function, ψ^{rot}	Nuclear weight	J values
			ψ^{ne}	β (spin)			
s	Σ_g^+	s	s	s	s	$\frac{1}{2}g(g + 1)$	Even
				a	a	$\frac{1}{2}g(g - 1)$	Odd
s	Σ_g^-	s	a	s	a	$\frac{1}{2}g(g + 1)$	Odd
				a	s	$\frac{1}{2}g(g - 1)$	Even
s	Σ_u^+	a	a	s	s	$\frac{1}{2}g(g + 1)$	Even
				a	a	$\frac{1}{2}g(g - 1)$	Odd
s	Σ_u^-	a	s	s	a	$\frac{1}{2}g(g + 1)$	Odd
				a	s	$\frac{1}{2}g(g - 1)$	Even

* For vibrational states with $v = 0, 2, 4, \ldots$; s = symmetric, a = antisymmetric.

Hetero (type AB)

$$Z^{\text{nu+rot}} = g_A{}^{\text{nu}} g_B{}^{\text{nu}} Z^{\text{rot}}$$

Homo (A odd, Σ_g^+ or Σ_u^+; or A even, Σ_g^- or Σ_u^-)

$$Z^{\text{nu+rot}} = \tfrac{1}{2}g(g - 1)Z^{\text{rot}}_{\text{even}} + \tfrac{1}{2}g(g + 1)Z^{\text{rot}}_{\text{odd}} \qquad \textbf{(18.50)}$$

Homo (A even, Σ_g^+ or Σ_u^+; or A odd, Σ_g^- or Σ_u^-)

$$Z^{\text{nu+rot}} = \tfrac{1}{2}g(g + 1)Z^{\text{rot}}_{\text{even}} + \tfrac{1}{2}g(g - 1)Z^{\text{rot}}_{\text{odd}} \qquad \textbf{(18.51)}$$

Since at high temperatures

$$Z^{\text{rot}}_{\text{odd}} = Z^{\text{rot}}_{\text{even}} = \tfrac{1}{2}Z^{\text{rot}}$$

these results reduce to a single equation for heteronuclear molecules and a single equation for homonuclear molecules.

Heteronuclear (high temperatures) $Z^{\text{nu+rot}} = g_A g_B Z^{\text{rot}}$ $\qquad \textbf{(18.52)}$
Homonuclear (high temperatures) $Z^{\text{nu+rot}} = \tfrac{1}{2}g^2 Z^{\text{rot}}$ $\qquad \textbf{(18.53)}$

Thus at sufficiently high temperatures the homonuclear molecule behaves like a heteronuclear one with only half the nuclear weight. This finding is in agreement with the classical use of the symmetry number, σ', in which $\sigma' = 1$ for the heteronuclear diatomic molecule and 2 for the homonuclear diatomic molecule. (See Eq. 17.53.)

18.15   Rotational Behavior of Homonuclear Molecules

One of the direct results of the preceding discussion is that the band spectra of homonuclear molecules should show alternating intensities of the lines in a branch. Thus we expect molecules in Σ_u^+ states, such as He_2, for which $S^{\text{nu}} = 0$ and $g_A{}^{\text{nu}} = g = 1$, to have rotational states with $J = 0, 3, 5, \ldots$ *missing* since these states have a statistical weight of zero. In other words, every other line in each branch should be *missing* entirely. (For O_2 and S_2, the state is a Σ_g^-, and the even rotational levels should be missing.) For H_2, $S^{\text{nu}} = \tfrac{1}{2}$, $g = 2$, and the ratio, g_s/g_a, of symmetric to antisymmetric rotational weights is

$$\frac{g_s}{g_a} = \frac{(g - 1)}{(g + 1)} = \frac{1}{3}$$

For N_2 (a $^1\Sigma_g^+$ state), with $S^{\text{nu}} = 1$ and $g = 3$,

$$\frac{g_s}{g_a} = \frac{4}{2} = \frac{2}{1}$$

A similar relation must hold for the rotational levels of D_2. In all these cases the band spectra reveal the expected intensity ratio. In fact, with the process reversed, observation of the intensity ratio provides one of the more direct methods of measuring nuclear spins.

Only in the case of H_2 and its isotopic variants can the rotational contribution to the heat capacity be observed directly. Since for H_2 $\Theta^{vib} = 6320°K$ and $\Theta^{rot} = 87.5°K$, measurements of C_V from low temperatures to room temperatures enable us to write

$$C_V{}^{rot} = C_V - \tfrac{3}{2}R$$

vibratory contributions being entirely negligible.

The proton has a spin of $s^{nu} = \tfrac{1}{2}$, and in the molecule of H_2 the nuclear spins line up along the nuclear axis to give a total nuclear spin for the molecule of $i = 1$ or 0. (See Fig. 18.19.) The first type is called orthohydrogen (ortho-H), and the second parahydrogen (para-H). We expect a nuclear weight of $g_{AA} = 2i + 1 = 3$ for the orthohydrogen molecule and of $g_{AA} = 2i + 1 = 1$ for parahydrogen. Since the nuclear weight for a single atom is $g_A = g = 2(\tfrac{1}{2}) + 1 = 2$, the total molecular statistical weight of 3 can come only from the factor $\tfrac{1}{2}g(g + 1)$ in Table 18.4. Consequently, *orthohydrogen* is the form for which the nuclear spin wave function must be *symmetric*, and accordingly it can have rotational levels with *odd J* values only. *Parahydrogen* is *antisymmetric* in the nuclear spins and can have rotational states of *even J* only. The nuclear rotational partition function should therefore be given by Eq. 18.50 as

$$Z_{\substack{\text{odd mass}}}^{nu+rot} = (1 \times Z_{\text{even } J}^{rot}) + (3 \times Z_{\text{odd } J}^{rot}) \tag{18.54}$$

Then
$$C_V{}^{rot} = Nk\frac{\partial}{\partial T}\left(T^2\frac{\partial \ln Z^{nu+rot}}{\partial T}\right) \tag{18.55}$$

The results are plotted as the dashed line, C_{eq}, in Fig. 18.20. This curve attains a maximum off the figure (below $T/\Theta^{rot} = 1$) and bears no resemblance to the experimental observations (circles in the figure). It was Dennison who pointed out the solution to this paradox.[11]

Eq. 18.54 is based on the implicit assumption of complete thermal equilibrium between parahydrogen and orthohydrogen. As a matter of fact, the quantum transition involving the flipping of a nuclear spin vector to cause a change from the para- to the ortho-form (or vice versa) is a rather rare one and in the absence of a suitable catalyst takes place very slowly indeed in comparison with the time of an experiment. Ordinary hydrogen is accordingly to be

FIGURE **18.19**

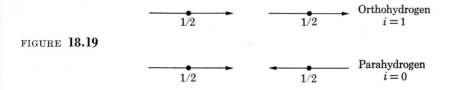

[11] Dennison, *Proc. Roy. Soc. (London),* **A115**, 483 (1927).

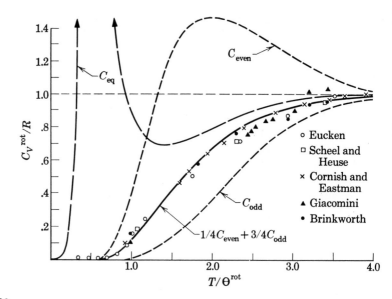

FIGURE **18.20**

treated as a mixture of two *noninteracting* gases, each with its own heat capacity, the two forms being in the theoretical high-temperature proportions of 1 part parahydrogen to 3 parts orthohydrogen. Thus with a mole of gas, $N_0/4$ molecules are in the para-form and $3N_0/4$ in the ortho-form. If then

$$C_{\text{even}} = N_0 k \frac{\partial}{\partial T} \left(T^2 \frac{\partial \ln Z_{\text{even}}^{\text{rot}}}{\partial T} \right)$$

and

$$C_{\text{odd}} = N_0 k \frac{\partial}{\partial T} \left(T^2 \frac{\partial \ln Z_{\text{odd}}^{\text{rot}}}{\partial T} \right)$$

as shown by the dotted lines in the figure, the heat capacity of the mixture should be

$$C_V^{\text{rot}} = \tfrac{1}{4} C_{\text{even}} + \tfrac{3}{4} C_{\text{odd}} \tag{18.56}$$

This was used to plot the solid curve in Fig. 18.20, a few of the extensive experimental values being shown for comparison.[12] There can be little doubt of the correctness of this interpretation.

The case of D_2 is somewhat more complicated than that of H_2. The spin of the deuterium nucleus is $S^{\text{nu}} = 1$, so that the statistical weight for an atom is $g_A = g = 3$, which gives for the two weights in Table 18.4 $\tfrac{1}{2} g(g + 1) = 6$ and $\tfrac{1}{2} g(g - 1) = 3$.

---

[12] Eucken, *Sitzber. preuss. Akad. Wiss. Physik.-math. Kl.*, **1912**, 41; Scheel and Heuse, *Ann. Physik*, **40**, 473 (1913); Giacomini, *Phil. Mag.*, **50**, 146 (1925); Brinkworth, *Proc. Roy. Soc. (London)*, **A107**, 510 (1925); and Cornish and Eastman, *J. Am. Chem. Soc.*, **0**, 627 (1928).

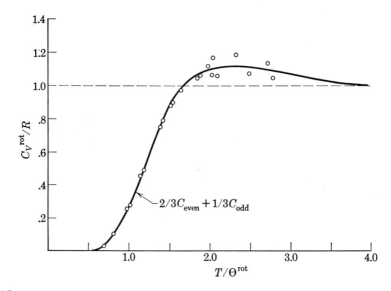

FIGURE 18.21

Since the mass number is now *even* and the electronic state is, as before, a $^1\Sigma_g^+$ state, the *symmetric* nuclear states (with molecular statistical weights 6) must be confined to rotational levels with $J = 0, 2, 4$. The resulting form is called orthodeuterium. The para-form, with weight of 3, is thus required to have J odd. The nuclear spins of the individual atoms combine to give $i = 0, 1$, and 2, with weights of 1, 3, and 5. This means that states with $i = 0$ and 2 (total weight 6) belong to *orthodeuterium*, whereas that with $i = 1$ (weight 3) belongs to the *para*-form. Ordinary deuterium should therefore consist of ortho- and para-forms in the ratio 2 to 1. We accordingly predict

$$C_V{}^{\text{rot}} = \tfrac{2}{3}C_{\text{even}} + \tfrac{1}{3}C_{\text{odd}}$$

This is shown in Fig. 18.21 along with the observations of Clusius and Bartholomé.[13] Again observations are in good agreement with the theoretical predictions.

18.16 Spectroscopic and Calorimetric Entropies

Returning to the general definition of entropy for an ideal gas,

$$S = Nk \left(\ln \frac{Z}{N} + T \frac{\partial \ln Z}{\partial T} + 1 \right) \tag{16.58}$$

if we write for the gas

$$Z^G = \frac{V}{N} \frac{(2\pi m k T)^{3/2}}{h^3} Z^{\text{rot+vib}} Z^{\text{el}} g_{AB}{}^{\mathbf{nu}}$$

[13] Clusius and Bartholomé, *Z. Elektrochem.*, **40**, 526 (1934).

with $V/N = kT/p$ and $Z^{el} = g_G^{el}$, we have

$$Z^G(T, p, N) = \frac{T^{5/2}}{p} \frac{(2\pi m)^{3/2} k^{5/2}}{h^3} Z^{rot+vib} g_{AB}{}^{nu} g_G^{el} \qquad (18.57)$$

The entropy expression then becomes

$$S^G(T, p, N) = Nk \left\{ \ln \frac{T^{5/2}}{p} + T \frac{\partial}{\partial T} \ln Z^{rot+vib} + \ln \left[\frac{(2\pi m)^{3/2} k^{5/2}}{h^3} g_G^{el} g_{AB}{}^{nu} \right] + \frac{7}{2} \right\} \qquad (18.58)$$

which may be calculated not from the approximate expressions for the rotational and vibrational energies but from the actually observed spectroscopic energy levels. Giauque has termed the difference between $S^G(T, p, N)$ so calculated and the nuclear term, $Nk \ln g_{AB}{}^{nu}$, the *spectroscopic* entropy of the gas, S_{spec}^G. Using $N = N_0$, we have

$$S_{spec}^G = S^G(T, p, N) - N_0 k \ln g_{AB}{}^{nu} \qquad (18.59)$$

The difference between the entropy of the gas, $S^G(T, p, N_0)$, and that of the solid (at $0°K$ and $p = 0$), $S_0^K(0,0)$, can be measured thermally by the integration of C_V/T over an appropriate path from $T = 0$ and $p_0 = 0$ to, say, T and $p = 1$ atm. (Here a superscript or subscript K refers to the solid.) Calling this difference the calorimetric entropy, S_{cal}^G, we have

$$S_{cal}^G = S^G(T, p, N_0) - S_0^K(0,0) \qquad (18.60)$$

This type of measurement, of course, always involves an extrapolation from the temperature at which the lowest data are available to $0°K$.

From the argument in Sec. 17.15, for the solid at $0°K$

$$\frac{S_0'''}{R} = \frac{S_0^K}{R} = \ln g_K{}^{nu} g_K^{el} g_K^{orn}$$

and therefore

$$S_{cal}^G = S^G(T, p, N_0) - R \ln g_K{}^{nu} g_K^{el} g_K^{orn} \qquad (18.61)$$

Forming the difference, $S_{spec}^G - S_{cal}^G$, we have simply

$$\boxed{S_{spec}^G - S_{cal}^G = N_0 k \ln g_K^{el} g_K^{orn}} \qquad (18.62)$$

since $g_K{}^{nu} = g_{AB}{}^{nu}$.

Thus an experimental method becomes available for evaluating the important product $g_K^{el} g_K^{orn}$. This type of calculation has been carried out by Giauque and his collaborators and has provided a great deal of interesting information. In the cases of the diatomic gases of Table 17.4, all except CO require $\ln g_K^{el} g_K^{orn}$ to be zero. The data for this gas and for H_2, D_2, and NO are collected in Table 18.5. Column 5 gives the difference on the left side of Eq.

TABLE **18.5**

Molar Entropies at $T = 298.1°K$ and $p = 1$ atm $(cal/mole\text{-}deg)$ *

Gas	State	S^G_{cal}	S^G_{spec}	Col. 3 − col. 2	g^{orn}, assumed	$R \ln g_K{}^{orn}$	$R \ln g_{A}g_{B}$
H_2	$^1\Sigma$	29.7	31.23	1.53	$3^{3/4}$	1.637	$R \ln 4$
D_2	$^1\Sigma$	33.9	34.62	0.72	$3^{1/3}$	0.728	$R \ln 9$
CO	$^1\Sigma$	46.2	47.32	1.12	2	1.379	$R \ln 1$
NO*	$^2\Pi^{1/2}$	43.0	43.75	0.75	$2^{1/2}$	0.689	$R \ln 3$

* Data refer to 121.36°K.

18.62, column 6 the assumed values of the orientational weight, g^{orn} (to be discussed later), column 7 the values of $R \ln g_K{}^{orn}$, and the last column the values of the last term in Eq. 18.59.

For H_2, D_2, and CO, $g_K{}^{el}$ is taken as 1, since each gas is in a $^1\Sigma$ state, which seems to carry over to the solid in all known cases. For H_2 the orientation factor is obtained as follows. We have a mixture of para- and ortho-molecules in the ratio of 1 to 3; for the parahydrogen the lowest state is a rotationless one, and therefore $g^{orn} = 1$, whereas for the orthohydrogen $J = 1$ and $g^{orn} = 3$. Accordingly, in the normal mixture the proper value of $\ln g^{orn}$ is

$$\ln g^{orn} = \tfrac{1}{4} \ln 1 + \tfrac{3}{4} \ln 3 = \ln 3^{3/4}$$

Since in D_2 the ortho-form has the lowest state rotationless, for it $\ln g^{orn} = \ln 1$ and for the para-form the value is $\ln 3$. Then for the 2 to 1 mixture

$$\ln g^{orn} = \tfrac{2}{3} \ln 1 + \tfrac{1}{3} \ln 3 = \ln 3^{1/3}$$

In the case of CO, as was explained in Sec. 17.15, it appears that the two orientations, CO and OC, in the crystal furnish the value of $R \ln g^{orn} = R \ln 2 = 1.379$. The value of 1.12 in column 5 of Table 18.5 seems to indicate that the samples of solid CO used in the calorimetric experiments did not have quite equal orientations in these two directions.

In the case of NO with its $^2\Pi$ electronic state, it is necessary to set $Z^{el} = 2(1 + e^{-178/T})$ as in the discussion of electronic heat capacities. Giauque and Johnson interpret the orientation factor of $2^{1/2}$ as due to the presence of N_2O_2 molecules in the crystal, which gives $\ln g^{orn} = \ln 2$ per mole of the *double* molecule or $\tfrac{1}{2} \ln 2 = \ln 2^{1/2}$ per mole of NO. The agreement between the values in columns 5 and 7 is thus on the whole fairly close.

With these values of g^{orn} and g^{el}, the observed vapor pressure constants of H_2 and NO, presented in Table 18.6, are interpretable (unfortunately no high-temperature data are available for D_2). Column 3 gives the observed

TABLE **18.6**

Vapor Pressure Data for Diatomic Gases

Gas	State	$(i_p')_{obs}$	$g_G{}^{el}$	σ'	1×10^{40}	g^{orn}	$(i_p')_{theor}$
H_2	$^1\Sigma$	$-3.68 \pm .03$	1	2	0.463	$3\frac{3}{4}$	-3.735
D_2	$^1\Sigma$		1	2	0.931	$3\frac{1}{3}$	-2.782
NO	$^2\Pi_{\frac{1}{2}}, {}^2\Pi_{\frac{3}{2}}$	$0.55 \pm .03$	$2(1 + e^{-178/T})$	2	16.42	$2\frac{1}{2}$	$+0.472$

values of i_p' for temperatures at which each gas is classical as far as rotation is concerned. Column 6 gives the values of the moment of inertia times 10^{40}, and column 8 gives the values of i_p' calculated from Eq. 17.58 with the constant terms as evaluated in Sec. 17.15, that is,

$$i_p' = -3.199 + \log \ M^{\frac{3}{2}} + \log \ \frac{I \times 10^{40}}{\sigma'} - \log \ g_K{}^{orn} + \log \ g_G{}^{el}$$

where, with $S'''/R = \log \ g_K{}^{nu} g_K{}^{el} g_K{}^{orn}$, it has been assumed that $g_K{}^{el} = g_G{}^{el}$ for the first two cases and that $g_K{}^{nu} = g_G{}^{nu}$.

We have then

for H_2 $(i_p')_{theor} = -3.199 + 0.457 - 0.635 - 0.358 = -3.735$

for D_2 $(i_p')_{theor} = -3.199 + 0.908 - 0.332 - 0.159 = -2.782$

and for NO $(i_p')_{theor} = -3.199 + 2.216 + 1.215 - 0.151 + 0.391 = +0.472$

[where the value 0.391 comes from $2(1 + e^{-178/T})$ at $121.36°K$].

The agreement between observed values and calculated values is reasonably good for H_2 and almost as satisfactory for NO.

In general, the calorimetric entropy does not include the nuclear spin term, $R \ln g_A g_B$, or the orientational term, $R \ln g^{orn}$, simply because the measured specific heat must always stop at some finite temperature, T_0 (see Fig. 18.22). Below this the heat capacity data are extrapolated smoothly by an appropriate curve, say, of the Debye cube type, to $0°K$ (dashed line in the figure). The effects of the various oriental energy levels, the nuclear spin orientations, etc., in general produce humps, such as the dotted curves. These effects do not appear in the calorimetric calculations from relations of the type of Eq. 18.61.

The reason that such humps in the heat capacity curve appear simply as constant terms in the theoretical entropy formulas may be explained as follows. Suppose that Z^i is a factor in the partition function due to a group of closely spaced energy levels for which the statistical weights, beginning with that of the ground state, are

$$g_0, g_1, g_2, \ . \ . \ . \ , g_n$$

and the characteristic temperatures are

$$0, \Theta_1, \Theta_2, \ . \ . \ . \ , \Theta_n$$

Then, whatever the origin of these levels may be, we write

$$Z^i = g_0 + g_1 e^{-\Theta_1/T} + \cdots + g_n e^{-\Theta_n/T}$$

and the contribution to the entropy, S^i, is

$$S^i = R \left(\ln Z^i + T \frac{\partial \ln Z^i}{\partial T} \right)$$

At temperatures where $T \gg \Theta_n$,

$$Z^i \to g_0 + g_1 + \cdots + g_n = \sum_1^n g_i$$

and the contribution to the theoretical entropy is thus

$$\lim_{T \to \text{large}} S^i = R \lim_{T \to \text{large}} Z^i = R \ln \sum_1^n g_i$$

If there are only two levels, for example, with $g_0 = g_1 = 1$, then $S^i = R \ln 2 = 1.379$ cal/mole-deg. Values are correspondingly larger for higher weights and more levels.

In other cases new sources of closely spaced levels arise owing to the internal Stark effect. With the Cr^{+++} ions of chromium methylamine alum discussed earlier (Sec. 18.11), $g_0 = g_1 = 2$, and $S^i = R \ln (g_0 + g_1) = R \ln 4 = 2.758$ entropy units. Any calorimetric extrapolation made from, say, $1°K$, would miss this contribution altogether. It is clear that we can never be sure that all effects such as this have been included in even the most complete theoretical entropy formula. The purely conventional nature of the zero of entropy therefore becomes apparent. We include all effects that are predictable at a given time or required for a given discussion, but *the value of entropy always remains relative.* Absolute entropy is without meaning.

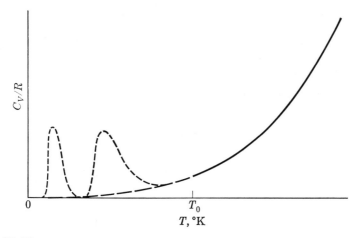

FIGURE **18.22**

References

ATOMIC

SEMAT, H., *Introduction to Atomic and Nuclear Physics*, Holt, Rinehart & Winston, New York, 1954, Chap. 8.

MOLECULAR

BAK, B., *Elementary Introduction to Molecular Spectra*, Interscience, New York, 1952.

Problems

18.1   Show that the wave equation for the rigid rotor in Cartesian coordinates,

$$\frac{\partial^2 \psi}{\partial x^2} + \frac{\partial^2 \psi}{\partial y^2} + \frac{\partial^2 \psi}{\partial z^2} + \frac{2m'w}{\hbar^2}\psi = 0 \qquad (18.29)$$

transforms to the spherical polar coordinate form,

$$\frac{1}{\sin\theta}\frac{\partial}{\partial\theta}\left(\sin\theta\frac{\partial\psi}{\partial\theta}\right) + \frac{1}{\sin^2\theta}\frac{\partial^2\psi}{\partial\phi^2} + \frac{2Iw}{\hbar^2}\psi = 0 \qquad (18.30)$$

(See H. Morgenau and G. H. Murphy, *Mathematics of Physics and Chemistry*, Van Nostrand, New York, 1943, p. 172, for a general method based on differential geometry.)

18.2   Solve Legendre's equation

$$(1 - x^2)\frac{d^2y}{dx^2} - 2x\frac{dy}{dx} + n(n+1)y = 0$$

in the form of a power series, and show that solutions in polynomials in odd or even descending powers of x can be found in the general form of Legendre's polynomials of degree n,

$$P_n(x) = 1 \times 3 \times 5 \times \cdots \times (2n-1)\left[x^n - \frac{n(n-1)}{2(2n-1)}x^{n-2} \right.$$
$$\left. + \frac{n(n-1)(n-3)}{2 \times 4(2n-1)(2n-3)}x^{n-4} + \cdots \right]$$

18.3   Determine the approximate angles that the vectors $\underline{L}$ and $\underline{S}$ bear to $\underline{J}$ in the following atomic cases:

(a) $L = 1$, $S = \frac{1}{2}$; and
(b) $L = 2$, $S = \frac{3}{2}$.

18.4   Follow through the argument in J. E. Mayer and M. G. Mayer, *Statistical Mechanics*, Wiley, New York, 1940, pp. 160 ff., for the case of the general diatomic molecule, taking into account stretching of the molecule and the effect of anharmonicity.

   1. If the general energy term of the rotation-vibration partition function is written

$$\epsilon_i = hc\omega_e(v + \tfrac{1}{2}) - hcx_e\omega_e(v + \tfrac{1}{2})^2 + B_e hcJ(J+1) - hcD_e J^2(J+1)^2$$
$$- \alpha hc(v + \tfrac{1}{2})J(J+1)$$

the rotation-vibration partition function may be written

$$Z^{\text{vib}} Z^{\text{rot}} Z^{\text{corr}}$$

the first two factors being the approximations obtained for the idealized diatomic case.

2. The third factor may be written as a logarithm in the form

$$\ln Z^{\text{corr}} = \frac{1}{u}\left[8\gamma + \delta\frac{u}{e^u - 1} + 2x\frac{u^2}{(e^u - 1)^2}\right]$$

where $u = hc\omega_0/kT$, $\gamma = \sigma/u = (D_0/B_0)^{1/2}$, $\sigma = hcB_0/kT$, $\delta = \alpha/B_e$, and $x = x_e$, the subscript zero indicating reference to the state with $v = 0$ and $J = 0$.

3. The corresponding correction for the internal energy, U^{corr}, becomes

$$U^{\text{corr}} = RT\left[u^{-1}(2x + 6(\gamma x)^{1/2} + 2x) - \frac{u}{6}(-3\gamma + 3(\gamma x)^{1/2} + 5x) + \frac{u^2 x}{3} - \frac{u^3}{40}(\gamma - (\gamma x)^{1/2} + x) + \cdots\right]$$

18.5 Show that if there are two Stark levels above the ground level, with characteristic temperatures Θ_1 and Θ_2, and if the statistical weights for the three levels are g_0, g_1, and g_2, we should expect

$$C_V^{\text{el}} = \frac{\text{constant}}{T^2} \tag{18.48}$$

for temperatures sufficiently above Θ_2 for the approximations to hold.

18.6 Calculate the practical vapor pressure constant for the gas tritium (T_2), which has $M = 3.0340$. Also determine the values of the entropy term

$$R(\ln g_A{}^{\text{nu}} + \ln g^{\text{orn}})$$

for this substance. For the tritium atom $S^{\text{nu}} = \frac{1}{2}$, as for H^1.

18.7 Calculate the value of $R \ln g^{\text{nu}}g^{\text{el}}$ for the following atomic gases (see Table 18.2):

(a) carbon,
(b) oxygen,
(c) nitrogen,
(d) chlorine-35,

and take the temperature to be 300°K.

18.8 Calculate and plot the curve for C_V^{el}/R for a mole of atomic chlorine gas (pure isotope 35).

18.9 In the treatment of the hyperfine structure of atomic spectrum lines, the nuclear momentum vector, $\mathcal{I}^{\text{nu}}$, is combined with the $\mathcal{J}$ vector for the external electrons to give $\mathcal{F}$, the fine-structure vector. Then $|\mathcal{F}|$ is given by

$$|\mathcal{F}| = \mathcal{F} = [f(f + 1)]^{1/2}\hbar$$

where f is the fine-structure (or inner) quantum number. If f takes on the values, integral or half-integral, from $j + i$ to $j - i$, show that if the weights of all the possible f values are added, the same value results for the combined nuclear and electronic weight as if the two cases were treated separately, that is,

$$g^{\text{nu}}g^{\text{el}} = (2i + 1)(2j + 1)$$

CHAPTER NINETEEN

Applications to Various Systems

19.1   Bose-Einstein and Fermi-Dirac Statistics

In Chap. 17 the Bose-Einstein statistics was shown to lead to a distribution function of the form

Bose-Einstein $$N_j = \frac{g_j}{B e^{\beta \epsilon_j} - 1}$$ $g_j \gg 1$ (17.14)

If the same argument is carried out for indistinguishable objects, but with *only a fixed number of objects* to a cell, the Fermi-Dirac statistics results. It will be shown in Sec. 19.15 that the corresponding distribution is

Fermi-Dirac $$N_j = \frac{g_j}{B e^{\beta \epsilon_j} + 1}$$ $g_j \gg N_j$ (19.1)

All systems made up of weakly interacting physical entities in thermal equilibrium obey one or the other of these distribution laws. Which type of statistics is to be expected depends upon the spin properties of the individual entities of which the system is composed. If these entities are material particles, the nuclear spins are important. When S^{nu} is an *even* multiple of $\frac{1}{2}$, Bose-Einstein statistics applies, whereas when S^{nu} is an *odd* multiple of $\frac{1}{2}$, Fermi-Dirac statistics holds. Since atoms with even mass numbers can have only even multiples, systems with atoms of *even mass number* are governed by Bose-Einstein statistics, and those of *odd mass number* obey the Fermi-Dirac law.

If, in a system of either type, conditions are such that $B e^{\beta \epsilon_j} \gg 1$, each of the distribution functions reduces to the Boltzmann form, with $B = 1/\alpha' = 1/(\alpha N \Delta \mu) = Z/N$. For the case of an ideal monatomic gas,

$$B = \frac{V}{N} \frac{(2\pi m k T)^{3/2}}{h^3} \propto (mT)^{3/2}$$ (19.2)

For a particular system, the larger the mass and the higher the temperature, the more justified does the Boltzmann approximation become. In practice, this means that for essentially all systems made up of particles heavier than H_2 or He, the Boltzmann approximation is adequate. For these two systems below a few degrees Kelvin, the approximation is not applicable; H_2 should obey Fermi-Dirac statistics, and He Bose-Einstein statistics.

As soon as the interactions among particles become greater than the feeble ones necessary to maintain thermal equilibrium, producing so-called cooperative systems, calculation of the effect of the mutual interactions must be carried out. In such cases the basic assumption that the probability of a particle's being in a given quantum state (or quantum cell in μ space) is independent of the location of neighbors ceases to be valid. It is necessary to discuss the energy of the system as a whole and to use the fundamental ideas of Γ space. In particular, the partition function summed over the accessible cells of μ space (or the permitted energy states of a single particle) is no longer adequate. It must be replaced by a new more general partition function summed over the accessible cells of Γ space (or the quantum states of the entire system). The first function we shall refer to as a *particle* (or μ space) partition function and designate as Z_μ, whether it is evaluated by classical or quantum methods or an appropriate mixture of the two. The new function we shall call a *system* (or Γ space) partition function, to be indicated by Z_γ. The system partition functions, as we shall see, are in theory applicable to the most complicated systems made up of interacting subsystems (which may be simple particles), however strong these interactions may be.

By means of the powerful method of the Gibbs ensemble, formulas for calculating thermodynamic quantities from Z_γ, analogous to those in terms of Z_μ collected at the end of Chap. 16, will be obtained. For systems with weak

TABLE **19.1**

System	Entities to be treated as	Statistics
Ideal gas	Independent	Boltzmann
Ideal paramagnetic solid	Independent	Boltzmann
Ideal gases in electric or magnetic fields	Independent	Boltzmann
Ideal gases reacting	Independent	Boltzmann
Adsorption	Cooperative	Gibbs-Boltzmann
Imperfect gas	Cooperative	Gibbs-Boltzmann
Compressed gases, liquids	Cooperative	Gibbs-Boltzmann
Solids (crystals)	Cooperative	Gibbs-Boltzmann
Black body radiation	Independent	Bose-Einstein $(S = 1)$
Electrons in conductors	Independent	Fermi-Dirac $(S = \frac{1}{2})$
Liquid He^4	Cooperative	Gibbs-Bose-Einstein $(S = 0)$
Liquid He^3	Cooperative	Gibbs-Fermi-Dirac $(S = \frac{1}{2})$

interactions Z_γ can be obtained simply from Z_μ. For those with stronger interactions useful results depend entirely upon the development of practical approximate methods for solving the often quite formidable (not to say insuperable) mathematical complications.

As an indication of the variety of physical and chemical problems open to statistical investigation, Table 19.1 presents a few of the more significant ones, along with the type of interactions postulated and the type of statistics required. Here for simplicity interactions are classed as *weak* and *nonweak*, the former leading to independent particles and the latter to *cooperative* assemblies. The following discussion will treat briefly a few of the many typical problems suggested in the table.

19.2   The Ideal Paramagnetic Solid

In the case of a crystal in which the lattice points are occupied by particles possessing electronic spin, the interaction between close neighbors is large, with all the complications encountered in the treatment of *ferromagnetic* materials. In the case of paramagnetic substances, however, units that possess nonvanishing electronic spins (the paramagnetically active ions) are separated from their nearest neighbors by other nonactive particles, and the troublesome interactions are often quite small. The *ideal* paramagnetic solid is defined as one in which these interactions are negligible.

In general, a magnetic dipole of strength μ when placed in a uniform magnetic field of strength $\mathcal{H}$ (see Fig. 19.1) acquires an energy relative to the

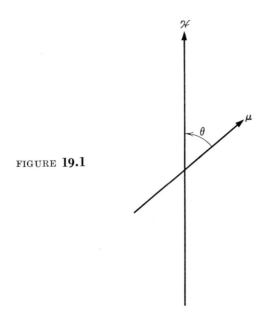

FIGURE **19.1**

zero-field value given by the relation

$$\epsilon = -\mu \mathcal{H} \cos \theta$$

so that its energy is $-\mu \mathcal{H}$ when parallel to the field and $+\mu \mathcal{H}$ when opposite. In an atomic or molecular system a similar relation holds except that now in general the magnetic moment is expressible in terms of the Bohr magnetron, μ_0, where

$$\mu_0 = \frac{|e|\hbar}{2m_e c}$$

$|e|$ being the absolute value of the charge on an electron, m_e its mass, and c the velocity of light. The total angular momentum vector, $\underline{\mathcal{J}}$, of size $[j(j+1)]^{1/2}$, precesses, as we have seen, about the field at angles such that j has only integral (or half-integral) projections on $\mathcal{H}$.

Thus the possible projections of j on $\mathcal{H}$ give the magnetic quantum numbers, $M_{\mathcal{H}}$ (written hereafter as M for brevity), of values

$$-j, \; -j+1, \; \ldots, \; j-1, \; j$$

a total of $2j + 1$ in number. See Fig. 18.8, where $j \equiv J$ and has the integral values of 0, 1, and 2. The energy of the system, ϵ_M, then becomes

$$\epsilon_M = M \mu_0 \mathcal{H} \tag{19.3}$$

when there is no spin (and $j = L$, giving a singlet state) or

$$\epsilon_M = 2M \mu_0 \mathcal{H} \tag{19.4}$$

when $L = 0$ and $j = S$, the total spin quantum number.[1] This last result holds for all atoms or ions in S or sharp states and therefore includes the case of most paramagnetic ions.

When S is *integral*, $2S + 1$ is odd, and these states are arranged symmetrically about the no-field position (here given by $M = 0$). When S is *half-integral*, there is an even number of states, also symmetric about the zero-field position although this no longer corresponds to a possible M value. (See Fig. 19.2.)

Despite the dissimilarity between the two systems, such an idealized paramagnetic solid may be treated, as far as its magnetic behavior is concerned, as was the equilibrium state of an ideal gas. With the basic energy equation given in Eq. 19.4, we set up the particle partition function for an ion in a

---

[1] Owing to the negative charge of the electron, its magnetic moment vector is opposite in direction to $\underline{\mathcal{J}}$, which measures the *mechanical* momentum. Thus the energy is positive when M is positive but the components of *magnetic* moment along $\mathcal{H}$ are $-2M\mu_0$ (or $-M\mu_0$, as the case may be).

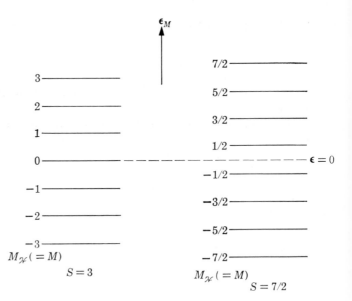

FIGURE **19.2**

magnetic field by summing the exponential $e^{-\epsilon_M/kT}$ over all the values of M for the ion. If this magnetic partition function is $Z_\mu^{\mathscr{H}}$, then

$$Z_\mu^{\mathscr{H}} = \sum_{M=-S}^{M=+S} e^{-2M\mu\mathscr{H}/kT} = \sum_{M=-S}^{M=+S} e^{-2Mx}$$

where $x = \mu_0\mathscr{H}/kT$ and is thus analogous to the ratios u and σ used in treating vibration and rotation, respectively. In fact, we may define a magnetic characteristic temperature, Θ^{mag}, by the relation

$$\Theta^{\text{mag}} = \frac{\mu_0\mathscr{H}}{k}$$

Unlike the other characteristic temperatures, this can be varied by altering the value of the magnetic field. Reversing the order, we obtain for the sum

$$Z_\mu^{\mathscr{H}} = e^{-2Sx} + e^{(-2S+2)x} + \cdots + e^{(2S-2)x} + e^{2Sx} \qquad (19.5)$$

and it can be shown (see Problem 19.1) that this is readily summed in closed form to give

$$Z_\mu^{\mathscr{H}} = \frac{\sinh\left[(2S+1)x\right]}{\sinh x} \qquad (19.6)$$

From the general theory developed in Chap. 16, we know that the number of dipoles, say, N_M, in a particular state, ϵ_M, fixed by the magnetic quantum number, M, is given simply as

$$N_M = \frac{Ne^{-2Mx}}{\Sigma e^{-2Mx}} = \frac{Ne^{-2Mx}}{Z_\mu{}^{\mathcal{H}}}$$

(since summation of N_M over all M's must reduce the equation to an identity). (See Eq. 16.65.)

Since for a given M the moment in the direction of $\mathcal{H}$ is $-2M\mu_0$ for a single dipole, the total moment of the solid along $\mathcal{H}$ due to N_M is

$$-N_M 2M\mu_0 = -\frac{Ne^{-2Mx}}{Z_\mu{}^{\mathcal{H}}} 2M\mu_0 = \frac{NkTe^{-2Mx}}{Z_\mu{}^{\mathcal{H}}}\left(-\frac{2M\mu_0}{kT}\right)$$

Summing this over all M values gives the total magnetic moment, $\mathbf{M}$, of the solid. Thus

$$\mathbf{M} = \sum_M -N_M 2M\mu_0 = NkT \frac{\Sigma e^{-2Mx}}{Z_\mu{}^{\mathcal{H}}}\left(-\frac{2M\mu_0}{kT}\right)$$

or

$$\mathbf{M} = NkT \frac{\partial \ln Z_\mu{}^{\mathcal{H}}}{\partial \mathcal{H}} = N\mu_0 \frac{\partial \ln Z_\mu{}^{\mathcal{H}}}{\partial x} \tag{19.7}$$

since $kT\, \partial/\partial\mathcal{H} = \mu_0\, \partial/\partial x$. Differentiation of $Z_\mu{}^{\mathcal{H}}$ from Eq. 19.6 with respect to x gives

$$\frac{\partial \ln Z}{\partial x} = (2S+1)\coth[(2S+1)x] - \coth x$$

and therefore

$$\mathbf{M} = N\mu_0\{(2S+1)\coth[(2S+1)x] - \coth x\} \tag{19.8}$$

Let us now examine this important formula for various values of the argument $x = \mu_0\mathcal{H}/kT$.

Small x. At ordinary temperatures x is small for the largest attainable fields. But for small values of an argument y, the hyperbolic cotangent of y can always be written

$$\coth y = \frac{1}{y} + \frac{y}{3} + \cdots \qquad y \ll 1$$

For such conditions the bracket on the right side of Eq. 19.8 becomes

$$2S+1\left[\frac{1}{(2S+1)x} + \frac{(2S+1)x}{3} + \cdots\right] - \frac{1}{x} - \frac{x}{3}\cdots = 4S(S+1)\frac{x}{3}$$

and therefore

$$\mathbf{M} = N_0\mu_0 4S(S+1)\frac{x}{3} \qquad x \ll 1$$

$$= \frac{N_0\mu_0{}^2 4S(S+1)}{3k}\frac{\mathcal{H}}{T} = C\frac{\mathcal{H}}{T} \qquad \frac{\mu_0\mathcal{H}}{kT} \ll 1 \tag{19.9}$$

which is *Curie's law* with the constant C now given explicitly by

$$C = \frac{4S(S + 1)\mu_0{}^2 N_0}{3k}$$

Large x.   Although large values of $x = \mu_0 \mathscr{H} / kT$ are not attainable at room temperatures, they may be obtained at sufficiently low temperatures. In this case (that is, for large values of x) the phenomenon of saturation is observed. In fact, since

$$\lim_{y \to \infty} \coth y = 1$$

Eq. 19.8 gives

$$\mathbf{M}_{\text{sat}} = N_0 \mu_0 (2S + 1 - 1) = N_0 \mu_0 2S$$

or

$$\boxed{\frac{\overline{\mu_{\text{sat}}}}{\mu_0} = \frac{\mathbf{M}_{\text{sat}}}{N_0 \mu_0} = 2S} \qquad (19.10)$$

where $\overline{\mu_{\text{sat}}} / \mu_0$ is the ratio of the average moment per ion for saturation to the moment of the Bohr magnetron. This ratio for the saturated paramagnetic solid is thus a dimensionless quantity fixed solely by the spin quantum number of the paramagnetic ion.

Suppose now that an idealized paramagnetic solid is magnetized from $\mathscr{H} = 0$ to saturation and then demagnetized to saturation in the reverse direction. We obtain the S-shaped curve drawn in Fig. 19.3 for a fixed value of

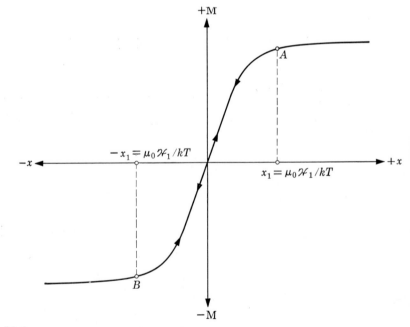

FIGURE **19.3**

S and T from Eq. 19.8. Here the vertical scale represents **M**, and the horizontal scale is $x = \mu_0\mathscr{H}/kT \propto \mathscr{H}$. If we execute a cycle from $+\mathscr{H}_1$ to $-\mathscr{H}_1$ and back, the curve is exactly retraced $(A \rightarrow B \rightarrow A)$, and we have a hysteresis loop of zero area. Experimentally many paramagnetic solids exhibit a very narrow loop, indicating the effects of the small interactions, neglected in the idealized case. As the interaction becomes stronger, whole domains begin to act as cooperative subsystems, magnetizing as a whole and producing sudden increases in magnetization here and there in the solid as the field is increased. On the reduction of $\mathscr{H}$, the demagnetization lags behind the field and takes place in a series of sudden, sharp (but microscopic) decreases, producing a quite different curve from the original one and giving rise on cyclic magnetization to the usual hysteresis loop such as is shown in Fig. 5.4.

Table 19.2 lists three paramagnetic salts, their corresponding active ions, and their electronic states in the solid condition, together with values of the spin

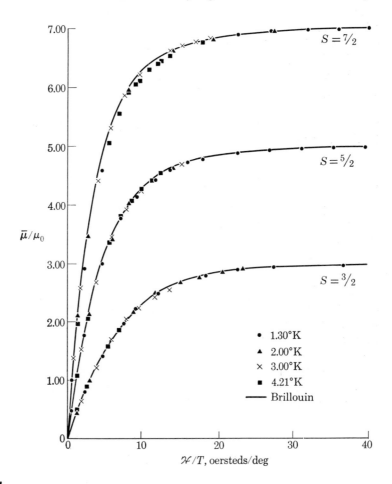

FIGURE **19.4**

TABLE **19.2**

Paramagnetic salt	Active ion	Electronic state	Spin quantum number, S	$\dfrac{\overline{\mu}_{\text{sat}}}{\mu_0}$
Potassium chrome alum, $Cr_2(SO_4)_3K_2SO_4 \cdot 24H_2O$	Cr^{+++}	$^4S_{3/2}$	$3/2$	3.00
Ammonium iron alum, $Fe_2(SO_4)_3(NH_4)_2SO_4 \cdot 24H_2O$	Fe^{+++}	$^6S_{5/2}$	$5/2$	5.00
Gadolinium sulfate, $Gd_2(SO_4)_3 \cdot 8H_2O$	Gd^{+++}	$^8S_{7/2}$	$7/2$	7.00

quantum number, S, and the limit ratio, $\overline{\mu}_{\text{sat}}/\mu_0$. The theoretical curves for $\overline{\mu}/\mu_0$ as calculated from the general expression in Eq. 19.8 are drawn as the solid curves in Fig. 19.4 for the S values of $3/2$, $5/2$, and $7/2$. The low-temperature data for the three salts of Table 19.2 (taken at 4.31°K and three lower temperatures) are indicated by the points. It is clear that the extensive data are beautifully represented by the theoretical curves.

For the more general case in which both L and S are different from zero, as well as a consideration of many other related phenomena, the reader is referred to Van Vleck.[2]

19.3   Black Body Radiation and the Photon Gas

Photons in nature are circularly polarized (right- or left-handed), and unpolarized light is a mixture of equal numbers of the two kinds. Since each such elementary quantum has an angular momentum of $1\hbar$, the Bose-Einstein statistics should apply. Furthermore, photons, unlike material particles, retain their identities only between emission and reabsorption by the walls. There is consequently no fixed condition on the total number, N, of photons of all frequencies in an enclosure. Accordingly, if we imagine a cavity of volume V with walls at temperature T, the equilibrium distribution should be governed by the type of result deduced in Sec. 17.6. This was obtained formally by maximizing the entropy of a system of indistinguishable and independent entities subject to the Bose-Einstein method of counting microstates and with no fixed condition on N. The result for N_j, the number of entities of energy ϵ_j, was obtained in the form of Eq. 17.15 as

$$N_j = \frac{g_j}{e^{\beta \epsilon_j} - 1} \tag{19.11}$$

---

[2] See Van Vleck, the reference cited at the end of the chapter.

where g_j is the degeneracy factor or statistical weight for the energy level of energy ϵ_j. Of course, there are numerous and basic differences between the entities (particles) in an actual gas and the entities (photons) in a photon gas.

Each photon of wave length λ_j has a momentum, p_j, where, by the de Broglie relation,

$$\lambda_j = \frac{h}{p_j}$$

or, since $\lambda_j = c/\nu_j$, c being the velocity of light,

$$p_j = \frac{h}{\lambda_j} = \frac{h\nu_j}{c} = \frac{\epsilon_j}{c} \tag{19.12}$$

In the case of a gas of material particles, the mass of each particle is constant; but the momentum (and hence the energy) varies from particle to particle owing to variations in velocity. In the case of a photon gas, all photons have the *same* speed; but the mass (and thus the momentum and energy) varies from photon to photon owing to frequency differences.

Suppose that the photon gas is set up in the interior of a cubic black body cavity with walls at a temperature, T.[3] Imagine a volume space and a momentum space, and locate the cavity in the volume space. Then every photon is *somewhere* in the volume space but has an image point fixed by its frequency (and hence its energy) in the momentum space. If we imagine a thin momentum shell of radius p_j and thickness Δp_j, each photon of energy between ϵ_j and $\epsilon_j + \Delta\epsilon_j$ has its image point in this shell. If these two spaces are now regarded as subspaces of a six-dimensional phase space, we *define* the "volume" of an energy shell as

$$V4\pi p_j{}^2 \Delta p_j$$

Any photon in a shell so defined must have an energy near ϵ_j.[4] The statistical weight of the energy states near ϵ_j are then defined in parallelism with the particle treatment (see Problem 17.2) as

$$g_j = \frac{V4\pi p_j{}^2 \Delta p_j}{h^3} \tag{19.13}$$

Here the difference between particles and photons mentioned at the beginning of this section must be taken into account. The photons occur in right- and left-handed forms in equal numbers, and Eq. 19.13 was deduced for one kind of entity only. To include both types of photons, the number in Eq.

---

[3] It can be shown that the particular shape of the enclosure has no influence on the result, but it is simpler to take the cavity as cubic.

[4] Since a photon cannot be localized in space, it is not possible to define its image point in the six-dimensional shell. We can say only that it is somewhere in V and definitely in the three-dimensional momentum shell of "volume" $4\pi p_j{}^2 \Delta p_j$.

19.13 must be doubled. Combining this with 19.11 gives

$$N_j = \frac{V 8\pi p_j{}^2 \, \Delta p_j}{h^3 (e^{\beta \epsilon_i} - 1)}$$

where now N_j is the total number of photons in volume V of momentum between p_j and $p_j + \Delta p_j$. Since from Eq. 19.12

$$p_j{}^2 \, \Delta p_j = \frac{h^3 \nu_j{}^2 \, \Delta \nu_j}{c^3}$$

this becomes

$$N_j = \frac{V 8\pi \nu_j{}^2 \, \Delta \nu_j}{c^3 (e^{\beta h \nu_i} - 1)} \tag{19.14}$$

Since there are a vast number of frequencies present, which we may take as forming essentially a continuous array, consider the ratio of N_j to $V \, \Delta \nu_j$ in the limit as $\Delta \nu_j \to 0$. The result is

$$\lim_{\Delta \nu_j \to 0} \frac{N_j}{V \, \Delta \nu_j} = \frac{dN_\nu}{V \, d\nu} = \frac{d\rho_\nu}{d\nu} = \frac{8\pi \nu^2}{c^3 (e^{\beta h \nu} - 1)} \tag{19.15}$$

where $d\rho_\nu / d\nu$ is the volume density of photons in the enclosure per unit frequency range at ν. Each photon of frequency ν has an energy $h\nu$, and therefore $h\nu \, dN_\nu$ is the total radiant energy in the system in the interval $d\nu$, and $h\nu \, dN_\nu / V$ is the *energy density* for radiation in the same interval. With this written as $u_\nu \, d\nu$, Eq. 19.15 gives

$$u_\nu \, d\nu = \frac{8\pi h \nu^3 \, d\nu}{c^3 (e^{\beta h \nu} - 1)} \tag{19.16}$$

It is customary to express this in terms of the wave length; since $\nu = c/\lambda$, $d\nu = -(c/\lambda^2) \, d\lambda$. If $u_\lambda \, d\lambda$ is the energy density in the corresponding wave length interval, $d\lambda$,

$$u_\lambda \, d\lambda = -\frac{8\pi hc \lambda^{-5} \, d\lambda}{e^{hc/\lambda kT} - 1} \tag{19.17}$$

or, with the minus sign disregarded since we are interested in the absolute density of radiation only,

$$\boxed{u_\lambda = \frac{8\pi hc \lambda^{-5}}{e^{hc/\lambda kT} - 1}} \tag{19.18}$$

This is Planck's energy density law for black body radiation, here obtained as a direct consequence of the Bose-Einstein statistics.

19.4 Planck's Radiation Law

Planck's radiation law for the equilibrium distribution of energy in a cavity at temperature T can now be converted to the form giving the actual radiancy from a black body surface (or opening in a cavity) by means of the result arrived at in Sec. 13.6. There it was shown that

$$R_c = \frac{uc}{4} \qquad\qquad (13.29)$$

R_c being the total *radiancy* (power radiated per unit area in all directions) from the cavity and u the total radiation density in the cavity. The same geometric argument applied to the radiation per unit wave length range at λ would give

$$R_\lambda = \frac{u_\lambda c}{4} \qquad\qquad (19.19)$$

where R_λ is the radiancy *from* and u_λ the radiation density *in* the cavity at wave length λ (each expressed per unit wave length interval). Combining Eq. 19.18 with Eq. 19.19 gives

$$R_\lambda = \frac{2\pi hc^2 \lambda^{-5}}{e^{hc/\lambda kT} - 1} = \frac{c_1 \lambda^{-5}}{e^{c_2/\lambda T} - 1} \qquad\qquad (19.20)$$

where $c_1 = 2\pi hc^2$ and $c_2 = hc/k$. This curve is shown in Fig. 19.5, plotted for temperatures of 1000 and 1200°K. The vertical scale is R_λ in watts per square centimeter per micron, and λ is in microns (10^{-4} cm).

To find the condition fixing the wave length, λ_m, for the maximum power radiated at a given T, it is necessary to calculate $\partial R_\lambda/\partial \lambda$ and set it equal to zero.

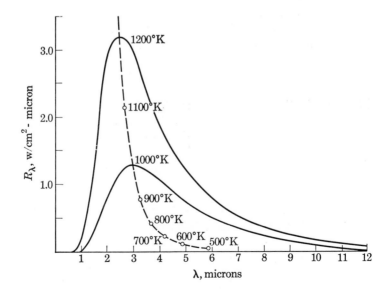

FIGURE **19.5**

This gives the condition

$$e^{-c_2/\lambda_m T} + 1 = \frac{c_2}{5\lambda_m T} \tag{19.21}$$

a transcendental equation that can be solved numerically by successive approximations to give

$$\lambda_m T = 0.20140 c_2 \tag{19.22}$$

This means of course that

$$\boxed{\lambda_m T = \text{constant}} \tag{19.23}$$

which is *Wien's displacement law*. It indicates that the maxima of the curves of R_λ versus λ lie on an equilateral hyperbola. This curve is shown as the dashed line in Fig. 19.5, where the locations of the maxima for a few temperatures between 1200 and 500°K are indicated. From Eq. 19.22, Wien's law may be written

$$\lambda_m T = 0.28976 \text{ cm-deg} = 2897.6 \text{ micron-deg}$$

according to whether λ is measured in centimeters or microns.

If Eq. 19.22 is substituted in Eq. 19.20, the value of the radiancy at λ_m, R_{λ_m}, becomes

$$R_{\lambda_m} = 1.287 T^5 \left(\frac{\text{watt}}{\text{cm}^2} \text{ micron}^{-1}\text{-deg}^{-5} \right) \tag{19.24}$$

Because of the T^5 factor, doubling the temperature increases R_{λ_m} *by a factor of 32*. (See Problem 19.2.)

If we integrate the quantity R_λ over the wave length range from 0 to ∞, we obtain the total radiancy, R_c, of a black body. Thus

$$R_c = \int_0^\infty R_\lambda \, d\lambda = c_1 \int_0^\infty \frac{\lambda^{-5} \, d\lambda}{e^{-c_2/\lambda T} - 1}$$

If the substitution $x = c_2/\lambda T$ is made, this becomes

$$R_c = \frac{c_1}{c_2^4} T^4 \int_0^\infty \frac{x^3 \, dx}{e^x - 1} = \frac{2\pi k^4}{h^3 c^2} T^4 \int_0^\infty \frac{x^3 \, dx}{e^x - 1}$$

We may evaluate the improper integral in x by showing that

$$\int_0^\infty \frac{x^3 \, dx}{e^x - 1} = \lim_{x \to \infty} \int_0^x \frac{x^3 \, dx}{e^x - 1} = \frac{\pi^4}{15}$$

(See Appendix 19.1.) We have therefore

$$\boxed{R_c = \frac{2\pi^5 k^4}{15 h^3 c^2} T^4 = \sigma T^4} \tag{19.25}$$

which is the *Stefan-Boltzmann* total radiation law, obtained by purely thermo-dynamic reasoning in Sec. 13.8. The constant σ is now, however, given explicitly as

$$\sigma = \frac{2\pi^5 k^4}{15 h^3 c^2} \qquad (19.26)$$

This and the value of c_2 in Planck's law

$$c_2 = \frac{hc}{k} \qquad (19.27)$$

give two equations in h and k. If the best experimental values of σ and c_2 are used, h and k may be determined directly from radiation measurements alone. Wensel, who has studied the experimental data, has adopted the experimental values[5]

$$c_2 = 1.436 \text{ cm-deg}$$
$$\sigma = 5.69 \; 10^{-5} \text{ erg-sec}^{-1}\text{-deg}^{-4}$$
$$R = 8.314 \; 10^7 \text{ erg-mole}^{-1}\text{-deg}^{-1}$$

and computed the values of h, k, and Avogadro's number, $N_0 \; (= R/k)$, using Eqs. 19.26 and 19.27. The results are given in Table 19.3 in column 2. Column 3 gives the values obtained by Dumond and Cohen from other physical measurements.

A short wave approximation to the Planck radiation law is obtained if we regard the exponent as large compared to unity; in this case Eq. 19.20 becomes

$$R_\lambda = c_1 \lambda^{-5} e^{-c_2/\lambda T} \qquad (19.28)$$

This is the emprical radiation law proposed by Wien before the advent of the quantum theory.

TABLE **19.3**

	Values from Eqs. 19.26 and 19.27	Values of Dumond and Cohen (1952)
h	6.598×10^{-27}	6.624×10^{-27}
k	1.377×10^{-16}	1.380×10^{-16}
N_0	6.036×10^{23}	6.025×10^{23}

[5] Wensel, *J. Research Natl. Bur. Standards,* **22,** 375 (1939).

If we assume that $c_2/\lambda T \ll 1$, in the original Planck law, so that the exponential can be expanded as a series,

$$1 + \frac{c_2}{\lambda T} + \frac{1}{2}\left(\frac{c_2}{\lambda T}\right)^2 + \cdots$$

the law reduces to the form

$$R_\lambda = \frac{c_1 \lambda T}{\lambda^5 c_2} = \frac{2\pi c k T}{\lambda^4} \tag{19.29}$$

where Planck's constant has disappeared. This is the *Rayleigh-Jeans* law, deduced originally from classical electromagnetic theory. We notice that it gives for the energy density per unit wave length interval, u_λ, the value

$$u_\lambda = \frac{4}{c} R_\lambda = \frac{8\pi}{\lambda^4} kT \tag{19.30}$$

and thus effectively assigns to a unit volume of radiation $8\pi/\lambda^4$ different vibrations, each with the classical energy for a vibration of kT.[6]

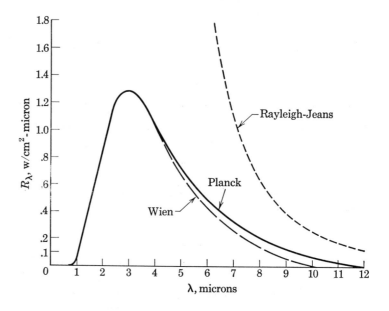

FIGURE **19.6**

---

[6] By an argument very similar to that given in Sec. 18.7 for standing matter waves, we take the number of standing electromagnetic waves in a cubic box of volume $L^3 = V$ to be $\frac{1}{8} 4\pi n^2 \Delta n$. If $n\lambda/2 = L$, $n^2 = 4L^2/\lambda^2$, and $|\Delta n| = (2L/\lambda^2)\Delta\lambda$ so that the number of such waves in $\Delta\lambda$ becomes $4\pi L^3 \Delta\lambda/\lambda^4$. Doubling this value to allow for two planes of polarization gives $8\pi/\lambda^4$ vibrations per unit volume per unit wave length interval. This is just the quantity in the Rayleigh-Jeans law. For the corresponding quantum version, see Problems 19.3 and 19.4.

In Fig. 19.6 the three laws of Planck, Wien, and Rayleigh-Jeans are plotted for a temperature of 1000°K. The law of Wien is indistinguishable from Planck's law at short wave lengths but is too low at large wave lengths. The Rayleigh-Jeans law is a good approximation for very large wave lengths but fails badly as the wave length gets shorter. In fact, u_λ is seen to go to infinity as $\lambda \to 0$, with the result that the total energy density in a black body is infinite at all finite temperatures! This anomalous situation indicates the necessity for some limitation at the short wave end such as that provided by the Planck quantum postulate. For with the energy of a quantum $h\nu$, the equilibrium number of quanta in any cavity diminishes rapidly with increasing frequency beyond the maximum in the radiation density curve.

19.5 Gibbs' Ensembles

For the study of the behavior of systems of particles that interact with one another, the treatment in μ space is inadequate simply because the probability of a particle's being in a given μ cell is affected by the number already there. For such systems Gibbs invented the concept of the ensemble, briefly referred to in Chap. 16. An ensemble consists of a great many, say, η, systems all occupying a volume of the *same* size, V, and having the *same* number of particles, N. If each system is isolated from its surroundings so that the total energy of each is fixed and all are alike as in Fig. 19.7(a), we have a *microcanonical* ensemble. If each of the systems is physically separated from the others by conducting walls [Fig. 19.7(b)], then, although V and N are alike (and constant), energies fluctuate about the mean for the entire system. This constitutes a *macrocanonical* ensemble and is for most purposes much easier to use than the microcanonical ensemble and more akin to the attainable in nature. In this case any one system of the ensemble may be thought of as in an extremely large temperature bath formed by the $(\eta - 1)$ others. The microcanonical ensemble, on the other hand, is rather artificial in that it is impossible to fix the energy of a given system precisely (whereas we *can* fix its temperature quite accurately). Finally there is the *grand canonical* ensemble, in which each system has small openings in its walls allowing molecules to diffuse back and forth from one system to another. In this case the number, N, of molecules as well as the internal energy of each system fluctuate. This is the type of ensemble most suited for systems with general physical and chemical processes underway. The macrocanonical ensemble, however, will be adequate for the discussions to follow.

In the macrocanonical ensemble, each system has its image point in Γ space, and each image point, as we have seen in Chap. 16, spends on the average the same amount of time in each Γ cell. In other words, all microstates of a system have equal probabilities, whether the elements (or particles, whatever they may be) of a system interact weakly (as in an ideal gas) or strongly as in dense gases, liquids, crystals, ferromagnetic substances, etc. It is for this reason that the use of Γ space and ensemble theory must in general replace the earlier use of molecular or μ space.

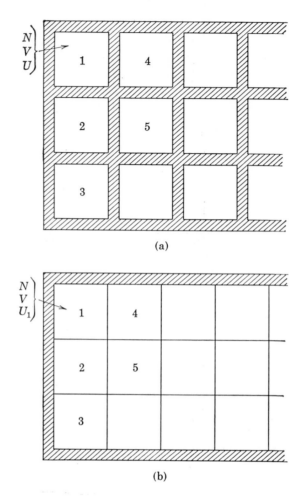

FIGURE **19.7** (b)

Since the energies in a macrocanonical ensemble fluctuate, Gibbs devised a method for calculating the most probable value for any system taken at random from the ensemble. The method bears a very close resemblance to that used in Chap. 16 in finding the most probable distribution in a system of particles and will be given here in rather condensed form. Since the energies fluctuate, image points move throughout Γ space (rather than being confined to a thin shell as with microcanonical ensembles) although they are denser in certain energy regions (or shells) than in others. We wish to find the energies where the density of image points is the greatest, that is, where a given system's image point is most likely to occur.

For this purpose imagine Γ space divided into energy shells, of which a typical one has energies between U_j and $U_j + \Delta U_j$. Suppose that there are η_j systems in this particular energy shell. Then the total number of systems is given by

$$\eta = \Sigma n_j \tag{19.31}$$

and the total energy, which we write ηU, becomes

$$\eta U = \Sigma \eta_j U_j \tag{19.32}$$

where U is thus the average energy of a system in the ensemble.

Unlike an ideal gas, in which the N identical molecules are in fact indistinguishable, the η systems of the ensemble are physically alike (that is, same N, same V, same permitted cells in Γ space, etc.) but are clearly distinguishable, since each occupies a particular location in the gridlike arrays of Fig. 19.7 and may be given a distinguishing number. This situation is, of course, not possible for the particles in a pure gas.

Now suppose that the volume of a given Γ space shell is of such size as to contain many quantum cells (which we now take to be not of size h^f, as for μ space, but of the appropriate size h^{Nf}). Let the number of quantum cells in the jth energy shell be Ω_j. Then Ω_j is the possible number of *microstates* for the system in this shell.[7] If we take the analog of the Boltzmann approximation, we must assume that $\Omega_j \gg \eta_j$, that is, that there are *many more available cells than systems* in a particular shell. Then the first system may be assigned in Ω_j ways, the second in Ω_j ways, etc., for a total of $\Omega_j^{\eta_j}$ distinct ways for the η_j (marked and distinguishable) systems. For the whole ensemble the number of assignments becomes

$$\prod_j \Omega_j^{\eta_j}$$

For the determination of the total number of ways of assigning the η marked systems in such an arrangement, the numbered systems must be permuted among the different shells, to give a factor

$$\frac{\eta!}{\Pi \eta_j!}$$

(just as in the original Boltzmann calculation, for which each molecule was marked; see Chap. 16). The result for the total number of meaningful ways, $\mathcal{W}$,

---

[7] Strictly speaking, in a quantized system (even when the interactions between the N subsystems are small) we must write down a single wave equation for the entire system. This wave equation contains the coordinates of all the N subsystems. Its solution gives the system wave functions, each of which determines a microstate of the system, all of equal a priori probability. The number of wave functions corresponding to U_j gives Ω_j, the statistical weight of that system energy (in just the same way as g_j was the statistical weight of an energy state, ϵ_j, of the individual subsystem in the earlier treatment).

is therefore

$$\mathscr{W} = \eta! \prod \frac{\Omega_j{}^{n_i}}{\eta_j!} \tag{19.33}$$

The entropy of the whole ensemble is then $k \ln \mathscr{W}$. Writing the total entropy as ηS (so that S is the average entropy of a system for this particular assignment), we have

$$\eta S = k \left(\ln \eta! \prod \frac{\Omega_j{}^{n_i}}{\eta_j!} \right)$$

or

$$\eta S = k \left(\eta \ln \eta + \sum \eta_j \ln \frac{\Omega_j}{\eta_j} \right) \tag{19.34}$$

on use of Stirling's formula for all factorials. Such a usage is now rigorously justified since we can make η and thus any η_j as large as we like. (For the Darwin-Fowler method, which avoids the use of the Stirling formula altogether, see Appendix 19.2.)

To find the equilibrium value of the η_j's we then proceed to maximize the entropy as given by Eq. 19.34 with the conditions of Eqs. 19.31 and 19.32. It is left as an exercise (Problem 19.5) to show that by the usual Lagrangian technique this maximization gives the condition

$$\ln \frac{\Omega_j}{\eta_j} = \lambda - \ln \eta + \beta U_j \tag{19.35}$$

or

$$\eta_j = \eta e^{-\lambda} \Omega_j e^{-\beta U_i} \tag{19.36}$$

To find λ, we must sum η_j to obtain

$$\eta = \sum \eta_j = \eta e^{-\lambda} \sum \Omega_j e^{-\beta U_i}$$

or

$$e^{\lambda} = \sum_{\text{all shells}} \Omega_j e^{-\beta U_i} = Z_\gamma = \sum_{\text{all cells}} e^{-\beta U_i} \tag{19.37}$$

where the sum of $\Omega_j e^{-\beta U_i}$ over all the shells of Γ space of energy U_j is now a partition function for Γ space (or a *system* partition function). As was mentioned at the beginning of the chapter, this function will be written Z_γ to distinguish it from Z_μ, the μ space or particle partition function used up to this point.

By means of this definition of Z_γ, the *system distribution law* becomes

$$\boxed{\eta_j = \frac{\eta e^{-\beta U_i}}{Z_\gamma}} \tag{19.38}$$

which is of the same form as the Maxwell-Boltzmann distribution law for molecules. Just as in the earlier case, the total energy, ηU, and the total entropy, ηS, of the ensemble may be expressed in terms of Z_γ and its derivatives. Thus use of Eqs. 19.32 and 19.37 gives us for the total energy of the ensemble

$$\eta U = \sum \eta_j U_j = \frac{\eta}{Z_\gamma} \sum U_j e^{-\beta U_j} = -\frac{\eta \partial \ln Z_\gamma}{\partial \beta}$$

or

$$U = -\frac{\partial \ln Z_\gamma}{\partial \beta} = kT^2 \frac{\partial \ln Z_\gamma}{\partial T} \qquad (19.39)$$

Likewise, insertion of the value of $\ln \Omega_j/\eta_j$ from Eq. 19.35 in the entropy expression Eq. 19.34 gives

$$\eta S = k(\eta \lambda + \beta \Sigma \eta_j U_j)$$

Since $\ln e^\lambda = \lambda = \ln Z_\gamma$ and $\Sigma \eta_j U_j = \eta U$, the number η cancels, leaving the entropy of a system at equilibrium as

$$S = k(\ln Z_\gamma + \beta U) \qquad (19.40)$$

Using the fact that $(\partial S/\partial U)_V = 1/T$ as in Sec. 15.11, we can readily show that $\beta = 1/kT$ as in the simpler case when we write Eq. 19.40

$$S = k\left(\ln Z_\gamma + \frac{U}{kT}\right) \qquad (19.41)$$

Since $A = U - TS$, we obtain for the Helmholtz function

$$A = -kT \ln Z_\gamma \qquad (19.42)$$

in appearance an even simpler result than that in terms of the molecular partition function, Z_μ. (See Eq. 16.65.)

19.6 The System Partition Function

In the case of the ideal monatomic gas, with which integration is justified for evaluation of the molecular partition function, we had

$$Z_\mu = \frac{1}{h^3} \int \cdots \int e^{-\beta H(p,q)} d\mu = \frac{1}{h^3} \int dV \iiint e^{-\beta H(p,q)} d\mu_p$$

$$= \frac{V}{h^3} (2\pi mkT)^{3/2} \qquad (19.43)$$

Here $d\mu_p$ refers to an element of momentum space, and the volume integral may be evaluated at once since the Hamiltonian is independent of the position coordinates in dV.

Now consider a system of N independent molecules, *all different,* to be designated as A, B, C, . . . , so that the energy of the entire system can be written

$$U = \epsilon_A + \epsilon_B + \epsilon_C + \cdots \qquad (19.44)$$

Then we define molecular partition functions of the form

$$Z_A = \sum_j e^{-\epsilon_{A_j}}$$

$$Z_B = \sum_j e^{-\epsilon_{B_j}}$$

$$\cdot \ \cdot \ \cdot \ \cdot \ \cdot$$

the summation being over all the energy states (or μ cells) of each molecule. When continuous integration is justified, these functions may be evaluated as integrals analogous to that given in Eq. 19.43 for the ideal monatomic gas. For the present discussion, however, they are best left as summations. If a product of these molecular partition functions is formed, it will in general contain in the exponentials all of the possible values that U in Eq. 19.44 can have.

For example, consider two molecules, A and B. Let the first have *two* possible states, ϵ_{A_1} and ϵ_{A_2}, and the second *three*, say, ϵ_{B_1}, ϵ_{B_2}, and ϵ_{B_3}. Then all the possible energies of this two-particle system are contained in the set of six energies,

$$\epsilon_{A_1} + \epsilon_{B_1} \qquad \epsilon_{A_1} + \epsilon_{B_2} \qquad \epsilon_{A_1} + \epsilon_{B_3}$$
$$\epsilon_{A_2} + \epsilon_{B_1} \qquad \epsilon_{A_2} + \epsilon_{B_2} \qquad \epsilon_{A_2} + \epsilon_{B_3}$$

since the product, $Z_A Z_B$, gives

$$Z_A Z_B = (e^{-\beta \epsilon_{A_1}} + e^{-\beta \epsilon_{A_2}})(e^{-\beta \epsilon_{B_1}} + e^{-\beta \epsilon_{B_2}} + e^{-\beta B_3})$$
$$= e^{-\beta(\epsilon_{A_1}+\epsilon_{B_1})} + e^{-\beta(\epsilon_{A_1}+\epsilon_{B_2})} + e^{-\beta(\epsilon_{A_1}+\epsilon_{B_3})} + e^{-\beta(\epsilon_{A_2}+\epsilon_{B_1})} + e^{-\beta(\epsilon_{A_2}+\epsilon_{B_2})} + e^{-\beta(\epsilon_{A_2}+\epsilon_{B_3})}$$

This relationship is true in general, and the system partition function may accordingly be written either as a product of the N particle partition functions or as a sum over all the energy states open to the entire system.[8]

In general the partition function for the system may be written in two ways, as we have seen,

$$Z_\gamma = \sum_{\text{all shells}} \Omega_j e^{-\beta U_j} = \sum_{\text{all cells}} e^{-\beta U_i}$$

depending on whether we sum over all *energy shells* in Γ space or all quantum states (that is, microstates). Using the latter summation, we can be sure that

---

[8] Here, in order to obtain complete factoring, it is necessary to permit more than one particle in the same energy state. For the argument underlying the Boltzmann approximation in the original discussion in Sec. 19.5 to hold, we now require that although this arrangement is possible, it is *very* rare.

the product of the particle functions will include all the terms in Z_γ, that is, that

$$Z_\gamma = \sum e^{-\beta U_i} = Z^A Z^B Z^C \cdots = \left(\sum_i e^{-\beta \epsilon_{A_i}}\right)\left(\sum_i e^{-\beta \epsilon_{B_i}}\right) \cdots \quad (19.45)$$

If the system is such that although all the molecules are *alike* (that is, have identical energy states), they are *distinguishable* (as, for example, by being bound to definite lattice points that may be numbered in a crystal), then $Z_A = Z_B = \cdots = Z_\mu$, and we write

$$Z_\gamma = Z_\mu{}^N = (Z_\mu)^N$$

N independent *identical* but *distinguishable* subsystems or particles   (19.46)

Now suppose that the molecules are not only *alike* but *indistinguishable* in the sense that they are free to move and are not attached to fixed localities that can be numbered. In this case *any* of the assignments of the N molecules to give a specific Γ cell fixes one of the system energy states or microstates, U_i, in the exponent of the sum that gives Z_γ. Permuting the N molecules gives *different* microstates when the molecules are *distinguishable*. But now there are $N!$ duplicates, and these must be counted only once. Therefore, Eq. 19.46 must be divided by $N!$ to give

$$Z_\gamma = \frac{1}{N!}(Z_\mu)^N$$

N *independent indistinguishable* subsystems or particles   (19.47)

Since we are justified in using Stirling's formula on $N!$, Eq. 19.47 may be written in the equivalent form,

$$\ln Z_\gamma = N\left(\ln \frac{Z_\mu}{N} + 1\right)$$

Thus if we take any pure ideal gas, the molecules are indistinguishable and Eq. 19.47 or its equivalent must be used in place of Eq. 19.46.

If the ideal *monatomic* gas is taken as an example, Z_μ is given by Eq. 19.43, and therefore

$$Z_\gamma = \frac{1}{N!}\frac{V^N(2\pi mkT)^{3N/2}}{h^{3N}}$$

or

$$\ln Z_\gamma = N\left[\ln \frac{VT^{3/2}}{N} + \ln \frac{(2\pi mk)^{3/2}}{h^3} + 1\right]$$

Then to find any desired thermodynamic function, we use the general Gibbs-Boltzmann equations obtained in Sec. 19.5. Thus A is given by

$$A = -kT \ln Z_\gamma$$

and therefore

$$A^{\text{mono}} = -NkT \left[\ln \frac{VT^{3/2}}{N} + \ln \frac{(2\pi mk)^{3/2}}{h^3} + 1 \right]$$

which is exactly the result found if we start with the earlier relation

$$A = -NkT \left(\ln \frac{Z_\mu}{N} + 1 \right) \tag{16.65}$$

obtained in Chap. 16.

In the case of a *cooperative* assembly made up of N *identical* but *interacting* particles, the particle energies cannot be separated in the same way as shown. In fact, the Hamiltonian for the entire system, $\mathbf{H}(q, q_1, \ldots, p_{Nf})$, must be used. In the classical case in which the partition function sum can be replaced by an integral, we write

$$Z_\gamma = \sum e^{-\beta U_i} = \frac{1}{N!} \frac{1}{h^{Nf}} \int \cdots \int e^{-\beta \mathbf{H}(q_1, \ldots, p_{Nf})} dq_1 \cdots dp_{Nf}$$

or

$$Z_\gamma = \frac{1}{N!} \frac{1}{h^{Nf}} \int e^{-\beta \mathbf{H}} \, d\Gamma \tag{19.48}$$

where again the factor $N!$ in the denominator is to take account of the duplicates that would otherwise be counted in the integration over Γ space. In general, this integral is seldom evaluable, and various approximations are required, depending on the interactions involved or assumed.

19.7 The Imperfect Monatomic Gas

One of the simpler cooperative assemblies is a monatomic gas at a density at which the interactions between the molecules, although not negligible, are small. In all gaseous problems the Hamiltonian may be written as the kinetic energy of the separate molecules plus the potential energy of the entire system. The first depends on the p's alone, and the second is a function of the q's only. Thus we write

$$\mathbf{H} = \sum_{i=1}^{3N} \frac{1}{2m} p_1{}^2 + U^{\text{pot}}(q_1 \cdots q_{3N}) \tag{19.49}$$

In this case the integral for Z_γ for the system as given in Eq. 19.48 separates into two independent factors, the first over the p's and the second over the q's; that is,

$$Z = Z_\gamma{}^p Z_\gamma{}^q$$

where with $f = 3$,

$$Z_\gamma{}^p = \frac{1}{N!} \frac{1}{h^{3N}} \int_{-\infty}^{+\infty} \cdots \int_{-\infty}^{+\infty} e^{-\beta \Sigma_i{}^2/2m} \, dp_1 \cdots dp_{3N}$$

and
$$Z_\gamma{}^q = \int \cdots \int e^{-\beta U^{\text{pot}}} \, dq_1 \cdots dq_{3N} \qquad \textbf{(19.50)}$$

Since the p's are all independent, the first of these factors breaks up into the product of $3N$ integrals of the type

$$\int_{-\infty}^{+\infty} e^{-\beta p^2/2m} \, dp = 2I(0) = (2\pi m k T)^{\frac{1}{2}}$$

when
$$Z_\gamma{}^p = \frac{1}{N!} \frac{(2\pi m k T)^{3N/2}}{h^{3N}}$$

The second factor, the so-called *configuration integral*, goes directly to V^N, when the gas is ideal and $U^{\text{pot}} \to 0$. In general it cannot be evaluated in closed terms, although it may be approximated in various ways, each of which leads to an equation of state for the gas.

Using the general Gibbs formula, Eq. 19.42, for A gives

$$-A = kT \ln Z_\gamma = kT \ln Z_\gamma{}^p Z_\gamma{}^q$$

where only the factor $Z_\gamma{}^q$ can involve the volume of the gas. Since $p = -(\partial A/\partial V)_T$,

$$p = kT \left(\frac{\partial \ln Z_\gamma{}^q}{\partial V} \right)_T \qquad \textbf{(19.51)}$$

is the general equation of state for the imperfect gas (note that for the ideal gas with $Z_\gamma{}^q = V^N$ this reduces to $p = NkT/V$ as it should). In other words, the factor $Z_\gamma{}^p$ does not enter the equation of state; this equation is determined solely by the *configuration integral*.

19.8   The van der Waals Approximation

Let us now attempt to find a simple approximation to the configuration integral, $Z_\gamma{}^q$, for the case in which the interactions between molecules are assumed *negligible* except when they are *very close together*. The simplest assumption to make is that the potential energy of the whole gas is the sum of a set of terms, each giving the potential of a *pair* of molecules as a function of their distance apart. Take the molecules i and j a distance r_{ij} apart, and let their mutual potential energy, $\epsilon(r_{ij})$, be some function of r_{ij}, the separation of their centers.[9]

---

[9] The near presence of a third molecule is assumed to have no appreciable effect on the function $\epsilon(r_{ij})$. Thus three molecules near to one another contribute three terms to the sum, each calculated as though the third were absent.

Now consider the number of such pairs in the gas. There are N ways of selecting the first, and $N - 1$ for the second, or $N(N - 1)/2$ *pairs*, since order is immaterial. Thus

$$U^{\text{pot}} = \sum_{i>j}^{N} \sum_{j=1}^{N-1} \epsilon(r_{ij}) \tag{19.52}$$

where only $N(N - 1)/2$ different terms are involved. The terms that Eq. 19.52 introduces into the exponent are such that we may write

$$e^{-\beta U^{\text{pot}}} = \prod_{N \geq i > j \geq 1} e^{-\beta \epsilon(r_{ij})} \tag{19.53}$$

that is, a product of $N(N - 1)/2$ terms, each of which approaches unity as r_{ij} becomes large and $\epsilon(r_{ij}) \to 0$. It is therefore convenient to write a given factor as

$$e^{-\beta \epsilon(r_{ij})} = e^{-\beta \epsilon_{ij}} = 1 + f_{ij} \tag{19.54}$$

where $f_{ij} \to 0$ as r_{ij} becomes large. Then Eq. 19.53 becomes

$$e^{-\beta U^{\text{pot}}} = 1 + \Sigma f_{ij} + \Sigma \Sigma f_{ij} f_{kl} + \cdot \cdot \cdot$$

Introduction of this expression in the configuration integral gives

$$Z_\gamma{}^q = \int \cdot \cdot \cdot \int (1 + \Sigma f_{ij} + \Sigma \Sigma f_{ij} f_{kl} \cdot \cdot \cdot) \, dq_1 \cdot \cdot \cdot dq_{3N}$$

Integration of this gives a series of terms, of which that from the unity term is just $\int \cdot \cdot \cdot \int dq_1 \cdot \cdot \cdot dq_N = V^N$ (the value for the ideal gas). The integration over the f_{ij} terms, the $f_{ij} f_{kl}$ terms, etc., gives what are known as *cluster* integrals. For the present purpose we assume that the gas is dilute enough that on the average only the terms in f_{ij} need be retained. This means that at any instant groups of *two* molecules exist that are close enough together for their mutual potential energies to be important, but that groups of *three or more* sufficiently close are rare enough to be neglected entirely.

With this simplification we replace each f_{ij} by $e^{\beta \epsilon_{ij}} - 1$ from Eq. 19.54 and obtain for the configuration integral

$$Z_\gamma{}^q = V^N + \sum_i \sum_j \int \cdot \cdot \cdot \int (e^{-\beta \epsilon_{ij}} - 1) \, dq_1 \cdot \cdot \cdot dq_{3N}$$

Here the double sum gives $N(N - 1)/2$ integrals all of the same value; each represents an integration over all Γ space.[10] These integrals represent corrections to the simple value of $Z_\gamma{}^q$ for the ideal gas (that is, V^N). Therefore, if I_{corr}

---

[10] This in reality assumes that all pairs in the gas are identical. Since pairs very near the surface are not identical, this equation amounts to treating all pairs as though they were *interior pairs*. This problem will be considered in more detail later.

is the common value of one of them,

$$Z_{\gamma^q} = V^N + \frac{N(N-1)}{2} I_{\text{corr}}$$

or

$$Z_{\gamma^q} = V^N + \frac{N^2}{2} I_{\text{corr}} \tag{19.55}$$

the difference between N and $N-1$ being negligible. Since

$$I_{\text{corr}} = \int \cdots \int (e^{-\beta \epsilon_{ij}} - 1)\, dq_1 \cdots dq_{3N}$$

and ϵ_{ij} depends on the coordinates of molecules i and j *only*, the integration over the coordinates of the other $(N-2)$ molecules may be carried out at once. Integration over the subspace of each molecule gives V, and thus the total factor produced is V^{N-2}. We therefore write

$$I_{\text{corr}} = V^{N-2} \int\int (e^{-\beta \epsilon_{ij}} - 1)\, dV_i dV_j$$

where $dV_i = dq_i\, dq_{i+1}\, dq_{i+2}$ and $dV_j = dq_j\, dq_{j+1}\, dq_{j+2}$

Since ϵ_{ij} depends only on r_{ij}, the distance between the two molecules, ϵ_{ij}, is constant on a sphere of radius r_{ij} about, say, molecule i as a center. (See Fig. 19.8.) We now transform to polar coordinates with the ith molecule as a center, and with $r_{ij} = r$ write

$$dV_j = 4\pi r^2\, dr$$

(which is equivalent to integration over the polar angles θ and ϕ). Then

$$I_{\text{corr}} = V^{N-2} \int_{V_i} \int_r (e^{-\beta \epsilon_{ij}(r)} - 1)4\pi r^2\, dr\, dV_i \tag{19.56}$$

This integral is impossible to evaluate as it stands, owing to the asymmetry of the force field for nearly all molecules, particularly those near the walls of

FIGURE **19.8**

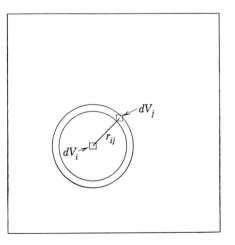

the container. Since we are assuming a purely local force field around each molecule, $\epsilon_{ij} \rightarrow 0$ for some modest value of r, say, r_1. Since r_1 is probably only a few tens of molecular diameters, this means that only surface molecules within a thin layer a few tens of angstroms in thickness are in an asymmetric field. These surface molecules, as was stated before, represent a negligible fraction of the whole. Accordingly, we may treat all molecules as though they were interior ones.

With this assumption (which was actually made earlier), we now proceed to the integration over the range from $r = 0$ to $r = r_1$. If there is some distance of closest approach of molecular centers during a collision, say, r_0, it is convenient to break the range into two parts, from 0 to r_0 and from r_0 to r_1. Clearly the center of j is prohibited from having its r in the range 0 to r_0, and ϵ_{ij} must be *indefinitely* large for this range. In general, unless the molecules are perfectly rigid and impenetrable, r_0 varies from collision to collision, depending on the relative approach velocity. To avoid this difficulty, we adopt the "*hard attracting sphere*" model of a molecule, with which r_0 becomes the same for all collisions and is just the diameter of one of the hard spheres. The form of the potential curve resulting for this simple model is shown in Fig. 19.9, where ϵ_{ij} is defined as follows.

$$\epsilon_{ij} = 0 \qquad r > r_1$$
$$\epsilon_{ij} < 0 \qquad r_0 < r < r_1$$
$$\epsilon_{ij} = +\infty \qquad r < r_0$$

Thus the force between the molecules is zero beyond the radius r_1 and is attractive between r_1 and r_0, where it suddenly changes to an infinite repulsion.

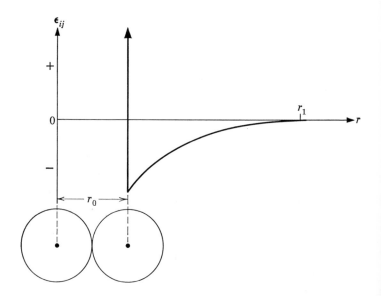

FIGURE **19.9**

We now write for the integral over r

$$\int_0^{r_1} (e^{-\beta \epsilon_i} - 1)4\pi r^2 \, dr = \int_0^{r_0} (e^{-\beta \epsilon_{ij}} - 1)4\pi r^2 \, dr + \int_{r_0}^{r_1} (e^{-\beta \epsilon_{ij}} - 1)4\pi r^2 \, dr$$

Since $e^{-\beta \epsilon_{ij}} - 1 = -1$ in the first range, the first integral reduces to $-4\pi r_0^3/3$. To evaluate the second integral, we assume that $\beta |\epsilon_{ij}| \ll 1$. Then, on expansion of the exponential,

$$e^{-\beta \epsilon_{ij}} - 1 = 1 - \beta \epsilon_{ij} + \cdots - 1 = -\beta \epsilon_{ij} = +\beta |\epsilon_{ij}|$$

since the potential energy must be negative in this entire range. If the average value of $|\epsilon_{ij}|$ over the range r_0 to r_1 is $|\overline{\epsilon_{ij}}|$, the second integral reduces to

$$\frac{4\pi r^3}{3} |\overline{\epsilon_{ij}}|\beta \Big]_{r_0}^{r_1}$$

and

$$I_{\text{corr}} = V^{N-2} \left\{ -\frac{4\pi r_0^3}{3} + \frac{4\pi r^3}{3} |\overline{\epsilon_{ij}}|\beta \Big]_{r_0}^{r_1} \right\} \int_V dV_i$$

$$= V^{N-1} \left[-\frac{4\pi r_0^3}{3} + \frac{4\pi (r_1^3 - r_0^3)|\overline{\epsilon_{ij}}|}{3kT} \right] \tag{19.57}$$

This gives for the configuration integral from Eq. 19.55

$$Z_\gamma{}^q = V^N \left\{ 1 + \frac{1}{V} \left[\frac{2\pi}{3} (r_1^3 - r_0^3)|\overline{\epsilon_{ij}}|N^2 \frac{1}{kT} - \frac{2\pi r_0^3}{3} NN \right] \right.$$

or simply

$$Z_\gamma{}^q = V^N \left[1 + \frac{1}{V} \left(\frac{a}{kT} - bN \right) \right] \tag{19.58}$$

where the abbreviations a and b are

$$a = \frac{2\pi}{3} (r_1^3 - r_0^3)|\overline{\epsilon_{ij}}|N^2$$

and

$$b = \frac{2\pi r_0^3 N}{3} \tag{19.59}$$

and are constants for the model we have adopted. The result in Eq. 19.58 constitutes the van der Waals approximation to the general configuration integral defined by Eq. 19.50.

19.9 The van der Waals Equation

Once the configuration integral has been evaluated, the equation of state can be written down from the general result obtained in Sec. 19.7 and given as

Eq. 19.51. Inserting the value for $Z_\gamma{}^q$ from Eq. 19.58 in Eq. 19.51 gives

$$p = kT\left(\frac{\partial \ln Z_\gamma{}^q}{\partial V}\right)_T = kT\frac{\partial \ln V^N}{\partial V} + kT\frac{\partial \ln\left[1 + \frac{1}{V}\left(\frac{a}{kT} - bN\right)\right]}{\partial V}$$

$$\text{or}\quad p = \frac{NkT}{V} - \frac{kT\left(\frac{a}{kT} - bN\right)}{V^2\left[1 + \frac{1}{V}\left(\frac{a}{kT} - bN\right)\right]} = \frac{NkT}{V} - \frac{a}{V^2} + \frac{NkTb}{V^2} + \cdots$$

provided that we neglect $1/V(a/kT - bN)$ compared with unity. Thus

$$\left(p + \frac{a}{V^2}\right)V = NkT\left(1 + \frac{b}{V}\right) = \frac{NkT}{\left(1 + \frac{b}{V}\right)^{-1}}$$

which may be written

$$\left(p + \frac{a}{V^2}\right)V\left(1 - \frac{b}{V} + \frac{b^2}{V^2} + \cdots\right) = NkT$$

When b^2/V^2 and higher powers are neglected, this reduces to

$$\boxed{\left(p + \frac{a}{V^2}\right)(V - b) = NkT}$$

which is van der Waals' equation for N molecules of gas. It is quite apparent that this results only from the ruthless neglect of all terms above the *first-order*

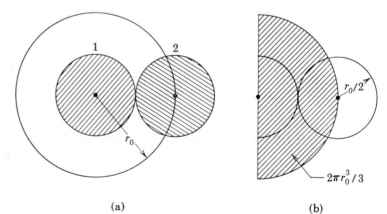

(a)   (b)

FIGURE **19.10**

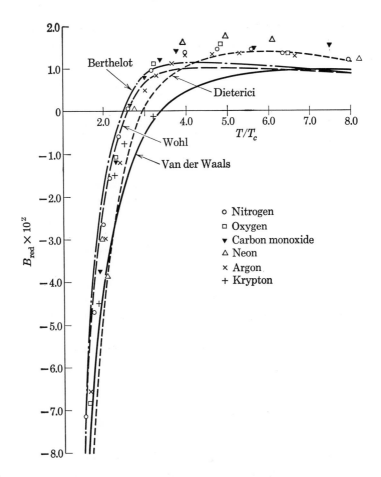

FIGURE **19.11**

correction ones, even for the infinitely hard attracting sphere model—which is itself, of course, a rather rough approximation to reality.

The van der Waals equation is none the less, as we have already seen, a remarkably good equation for the qualitative and semiquantitative discussion of a real gas. Incidentally it is now clear why van der Waals' a represents the effect of attraction, since from Eq. 19.59 it is fixed by parameters determined by the properties assigned to the *attractive potential function.* It varies with N^2, and this variation must be considered when the constants are changed from one unit of mass to another. Van der Waals' b, on the other hand, is not the total volume of the N dense spheres that we have assumed to comprise the gas. This would be

$$4 \frac{\pi}{3} \left(\frac{r_0}{2} \right)^3 N = \frac{\pi}{3} r_0{}^3 N = \frac{b}{2}$$

Nor is it the total volume of the spheres from which the *center* of a second molecule is excluded [see Fig. 19.10(a)]. This would be

$$4 \frac{\pi}{3} r_0{}^3 = 2b$$

The volume b represents the "statistical exclusion volume," which, in the state of the gas assumed, is denied the centers of colliding molecules. Since we are neglecting the presence of clusters of three or more molecules, only the effect of *bimolecular* collisions is included in van der Waals' equation. Statistically, therefore, one half of $4\pi r_0{}^3/3$ gives the effective value of b [Fig. 19.10(b)], since this is all the volume actually "seen" from the center of approaching molecules in bimolecular collisions.

Of course, more suitable (and more complicated) potential functions may be assumed than the one we have discussed here. The whole subject is a vast and ever growing one in which, as greater precision is sought, the forces acting must eventually be treated by quantum mechanical methods. It is none the less interesting to compare the van der Waals equation on the basis of the second virial coefficient that it predicts with observations and with other simple equations of state. Accordingly, Fig. 19.11 has been drawn to show the course of the second virial coefficients for the three two-constant equations of van der Waals, Berthelot, and Dieterici and the *three*-constant formula of Wohl. The necessary values for the B's are taken from Table 3.2, converted to reduced pressure, and plotted as $B_{\mathrm{red}} \times 10^2$ vertically versus the reduced temperature, T/T_c, horizontally. The four curves result; the observed points for N_2, O_2, CO, Ne, Ar, and K are calculated for the most part from the data of Holborn and Otto (see Appendix 2.1).

Much more precise calculations of the effects of various assumed potential functions give better agreement with experiment. Ultimately, however, the differences among monatomic, polar, and nonpolar gases render any universal type of equation impossible, in theory at least.

19.10 The Einstein Model of a Monatomic Solid

The consideration of the dilute gas was made simple (and feasible) because we restricted ourselves to densities at which the interaction between particles was relatively small. The other extreme is that of a solid body—taken here as a regular monatomic crystal. Although the interactions are very large, the force field set up in the interior of the crystal attains a simple periodic structure throughout the interior of the sample. This permits certain rather simple approximations to the actual physical situation.

For simplicity let us consider a perfect cubic crystal in which the elements occupying the points of the crystal lattice are atoms in ^1S states. The atoms vibrate about these lattice points as a result of the internal forces in the crystal. Since the atoms are close together, the field in which a given one moves depends on the locations of its neighbors. Accordingly, both its equilibrium position and its frequency are determined by the locations of its nearest neighbors in the lattice and are changing all the time. To simplify this complicated behavior, we consider a static field with a fixed equilibrium position at the appropriate lattice point, this field representing a suitable time average of the real one. Owing to the crystal symmetry, we expect this field to be the same along the three crystal axes. Thus the general oscillations of the atom are resolvable into three vibrations along the three orthogonal axes, which, if the amplitudes are sufficiently small, are simple harmonic and all of the same frequency. Therefore, the crystal system made up of N atoms (the near surface effect again being neglected) may be represented by a system of $3N$ independent harmonic oscillators of the same frequency, ν. This is essentially the approximation made by Einstein.

The Einstein model of the crystal then consists of a system of $3N$ *independent linear oscillators* that are *distinguishable* because of their assumed identification with definite lattice points.

For simplicity we agree to measure the total energy of the system relative to the zero-point energy and write

$$U = \epsilon_{A_{v_1}} + \epsilon_{B_{v_2}} + \epsilon_{C_{v_3}} + \cdots$$

where $\epsilon_{A_{v_1}}$ is the energy of vibrator A in state v_1, $\epsilon_{B_{v_2}}$ that of B in state v_2, etc. Thus with Eqs. 19.45 and 19.46 as the pair of expressions for the system partition function, we write for the system of $3N$ independent distinguishable oscillators

$$Z_\gamma' = (Z_\mu')^{3N}$$

Here Z_μ' is the (relative) vibratory partition function given in Eq. 17.41 of Sec. 17.12 for the linear oscillator, for which

$$\epsilon' = \epsilon^{\text{vib}} - \epsilon_0 = v h\nu$$

and

$$Z' \equiv Z_\mu' = (1 - e^{-u})^{-1} = (1 - e^{-\beta h\nu})^{-1}$$

Thus

$$Z_\gamma' = (1 - e^{-\beta h\nu})^{-3N} \qquad (19.60)$$

From the general Gibbs relation in Eq. 19.39,

$$U' = -\frac{\partial \ln Z_\gamma'}{\partial \beta} = \frac{3N e^{-\beta h\nu} h\nu}{1 - e^{-\beta h\nu}} = \frac{3N h\nu}{e^{\beta h\nu} - 1} \qquad (19.61)$$

This gives for the molar heat capacity of the solid

$$C_V = \frac{\partial U'}{\partial T} = \frac{3N_0 k (\beta h\nu)^2 e^{\beta h\nu}}{(e^{\beta h\nu} - 1)^2} = 3R \frac{u^2 e^u}{(e^u - 1)^2} \qquad (19.62)$$

or

$$\frac{C_V}{R} = 3E(u)$$

and

$$u = \beta h\nu = \frac{h\nu}{kT} = \frac{\Theta}{T}$$

Here $E(u)$ is the Einstein function discussed in Sec. 7.7, and $3RE(u)$ is plotted versus $1/u = T/\Theta$ as the lower curve in Fig. 7.6.

By means of this simple model, Einstein was able to show why the heat capacities of solids diminished from the classical Dulong and Petit value of $3R$ as the temperature was lowered. As Fig. 7.6 shows, the Einstein formula predicts too rapid a fall and the attainment of essentially zero heat capacities at too high a temperature. None the less Einstein's formula was very important historically in directing attention to the desirability of low-temperature thermal measurements as well as in acting as a starting point for more refined calculations.

19.11   The Debye Model of a Solid

In practice most solids are aggregates of small crystals having thermal properties that are not greatly different from those of an equivalent cubic crystal with the same elastic properties along the three axes of the solid. Let the positions of each atom be designated by Cartesian coordinates $x_1 \cdots x_{3N}$, measured relative to the equilibrium position in the space lattice, where the energy by definition is zero. For small disturbances from these positions, the potential energy can always be expanded as a sum of terms of the form $a_{ij}x_ix_j$. All linear terms must be zero since no forces exist at the equilibrium positions, and cubic and higher-order terms may be neglected for small enough amplitudes of vibration. For the velocity components $\dot{x}_1$, $\dot{x}_2$, $\ldots$, $\dot{x}_{3N}$, there are the momenta p_1, p_2, $\ldots$, p_{3N}, and the Hamiltonian for the system becomes

$$\mathrm{H}(p_{x_i}, x_i) = \sum_i^{3N} \frac{1}{2m}\, p_{x_i} + \sum_j \sum_i a_{ij}x_ix_j \tag{19.63}$$

where m is the mass of a single particle. Whatever the array of constants a_{ij} may be, it is always possible, as we have seen elsewhere, to transform to a new set of normal coordinates, say, p_i and q_i, so that the new Hamiltonian is a sum of squares only, that is,

$$\mathrm{H}(p_i, q_i) = \sum_i^{3N} \frac{1}{2m_i} p_i{}^2 + \sum_i^{3N} \frac{1}{2} K_i q_i{}^2 \tag{19.64}$$

where the force constants fix the frequency, ν_i, by the usual relation,

$$K_i = 4\pi^2 m \nu_i{}^2$$

This indicates that the cooperative assembly of N strongly coupled particles is equivalent for *infinitely small* vibrations to Einstein's $3N$ independent monochromatic oscillators. It is the higher terms, neglected in Eq. 19.63, that cause the vibrators to interact and ultimately come to equilibrium as a system at temperature T. The interactions thus play much the same role as the assumed momentary and infrequent collisions in an extremely dilute gas.

Since the linear oscillators are governed by the quantum theory, the amplitudes cannot be treated as infinitely small, and the oscillations are neither alike nor harmonic. We therefore imagine the real solid replaced by a collection of $3N$ harmonic oscillators, *all of different* frequencies. In this case, for a given frequency, ν_i, the energy is

$$\epsilon_i = vh\nu_i \qquad v = 0, 1, 2, \ldots$$

and the partition function for the particular oscillator is

$$Z_{\mu_i}' = \sum_{j=1}^{\infty} e^{-\beta v_j h \nu_i} = (1 - e^{-\beta h \nu_i})^{-1}$$

The corresponding partition function for the system is then the product of these values over the $3N$ oscillators, that is,

$$Z_\gamma' = \prod_{i=1}^{N3} (1 - e^{-\beta h \nu_i})^{-1} \tag{19.65}$$

Of course, the main question remains. Can we so determine the possible frequencies $\nu_1, \nu_2, \ldots, \nu_{3N}$ as to obtain a model that resembles the actual solid?

Debye proposed fixing the spectrum of frequencies for the system by going to the other extreme of treating it as a classically continuous solid. Its independent modes of vibration would then be due to all the possible *elastic standing waves* that the solid could sustain. From this standpoint the actual amplitude of any particular atom is compounded of the local amplitudes of all of these independent elastic vibrations and can in general be very complicated indeed.

The Debye model of a solid, therefore, is an elastically vibrating continuum for which the first $3N$ modes of vibration, counting from the lowest in frequency, are taken as the $3N$ independent vibrations required in the product for Z_γ' in Eq. 19.65. A mechanical standing wave in a continuous solid is limited by the same mathematical relations discussed for the quantum mechanical motion of a particle in a box in Sec. 18.4. Each standing wave must produce an integral number of half waves in the dimension considered. Whether the surfaces of the solid are planes of nodes or loops in these waves is immaterial. If the solid body is taken, for simplicity, in the form of a cube of length L on an edge, a standing wave, say, along the x axis must satisfy a relation of the usual form,

$$n_1 \frac{\lambda}{2} = L$$

or

$$n_1 = \frac{2L}{\lambda}$$

where n_1 is an integer. When $n_1 = 1$, $\lambda = 2L$, and no longer wave is permitted. The conditions for waves along the other axes are similar.

$$n_2 = \frac{2L}{\lambda}$$

and

$$n_3 = \frac{2L}{\lambda}$$

The general condition for a wave in a direction not necessarily along the axis is obtained by squaring these single conditions and adding to give

$$n_1{}^2 + n_2{}^2 + n_3{}^2 = \left(\frac{2L}{\lambda}\right)^2 = \left(\frac{2L\nu}{c}\right)^2 \tag{19.66}$$

where c is the speed of propagation and ν the frequency of the wave. The permitted independent frequencies are then found by assigning all possible integers to the set n_1, n_2, n_3, beginning with $0,0,0$, $1,0,0$, etc.[11]

Again, as in the case of the particle in a box,[12] the number of possible frequencies is very large for physical bodies of ordinary size, and we may treat them as forming essentially a continuous spectrum. This approach permits the use of the "n space" discussed in Sec. 18.7 and illustrated in Fig. 18.6. We therefore calculate the number of frequencies lying between ν and $\nu + d\nu$ on this basis. In this case Eq. 19.66 gives the condition on n,

$$n^2 = n_1{}^2 + n_2{}^2 + n_3{}^2 = \left(\frac{2L}{c}\right)^2 \nu^2$$

or

$$n = \left(\frac{2L}{c}\right)\nu \tag{19.67}$$

The number of frequencies in the range between n and $n + \Delta n$ is just one eighth the volume of the thin shell of radius n and thickness Δn illustrated in Fig. 18.6, that is,

$$\frac{1}{8}\,4\pi n^2\,\Delta n = \frac{\pi}{2} n^2\,\Delta n$$

With Eq. 19.67, this gives in the limit

$$\frac{\pi}{2}\left(\frac{2L}{c}\right)^3 \nu^2\,d\nu = \frac{4\pi V}{c^3}\,\nu^2\,d\nu \tag{19.68}$$

---

[11] In the case of the quantum problem of the particle in a cubic box, no solutions of the type $0, 0, 0$, $1, 0, 0$, etc., are possible, since if one or more of the product wave functions vanishes the whole solution vanishes. Thus the longest particle wave possible is that for the number set $1, 1, 1$, and there is no analog of the vibrationless solid. This situation has no effect on the present argument.

[12] Or the case of black body radiation in a cubic vessel with reflecting walls. See footnote 6, on the classical treatment of black body radiation in a cubic cavity.

For a solid body there are both transverse and longitudinal waves. The transverse waves may be described in terms of two independent transverse waves polarized at right angles to one another. Since they have identical velocities of propagation, say, c_t, the number of frequencies due to them is just twice that given in Eq. 19.68. If c_l is the velocity of the longitudinal waves, we now write for the total number of independent frequencies for a continuous solid of volume $V = L^3$ in the range between ν and $\nu + d\nu$, say, dN_2,

$$dN_\nu = 4\pi V \left(\frac{2}{c_t^3} + \frac{1}{c_l^3} \right) \nu^2 \, d\nu$$

If an average velocity, c, for these three waves is defined by

$$\frac{3}{c^3} = \frac{2}{c_t^3} + \frac{1}{c_l^3}$$

then

$$dN_\nu = \frac{12\pi V \nu^2 \, d\nu}{c^3} \tag{19.69}$$

If for simplicity V and c are both taken to be constant (although in fact they must vary with temperature), the number of independent modes per unit frequency range is proportional to ν^2.

19.12   The Debye Formula for Internal Energy

With the result just obtained, we are able to understand the Debye model for a solid. The actual solid with its N particles performing three-dimensional dependent vibrations is replaced by a continuous elastic body of the same dimensions, for which the number of independent modes of vibration in any frequency range, $d\nu$, is given by Eq. 19.69. Although the continuous solid has theoretically an infinite number of modes of elastic vibration, the elastic body can have only $3N$, and therefore Eq. 19.69 must be summed from 0 to a maximum frequency, ν_m, such that the total number of possible modes becomes exactly $3N$. Thus integrating Eq. 19.69 over the range 0 to ν_m gives the condition

$$3N = \int_0^{\nu_m} dN_\nu = \frac{12\pi V}{c^3} \int_0^{\nu_m} \nu^2 \, d\nu = \frac{4\pi V \nu_m^3}{c^3}$$

or

$$\nu_m = \left(\frac{3Nc^3}{4\pi V} \right)^{1/3} \tag{19.70}$$

This produces the spectrum shown previously in Fig. 7.7 of Sec. 7.7, with its sharp cutoff at $\nu_m = \nu_{max}$.

We now return to the system partition function given in Eq. 19.65. Its logarithm becomes

$$\ln Z_\gamma' = \sum_{i=1}^{3N} \ln (1 - e^{-\beta h \nu_i})^{-1}$$

With the number of frequencies in a region between ν_i and $\nu_i + d\nu_i$ given by the limit in Eq. 19.69, the sum is replaceable by an integral from $\nu = 0$ to ν_m, and we write

$$\ln Z_\gamma' = - \frac{12\pi V}{c^3} \int_0^{\nu_m} \nu^2 \ln (1 - e^{-\beta h \nu}) \, d\nu$$

Using Eq. 19.70 to replace the coefficient of the integral by $9N/\nu_m{}^3$, we obtain

$$\ln Z_\gamma' = - \frac{9N}{\nu_m{}^3} \int_0^{\nu_m} \nu^2 \ln (1 - e^{-\beta h \nu}) \, d\nu \tag{19.71}$$

It is convenient to make the usual substitution, $h\nu/kT = u$, where u_m is the maximum value of u, and

$$\ln Z_\gamma' = - \frac{9N}{u_m{}^3} \int_0^{u_m} u^2 \ln (1 - e^{-u}) \, du \tag{19.72}$$

or, on integration by parts,

$$\ln Z_\gamma' = - 3N \ln (1 - e^{-u_m}) + \frac{3N}{u_m{}^3} \int_0^{u_m} \frac{u^3 \, du}{e^u - 1} \tag{19.73}$$

A glance back at Eq. 19.60 shows that the first term is just the Einstein approximation with the single Einstein frequency equal to ν_m, the maximum of the Debye spectrum. Thus the Einstein spectrum is a *single line* where the Debye spectrum has its maximum intensity. The second term in Eq. 19.73 gives the extra contribution to $\ln Z_\gamma'$ due to the frequencies below ν_m and is relatively small in magnitude.

To find U' for the atomic crystal, it is simply necessary to make use of the general Gibbs relation in Eq. 19.39 as before.

$$U' = - \frac{\partial \ln Z_\gamma'}{\partial \beta} = - h\nu_m \frac{\partial \ln Z_\gamma'}{\partial u_m}$$

since $u_m = h\nu_m/kT$. Inserting Z_γ' from Eq. 19.73 and setting $\Theta_m = h\nu_m/k$, where Θ_m is the Debye temperature for the solid, give the relative internal energy due to vibration as

$$U' = \frac{9NkT^4}{\Theta_m{}^3} \int_0^{u_m} \frac{u^3 \, du}{e^u - 1} \qquad u_m = \frac{h\nu_m}{kT} \tag{19.74}$$

19.13   The Debye Function

To obtain the value of C_V for a mole of the crystal, we must now differentiate Eq. 19.74 with respect to T. Writing the integral in this expression as $I(u_m)$, we have

$$C_V = \frac{\partial U'}{\partial T} = \frac{9N_0 k}{\Theta_m{}^3} \left\{ 4T^3 I(u_m) + T^4 \left[\frac{\partial I(u_m)}{\partial T} \right] \right\}$$

However,

$$\frac{\partial I(u_m)}{\partial T} = \frac{\partial I(u_m)}{\partial u_m} \frac{\partial u_m}{\partial T} = - \frac{\Theta_m}{T^2} \frac{\partial I(u_m)}{\partial u_m}$$

where $\Theta_m = h\nu_m/k$ is again the Debye temperature for the solid (written simply as Θ in Chap. 7). Thus

$$\frac{\partial I(u_m)}{\partial T} = - \frac{\Theta_m}{T^2} \frac{u_m{}^3}{e^{u_m} - 1} = - \frac{\Theta_m{}^4}{T^5} \frac{1}{e^{\Theta_m/T} - 1}$$

and

$$C_V = 3R \left[12 \left(\frac{T}{\Theta_m} \right)^3 \int_0^{u_m} \frac{u^3\, du}{e^u - 1} - \frac{3 \left(\frac{\Theta_m}{T} \right)}{e^{\Theta_m/T} - 1} \right] \tag{19.75}$$

This we write as

$$\frac{C_V}{3R} = D \left(\frac{\Theta_m}{T} \right)$$

where

$$D \left(\frac{\Theta_m}{T} \right) = D(u_m) = \left[12 \left(\frac{T}{\Theta_m} \right)^3 \int_0^{u_m} \frac{u^3\, du}{e^u - 1} - \frac{3 \left(\frac{\Theta_m}{T} \right)}{e^{\Theta_m/T} - 1} \right] \tag{19.76}$$

and is the *Debye function*. This function unfortunately cannot be evaluated except by numerical calculation. Debye has made the calculation,[13] and some of his values are used for Table 19.4, columns 3 and 6 giving $3RD(\Theta_m/T)$, with Θ_m/T and its reciprocal T/Θ_m as the independent variables.

The behavior of C_V for a few typical solids is shown graphically in Fig. 7.6, where the large difference between the Debye and the Einstein predictions is evident.

To obtain the behavior of the Debye formula at low temperatures, we notice that as T becomes small, the *second* term in the Debye function (Eq. 19.76) becomes $-3(\Theta_m/T)e^{-\Theta_m/T}$, which clearly goes to zero as $T \to 0$. The *first* term contains the same integral that arose in the discussion of black body

---

[13] Debye, *Ann. Physik*, **39**, 789 (1912).

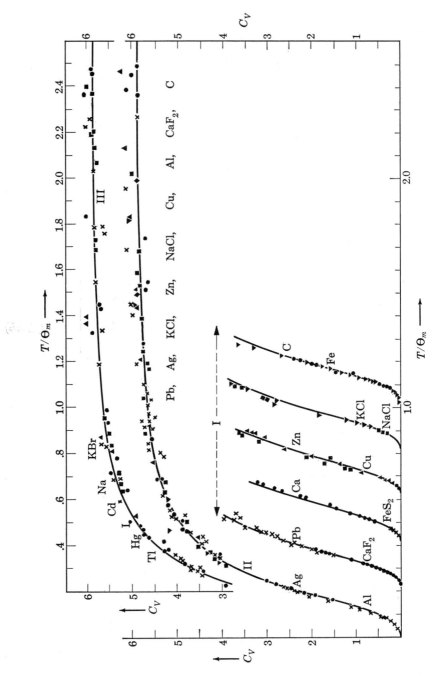

FIGURE 19.12

TABLE **19.4**

Molar Heat Capacity of a Solid from Debye's Formula, Eq. 19.75 (cal/mole-deg)

Θ_m/T	T/Θ_m	C_V	Θ_m/T	T/Θ_m	C_V
30	0.0333	0.0172	9		0.605
25	.0400	.0298	8	0.125	.824
20	.0500	.0581	7		1.138
15		.137	6		1.584
14		.169	5	.200	2.199
13		.211	4	.250	2.999
12	.125	.267	3	.333	3.952
11		.345	2	.500	4.923
10	.100	.452	1	1.000	5.676
			0		5.961

radiation in Sec. 19.3 and, as shown in Appendix 19.1, goes to $\pi^4/15$ as the upper limit, u_m, proceeds to infinity. Thus

$$\lim_{T \to \text{small}} C_V = 36R \left(\frac{T}{\Theta_m}\right)^3 \frac{\pi^4}{15} = \frac{12}{5} \frac{\pi^4 R}{\Theta_m{}^3} T^3 = \text{constant } T^3$$

This is the origin of the *Debye cube law*, which has been quoted so often in previous discussions. It is now seen to be a necessary consequence of the Debye model.

Experimentally a great many materials follow the Debye formula quite satisfactorily. In particular, Schrödinger (see Table 7.3) examined the data for the materials given in Table 7.3 and presented his results in graphical form. His now famous graph is reproduced in Fig. 19.12, and the data are seen to be represented well by the solid (theoretical) curves not only for the simple elementary substances but also for a number of compounds. (Here the horizontal scales for the curves in group I are shifted successively 0.2 divisions each as we proceed to the right.)

19.14   Extension of the Theory for Solids

As was pointed out in Chap. 7 (see particularly Secs. 7.6 and 7.7), many solids do not obey the Debye law for C_V. In the case of metals, an extra small term is needed at low temperatures to take care of the contribution of conduction electrons. (This will be obtained in Sec. 19.18.) In other cases the value of Θ_m that is adequate at low temperatures fails to fit the data at higher temperatures. In still other cases the C_V curves show various maxima or exhibit no tendency to level off at a limiting value, etc.

In general, we expect the actual frequency spectrum for the atomic solid to be dependent on the specific crystal lattice involved. If, instead of the simple spectrum given by Eq. 19.69, we introduce a general function, $f(\nu)$, so that the number of modes in a range $d\nu$ at ν becomes

$$dN_\nu = Nf(\nu)\,d\nu$$

then for a model with $3N$ modes the normalization requirement on the spectrum function is that

$$3N = \int_0^\infty Nf(\nu)\,d\nu$$

or

$$\int_0^\infty f(\nu)\,d\nu = 3$$

With this spectrum function the Debye partition function of Eq. 19.71 becomes a special case of a more general so-called acoustic or lattice function, given by

$$\ln Z_\gamma' = \ln Z_\gamma{}^{ac} = -N \int_0^\infty f(\nu) \ln\left(1 - e^{-\beta h\nu}\right) d\nu \qquad \textbf{(19.77)}$$

Blackman has investigated the possible forms of the function $f(\nu)$ for specific crystal lattices and found marked variations from the Debye type. He has succeeded in carrying out the difficult and laborious calculations for a cubic lattice model, and the results of the calculation of some 90,000 modes are shown in Fig. 19.13 and are seen to be quite different from the Debye spectrum. In the determination of this curve, $f(\nu)$ was calculated with $\Delta\nu$ in steps of 0.1, and the smoothed curve drawn so as to give the proper area under it. When the specific heat was calculated from this spectrum, Θ_m was found to vary with temperature as shown by the curve in Fig. 19.14. The circles represent the values obtained from measured values of C_V, and the agreement is seen to be

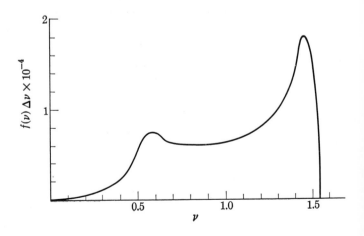

FIGURE **19.13**

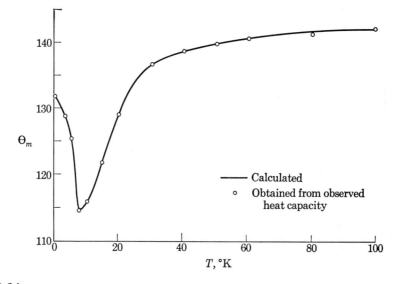

FIGURE **19.14**

very satisfactory indeed. For further details see an excellent review by Blackman.[14]

The complete partition function for a general crystal system must include a factor for the internal degrees of freedom, say, Z_γ^{int}, and so in place of Eq. 19.77, we write Z_γ^K for the crystal system as

$$Z_\gamma^K = Z_\gamma^{ac} Z_\gamma^{int}$$

If the lattice points are occupied by molecules, radicals, or groups of atoms, there are in general internal vibrations, and a factor of the Einstein type is needed for each. A final factor is necessary for the contributions due to electronic and nuclear states. Since for all of these internal contributions the system may be treated approximately as though it were made up of N independent but *identical* and *distinguishable* particles, Z_γ^{int} is found by raising the appropriate particle partition function to the Nth power as in Eq. 19.46. Thus for a diatomic crystal, we should have

where
$$Z_\gamma^{int} = (Z_\mu^{vib} g^{orn} g_K^{el} g_K^{nu})^N = (Z_\mu^{int})^N$$
$$Z_\mu^{vib} = (1 - e^{-u})^{-1}$$
$$g_K^{el} = g_0^{el} + g_1^{el} e^{-\theta_1^{el}/T} + \cdots$$
$$g_K^{nu} = g_A g_B$$

and where g_K^{el} includes any internal Stark effect levels that may be present, etc.

---

[14] Blackman, *Repts. Progr. in Phys.*, **8**(1941), 11.

Finally the total system partition function for the diatomic crystal becomes

$$Z_\gamma{}^K = Z_\gamma{}^{ac}(Z_\mu{}^{vib} g^{orn} g_K{}^{el} g_K{}^{nu})^N$$

With this available all the thermodynamic properties of the crystal, including of course the equation of state itself, are in principle calculable.

19.15   Fermi-Dirac Statistics

In contrast to the other types of statistics we have been considering, a Fermi-Dirac system is one in which the number of particles to be assigned to a particular energy state (or quantum cell in μ space) is fixed by the exclusion principle of Pauli. If an object with a spin of $\frac{1}{2}$ is assigned to a cell, only one other may occupy this cell, and it must have its spin reversed in direction. Further objects must be assigned to different cells; this particular one is *full*.

For simplicity in what follows, we begin with particles with no spin; the factor of 2 (or $2S + 1$ in general) can always be inserted later. Consider therefore the simple example of two objects to be distributed among three equal energy levels (or cells) discussed in Sec. 17.4 and illustrated for Boltzmann and Bose-Einstein methods of assignments in Figs. 17.1 and 17.2. A glance at the latter figure shows that only three possibilities, as shown in Fig. 19.15, remain for this new statistics, since no two particles may occupy the same cell.

In general consider N_j *distinguishable* objects to be distributed among g_j cells of energy ϵ_j (assuming $g_j \gg N_j$), only one object to be assigned to each cell. For this assignment the first object may be assigned in g_j ways, the second in $g_j - 1$ ways, etc., down to $g_j - N_j + 1$ for the last one. The total is

$$g_j(g_j - 1) \cdot \cdot \cdot (g_j - N_j + 1) = \frac{g_j!}{(g_j - N_j)!}$$

If now the objects are allowed to become indistinguishable, this number includes $N_j!$ duplicates, and the number of ways, W_j, of distributing the N_j identical objects is

$$W_j = \frac{g_j!}{N_j!(g_j - N_j)!} \tag{19.78}$$

For a general distribution with the numbers

$$N_1, N_2, \ldots, N_j, \ldots$$

and energies

$$\epsilon_1, \epsilon_2, \ldots, \epsilon_j, \ldots$$

this gives

$$W = \prod_j \frac{g_j!}{N_j!(g_j - N_j)!} \tag{19.79}$$

and therefore the entropy for the system is

$$S = k \sum \left[\ln \frac{g_j!}{N_j!(g_j - N_j)!} \right]$$

$$\underline{\quad a \quad} \quad \underline{\quad a \quad} \quad \underline{\qquad} \quad \underline{\quad a \quad} \quad \underline{\qquad} \quad \underline{\quad a \quad} \quad . \quad \underline{\qquad} \quad \underline{\quad a \quad} \quad \underline{\quad a \quad}$$

FIGURE **19.15**

Assuming Stirling's approximation is legitimate as before, this may be written

$$S = k \sum_j \left[- g_j \ln \left(1 - \frac{N_j}{g_j} \right) + N_j \ln \left(\frac{g_j}{N_j} - 1 \right) \right] \qquad \textbf{(19.80)}$$

subject, of course, to the restrictions

$$\Sigma N_j = N$$

and

$$\Sigma N_j \epsilon_j = U$$

If this expression for entropy is maximized as before with the multipliers -1, $-\lambda$, and $-\beta$, the following single condition results:

$$\sum \left[\ln \left(\frac{g_j}{N_j} - 1 \right) - \lambda - \beta \epsilon_j \right] \delta N_j = 0$$

or

$$\boxed{N_j = \frac{g_j}{B e^{\beta \epsilon_j} + 1}} \qquad B = e^\lambda \qquad \textbf{(19.81)}$$

This is the Fermi-Dirac distribution law quoted earlier. Obviously it is needed to replace the Boltzmann expression only when $B e^{\beta \epsilon_j}$ becomes comparable to 1 (instead of being much larger, as is usual for material systems at most temperatures).

19.16 The Electron Gas

Sommerfeld was the first to show that the conducting electrons in a metal could be regarded essentially as forming a quantum gas of free electrons confined to the volume occupied by the metal.[15] From the classical theory of electrons it was predicted that N free electrons should make a contribution of $3NkT/2$ to the internal energy of the metal and thus of $3Nk/2$ to the heat capacity, doubling the Dulong and Petit value. This prediction is, of course, contrary to experience.

If, however, these electrons are subject to quantum theory and obey the Fermi-Dirac statistics rather than the Boltzmann statistics, the situation is radically altered. To make Eq. 19.81 apply to electrons, each of which has a spin of $\pm \tfrac{1}{2}$ when assigned to an energy level, or cell, we must simply multiply

---

[15] Sommerfeld, *Z. Physik*, **47**, 1 (1928).

by a factor of 2, so that

$$N_j = 2 \frac{g_j}{Be^{\beta \epsilon_j} + 1} \tag{19.82}$$

The permitted energies are to be found by the general wave mechanical treatment for a particle in a cubic box (now defined by the boundaries of the metal). Thus, turning to the earlier result, we have

$$\epsilon_{n_1 n_2 n_3} = (n_1{}^2 + n_2{}^2 + n_3{}^2) \frac{h^2}{8mL^2} = n^2 \frac{h^2}{8mL^2} \tag{18.20}$$

In Sec. 18.7 the number of energy states Δg_n in the range between n and $n + \Delta n$ was found and given in Eq. 18.40 as

$$\Delta g_n = \frac{\pi}{4} \frac{(\epsilon_n{}^{\text{trn}})^{1/2} \Delta \epsilon_n{}^{\text{trn}}}{(\Theta^{\text{trn}} k)^{3/2}} \qquad \Theta^{\text{trn}} = \frac{h^2}{8mV^{2/3}k}$$

or, on dropping of the superscript and elimination of Θ^{trn},

$$\Delta g_n = \frac{\pi (8m)^{3/2} V}{4h^3} \epsilon_n{}^{1/2} \Delta \epsilon_n \tag{19.83}$$

Insertion of this result in Eq. 19.82, with the subscript n replaced by j and $\Delta g_n = g_j$, gives

$$N_j = \frac{\frac{\pi}{2} \left(\frac{8m_e}{h^2} \right)^{3/2} V \epsilon_j{}^{1/2} \Delta \epsilon_j}{(Be^{\beta \epsilon_j} + 1)} \tag{19.84}$$

where m_e is the mass of an electron. If now we let

$$\lim_{\Delta \epsilon_j \to 0} \frac{N_j}{\Delta \epsilon_j} = \frac{dN_\epsilon}{d\epsilon}$$

the number of electrons per unit energy range at ϵ_j, Eq. 19.84 becomes

$$dN_\epsilon = \frac{\pi}{2} \frac{(8m_e)^{3/2}}{h^3} V \frac{\epsilon^{1/2} d\epsilon}{Be^{\beta \epsilon} + 1} \tag{19.85}$$

On integrating this over the total energy range, we obtain

$$N = \frac{\pi}{2} \frac{(8m_e)^{3/2}}{h^3} V \int_0^\infty \frac{\epsilon^{1/2} d\epsilon}{Be^{\beta \epsilon} + 1} \tag{19.86}$$

as the condition for fixing the parameter B.

Since in this statistics only two particles can occupy an energy level, suppose that we assign the N electrons to each level from the lowest until the Nth has been assigned. Let the energy of the topmost be designated by ϵ^*. Then ϵ^* is a very important quantity, the so-called *Fermi energy*, this top level being the *Fermi level*. There are exactly as many energy states at or below ϵ^* as there are free electrons. To find ϵ^*, we write Eq. 19.83 in differential form,

$$dg = \frac{\pi}{2} \frac{(8m_e)^{3/2}}{h^3} V \epsilon^{1/2} d\epsilon$$

(the factor of 2 being included to allow for electron spins). Integrating from $\epsilon = 0$ to $\epsilon = \epsilon^*$ and setting the integral of dg equal to N, the number of electrons, we find

$$\epsilon^* = \frac{h^2}{8m_e} \left(\frac{3N}{\pi V}\right)^{2/3} \tag{19.87}$$

where it is to be noted that ϵ^* is independent of temperature and fixed by N/V, the *volume density of free electrons in the metal*. On substituting Eq. 19.87 in Eq. 19.86 and setting $x = \beta\epsilon = \epsilon/kT$, we obtain for the *normalization condition on B*

$$1 = \frac{3}{2} \left(\frac{kT}{\epsilon^*}\right)^{3/2} \int_0^\infty \frac{x^{1/2}\,dx}{Be^x + 1} \qquad x = \frac{\epsilon}{kT} \tag{19.88}$$

To find the average kinetic energy of an electron in the metal, say, $\overline{\epsilon^{kin}}$, it is simply necessary to multiply both sides of Eq. 19.85 by ϵ and integrate over all energies. This gives, on the replacement of ϵ/kT by x,

$$\overline{\epsilon^{kin}} = \frac{3}{2} kT \left(\frac{kT}{\epsilon^*}\right)^{3/2} \int_0^\infty \frac{x^{3/2}\,dx}{Be^x + 1} \tag{19.89}$$

Once B is determined from Eq. 19.88, it can be substituted in Eq. 19.89 to give the average energy of an electron and hence the contribution of free electrons to the metal's internal energy. The heat capacity due to the free electrons is then found by a simple differentiation. Unfortunately Eq. 19.88 is difficult to solve for B.

19.17   Approximation to the Value of the Parameter B

As a first and rather crude approximation to the value of B, let us assume that $Be^x \ll 1$. This is equivalent to the assumption that $x \ll \ln 1/B$, but with the denominator in Eq. 19.88 reduced to unity, the integrand becomes simply $x^{1/2}$. Therefore, let us assume that the integrand is $x^{1/2}$ from zero to $\ln 1/B$ and entirely negligible above that (x does, of course, diminish with T). Then the integral becomes $2x^{3/2}/3$ over the range from zero to $\ln 1/B$, and from Eq. 19.88 the condition results that

$$1 = \frac{3}{2} \left(\frac{kT}{\epsilon^*}\right)^{3/2} \frac{2}{3} \ln \left(\frac{1}{B}\right)^{3/2}$$

or

$$B = e^{-\epsilon^*/kT}$$

or

$$\ln \frac{1}{B} = \frac{\epsilon^*}{kT} \tag{19.90}$$

To see that B is really small enough to justify these assumptions, we define, from Eq. 19.87, a *Fermi characteristic temperature*, Θ^*, where

$$\Theta^* = \frac{\epsilon^*}{k} = \frac{h^2}{8 m_e k} \left(\frac{3N}{\pi V} \right)^{2/3}$$

For the case of copper with $V/N = 63/8.9$ (where 8.9 is the density and 63 the atomic weight), this gives

$$\Theta^* = 8 \times 10^4 \text{ deg}$$

or

$$B = \exp - \frac{8 \times 10^4}{T}$$

which is certainly small for even high temperatures (that is, $B = e^{-40}$ even when $T = 2000°$K).

With this approximation to B and the same processes as before, the integral in Eq. 19.89 for the energy becomes

$$\int_0^{\ln 1/B} x^{3/2} \, dx = \frac{2}{5} \ln \left(\frac{1}{B} \right)^{5/2}$$

and

$$\overline{\epsilon^{\text{kin}}} = \frac{3}{2} kT \left(\frac{kT}{\epsilon^*} \right)^{3/2} \frac{2}{5} \left(\frac{\epsilon^*}{kT} \right)^{5/2} = \frac{3}{5} \epsilon^* = \text{constant} \qquad \textbf{(19.91)}$$

A second approximation to B can be carried out similarly, although it is rather long. Omitting the details, we arrive at Sommerfeld's result,

$$\overline{\epsilon^{\text{kin}}} = \frac{3}{5} \epsilon^* \left[1 + \frac{5\pi^2}{12} \left(\frac{kT}{\epsilon^*} \right)^2 \right] \qquad \textbf{(19.92)}$$

19.18 Significance of the Fermi Level

If we use the *first* approximation for B,

$$B = e^{-\epsilon^*/kT}$$

the energy distribution law (Eq. 19.85) becomes

$$\frac{dN_\epsilon}{d\epsilon} = \frac{\frac{\pi}{2} \left(\frac{8 m_e}{h^2} \right)^{3/2} V \epsilon^{1/2}}{e^{\beta(\epsilon - \epsilon^*)} + 1} \qquad \textbf{(19.93)}$$

As $T \to 0°$K, the result becomes very simple; for any energy *below* ϵ^* the exponent in the denominator approaches $-\infty$ as $T \to 0$. Thus Eq. 19.93 has the limit

$$\frac{dN_\epsilon}{d\epsilon} = \frac{\pi}{2} \left(\frac{8 m_e}{h^2} \right)^{3/2} V \epsilon^{1/2} \qquad T = 0°\text{K} \qquad \epsilon < \epsilon^*$$

and the number in a unit energy range varies with $\epsilon^{1/2}$ up to ϵ^*. Beyond this the exponent approaches $+\infty$ for all $\epsilon > \epsilon^*$, and $dN_\epsilon/d\epsilon \to 0$. The resulting distribution law is plotted versus the energy in Fig. 19.16. At $0°$K every level is filled up to the Fermi level, and there are *no* electrons beyond this. As the temperature rises, a few electrons begin to be excited to states above the Fermi level, and the new distribution is rounded off as shown by the lighter curves for two temperatures T_1 and T_2 ($T_2 > T_1$). The important thing is that with $\theta^* = 80,000°K$ (as for copper) only a *very few electrons* move up to these higher levels, and thus the contributions to heat capacities are extremely small.

Returning to the average energy, $\overline{\epsilon^{kin}}$, as given in Eq. 19.92, we have for the contribution of the free electrons to the total internal energy of the solid

$$U^{el} = \frac{3}{5} N\epsilon^* + \frac{N\pi^2}{4} \frac{k^2}{\epsilon^*} T^2 + \cdots \tag{19.94}$$

This leads to the molar heat capacity contribution of the free electrons (assuming one free electron per atom) of

$$C_V{}^{el} = R\frac{\pi^2}{2} \frac{k}{\epsilon^*} T = R\frac{\pi^2}{2} \frac{T}{\theta^*} \tag{19.95}$$

With $\theta^* = 80,000°K$ for copper,

$$C_V{}^{el} = R(6 \times 10^{-5}T)$$

$C_V{}^{el}$ is thus a negligible percentage at all ordinary temperatures, in confirmation of experience. At very low temperatures it must be added to the Debye cube term and is the origin of the linear term in T mentioned in Sec. 7.7. The absolute values predicted from Eq. 19.95 for around 1°K agree within a factor of two with experiment, despite the rather rough approximations made in arriving at this formula.

Other valuable applications of Fermi-Dirac statistics include the Fermi-Thomas model of the atom, the Fermi nucleon gas model of a nucleus, photoelectricity, and photoelectric emission, not to mention the fascinating and ever-growing field of solid state physics itself. The discussion of the electron gas theory of a metal must serve to suggest the nature of the many applications, for details of which the reader must turn to more specialized sources.

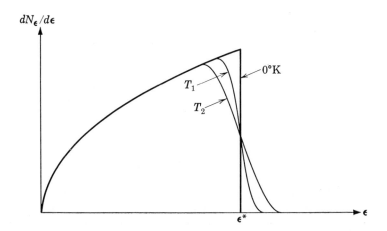

FIGURE **19.16**

References

FOWLER, R. H., and E. A. GUGGENHEIM, *Statistical Thermodynamics*, Cambridge Univ. Press, Cambridge, 1949, Chaps. IV, VII, and XIV.

KEESON, J. H., and N. PERLMAN, "Low Temperature Heat Capacity of Solids," in S. Flügge, ed., *Encyclopedia of Physics*, Springer, Berlin-Göttingen-Heidelberg, 1956, Vol. XIV, pp. 282–337.

KITTEL, C., *Introduction to Solid State Physics*, 2nd ed., Wiley, New York, 1956.

SEITZ, *Revs. Modern Phys.*, **27**, 249 (1955).

VAN VLECK, J. H., *Electric and Magnetic Susceptibilities*, Oxford Univ. Press, Oxford, 1932, Chaps. IX and X.

Problems

19.1 The particle partition function for the idealized paramagnetic solid in a magnetic field is

$$Z_\mu \mathcal{H} = e^{-2Sx} + e^{(-2S+2)x} + \cdots + e^{(2S-2)x} + e^{2Sx}$$
$$= e^{-Sz}(1 + e^z + e^{2z} + \cdots + e^{2Sz}) \tag{1}$$

where $z = 2x = 2\mu_0\mathcal{H}/kT$.

Show by direct division that

$$\frac{1 - y^{2n+1}}{1 - y} = 1 + y + y^2 + \cdots + y^{2n}$$

and hence that

$$y^{-n}(1 + y + y^2 + \cdots + y^{2n}) = \frac{y^{-n} - y^{n+1}}{1 - y}$$

Use this result to show that Eq. 1 may be put in the closed form

$$Z_\mu \mathcal{H} = \frac{\sinh\,[(2S + 1)x]}{\sinh x} \tag{19.6}$$

19.2 Verify the numerical result given in Eq. 19.24 that the radiancy at the maximum of the radiancy curve for a black body, R_{λ_m}, is given as

$$R_{\lambda_m} = 1.287\,T^5 \times 10^{-5}\left(\frac{\text{watt}}{\text{cm}^2}\,\text{micron}^{-1}\text{-deg}^{-5}\right) \tag{19.24}$$

19.3 The system partition function for the acoustic vibrations of a continuous solid is given in Sec. 19.12 as

$$\ln Z_\gamma' = -\frac{12\pi V}{c^3}\int_0^{\nu_m} \nu^2 \ln\,(1 - e^{-\beta h\nu})\,d\nu \tag{2}$$

In the case of a cubic cavity filled with equilibrium radiation at temperature T, the same type of relation should hold but with two modifications: (1) the coefficient in front of the integral must be reduced by a third since no *longitudinal* electromagnetic waves exist (then c is the velocity of light); and (2) with no finite number of particles, as in a solid, the limit ν_m must go to ∞. Thus the classical partition function for temperature radiation becomes

$$\ln Z_\gamma{}^{\text{rad}} = - 8\pi \left(\frac{kT}{ch}\right)^3 V \int_0^\infty x^2 \ln (1 - e^{-x})\, dx \tag{3}$$

if we substitute $x = \beta h\nu = h\nu/kT$.

Using the power series expansion for a logarithm, show that on integration termwise we have

$$- \int_0^\infty x^2 \ln (1 - e^{-x})\, dx = \int_0^\infty \sum_{n=1}^\infty \frac{x^2}{n} e^{-nx}\, dx = \sum_{n=1}^\infty \frac{1}{n^4} \int_0^\infty y^2 e^{-y}\, dy$$

$$= 2 \sum_{n=1}^\infty \frac{1}{n^4} = \frac{\pi^4}{45}$$

when Eq. 3 becomes

$$\ln Z_\gamma{}^{\text{rad}} = \frac{8\pi^5}{45} \left(\frac{k}{hc}\right)^3 V T^3 \tag{4}$$

Show

(a) that Eq. 4 leads to the expression for the internal energy of the system,

$$U^{\text{rad}} = \frac{8\pi^5 k^4}{15 c^3 h^3} V T^4$$

which is the Stefan-Boltzmann law for the volume, V (compare with Eq. 19.25); and

(b) that the Helmholtz potential for the radiation is

$$A^{\text{rad}} = - kT \ln Z_\gamma{}^{\text{rad}} = - \frac{8\pi^5 k^4}{45 c^3 h^3} V T^4$$

and hence that the pressure of the radiation becomes

$$p^{\text{rad}} = \frac{u}{3}$$

(See Sec. 13.7, where this result was obtained in a quite different way.)

19.4 Obtain the black body radiation density law,

$$u_\lambda = \frac{8\pi h c \lambda^{-5}}{e^{hc/\lambda kT} - 1} \tag{19.18}$$

from the system partition function given in Problem 19.3. (*Question:* Why does not this argument lead to the Rayleigh-Jeans law?)

19.5   The total entropy, total energy, and number of systems in a macrocanonical ensemble are given by

$$1 \quad \eta S = k \left(\eta \ln \eta + \Sigma \eta_i \ln \frac{\Omega_i}{\eta_i} \right) \tag{19.34}$$

$$-k\lambda \quad \eta = \Sigma \eta_i \tag{19.31}$$

$$-k\beta \quad \eta U = \Sigma \eta_i U_i \tag{19.32}$$

Show that the earlier method of maximizing entropy subject to Eqs. 19.31 and 19.32 is equivalent to combining these three equations by the Lagrangian multipliers shown at the left, differentiating the sum *partially* with respect to η_i, and setting the result equal to zero, to give

$$\frac{\partial}{\partial \eta_i} (\eta S - k\lambda \eta - k\beta \eta U) = k \left(\ln \frac{\Omega_i}{\eta_i} + \ln \eta - \lambda - \beta U_i \right) = 0$$

(*Note:* In this method it is essential to regard $\eta = \Sigma \eta_i$ with *every* η_i independent. Why is this treatment justified?)

Appendixes

APPENDIX **2.1**

Smoothed Second Virial Coefficients (B_1 Values $\times$ 10^5) for Thermometric Gases*

t, °C	He	H_2	Ne	N_2
400	58.7		81.6	138.4
300	61.8		80.3	120.2
200	64.8	92.2	77.5	90.0
100	67.5	90.7	72.2	37.8
50	69.6	87.7		-3.4
0	69.5	82.1	61.3	-62.7
-50	70.0	72.2	51.3	-153.8
-100	69.8	54.0	34.6	-309.5

* From Holborn and Otto, *Z. Physik*, **33**, 1 (1925); **38**, 359 (1926). Calculated for a gram-mole with pressure in meters of mercury from the relation

$$B_1 \times 10^5 = a + bT' + \frac{c}{T'} + \frac{e}{T'^3} \qquad T' = \frac{t + 273}{100}$$

where the empirical constants a, b, c, and e are as follows:

Gas	a	b	c	e
He	87.01	-3.81	-18.77	
H_2	166.00	-7.66	-172.33	
Ne	102.10	-0.80	-100.00	-31.33
N_2	357.46	-9.36	-1044.84	-242.53

The blanks in the e column indicate that only three terms are needed.

APPENDIX **4.1**

Specific Heat, c_p, and Specific Enthalpy, h, of Water at Atmospheric Pressure*

t, °C	c_p, 15° cal/g-deg	h, 15° cal/g	t, °C	c_p, 15° cal/g-deg	h, 15° cal/g
0	1.0076	0	35	82	35.0216
1	66	1.0072	36	82	36.0199
2	59	2.0137	37	82	37.0181
3	52	3.0193	38	83	38.0165
4	45	4.0243	39	0.9983	39.0418
5	39	5.0286			
6	34	6.0323	40	0.9983	40.0132
7	28	7.0355	41	83	41.0115
8	24	8.0382	42	84	42.0099
9	1.0019	9.0404	43	84	43.0083
			44	84	44.0068
10	1.0015	10.0422	45	85	45.0053
11	12	11.0436	46	85	46.0039
12	08	12.0446	47	86	47.0025
13	05	13.0454	48	86	48.0012
14	03	14.0458	49	0.9987	49.0000
15	1.0000	15.0467			
16	0.9998	16.0460	50	0.9988	49.9998
17	96	17.0458	51	89	50.9978
18	94	18.0453	52	89	51.9967
19	92	19.0447	53	90	52.9958
			54	90	53.9949
20	0.9991	20.0439	55	92	54.9941
21	89	21.0429	56	93	55.9934
22	88	22.0419	57	94	56.9928
23	87	23.0407	58	95	57.9923
24	86	24.0394	59	0.9996	58.9919
25	85	25.0381			
26	84	26.0366	60	0.9997	59.9915
27	84	27.0351	61	98	60.9913
28	83	28.0335	62	0.9999	61.9913
29	0.9983	29.0319	63	1.0000	62.9913
			64	01	63.9915
30	0.9983	30.0303	65	02	64.9917
31	82	31.0286	66	04	65.9921
32	82	32.0268	67	05	66.9926
33	82	33.0251	68	06	67.9932
34	82	34.0234	69	1.0008	68.9940

* Reduced from data of Stimson, *Am. J. Phys.*, **23**, 614 (1955), and Osborn, Stimson, and Ginnings, *J. Research Natl. Bur. Standards*, **23**, 197 (1939). For the conversion of absolute joules to 15° calories, the factor was 0.23892 cal/absolute joule, and for the conversion of international steam table calories (IT calories) to 15° calories, the factor was 1.000309 15° cal/IT cal. The enthalpy is taken as zero at 0°C and 1 atm.

APPENDIX **4.1** (*continued*)

t, °C	c_p, 15° cal/g-deg	h, 15° cal/g	t, °C	c_w, 15° cal/g-deg	h, 15° cal/g
70	1.0009	69.9948	86	37	86.0316
71	11	70.9959	87	39	87.0355
72	12	71.9971	88	42	88.0396
73	14	72.9985	89	1.0044	89.0440
74	15	74.0000			
75	17	75.0017	90	1.0046	90.0485
76	18	76.0035	91	48	91.0533
77	20	77.0055	92	51	92.0584
78	22	78.0076	93	54	93.0637
79	1.0024	79.0099	94	56	94.0693
			95	59	95.0750
80	1.0025	80.0125	96	61	96.0810
81	27	81.0152	97	64	97.0874
82	29	82.0180	98	66	98.0940
83	31	83.0212	99	1.0069	99.1008
84	33	84.0245			
85	35	85.0280	100	1.0072	100.1079

APPENDIX **11.1**

The Reciprocity Theorem for Jacobians

To prove the reciprocity theorem for Jacobians, we first prove the truth of
Eq. 11.36,

$$\frac{\partial(A, B)}{\partial(X, Y)} = \left[\frac{\partial(A, B)}{\partial(x, y)}\right]\left[\frac{\partial(x, y)}{\partial(X, Y)}\right] \tag{11.36}$$

Therefore, we need the theorem on the multiplication of two determinants,
which states that

$$\begin{vmatrix} a_1 & b_1 \\ a_2 & b_2 \end{vmatrix}\begin{vmatrix} A_1 & B_1 \\ A_2 & B_2 \end{vmatrix} = \begin{vmatrix} (a_1A_1 + b_1B_1) & (a_2A_1 + b_2B_1) \\ (a_1A_2 + b_1B_2) & (a_2A_2 + b_2B_2) \end{vmatrix}$$

The right side of Eq. 11.36 is written

$$\begin{vmatrix} \dfrac{\partial A}{\partial x} & \dfrac{\partial B}{\partial x} \\ \dfrac{\partial A}{\partial y} & \dfrac{\partial B}{\partial y} \end{vmatrix}\begin{vmatrix} \dfrac{\partial x}{\partial X} & \dfrac{\partial y}{\partial X} \\ \dfrac{\partial x}{\partial Y} & \dfrac{\partial y}{\partial Y} \end{vmatrix} = \begin{vmatrix} \dfrac{\partial A}{\partial x} & \dfrac{\partial A}{\partial y} \\ \dfrac{\partial B}{\partial x} & \dfrac{\partial B}{\partial y} \end{vmatrix}\begin{vmatrix} \dfrac{\partial x}{\partial X} & \dfrac{\partial y}{\partial X} \\ \dfrac{\partial x}{\partial Y} & \dfrac{\partial y}{\partial Y} \end{vmatrix}$$

where the columns and rows of the first Jacobian are interchanged and the
variables held constant are omitted for compactness.

Application of the multiplication theorem to the last result gives

$$
\begin{vmatrix}
\left(\dfrac{\partial A}{\partial x}\dfrac{\partial x}{\partial X} + \dfrac{\partial A}{\partial y}\dfrac{\partial y}{\partial X}\right) & \left(\dfrac{\partial B}{\partial x}\dfrac{\partial x}{\partial X} + \dfrac{\partial B}{\partial y}\dfrac{\partial y}{\partial X}\right) \\[2ex]
\left(\dfrac{\partial A}{\partial x}\dfrac{\partial x}{\partial Y} + \dfrac{\partial A}{\partial y}\dfrac{\partial y}{\partial Y}\right) & \left(\dfrac{\partial B}{\partial x}\dfrac{\partial x}{\partial Y} + \dfrac{\partial B}{\partial y}\dfrac{\partial y}{\partial Y}\right)
\end{vmatrix}
=
\begin{vmatrix}
\dfrac{\partial A}{\partial X} & \dfrac{\partial B}{\partial X} \\[2ex]
\dfrac{\partial A}{\partial Y} & \dfrac{\partial B}{\partial Y}
\end{vmatrix}
$$

which is just $[\partial(A, B)]/[\partial(X, Y)]$. Thus Eq. 11.36 is verified.

To arrive at the reciprocity theorem, Eq. 11.34, we must simply reverse the argument in Sec. 11.14 whereby Eq. 11.36 was deduced from Eq. 11.34.

The same general theorem may be applied to an nth-order Jacobian, that is,

$$
\frac{\partial(A, B, C, \ldots)}{\partial(X, Y, Z, \ldots)} = \left[\frac{\partial(A, B, C, \ldots)}{\partial(x, y, z, \ldots)}\right]\left[\frac{\partial(x, y, z, \ldots)}{\partial(X, Y, Z, \ldots)}\right]
$$

and the method extended accordingly.

APPENDIX **13.1**

Forms of Maxwell's Relations for n = 3

Let dU be given by the relation

$$
dU = T\,dS - p\,dV + F\,dL \tag{1}
$$

as for a typical unrestricted system with $n = 3$. Transform to the variables x, y, and z when

$$
dS = \left(\frac{\partial S}{\partial x}\right)_{yz} dx + \left(\frac{\partial S}{\partial y}\right)_{xz} dy + \left(\frac{\partial S}{\partial z}\right)_{xy} dz
$$

with similar relations for dV and dL. On substitution in Eq. 1 and collection of terms (with subscripts omitted),

$$
\begin{aligned}
dU = &\left[T\left(\frac{\partial S}{\partial x}\right) - p\left(\frac{\partial V}{\partial x}\right) + F\left(\frac{\partial L}{\partial x}\right)\right] dx \\
&+ \left[T\left(\frac{\partial S}{\partial y}\right) - p\left(\frac{\partial V}{\partial y}\right) + F\left(\frac{\partial L}{\partial y}\right)\right] dy \\
&+ \left[T\left(\frac{\partial S}{\partial z}\right) - p\left(\frac{\partial V}{\partial z}\right) + F\left(\frac{\partial L}{\partial z}\right)\right] dz \tag{2}
\end{aligned}
$$

This is of the general form

$$
dU = A\,dx + B\,dy + C\,dz
$$

where the cross derivative theorem gives

$$
\left(\frac{\partial A}{\partial y}\right)_{xz} = \left(\frac{\partial B}{\partial x}\right)_{yz} \tag{3}
$$

$$
\left(\frac{\partial A}{\partial z}\right)_{xy} = \left(\frac{\partial C}{\partial x}\right)_{yz} \tag{4}
$$

$$
\left(\frac{\partial B}{\partial z}\right)_{xy} = \left(\frac{\partial C}{\partial y}\right)_{xz} \tag{5}
$$

On substitution of the bracketed terms in Eq. 2 for A and B, the top equation (z is constant throughout) reduces to a sum of three second-order Jacobians, of which the first is

$$\left(\frac{\partial T}{\partial x}\right)_{yz}\left(\frac{\partial S}{\partial y}\right)_{xz} - \left(\frac{\partial T}{\partial y}\right)_{xz}\left(\frac{\partial S}{\partial x}\right)_{yz} = \frac{\partial(T, S)}{\partial(x, y)_z}$$

whereas the other two are recognized as

$$-\frac{\partial(p, V)}{\partial(x, y)_z}$$

and

$$\frac{\partial(F, L)}{\partial(x, y)_z}$$

Thus condition 3 becomes

$$\frac{\partial(T, S)}{\partial(x, y)_z} - \frac{\partial(p, V)}{\partial(x, y)_z} + \frac{\partial(F, L)}{\partial(x, y)_z} = 0 \qquad (6)$$

Similarly, conditions 4 and 5 become, respectively,

$$\frac{\partial(T, S)}{\partial(x, z)_y} - \frac{\partial(p, V)}{\partial(x, z)_y} + \frac{\partial(F, L)}{\partial(x, z)_y} = 0 \qquad (7)$$

and

$$\frac{\partial(T, S)}{\partial(y, z)_x} - \frac{\partial(p, V)}{\partial(y, z)_x} + \frac{\partial(F, L)}{\partial(y, z)_x} = 0 \qquad (8)$$

These are the appropriate Maxwellian relations for three variables.

It is easily verified that if x, y, and z are chosen as a *force* set (T, p, and F), a *geometric* set (S, V, and L), or in fact as any *nonconjugate* set, each of the sums in Eqs. 6, 7, and 8 reduces to the sum or difference of *two single derivatives*.

In the case of n variables, there are $n(n-1)/2$ Maxwellian equations, each involving the sum of n second-order Jacobians. With a nonconjugate choice of independent variables, each of these equations likewise reduces to the sum or difference of two single derivatives.

APPENDIX **15.1**

Stirling's Formula

The formula of Stirling for the approximation to $\ln n!$ when n is large can be arrived at as follows.

The fact that

$$\ln n! = \ln 1 + \ln 2 + \cdots + \ln n$$

suggests writing the sum as

$$\sum_{x=1}^{x=n} \ln x \, \Delta x$$

where $\Delta x = 1$. This represents the total area of a series of rectangles of unit width and of height $\ln x$. If we form the integral $\int_1^x \ln x \, dx$, integration by parts gives

$$\int_1^x \ln x \, dx = x \ln x - x + 1 = x \ln x - x \qquad x \gg 1$$

Geometrically speaking, the integral is the area between a curve $y = \ln x$ and the x axis. The sum itself is the area under a step curve, the successive units of which have heights $\ln 1(= 0)$, $\ln 2$, $\ln 3$, etc. As n becomes large, the difference between these two areas becomes less and less. Thus we arrive at Stirling's approximation to $\ln n!$ as

$$\ln n! = n (\ln n - 1) \qquad n \gg 1$$

From another point of view we may replace the factorial by the π function defined by the integral

$$\pi(x) = \int_0^\infty e^{-t} t^x \, dt$$

Since $\pi(x) = x!$ for integral x, this defines a smooth function between the discrete values of $x!$. Eq. 15.19 thus becomes

$$S = k[2 \ln \pi(N) - \sum_i \ln \pi(n_i) - \sum_j \ln \pi(N_j)]$$

The argument of Sec. 15.8 for maximizing S by varying the N_j's then carries through to give in place of Eq. 15.29 the condition

$$\frac{d \ln \pi(N_j)}{dN_j} = -\lambda - \beta \epsilon_j \tag{1}$$

The quantity on the left is the logarithmic derivative of $\pi(N_j)$, say, $\psi(N_j)$, a well-known function, where

$$\psi(N_j) = \frac{d \ln \pi(N_j)}{dN_j} = \frac{d \ln N_j!}{dN_j}$$

Fortunately $\pi(N_j)$ can be expanded as follows:

$$\psi(N_j) = \ln N_j + \frac{1}{2N_j} - \frac{1}{12N_j^2} + \frac{1}{120N_j^4} + \cdots \qquad N_j \gg 1 \tag{2}$$

and thus

$$\lim_{N_j \to \infty} \psi(N_j) = \ln N_j$$

On use of exponentials, Eq. 1 becomes

$$e^{\psi(N_j)} = e^{-\lambda} e^{-\beta \epsilon_j} = A e^{-\beta \epsilon_j} \tag{3}$$

and with Eq. 2 this may be written

$$N_j = F(N_j) A e^{-\beta \epsilon_j} \tag{4}$$

where

$$F(N_j) = e^{-1/2N_j} e^{1/12N_j^2} \cdots$$

The factor $F(N_j)$ can be seen to approach unity as N_j becomes large, when Eq. 4 reduces to Eq. 15.29. Even for rather small values of N_j, $F(N_j) \approx 1$, as can be seen in the following table.

N_j	$F(N_j)$
3	0.854
10	.952
20	.975
50	.9900
100	.9950
1000	.99950

Various methods have been employed to ensure the validity of the Stirling approximation, including the use of phase cells containing all particles of the *same energy* (that is, the substitution of a spherical *shell* in momentum space for a small rectangular cell), as in Chap. 16. An even more satisfactory solution is to use, not a single system, but a Gibbs ensemble of η equivalent systems (with η as large as desired) taken together (see Chap. 19) or to use the elegant but more difficult method of Darwin and Fowler (see also Appendix 19.2).

APPENDIX **16.1**

Liouville's Theorem

Consider a general phase space of $2F$ dimensionality where $2F = 2Nf$. Let A be a subportion of this space with volume Γ_t at time t. At a later time, t', each point in A will have moved to a new point in a new subregion, B, of volume $\Gamma_{t'}$. The theorem of Liouville states that

$$\Gamma_t = \int_A d\Gamma = \int_B d\Gamma' = \Gamma_{t'}$$

In other words, as a result of the laws of motion, the volume *retains its original value* as it moves through Γ space.

For the present purpose we may regard this change as simply a mathematical transformation brought about by the operation of the laws of mechanics, which transform the set of points $(p_1, p_2, \ldots, q_F)$ in A to a new set $(p_1', p_2', \ldots, q_F')$ in B. From the theory of the transformation of coordinates in integration, we have

$$\int_B d\Gamma' = \int_A J(q_i', p_i') \, d\Gamma$$

where

$$J(q_i', p_i') = \frac{\partial(q_1', \ldots, p_F')}{\partial(q_1, \ldots, p_F)}$$

is simply the Jacobian of the transformation. If we can show that owing to the form of the laws of mechanics the time derivative of J must vanish, that is, that

$$\frac{d}{dt} J(q_i', p_i') = 0$$

then the Jacobian must be a constant. Since it was *unity at* t, it must be *unity for all times* (subsequent or earlier), and hence the theorem.

The proof of the theorem depends on the differentiation of a Jacobian and is no more difficult in principle for many degrees of freedom than for $F = 1$. Let us take this very simple case. Then

$$J = \frac{\partial(q', p')}{\partial(q, p)} = \begin{vmatrix} \dfrac{\partial q'}{\partial q} & \dfrac{\partial p'}{\partial q} \\ \dfrac{\partial q'}{\partial p} & \dfrac{\partial p'}{\partial p} \end{vmatrix} = J(q', p')$$

and

$$\frac{dJ}{dt} = \frac{\partial(\dot{q}', p')}{\partial(q, p)} + \frac{\partial(q', \dot{p}')}{\partial(q, p)}$$

The first Jacobian can always be transformed as follows:

$$\frac{\partial(\dot{q}',p')}{\partial(q,p)} = \left[\frac{\partial(\dot{q}',p')}{\partial(q',p')}\right]\left[\frac{\partial(q',p')}{\partial(q,p)}\right] = \left(\frac{\partial\dot{q}'}{\partial q'}\right)J(q',p')$$

and similarly the second reduces to

$$\left(\frac{\partial\dot{p}'}{\partial p'}\right)J(q',p')$$

As a result, the time derivative becomes

$$\frac{dJ}{dt} = \left(\frac{\partial\dot{q}'}{\partial q'} + \frac{\partial\dot{p}'}{\partial p'}\right)J(q',p')$$

From Hamilton's equations the sum may be written

$$\left(\frac{\partial\dot{q}'}{\partial q'} + \frac{\partial\dot{p}'}{\partial p'}\right) = \frac{\partial}{\partial q'}\left(\frac{\partial H}{\partial p'}\right) - \frac{\partial}{\partial p'}\left(\frac{\partial H}{\partial q'}\right) = 0$$

Therefore,

$$\boxed{\frac{dJ}{dt} = 0}$$

and the theorem is established.

As a consequence of this theorem, the volume of any part of Γ space is an *invariant* of the *natural motion* of the image points within it. With image points scattered throughout Γ space, the density, D, at any point in region A is the same as that at the corresponding point in B. Thus D is constant along a trajectory in Γ space.

APPENDIX **18.1**

Solution of the Hermitian Equation

To find a polynomial solution of the Hermitian equation,

$$H'' - 2\xi H' + \left(\frac{a}{b} - 1\right)H = 0 \tag{1}$$

we first seek a solution in the form of a power series,

$$H = a_0 + a_1\xi + a_2\xi^2 + a_3\xi^3 + \cdots \tag{2}$$

Calculating the first and second derivatives, substituting these and Eq. 2 in Eq. 1, and collecting terms give the following conditions for the vanishing of the coefficients of the various powers of ξ:

$$a_2 = -\frac{1}{2}\left(\frac{a}{b} - 1\right)a_0$$

$$a_3 = -\frac{1}{2\times 3}\left(\frac{a}{b} - 1 - 2\right)a_1$$

$$a_4 = -\frac{1}{3\times 4}\left[\frac{a}{b} - 1 - (2\times 2)\right]a_2$$

$$a_5 = -\frac{1}{4\times 5}\left[\frac{a}{b} - 1 - (2\times 3)\right]a_3$$

or the general recursion formula,

$$a_{n+2} = \frac{\left(\dfrac{a}{b} - 1 - 2n\right)}{(n+1)(n+2)} a_n \tag{3}$$

Since each coefficient is related to another with a subscript smaller by 2, the coefficients with *even* subscripts may be expressed in terms of a_0, and those with *odd* subscripts in terms of a_1. The result is two series and two arbitrary constants, a_0 and a_1, from which a general solution may be made up.

To terminate the infinite series and obtain a polynomial solution, we must merely cause the numerator on the right of Eq. 3 to vanish, that is, set

$$\frac{a}{b} = 2n + 1 \tag{4}$$

This step ensures (for whatever n we select) that

$$a_{n+2} = a_{n+4} = \cdots = 0$$

Therefore, all the *even* coefficients, say, above a_n vanish, and one series terminates. Thus with n *even* we set $a_1 = 0$ arbitrarily and for every even value of n have a condition on the ratio

$$\frac{a}{b} = \frac{\dfrac{8\pi^2 mw}{h^2}}{\dfrac{4\pi^2 m\nu}{h}} = \frac{2w}{h\nu}$$

to fix the a's with even subscripts. With Eq. 4 this gives

$$\frac{2w}{h\nu} = 2n + 1$$

which is the energy condition for the linear oscillator, Eq. 17.27.

If we take $n = 0$,

$$\frac{a}{b} = (2 \times 0) + 1 = 1$$

and the series terminates with a_0; that is, the first polynomial is a constant. If $n = 2$,

$$\frac{a}{b} = (2 \times 2) + 1 = 5$$

and the series terminates with $a_2 \xi^2$. Using Eq. 3 to find $a_2 (= a_{0+2})$ gives

$$a_2 = -\left(\frac{5 - 1 - 0}{1 \times 2}\right) a_0 = -2a_0$$

This polynomial is therefore $a_0 - 2a_0 \xi^2$, etc.

We now carry out this process for the odd values of n (with $a_0 = 0$ to eliminate the other series). With $n = 1$, the condition in Eq. 4 makes

$$\frac{a}{b} = 3$$

and
$$a_3 = a_5 = \cdots = 0$$

The first odd polynomial is therefore simply $a_1 \xi$. With $n = 3$, $a/b = 7$ from Eq. 4, and

$$a_3 = a_{1+2} = -\left(\frac{7 - 1 - 2}{2 \times 4}\right) a_1 = -\tfrac{2}{3} a_1$$

The second odd polynomial is $a_1(\xi - \tfrac{2}{3}\xi^3)$, etc.

With this procedure we obtain

a_0	a_1
$a_0(1 - 2\xi^2)$	$a_1(\xi - \tfrac{2}{3}\xi^3)$
$a_0(1 - 4\xi^2 + \tfrac{4}{3}\xi^4)$	$a_1\left[\xi - \tfrac{4}{3}\xi^3 + \left(\dfrac{4}{3 \times 5}\right)\xi^5\right]$
$\cdots\cdots$	$\cdots\cdots$

We throw these into their so-called standard forms by setting

$$a_0 = (-1)^{n/2} \frac{n!}{\left(\dfrac{n}{2}\right)!}$$

and
$$a_1 = (-1)^{(n-1)/2} \frac{2n!}{\left(\dfrac{n-1}{2}\right)!}$$

so that

$$H_0(\xi) = 1 \qquad\qquad H_1(\xi) = 2\xi$$
$$H_2(\xi) = 4\xi^2 - 2 \qquad\qquad H_3(\xi) = 8\xi^3 - 12\xi$$
$$H_4(\xi) = 16\xi^4 - 48\xi^2 + 12 \qquad H_5(\xi) = 32\xi^5 - 160\xi^3 + 120\xi$$
$$\cdots\cdots \qquad\qquad\qquad \cdots\cdots$$

The general member of the set then takes the form

$$H_n(\xi) = (2\xi)^n - \frac{n(n-1)(2\xi)^{n-2}}{1!} + \frac{n(n-1)(n-2)(n-3)(2\xi)^{n-4}}{2!} - \cdots$$

whether n is even or odd. (This convenient fact results from the choices of a_0 and a_1.)

Solution of the Associated Legendre Equation

The associated Legendre equation (Eq. 18.33),

$$(1 - x^2)\frac{d^2y}{dx^2} - 2x\frac{dy}{dx} + \left[n(n+1) - \frac{m^2}{1 - x^2}\right]y = 0 \qquad (1)$$

is best solved by beginning with Legendre's equation itself:

$$(1 - x^2)\frac{d^2y}{dx^2} - 2x\frac{dy}{dx} + n(n + 1)y = 0 \qquad (2)$$

By the method of terminating an infinite series used in Appendix 18.1, it can be shown that Eq. 2 is satisfied by the set of polynomials known as Legendre's polynomials, the first few of which in their standard forms are as follows:

$$P_0(x) = 1$$
$$P_1(x) = x$$
$$P_2(x) = \tfrac{3}{2}x^2 - \tfrac{1}{2}$$
$$P_3(x) = \tfrac{5}{2}x^3 - \tfrac{3}{2}x$$
$$P_4(x) = \left(\frac{7 \times 5}{4 \times 2}\right)x^4 - \left(\frac{2 \times 5 \times 3}{4 \times 2}\right)x^2 + \frac{3 \times 1}{4 \times 2}$$
$$\cdot\ \cdot\ \cdot\ \cdot\ \cdot$$

The general Legendre polynomial of degree n, $P_n(x)$, is given as

$$P_n(x) = \frac{1 \times 3 \times 5 \cdots (2n - 1)}{n!}\left[x^n - \frac{n(n - 1)}{2(2n - 1)}x^{n-2} \right.$$
$$\left. + \frac{n(n - 1)(n - 2)(n - 3)}{2 \times 4(2n - 1)(2n - 3)}x^{n-4} - \cdots \right]$$

We wish to show that a particular solution of Eq. 1 is of the form

$$y = \Theta = (1 - x)^{m/2}\frac{d^m P_n(x)}{dx^m}$$

where $P_n(x)$ is a solution of Legendre's equation, Eq. 2, and d^m/dx^m indicates the mth-order derivative.

Thus we write

$$\frac{d^m P_n(x)}{dx^m} = P_n{}^{(m)}(x)$$

where $P_n{}^{(m)}(x)$ is frequently called the *Helmholtz function of degree* $(n - m)$. Since $P_n(x)$ satisfies Eq. 2, we differentiate that equation m times. The first differentiation gives

$$(1 - x^2)P_n{}^{(3)} - 2(1 + 1)xP_n{}^{(2)} + [n(n + 1) - 1(1 + 1)]P_n{}^{(1)} = 0$$

the second gives

$$(1 - x^2)P_n{}^{(4)} - 2(2 + 1)xP_n{}^{(3)} + [n(n + 1) - 2(2 + 1)]P_n{}^{(2)} = 0$$

and finally the mth gives

$$(1 - x^2)P_n{}^{(m+2)} - 2(m + 1)xP_n{}^{(m+1)} + [n(n + 1) - m(m + 1)]P_n{}^{(n)} = 0 \qquad (3)$$

This is the differential equation that $P_n{}^{(m)}$ must satisfy.

To show the relation to the associated equation, we let

$$P_n{}^{(m)}(x) = (1 - x^2)^r y$$

and seek the form that y must have by substitution of this relation in Eq. 3.

The result is the following differential equation:

$$(1 - x^2)^{r-1}\{(4r^2x^2 - 2r - 2rx^2)y - 4r(1 - x^2)xy'$$
$$+ (1 - x^2)^2 y'' - 2(m + 1)(1 - x^2)xy' + 4r(m + 1)x^2 y$$
$$+ [n(n + 1) - m(m + 1)](1 - x^2)y\} = 0$$

If r is now given the special value $-m/2$, the very formidable expression in the braces reduces to Eq. 1. This, of course, means that

$$y = (1 - x^2)^{m/2} P_n^{(m)}(x) = \Theta_n^m(x)$$

must satisfy the original associated equation of Legendre.

These solutions represent the *associated spherical harmonics* or *associated Legendre functions*, and this argument justifies the form of Eq. 18.36 in Sec. 18.6.

APPENDIX **19.1**

Evaluation of the Improper Integral in Sec. 19.4

To evaluate the improper integral

$$I = \int_0^\infty \frac{x^3 \, dx}{e^x - 1}$$

we must regard it as the limit as $x \to \infty$ of $I(x)$, where

$$I = \lim_{x \to \infty} I(x) = \lim \int_0^x \frac{x^3 \, dx}{e^x - 1}$$

To evaluate $I(x)$, we first write

$$\frac{1}{e^x - 1} = e^{-x}(1 - e^{-x})^{-1} = e^{-x} + e^{-2x} + e^{-3x} + \cdots = \sum_{n=1}^\infty e^{-nx}$$

Then

$$I(x) = \int_0^x x^3 \sum_{n=1}^\infty e^{-nx} \, dx = \sum_{n=1}^\infty \int_0^x x^3 e^{-nx} \, dx = \sum_{n=1}^\infty I_n(x)$$

On integration of the last integral by parts, we obtain

$$I_n(x) = \int_0^x e^{-nx} x^3 \, dx = - \frac{e^{-nx}}{n} \left[x^3 + \frac{3x^2}{n} + \frac{(2 \times 3)x}{n^2} + \frac{2 \times 3}{n^3} \right]_0^x$$

and

$$\lim_{x \to \infty} I_n(x) = 0 + \frac{2 \times 3}{n^4} = \frac{6}{n^4}$$

Therefore,

$$I = \lim_{x \to \infty} I(x) = \sum_{n=1}^\infty \frac{6}{n^4} = 6 \left(\frac{1}{1^4} + \frac{1}{2^4} + \frac{1}{3^4} + \cdots \right) = \frac{\pi^4}{15}$$

since the series in parentheses is a known expansion of $\pi^4/90$. (See, for example, K. Knopp, *Theory and Application of Infinite Series*, 2nd ed., Hafner, New York, 1948, p. 387, Sec. II, Eq. 166c.)

APPENDIX **19.2**

The Method of Darwin and Fowler

The method of Darwin and Fowler permits the calculation of averages over microcanonical ensembles without the use of Stirling's approximation for the factorial. It further has the advantage of dealing directly with average values rather than with most probable values and is particularly suited to the calculation of fluctuations from the average. The method makes use of two mathematical devices, the multinomial theorem and the evaluation of certain generating integrals in the complex domain.

The multinomial theorem is a generalization of the binomial theorem to the expansion of polynomial sums. Thus, if we write out the binomial theorem for $(x_1 + x_2)^N$, we have

$$(x_1 + x_2)^N = x_1^N + A_1 x_1^{N-1} x_2 + A_2 x_1^{N-2} x_2^2 + \cdots + x_2^N$$

where the general coefficient A_i may be written

$$A_i = \frac{N(N-1)(N-2)\cdots(N-i+1)}{i!} = \frac{N!}{i!\,(N-i)!}$$

Let $i = n_1$ and $N - i = N - n_i = n_2$, where

$$n_1 + n_2 = N \tag{1}$$

Then
$$A_{n_1} = \frac{N!}{n_1! n_2!}$$

and the binomial theorem becomes

$$(x_1 + x_2)^N = \sum \frac{N!}{n_1! n_2!} x_1^{n_1} x_2^{n_2} \tag{2}$$

the summation to be carried out over all values of n_1 and n_2 satisfying Eq. 1.

Now consider the trinomial expression

$$(x_1 + x_2 + x_3)^N = [x_1 + (x_2 + x_3)]^N$$

Expanding the right side by the binomial theorem makes it

$$\sum \frac{N!}{n_1! n_2'!} x_1^{n_1} (x_2 + x_3)^{n_2'}$$

the summation to be made over all n_1 and n_2' values for which $n_1 + n_2' = N$. Apply the binomial theorem to the factor $(x_2 + x_3)^{n_2'}$ so that the last result becomes

$$\sum_{n_1 n_2'} \frac{N! x_1^{n_1}}{n_1! n_2'!} \sum \frac{n_2'!}{n_2! n_3!} x_2^{n_2} x_3^{n_3}$$

where the second summation is over all n_2 and n_3 values for which

$$n_2 + n_3 = n_2' = N - n_1$$

that is, for which

$$n_1 + n_2 + n_3 = N \tag{3}$$

For every $n_2'!$ in the denominator of the first sum, there will be a similar $n_2'!$ in the numerator of a term in the second. These cancel to give

$$(x_1 + x_2 + x_3)^N = \sum \frac{N}{n_1!n_2!n_3!} x_1^{n_1} x_2^{n_2} x_3^{n_3}$$

By similar technique this result may be extended to sums of any number of terms. The multinomial theorem for any number of terms, c, raised to the Nth power arises; that is,

$$(x_1 + x_2 + \cdots + x_c)^N = \sum \frac{N!}{n_1!n_2! \ldots n_c!} x_1^{n_1} x_2^{n_2} \ldots x_c^{n_c}$$

where the summation is over all positive n_i's for which

$$\Sigma n_i = N \tag{4}$$

Consider the application of these results to finding the average distribution of ideal gas molecules in a volume, V. Suppose the total volume to be broken up into a set of volumes, $v_1, v_2, v_3, \ldots, v_c$ (which may be alike or unlike, large or small; this is immaterial). Let a macrodistribution, D, be defined as having $n_1, n_2, n_3, \ldots, n_c$ molecules in the volumes $v_1, v_2, v_3, \ldots, v_c$, where, of course,

$$n_1 + n_2 + n_3 + \cdots + n_c = N$$

and
$$v_1 + v_2 + v_3 + \cdots + v_c = V$$

The argument of Sec. 15.5 shows that if the molecules are distinguishable the number of microstates in D is simply

$$\frac{N!}{n_1!n_2! \ldots n_c!} \tag{15.10}$$

Since some microstates are more probable than others, owing to the variable sizes of the volumes v_1 to v_c, we want a statistical weight factor for the microstates in any given distribution. The probability that a given molecule will be in v_1 by pure chance is simply v_1/V, and the probability that n_1 molecules will be in the volume is $(v_1/V)^{n_1}$. Thus the mathematical probability of the distribution D becomes the product of a set of similar factors,

$$\left(\frac{v_1}{V}\right)^{n_1} \left(\frac{v_2}{V}\right)^{n_2} \cdots \left(\frac{v_c}{V}\right)^{n_c} = \frac{v_1^{n_1} v_2^{n_2} \ldots v_c^{n_c}}{V^N}$$

We regard the variable part of this result (that is, the numerator) as the appropriate statistical weight for any microstate in D. This then gives for the weighted number of microstates in D

$$\frac{N!}{n_1!n_2! \ldots n_c!} v_1^{n_1} v_2^{n_2} \ldots v_c^{n_c}$$

Consequently, the weighted sum of all the microstates, say, C, is just the sum of terms of this sort over all the n_i's that satisfy Eq. 4. Thus

$$C = \sum \frac{N!}{n_1!n_2! \ldots n_c!} v_1^{n_1} v_2^{n_2} \cdots v_c^{n_c} = (v_1 + v_2 + \cdots + v_c)^N \tag{5}$$

by the multinomial theorem.

To find the average number of particles, $\overline{n_i}$, in the ith volume, v_i, we have by definition

$$C\overline{n_i} = \sum \frac{n_i(v_1{}^{n_1} \ldots v_c{}^{n_c})N!}{n_1!n_2! \ldots n_c!}$$

The term n_i will cancel $n_i!$ in the denominator to $(n_i - 1)!$, which with $N! = N(N - 1)!$ and $v_1{}^{n_i} = v_1{}^{n_i-1}v_i$ reduces the result to

$$C\overline{n_i} = Nv_i \sum \frac{v_1{}^{n_1} \ldots v_i{}^{n_i-1} \ldots v_c{}^{n_c}}{n_1! \ldots (n_i - 1)! \ldots n_c!}(N - 1)!$$
$$= Nv_i(v_1 + v_2 + \cdots + v_c)^{N-1} = Nv_iV^{N-1}$$

by the multinomial theorem. Thus with $C = V^N$,

$$V^N\overline{n_i} = Nv_iV^{N-1}$$

or

$$\overline{n_i} = \left(\frac{N}{V}\right)v_i$$

and

$$\overline{n_i} = \hat{n}v_i$$

where $\hat{n}$ is the average particle density in the gas, which is clearly n_i/v_i, the average density in v_i. This calculation of uniform density in the gas is given here to illustrate the use of a *generating function*. A generating function is a quantity, having coefficients of expansion that by the multinomial theorem give the coefficients of the variable terms in the sum C. In this case the generating function appropriate to the discussion of particle density is evidently

$$(v_1 + v_2 + v_3 + \cdots + v_c)^N$$

For the calculation of other averages in other systems, still other generating functions are needed. For discussing the equilibrium of N of Planck's linear oscillators, n_0, n_1, n_2, n_3, etc., with energies 0, ϵ, 2ϵ, 3ϵ, etc., respectively, the proper generating function is the infinite series

$$(1 + Z + Z^2 + Z^3 + \cdots)^N = \frac{1}{(1 - Z)^N}$$

For a system made up of two types of oscillators (N each in number) with energies that are multiples of two different quantities, ϵ and η, the generating function to be used is

$$(1 + Z^\epsilon + Z^{2\epsilon} + \cdots)^N(1 + Z^\eta + Z^{2\eta} + \cdots)^N = \frac{1}{(1 - Z^\epsilon)^N}\frac{1}{(1 - Z^\eta)^N}$$

In such cases and in general, the sum of the weighted microstates can be expressed most readily as a complex integral. This must be evaluated by an appropriate contour integration in the complex plane. The details are beyond a short appendix, and the reader is referred elsewhere. See, in particular, Darwin and Fowler, *Phil. Mag.*, **44**, 450, 823 (1922), and many later papers; R. H. Fowler, *Statistical Mechanics*, 2nd ed., Cambridge Univ. Press, Cambridge, 1936; D. ten Haar, *Elements of Statistical Mechanics*, Holt, Rinehart & Winston, New York, 1954, p. 408; and H. Morgenau and G. M. Murphy, *The Mathematics of Physics and Chemistry*, 2nd ed., Van Nostrand, New York, 1956.

Notation List

Throughout the text capital letters represent extensive properties of a whole system, and lower-case letters represent extensive properties of unit masses. Superscript circles identify ideal gas properties (for example, $U°$). When more than one phase is present, single, double, etc., primes distinguish the phases, the single prime denoting the state stable at the high temperature. In general, $a_0, a_1, a_2, \ldots, b_0, b_1, b_2, \ldots, c_0, c_1, c_2, \ldots, A, B, C$, etc., are coefficients in various series expansions. The numbers in parentheses after each definition indicate the section (or equation or problem, as noted) where it first appears.

A	area (1.13); Helmholtz's potential (9.17)
a, b	van der Waals' constants (3.9)
B	magnetic induction (5.5); rotational constant for diatomic molecule (17.9); Fermi-Dirac normalization factor (Eq. 19.81)
$B_1, B_2, \ldots$	second, third, etc., virial coefficients for powers of pressure (Eq. 3.18)
$\mathscr{B}_1, \mathscr{B}_2, \ldots$	second, third, etc., molar virial coefficients for powers of $1/V$ (Eq. 3.19)
c	speed of light (13.6); number of chemical components (13.15); average speed of transverse and longitudinal waves in solid (19.11)
C_p	system heat capacity at constant pressure (4.2)
c_p	specific heat at constant pressure (4.2)
C_V	system heat capacity at constant volume (Eq. 5.31)
c_V	specific heat at constant volume (5.11)
$c'_{\text{sat}}, c''_{\text{sat}}$	specific heats of saturated vapor and liquid (11.3)
$C_y^{(x)}$	heat capacity at constant y per unit increase in x (5.10)
D	Debye's function (7.6, Eq. 19.76); electric induction (13.10); atomic diffuse series state with $L = 2$ (18.9)

E	potential drop (4.5); emf (5.4); Einstein's function (7.7)
e	base of Naperian logarithms $= 2.71828 \ldots$; charge on electron (19.2)
$\mathcal{E}$	electric field strength (13.10); virial correction in vapor pressure formula of helium (Eq. 14.4)
F	force (1.13); atomic electronic state with $L = 3$ (18.9)
$F_1, F_2, \ldots$	generalized forces (5.6)
$F, F_\omega, F_\parallel$	general, directional, and parallel beam mass flux coefficients (15.16)
$\mathbf{F}$	Faraday (13.4)
$\underline{\mathcal{F}}$	total angular momentum (fine-structure) vector for atom (Problem 18.9)
f	number of degrees of freedom of molecule (6.13); fine-structure quantum number (Problem 18.9)
G	Gibbs' potential (9.17)
g	specific Gibbs' potential for pure substance (13.13); local acceleration of gravity (16.9)
g_0	standard acceleration of gravity (3.3)
g_j	statistical weight for jth cell or energy state (17.6)
g^{nu}, g^{el}	nuclear and electronic statistical weights for atom (18.9)
g^{orn}	orientational statistical weight for molecule (17.15)
H	system enthalpy (Eq. 7.21)
$\mathbf{H}$	Hamiltonian (Eq. 16.3)
$\mathcal{H}$	magnetic field intensity (5.5)
h	specific enthalpy (Eqs. 4.8, 7.21); Planck's constant (6.15)
$\hbar$	$h/2\pi$
I	moment of inertia (6.15)
$I(n)$	kinetic theory integral of index n (15.10)
$\underline{\mathcal{I}}$	total angular momentum vector for nucleus (18.9)
i	electric current (4.5); total nuclear quantum number (18.9)
i_p, i_p'	absolute and conventional vapor pressure constants (Eqs. 12.84, 12.86)
J	mechanical equivalent of heat (4.4); rotational quantum number for diatomic molecule (17.9)
$J(X, Y)$	Jacobian of dependent variables X and Y (11.13)
J_0, J_0'	fundamental and modified symmetric Jacobians (11.17)
$\underline{\mathcal{J}}$	total angular momentum vector for extranuclear electrons (18.9)
j	total angular quantum number for extranuclear electrons (18.9)
K, K_e	dielectric constant (1.11, 13.10)
K	Kelvin thermodynamic temperature scale (2.9)
K_{ref}, K_{hp}	coefficients of performance of refrigerator and heat pump (8.12)
k	Boltzmann's constant (6.15)

L	length (1.13); total orbital quantum number for extranuclear electron (18.9)
L_p	latent heat of pressure rise (Eq. 5.28)
L_V	latent heat of expansion (Eq. 5.33)
$\underline{\mathcal{L}}$	total orbital momentum vector for extranuclear electrons (18.9)
l	angular quantum number for single electron (18.12)
M	molecular weight (3.1)
$M_{\mathcal{H}}$	magnetic quantum number (18.8)
$\mathbf{M}$	magnetic moment of system (Eq. 5.15)
$\mathbf{M}'$	electric moment of system (13.10)
m	mass (1.8)
m'	reduced mass (6.14); apparent or effective mass (16.11)
N, N_j	numbers of molecules in system and at energy state ϵ_j (15.5)
N_0	Avogadro's number (6.11)
N_0'	number of particles in ground state (17.12)
n	number of independent thermodynamic variables (Eq. 1.19)
n_{eq}	total number of independent equations (1.11)
n_{var}	total number of thermodynamic variables (1.11)
n_{int}	number of independent intensive variables (Eq. 13.64)
$\hat{n}$	particle density in gas (16.2)
P	pressure in atmospheres (17.15); atomic principal series state with $L = 1$ (18.9)
$P_A, P_B, \ldots$	mathematical probabilities of events $A, B, \ldots$ (15.2)
p	pressure in general (1.8); momentum of particle (16.3)
p_0	value of 1 atm in cgs units (17.2)
Q	heat gained by system (4.2)
Q_C	heat absorbed by system along curve C (4.11)
q	Hamiltonian position coordinate (16.3)
q_C	heat absorbed per unit mass along curve C (5.11)
R	universal gas constant (3.1)
$R_c, R_\omega, R_\parallel$	cavity, directional, and parallel beam radiancies (13.5, 13.6)
R_λ	radiancy per unit wave length interval (19.4)
r	radius (1.13); electrical resistance (Eq. 2.9); number of squared terms in energy expression for molecule (6.12); nuclear separation for diatomic molecules (6.14); compression ratio (8.5); number of cells in volume space of gas (15.5)
S	system entropy (9.4); atomic sharp series state with $L = 0$ (18.9); total spin quantum number for extranuclear electrons (18.9)
S_{0Tp}	entropy constant for ideal gas variables T and p (Eq. 9.50)
S_{0TV}	entropy constant for ideal gas variables T and V (Eq. 9.49)
$\mathcal{S}$	surface tension (1.13)
$\underline{\mathcal{S}}$	total spin vector for extranuclear electrons (18.9)

s	number of cells in velocity space (15.7); spin quantum number for electron or nucleon $= \frac{1}{2}$ (18.9)
$\underline{s}^{nu}$	spin vector for single nucleon (18.9)
T	temperature on Kelvin or absolute thermodynamic scale (Eq. 2.27)
t	general and Celsius temperatures (1.8, 2.6)
U	system internal energy (4.6)
u	vibratory parameter (6.15); specific internal energy (7.9); radiation density (Eq. 13.28)
V	system volume (1.8)
$\mathscr{V}$	speed of large-scale motion (7.16)
v	specific volume (1.10); molecular speed (6.11)
v_{mp}	most probable speed (15.13)
v_{rms}	root-mean-square speed (15.14)
v_0, v_0'	sizes of cells in volume and velocity spaces (15.5)
W	mechanical work (4.4); thermodynamic probability of system's state (disorder number) (15.4)
W_c	work done on system along curve C (4.10)
$\mathscr{W}$	thermodynamic probability of ensemble (19.5)
$w_1, w_2, \ldots$	characteristic values in Schrödinger's equation (18.3)
X, Y, Z	general variables
x, y, z	Cartesian coordinates
Z	general partition function (Eq. 16.24)
Z_μ, Z_γ	partition functions in μ and Γ spaces (19.6)
z	electric charge (1.13)
α, α'	parameters in Boltzmann distribution law (15.9, 15.10)
α_F	coefficient of linear expansion at constant force (5.12)
α_p	coefficient of linear expansion at constant pressure (5.12)
α_V	isochoric coefficient of pressure rise (Eq. 3.16)
β	$1/kT$ (15.11)
β_p	isobaric coefficient of volume expansion (Eq. 3.15)
Γ	symbol for gas space (16.4)
γ	ratio of C_p to C_V for gas (5.15)
Δ	electronic state of diatomic molecule with $\Lambda = 2$ (18.10)
$\Delta\mu$	fixed size of cell in μ (molecular) space (16.4)
$\Delta\Gamma$	fixed size of cell in Γ (gas) space (16.4)
ϵ	electric susceptibility (13.10)
$\epsilon, \epsilon^{vib}, \epsilon^{pot}, \epsilon^{kin}, \ldots$	total vibratory, potential, kinetic, etc., energies of single particle (Eqs. 6.19, 6.25, $\ldots$)
ϵ_j	energy in jth state (15.5)
ϵ^*	Fermi energy (19.16)
ζ	running dynamic variable (16.10)
η	thermal efficiency (8.2); viscosity (14.8); number of systems in Gibbs' ensembles (19.5)

Θ	characteristic temperature (6.15)
Θ_m	Debye temperature for solid (19.12)
$\Theta_n{}^m$	associated spherical harmonic of order m and degree n (18.6)
θ	reduced temperature (Problem 3.9); generalized geometric variable (5.6); angular coordinate (16.3)
κ_T	isothermal coefficient of compressibility (Eq. 3.14)
Λ	molar latent heat (7.10)
λ	specific latent heat (6.2); general parameter (6.12); wave length (6.15)
μ	Joule-Kelvin (or Joule-Thomson) coefficient (Eq. 12.48); symbol for molecular space (16.1); magnetic dipole moment (19.2)
μ_0	Bohr magneton (19.2)
$\mu_j{}^\alpha$	chemical potential of jth component in αth phase (13.15)
ν	frequency (6.14); number of moles (7.15)
$\tilde{\nu}$	frequency in wave numbers (17.10)
ξ	general dynamic variable (6.12)
Π	general multiplication sign; Peltier coefficient (13.18); molecular electronic state with $\Lambda = 1$ (18.10)
π	3.1416 . . . ; reduced pressure (Problem 3.9)
ρ	mass density (1.10)
ρ'	image point density (15.10)
Σ	general summation sign; molecular electronic state with $\Lambda = 0$ (18.10)
σ	Stefan-Boltzmann radiation constant (Eq. 13.34); rotational parameter (17.14)
σ_A	Thomson coefficient for substance A (13.18)
σ'	symmetry number for molecule (17.8)
τ	time (in nondynamic equations) (4.5)
Υ	velocity of sound (1.11)
Φ	molecular electronic state with $\Lambda = 3$ (18.10)
ϕ	reduced volume (Problem 3.9); number of phases (13.15); angular coordinate (16.3); time-dependent wave function (18.3)
χ	molar magnetic susceptibility (14.3)
Ψ	general wave function (18.3)
ψ	radiant flux (13.5); space-dependent wave function (18.3)
Ω_j	number of microstates in jth energy shell of ensemble (19.5)
ω	vibrational constant for diatomic molecules (17.9)

Useful Constants[*]

c	speed of light *in vacuo*	$= 2.997923(\pm 8) \times 10^{10}$ cm/sec
$\mathbf{F}$	Faraday	$= 96{,}522(\pm 2)$ coul/g-equivalent
h	Planck's constant	$= 6.6253(\pm 3) \times 10^{-27}$ erg-sec
J	mechanical equivalent of heat	$= 4.1855(\pm 4)$ absolute joules/cal
		($\log_{10} 4.1855 = 0.62175$)
k	Boltzmann's constant	$= 1.38041(\pm 7) \times 10^{-16}$ erg/deg
N_0	Avogadro's number	$= 6.0248(\pm 3) \times 10^{23}$ molecules/mole
R	gas constant per mole	$= 8.3167(\pm 3) \times 10^{7}$ ergs/mole-deg
		$= 8.2077 \times 10^{-2}$ liter-atm/mole-deg
		$= 8.2079 \times 10^{1}$ cm³-atm/mole-deg
		$= 1.9870$ cal/mole-deg
V_0	molar volume	$= 2.24208(\pm 3) \times 10^{4}$ cm³/mole
$1/J$		$= 0.23892$ cal/absolute joule
		($\log 0.23892 = \overline{1}.37823$)
hc/k		$= 1.4389$ deg-cm
$\mathbf{F}/R \times 10^{7}$v		$= 11{,}606(\pm 1)°$ (≈ 1 ev in degrees)

---

[*] Evaluated by J. A. Bearden, M. D. Earle, J. M. Minkowski, and J. S. Thomsen of The Johns Hopkins University in October, 1954. From D. E. Gray, ed., *American Institute of Physics Handbook*, McGraw-Hill, New York, 1957.

Index

absolute thermodynamic scale, 36–38, 39, 50, 51, 222–25, 415, 416, 440
absolute vapor pressure constant, 360; and entropy, 364–66
absorption intensities, 549–50
acetylene, and experimental values of C_V and γ, 150; modes of molecular vibration of, 157
action, volume in phase space in terms of, 501
adiabatic change of magnetic field, 437–39
adiabatic curve, and Berthelot gas, 147; and equation of for ideal gas, 135; slope of, 133–35; and van der Waals gas, 336
adiabatic demagnetization, magnetic cooling by, 435–39
adiabatic expansion, 126, 127; measurement of γ by, 145–47
adiabatic processes, and entropy, 398
adiabatic vacuum calorimeter, 168–69
adiabatic walls, 4, 6, 7
adsorption, positive surface, 393
Advisory Committee on Thermometry, 96
aerostatic equation, 514–15
air, and experimental values of C_V and γ, 150; maximum inversion temperature of, 350
air standard Diesel cycle, 207–09
air standard Otto cycle, 206–07
alcohols, vapor pressure of, 354; see also ethyl alcohol
Allen, and Jones, 429; and Reekie, 429n.
alternating intensity, 608
aluminum, atomic heat of, 171; Debye temperatures of, 175; temperature variation of heating capacity of, 173
Amagat units, 35, 53

ammonia, critical constants of, 71; heat capacity of, at 1 atm, 163; as refrigerant, 286, 289, 290
ammonium iron alum, 440, 626
angular momentum, 586–88
antimony, freezing point of, 47
antisymmetric wave function, molecular, 579, 580, 584; nuclear, 604, 605
argon, 141, 144, 149, 178, 342, 343, 344; critical constants of, 71; empirical behavior of, 34, 36; and experimental values of C_V and γ, 150; heat capacity of, 179; maximum inversion temperature of, 350; and observed values of $100a$, 36; vapor pressure constants for, 364, 532
associated spherical harmonics, 583, 680
atom(s), Fermi-Thomas model of, 665; formation of molecule from, 600–03; statistical weights for, 588–93
atomic heats of elements, 171
average speed, from speed distribution law, 479, 480
Avogadro's law, 55
Avogadro's number, 151; from black body radiation, 631; and Boltzmann's constant, 472; from Brownian movement, 515

bands, alternating intensity in, 608; rotation and rotation-vibration, 546–50
Barnes, H. T., mechanical equivalent, 91, 93
Barnes and Silverman, and Brownian movement, 521
Bartholomé, see Clusius and Bartholomé
Beattie, J. A., absolute temperature of ice point, 37
Beattie-Bridgeman equation of state, 75, 76, 342, 343, 350, 351

benzene, heat capacity of, 178
Bernoulli flow, 199
Berthelot, P., 142
Berthelot's equation of state, 72–74, 76, 77; maximum inversion temperatures from, 350, 351; thermodynamic tests of, 342
bimolecular collisions, 648
Birge, R. T., recommended value of J, 92
bismuth, atomic heat of, 171
bivariant system, 18
Black, Joseph, 88 and n.
black body radiation, 381, 384, 626, 627, 628, 629, 630
Blackman, heat capacity of crystals, 658
Bohr correspondence principle, 582
Bohr magneton, 621, 624
Bohr quantum postulate, 544
bolometer, 147
Boltzmann, Ludwig, and entropy and disorder, 448; and entropy and probability, 261; and finite size of μ cells, 529; and indistinguishability of identical particles, 534–35; and thermodynamic probability, 456, 513; see also Boltzmann entries below
Boltzmann's approximation, 539–42, 619
Boltzmann's constant, 152, 161, 472 and n., 515
Boltzmann's entropy expression, 461, 473, 506, 512; and entropy paradox, 522
Boltzmann's equipartition of energy theorem, 152–54, 481, 482, 511, 516–18
boron, atomic heat of, 171
Bose-Einstein distribution law, 537–39, 618, 619; Boltzmann's approximation to, 539–42, 619
boundary of system, 3
Boyle, Robert, 10

690